ANDERSON COLLEGE

ANDERSON UNIVERSITY

3 2197 01027107 6

D1264203

In this volume

NELSON DOUBLEDAY, INC.

GARDEN CITY   NEW YORK

Printed in the U.S.A.

THE BRIDGES AT TOKO-RI

THE BRIDGES
AT TOKO-RI

JAMES A. MICHENER, 1907–

NELSON DOUBLEDAY, INC.
GARDEN CITY, NEW YORK

THE BRIDGES AT TOKO-RI

COPYRIGHT, 1953, BY JAMES A. MICHENER AND

PUBLISHED BY RANDOM HOUSE, INC., NEW YORK.

ANDERSON COLLEGE
LIBRARY
ANDERSON, INDIANA

PS
3525
.I19
B72
1953

THE BRIDGES AT TOKO-RI

ANDERSON COLLEGE
LIBRARY
ANDERSON, INDIANA

43444

SEA

THE SEA was bitter cold. From the vast empty plains of Siberia howling winds roared down to lash the mountains of Korea, where American soldiers lost on patrol froze into stiff and awkward forms. Then with furious intensity the arctic wind swept out to sea, freezing even the salt spray that leaped into the air from crests of falling waves.

Through these turbulent seas, not far from the trenches of Korea, plowed a considerable formation of American warships. A battleship and two cruisers, accompanied by fourteen destroyers to shield against Russian submarines, held steady course as their icy decks rose and fell and shivered in the gale. They were the ships of Task Force 77 and they had been sent to destroy the communist-held bridges at Toko-ri.

Toward the center of this powerful assembly rode two fast
carriers, the cause of the task force and its mighty arm. Their
massive decks pitched at crazy angles, which for the present
made take-offs or landings impossible. Their planes stood useless, huddled together in the wind, lashed down by steel cables.

It was strange, and in some perverse way resolutely American, that these two carriers wallowing in the dusk bore names
which memorialized not stirring victories but humiliating de-
feats, as if by thus publishing her indifference to catastrophe
and her willingness to surmount it, the United States were
defying her enemies. To the east, and farther out to sea, rode
the *Hornet*, whose predecessor of that name had absorbed a
multitude of Japanese bombs and torpedoes, going down off
Guadalcanal, while the inboard carrier, the *Savo*, would forever
remind the navy of its most shameful defeat in history, when
four cruisers sank helpless at Savo Island, caught sleeping by
the audacious Japanese.

Now, as night approached the freezing task force, the bull
horn on the *Savo* rasped out, "Prepare to launch aircraft!" And
it was obvious from the way her deck was arranged that the
carrier already had some planes in the skies over Korea, and
every man who watched the heaving sea wondered how those
planes could possibly get back aboard.

The bull horn, ignoring such problems, roared, "Prepare to
launch helicopter!" and although the deck pitched in abandon,
rotors began to turn, slowly at first and then with lumbering
speed.

Now the great carrier struck a sea trough and slid away, her
deck lurching, but relentlessly the bull horn cried, "Move jets
into position for launching," and the catapult crew, fighting
for footing on the sliding deck, sprang swiftly into action, inch-
ing two heavy Banshees onto the catapults, taking painful care
not to allow the jets to get rolling, lest they plunge overboard
with some sudden shifting of the deck.

"Start jet engines," roared the insistent bull horn.

The doctor, who had to be on deck in case of crash, looked

at the heaving sea and yelled to the crane operator, "They may launch these jets, but they'll never get 'em back aboard."

The craneman looked down from his giant machine, which could lift a burning plane and toss it into the sea, and shouted, "Maybe they're planning to spend the night at some air force field in Korea. Along with the ones that are already up."

But at this instant all ships of the task force swung in tight circles and headed away from the open sea, straight for the nearby cliffs of Korea, and when the turn was completed, the deck of the *Savo* mysteriously stabilized. The effects of wind and sea neutralized each other, and planes returning from the bombardment of Korea now had a safe place to land.

But before they could do so the bull horn cried eerily into the dusk, "Launch helicopter!" and the crazy bird, its two rotors spinning so slowly the blades could be seen, stumbled into the air, and the horn cried, "Launch jets!"

Then, as the great carrier rode serenely amid the storms, the catapult officer whirled one finger above his head and a tremendous, almost unbearable roar arose and twin blasts of heat leaped from each Banshee, burning the icy air more than a hundred feet aft. Now the officer whirled two fingers and the roar increased and white heat scorched the deck of the carrier and the twin engines whipped to a meaningless speed of 13,000 revolutions a minute and the Banshee pilot, forcing his head back against a cushion, saluted and the catapult officer's right hand whipped down and the catapult fired.

Nine tons of jet aircraft were swept down the deck at a speed of more than 135 miles an hour. Within less than 150 feet the immense Banshee was airborne, and by the time it reached the forward edge of the carrier, it was headed toward its mission. Four times the catapults fired and four times heavy jets leaped into the darkening sky and headed for the coastline of Korea.

As soon as they had left, the bull horn wailed, "Respot planes. On the double. We must recover the Korea jets immediately."

When this announcement was made thirty old-fashioned propeller planes were already lashed down on the after part of the flight deck in precisely that area needed for landing the jets which now appeared overhead. The prop planes had been stowed there to permit catapult take-offs, and now they must be moved forward. So on the wooden deck, swept by icy winds, hundreds of young men in varicolored uniforms sped to the task of clearing the landing space. Men in green stowed the catapult gear so that no remnant of the powerful machine was visible. Other men in yellow leaped upon the deck and began to indicate the course each plane must follow on its way to forward stowage. Dozens of tough young men in blue leaned their shoulders against the planes, swung them laboriously into position and pushed them slowly into the biting wind. In blazing red uniforms other men checked guns or fueled empty craft while plane captains in brown sat in cockpits and worked the brakes to prevent accident. Darting about through the milling, pushing, shouting deck hands three-wheeled jeeps of vivid yellow and lumbering tractors in somber gray hurried to their jobs, while over all towered the mighty arms of the enormous black and sinister crane. Behind it lurked two weird men in fantastic suits of ashen gray asbestos, their faces peering from huge glassine boxes, ready to save the pilot if a crashed plane should burn, while in back of them, clothed in snowy white, the doctor waited, for death was always close upon the carrier deck.

So in an age of flight, in the jet age of incredible speed, these men pushed and pulled and slipped upon the icy deck and ordered the heavy planes with their bare hands. Upon trailing edges burdened with ice they pushed, their faces open to the freezing wind, their eyes heavy with frozen salt and the knuckles of their hands covered long since with protecting scars. And as they moved, their bright colors formed the pattern of a dance and after they had swarmed upon the deck for some minutes the *Savo* was transformed and from the lowering shadows the jets prepared to land.

This intricate operation was guided by one man. From the admiral's country he had directed the task force to run toward the communist coast. The last four jets had been dispatched at his command. He had placed the ships so that the operations of one would not trespass the allotted space of the other, and it was his responsibility to see that his carriers faced the wind in such position that smoke trailed off to one side rather than directly aft and into the faces of incoming pilots. Now he stood upon his bridge and watched the mountains of Korea moving perilously close.

Admiral George Tarrant was a tall narrow man with a sharp face that was sour and withdrawing like those of his Maine ancestors. Battle-wizened, he had fought the Japanese with his own carrier at Saipan, at Iwo Jima and at Okinawa, where his austere and lonely presence had brought almost as much terror to his own fliers as it had to the enemy.

He was known through the navy as George the Tyrant, and any aviator who wanted to fetch a big laugh would grab a saucer in his left hand, a coffee cup in his right, lean back in his chair and survey the audience sourly, snorting, "Rubbish." Then the mimic would stare piercingly at some one pilot, jab the coffee cup at him and growl, "You, son. What do you think?"

But men who served with Tarrant soon forgot his tyranny and remembered his fantastic skill in operating a task force. His men said flatly, "He can do it better than anyone else in the world." He knew the motion of the sea and could estimate whether a morning swell would rise to prevent recovery of afternoon planes or subside so that even jets could land freely. He was able to guess when new gales of bitter Siberian air would rush the line of snowstorms out to sea and when the snow would come creeping softly back and throw a blizzard about the task force as it slept at night. And he had a most curious ability to foresee what might trouble the tin-can sailors serving in the remote destroyers.

He fought upon the surface of the sea and in the sky. He sent his planes inland to support ground troops or far out to sea to spot Russian submarines. His was the most complex combat command of which one man's mind was capable and on him alone depended decisions of the gravest moment.

For example, the position he was now in, with mountains closing down upon him, was his responsibility. Early that morning his aerologist had warned, "Wind's coming up, sir. You might run out of ocean by late afternoon."

He studied the charts and growled, "We'll make it."

Now his navigator warned, "We can't hold this course more than sixteen minutes, sir." The young officer looked at the looming coastline as if to add, "After that we'll have to turn back and abandon the planes."

"We'll make it," Tarrant grumbled as his ships plowed resolutely on toward the crucial hundred fathom curve which he dare not penetrate for fear of shoals, mines and submarines. But he turned his back upon this problem, for he could do nothing about it now. Instead, he checked to be sure the *Savo's* deck was ready and in doing so he saw something which reassured him. Far aft, standing upon a tiny platform that jutted out over the side of the carrier, stood a hulking giant, muffled in fur and holding two landing-signal paddles in his huge hands. It was Beer Barrel, and if any man could bring jets surely and swiftly home, it was Beer Barrel.

He was an enormous man, six feet three, more than 250 pounds, and his heavy suit, stitched with strips of fluorescent cloth to make his arms and legs easier to read, added to his bulk. He was a farmer from Texas who before the perilous days of 1943 had never seen the ocean, but he possessed a fabulous ability to sense the motion of the sea and what position the carrier deck would take. He could judge the speed of jets as they whirled down upon him, but most of all he could imagine himself in the cockpit of every incoming plane and he seemed to know what tired and jittery pilots would do next and he saved their lives. He was a fearfully bad naval officer and in some ways a disgrace to his uniform, but everyone felt better when he came aboard a carrier, for he could do one thing. He could land planes.

He could reach out with his great hands and bring them safely home the way falconers used to bring back birds they loved. In the Pentagon they knew he broke rules and smuggled beer aboard each ship he served upon. Carrier captains knew it, and even Admiral Tarrant, who was a terror on navy rules, looked the other way when Beer Barrel staggered back after each drunken liberty, lugging his two ridiculous golf bags. The huge Texan had never once played golf and the two clubs sticking out were dummies. Once a deck hand, fearful that drunken Beer Barrel might slide back down the gangplank, had grabbed one of the outsize golf bags to help, but the surprising weight of it had crumpled him to the deck. Beer Barrel, barely able to heft the bag himself, had got it onto his massive shoulder, whispering beerily to the boy, "Thanks, Junior, but this is man's work." And he had carried the bags full of beer into his quarters.

For he believed that if he had a can of cold beer in his belly it formed a kind of gyroscope which made him unusually sensitive to the sea and that when this beer sloshed about it harmonized with the elements and he became one with the sea and the sky and the heaving deck and the heart of the incoming pilot.

"Land jets!" moaned the bull horn.

"Let's hear the checks," Beer Barrel said to his spotters, staring aft to catch the first jet as it made its 180° turn for the cross leg and the sharp final turn into the landing run. Now the jet appeared and Beer Barrel thought, "They're always pretty comin' home at night."

"All down!" the first watcher cried as he checked the wheels, the flaps and the stout hook which now dangled lower than the wheels.

"All down," Beer Barrel echoed unemotionally.

"Clear deck!" the second watcher shouted as he checked the nylon barriers and the thirteen heavy steel wires riding a few inches off the deck, waiting to engage the hook.

"Clear deck," Beer Barrel grunted phlegmatically.

He extended his paddles out sideways from his shoulders, standing like an imperturbable rock, and willed the plane onto the deck. "Come on, Junior," he growled. "Keep your nose up so's your hook'll catch. Good boy!" Satisfied that all was well, he snapped his right paddle dramatically across his heart and dropped his left arm as if it had been severed clean away from his body. Instantly the jet pilot cut his flaming speed and slammed his Banshee onto the deck. With violent grasp the protruding hook engaged one of the slightly elevated wires and dragged the massive plane to a shuttering stop.

Beer Barrel, watching from his platform, called to the clerk who kept records on each plane, "1593. Junior done real good. Number three wire." Never did Beer Barrel feel so content, not even when guzzling lager, as when one of his boys caught number three wire. "Heaven," he explained once, "is where everybody gets number three wire. Hell is where they fly wrong and catch number thirteen and crash into the barrier and burn. And every one of you's goin' straight to hell if you don't follow me better."

From his own bridge, Admiral Tarrant watched the jets come home. In his life he had seen many fine and stirring things: his wife at the altar, Japanese battleships going down, ducks rising from Virginia marshes and his sons in uniform. But nothing he knew surpassed the sight of Beer Barrel bringing home the jets at dusk.

There always came that exquisite moment of human judgment when one man—a man standing alone on the remotest corner of the ship, lashed by foul wind and storm—had to decide that the jet roaring down upon him could make it. This solitary man had to judge the speed and height and the pitching of the deck and the wallowing of the sea and the oddities of this particular pilot and those additional imponderables that no man can explain. Then, at the last screaming second he had to make his decision and flash it to the pilot. He had only two choices. He could land the plane and risk the life of the pilot and the plane and the ship if he had judged wrong. Or he could wave-off and delay his decision until next time around. But he could defer his job to no one. It was his, and if he did judge wrong, carnage on the carrier deck could be fearful. That was why Admiral Tarrant never bothered about the bags of beer.

On they came, the slim and beautiful jets. As they roared upwind the admiral could see their stacks flaming. When they made their far turn and roared downwind he could see the pilots as human beings, tensed up and ready for the landing that was never twice the same. Finally, when these mighty jets hit the deck they weighed well over seven tons and their speed exceeded 135 miles an hour, yet within 120 feet they were completely stopped and this miracle was accomplished in several ways. First, Tarrant kept his carriers headed into the wind, which on this day stormed in at nearly 40 miles an hour, which cut the plane's relative speed to about 95 miles. Then, too, the carrier was running away from the plane at 11 miles an hour, which further cut the plane's speed to 84, and it was this actual speed that the wires had to arrest. They did so with brutal strength, but should they miss, two slim nylon barriers waited to drag the plane onto the deck and chop its impetus, halting it so that it could not proceed forward to damage other planes. And finally, should a runaway jet miss both the wires and the barriers, it would plunge into a stout nylon barricade which would entwine itself about the wings and wheels and tear the jet apart as if it were a helpless insect.

But it was Beer Barrel's job to see that the barriers and the barricade were not needed and he would shout curses at his pilots and cry, "Don't fly the deck, Junior. Don't fly the sea. Fly me." An air force colonel watching Beer Barrel land jets exclaimed, "Why, it isn't a landing at all! It's a controlled crash." And the big Texan replied in his beery voice, "Difference is that when I crash 'em they're safe in the arms of God."

Now he brought in three more, swiftly and surely, and Admiral Tarrant, watching the looming mountains of Korea as they moved in upon his ships, muttered, "Well, we'll make it again."

ANDERSON COLLEGE
LIBRARY
ANDERSON, INDIANA

43444

But as he said these words his squawk box sounded, and from deep within the *Savo* the combat intelligence director reported coolly, "1591 has been hit. Serious damage. May have to ditch."

"What's his position?"

"Thirty-five miles away."

"Who's with him?"

"His wingman, 1592."

"Direct him to come on in and attempt landing."

The squawk box clicked off and Admiral Tarrant looked straight ahead at the looming coast. Long ago he had learned never to panic, but he had trained himself to look at situations in their gloomiest aspects so as to be prepared for ill turns of luck. "If this jet limps in we may have to hold this course for ten or fifteen more minutes. Well, we probably can do it."

He studied the radar screen to estimate his probable position in fifteen minutes. "Too close," he muttered. Then into the squawk box which led to the air officer of the *Savo* he said, "Recovery operations must end in ten minutes. Get all planes aboard."

"The admiral knows there's one in trouble?"

"Yes. I've ordered him to try to land."

"Yes, sir."

The bull horn sounded. "All hands. We must stop operations within ten minutes. Get those barriers cleared faster. Bring the planes in faster."

The telephone talker at the landing platform told Beer Barrel, "We got to get 'em all aboard in ten minutes."

"What's a matter?" Beer Barrel growled. "Admiral running hisself out of ocean?"

"Looks like it," the talker said.

"You tell him to get the planes up here and I'll get 'em aboard."

So the nineteen dark ships of the task force sped on toward the coastline and suddenly the squawk box rasped, "Admiral, 1591 says he will have to ditch."

"Can he ditch near the destroyers?"

"Negative."

"Is his wingman still with him?"

"Affirmative."

"How much fuel?"

"Six hundred pounds."

"Have you a fix on their positions?"

"Affirmative."

"Dispatch helicopter and tell wingman to land immediately."

There was a long silence and the voice said, "Wingman 1592 requests permission stay with downed plane till copter arrives."

The admiral was now faced with a decision no man should have to make. If the wingman stayed on, he would surely run out of fuel and lose his own plane and probably his life as well. But to command him to leave a downed companion was inhuman and any pilot aboard the *Savo* would prefer to risk his own life and his plane rather than to leave a man adrift in the freezing sea before the helicopter had spotted him.

For in the seas off Korea a downed airman had twenty minutes to live. That was all. The water was so bitterly cold that within five minutes the hands were frozen and the face. In twelve minutes of immersion in these fearful waters the arms became unable to function and by the twentieth minute the pilot was frozen to death.

The decision could not be deferred, for the squawk box repeated, "Wingman 1592 requests permission to stay."

The admiral asked, "What is the absolute minimum of gas with which the wingman can make a straight-in landing?"

There was a moment's computation. "Assuming he finds the carrier promptly, about four hundred pounds."

"Tell him to stay with the downed man . . ."

The voice interrupted, "Admiral, 1591 has just ditched. Wingman says the plane sank immediately."

There was a moment's silence and the admiral asked, "Where's the helicopter?"

"About three more minutes away from the ditching."

"Advise the helicopter . . ."

"Admiral, the wingman reports downed pilot afloat."

"Tell the wingman to orbit until helicopter arrives. Then back for a straight-in landing."

The bull horn echoed in the gathering dusk and mournful sounds spread over the flight deck, speaking of disaster. "Get those last two jets down immediately. Then prepare for emergency straight-in landing. A plane has been lost at sea. Wingman coming in short of fuel."

For a moment the many-colored figures stopped their furious motions. The frozen hands stopped pushing jets and the yellow jeeps stayed where they were. No matter how often you heard the news it always stopped you. No matter how frozen your face was, the bull horn made you a little bit colder. And far out to sea, in a buffeted helicopter, two enlisted men were coldest of all.

At the controls was Mike Forney, a tough twenty-seven-year-old Irishman from Chicago. In a navy where enlisted men hadn't much chance of flying, Mike had made it. He had bullied his way through to flight school and his arrival aboard his first ship, the *Savo*, would be remembered as long as the ship stayed afloat. It was March 17 when he flew his copter onto the flight deck, wearing an opera hat painted green, a Baron von Richthofen scarf of kelly green, and a clay pipe jammed into his big teeth. He had his earphones wrapped around the back of his neck and when the captain of the *Savo* started to chew him out Forney said, "When I appear anywhere I want the regular pilots to know it, because if they listen to me, I'll save 'em." Now, as he sped toward the ditched pilot, he was wearing his green stovepipe and his World War I kelly green scarf, for he had found that when those astonishing symbols appeared at a scene of catastrophe everyone relaxed, and he had already saved three pilots.

But the man flying directly behind Mike Forney's hat wasn't relaxed. Nestor Gamidge, in charge of the actual rescue gear, was a sad-faced inconsequential young man from Kentucky, where his unmarried schoolteacher mother had named him Nestor after the wisest man in history, hoping that he would justify everything. But Nestor had not lived up to his name and was in fact rather stupid, yet, as the copter flew low over the bitter waves to find the ditched plane, he was bright enough to know that if anyone were to save the airman pitching about in the freezing water below it would be he. In this spot the admiral didn't count nor the wingman who was orbiting upstairs nor even Mike Forney. In a few minutes he would lean out of the helicopter and lower a steel hoisting sling for the pilot to climb into. But from cold experience he knew that the man below would probably be too frozen even to lift his arms, so he, Nestor Gamidge, who hated the sea and who was dragged into the navy by his draft board, would have to jump into the icy waves and try to shove the inert body of the pilot into the sling. And if he failed—if his own hands froze before he could accomplish this—the pilot must die. That's why they gave Nestor the job. He was dumb and he was undersized but he was strong.

"I see him," Nestor said.

Mike immediately called to the wingman: "1592. Go on home. This is Mike Forney and everything's under control."

"Mike!" the wingman called. "Save that guy."

"We always save 'em. Scram."

"That guy down there is Harry Brubaker. The one whose wife and kids are waiting for him in Yokosuka. But he don't know it. Save him!"

Mike said to Nestor, "You hear that? He's the one whose wife and kids came out to surprise him."

"He looks froze," Nestor said, lowering the sling.

Suddenly Mike's voice lost its brashness. "Nestor," he said quietly, "if you have to jump in . . . I'll stay here till the other copter gets you."

In dismay, Nestor watched the sling drift past the downed pilot and saw that the man was too frozen to catch hold. So he hauled the sling back up and said, "I'll have to go down."

Voluntarily, he fastened the sling about him and dropped into the icy waves.

"Am I glad to see you!" the pilot cried.

"He's OK," Nestor signaled.

"Lash him in," Mike signaled back.

"Is that Mike? With the green hat?"

"Yep."

"My hands won't . . ."

They tried four times to do so simple a thing as force the sling down over the pilot's head and arms but the enormous weight of watersoaked clothing made him an inert lump. There was a sickening moment when Nestor thought he might fail. Then, with desperate effort, he jammed his right foot into the pilot's back and shoved. The sling caught.

Nestor lashed it fast and signaled Mike to haul away. Slowly the pilot was pulled clear of the clutching sea and was borne aloft. Nestor, wallowing below, thought, "There goes another."

Then he was alone. On the bosom of the great sea he was alone and unless the second helicopter arrived immediately, he would die. Already, overpowering cold tore at the seams of his clothing and crept in to get him. He could feel it numb his powerful hands and attack his strong legs. It was the engulfing sea, the icy and deadly sea that he despised and he was deep into it and his arms were growing heavy.

Then, out of the gathering darkness, came the *Hornet's* copter.

So Mike called the *Savo* and reported, "Two copters comin' home with two frozen mackerel."

"What was that?" the *Savo* asked gruffly.

"What I said," Mike replied, and the two whirly birds headed for home, each dangling below it the freezing body of a man too stiff to crawl inside.

Meanwhile Admiral Tarrant was faced with a new problem. The downed pilot had been rescued but the incoming wingman had fuel sufficient for only one pass, and if that pass were waved off the pilot would have to crash land into the sea and hope for a destroyer pickup, unless one of the copters could find him in the gathering dusk.

But far more important than the fate of one Banshee were the nineteen ships of the task force which were now closing the hundred fathom mark. For them to proceed farther would be to invite the most serious trouble. Therefore the admiral judged that he had at most two minutes more on course, after which he would be forced to run with the wind, and then no jet could land, for the combined speed of jet and wind would be more than 175 miles, which would tear out any landing hook and probably the barriers as well. But the same motive that had impelled the wingman to stay at the scene of the crash, the motive that forced Nestor Gamidge to plunge into the icy sea, was at work upon the admiral and he said, "We'll hold the wind a little longer. Move a little closer to shore."

Nevertheless, he directed the four destroyers on the forward edge of the screen to turn back toward the open sea, and he checked them on the radar as they moved off. For the life of one pilot he was willing to gamble his command that there were no mines and that Russia had no submarines lurking between him and the shore.

"1592 approaching," the squawk box rasped.

"Warn him to come straight in."

Outside the bull horn growled, "Prepare to land last jet, straight in."

Now it was the lead cruiser's turn to leave the formation but the *Savo* rode solemnly on, lingering to catch this last plane. On the landing platform Beer Barrel's watcher cried, "Hook down, wheels down. Can't see flaps."

The telephone talker shouted, "Pilot reports his flaps down."

"All down," Beer Barrel droned.

"Clear deck!"

"Clear deck."

Now even the carrier *Hornet* turned away from the hundred fathom line and steamed parallel to it while the jet bore in low across her path. Beer Barrel, on his wooden platform, watched it come straight and low and slowing down.

"Don't watch the sea, Junior," he chanted. "Watch me. Hit me in the kisser with your left wing tank and you'll be all right, Junior." His massive arms were outstretched with the paddles parallel to the deck and the jet screamed in, trying to adjust its altitude to the shifting carrier's.

"Don't fly the deck, Junior!" roared Beer Barrel and for one fearful instant it looked as if the onrushing jet had put itself too high. In that millionth of a second Beer Barrel thought he would have to wave the plane off but then his judgment cried that there was a chance the plane could make it. So Beer Barrel shouted, "Keep comin', Junior!" and at the last moment he whipped the right paddle across his heart and dropped the left.

The plane was indeed high and for one devastating moment seemed to be floating down the deck and into the parked jets. Then, when a crash seemed inevitable, it settled fast and caught number nine. The jet screamed ahead and finally stopped with its slim nose peering into the webs of the barrier.

"You fly real good, Junior," Beer Barrel said, tucking the paddles under his arm, but when the pilot climbed down his face was ashen and he shouted, "They rescue Brubaker?"

"They got him."

The pilot seemed to slump and his plane captain ran up and caught him by the arm and led him to the ladder, but as they reached for the first step they stumbled and pitched forward, so swift was the *Savo's* groaning turn back out to sea.

As soon as the copters appeared with little Gamidge and the unconscious body of the pilot dangling through the icy air, Admiral Tarrant sent his personal aide down to sick bay to tell the helicopter men he would like to see them after the flight doctor had taken care of them. In a few minutes they arrived in flag plot, Forney in trim aviator's flight jacket and Gamidge in a fatigue suit some sizes too large.

The admiral poured them coffee and said, "Sit down." Forney

grabbed the comfortable corner of the leather davenport on which the admiral slept when he did not wish to leave this darkened room of radar screens, repeating compasses and charts, but Gamidge fumbled about until the admiral indicated where he was to sit. Pointing at the squat Kentuckian with his coffee cup, the admiral said, "It must have been cold in the water."

"It was!" Forney assured him. "Bitter."

"I hope the doctor gave you something to warm you up."

"Nestor's too young to drink," Forney said, "but I had some."

"You weren't in the water."

"No, sir, but I had the canopy open."

"How's the pilot?"

"When me and Gamidge go out for them we bring them back in good shape."

"They tell me he wasn't able to climb into the sling."

"That pilot was a real man, sir. Couldn't move his hands or arms but he never whimpered."

"Because he fainted," Nestor explained.

The admiral invariably insisted upon interviewing all men who did outstanding work and now he pointed his cup at Gamidge again. "Son, do you know any way we could improve the rescue sling?"

The little Kentuckian thought a long time and then said slowly, "Nope. If their hands freeze somebody's got to go into the water to get them."

The admiral put his cup down and said brusquely, "Keep bringing them back. Navy's proud of men like you."

"Yes, sir!" Forney said. He always pronounced *sir* with an insinuating leer, as if he wished to put commissioned officers at ease. Then he added, "There is one thing we could do to make the chopper better."

"What's that?"

"I got to operate that sling quicker. Because it seems like Nestor goes into the sea almost every time."

"You know what changes to make?"

"Yes, sir."

"Then make them."

The two enlisted men thanked the admiral and as they went down the ladder Tarrant heard Forney ask, "Nestor, why'd you stand there with your mouth shut, like a moron? Suppose he is a mean old bastard. No reason to be scared of him."

"By the way," the admiral called. "Who was the pilot?"

"Brubaker, sir," Forney cried, unabashed.

The name struck Tarrant with visible force. He backed into the darkened flag plot and steadied himself for a moment. "Brubaker!" he repeated quietly. "How strange that it should have been Brubaker!"

Shaken, he slumped onto the leather davenport and reached for some papers which had been delivered aboard ship by dispatch plane that afternoon. "Brubaker!" He scanned the papers and called sick bay.

"Doctor," he asked, "any chance I could talk with Brubaker?"

A crisp voice snapped back, "Admiral, you know the man's suffered exposure."

"I know that, but there's an urgent matter and I thought that when he found himself in good shape . . ." He left it at that.

Then he thought of Brubaker, a twenty-nine-year-old civilian who had been called back into service against his will. At the start of the cruise he had been something of a problem, griping ceaselessly about the raw deal the navy had given him, but gradually he had become one of the two or three finest pilots. He still griped, he still damned the navy, but he did his job. The admiral respected men like that.

But Brubaker had a special significance, for on recent cruises Admiral Tarrant had adopted the trick of selecting some young man of about the age and rank his older son would have attained had the Japs not shot him down while he was trying to launch a navy fighter plane on the morning of Pearl Harbor. Tarrant found satisfaction in watching the behavior of such pilots, for they added meaning to his otherwise lonely life.

But in the case of Harry Brubaker the trick had come close to reality. The Banshee pilot had the quick temper of his sons, the abiding resentments, the courage.

Admiral Tarrant therefore desperately wanted to leave flag plot and go down into the ship and talk with Brubaker, but custom of the sea forbade this, for the captain of any ship must be supreme upon that ship, and even the flag admiral who chances to make his quarters aboard is a guest. So Admiral Tarrant was cooped up in flag plot, a tiny bedroom and a special bridge reserved for his use. That was his country and there he must stay.

There was a knock upon the door and the aide said, "Sir, it's Brubaker!"

The good-looking young man who stuck his head in was obviously a civilian. He wore two big bathrobes and heavy woolen socks but even if he had worn dress uniform he would have been a civilian. He was a little overweight, his hair was a bit too long and he wasn't scared enough of the admiral. Indelibly, he was a young lawyer from Denver, Colorado, and the quicker he got out of the navy and back into a courtroom, the happier he'd be.

"You can scram now," he told the medical corpsman who had brought him up to the admiral's country.

"Come in, Brubaker," the admiral said stiffly. "Cup of coffee?" As he reached for the cup Brubaker didn't exactly stand at attention but the admiral said quickly, "Sit down, son. How's the Banshee take the water?"

"All right, if you fly her in."

"You keep the tail down?"

"I tried to. But as you approach the water every inclination is to land nose first. Then from way back in the past I remembered an October night when our family was burning leaves and at the end my mother pitched a bucket of water on the bonfire. I can still recall the ugly smell. Came back to me tonight. I said, 'If I let water get into the engines I'll smell it again.' So I edged the plane lower and lower. Kept the engines up and the tail way down. When the nose finally hit I was nearly stopped. But I was right. There was that same ugly smell."

"How was the helicopter?"

"That kid in back deserves a medal."

"They handle the rescue OK?"

"This man Forney. When I looked up and saw that crazy hat I knew I had it knocked."

Admiral Tarrant took a deep gulp of coffee and studied Brubaker across the rim of his cup. He knew he oughtn't to discuss this next point with a junior officer but he had to talk with someone. "You say the green hat gave you a little extra fight?"

"You're scared. Then you see an opera hat coming at you out of nowhere. You relax."

"I would. Forney was in here a few minutes ago. Put me right at ease. Implied I was doing a fair job. You've got to respect a character like that. But the funny thing is . . ." He looked into his cup and said casually, "Captain of the ship's going to get rid of Forney. Says the hat's an outrage."

Brubaker knew the admiral was out of line so he didn't want to press for more details but he did say, "The pilots'd be unhappy."

The admiral, far back in his corner of the davenport, studied the bundled-up young man and jabbed his coffee cup at him. "Harry, you're one of the finest pilots we have. You go in low, you do the job."

Brubaker grinned. He had a generous mouth and even teeth. His grin was attractive. "From you, sir, I appreciate that."

"Then why don't you stay in the navy? Great future here for you."

The grin vanished. "You know what I think of the navy, sir."

"Still bitter?"

"Still. I was unattached. The organized units were drawing pay. They were left home. I was called. Sometimes I'm so bitter I could bitch up the works on purpose."

"Why don't you?" Tarrant asked evenly.

"You know why I don't, sir. The catapult fires. There's that terrific moment and you're out front. On your way to Korea. So you say, 'What the heck? I'm here. Might as well do the job.'"

"Exactly. The President once rebuked me publicly. I'd had that big fight with the battleship boys because they didn't think aviation was important. Then the brawl with the air force who thought it too important. I know I'll never get promoted again. But you're here and you do the job."

"It would be easier to take if people back home were helping. But in Denver nobody even knew there was a war except my wife. Nobody supports this war."

At the mention of Brubaker's wife the admiral unconsciously reached for the file of papers, but he stopped because what the young pilot said interested him. "Every war's the wrong one," he said. "Could anything have been stupider than choosing Guadalcanal for a battleground? And look at us today!" With his cup he indicated on the chart where the permanent snow line, heavy with blizzards and sleet, hung a few miles to the east, while to the west the mountains of Korea hemmed in the ships. "Imagine the United States navy tied down to a few square miles of ocean. The marines are worse. Dug into permanent trenches. And the poor air force is the most misused of all. Bombers flying close air support. Militarily this war is a tragedy."

"Then why don't we pull out?" Harry asked bluntly.

Admiral Tarrant put his cup and saucer down firmly. "That's rubbish, son, and you know it. All through history free men have had to fight the wrong war in the wrong place. But that's the one they're stuck with. That's why, one of these days, we'll knock out those bridges at Toko-ri."

Flag plot grew silent. The two men stared at each other. For in every war there is one target whose name stops conversation. You say that name and the men who must fly against that target sit mute and stare ahead. In Europe, during World War

II it was Ploesti or Peenemunde. In the Pacific it was Truk or the Yawata steel works. Now, to the navy off Korea, it was the deadly concentration of mountains and narrow passes and festering gun emplacements that hemmed the vital bridges at Toko-ri. Here all communist supplies to the central and eastern front assembled. Here the communists were vulnerable.

Finally Brubaker asked, "Do we have to knock out those particular bridges?"

"Yes, we must. I believe without question that some morning a bunch of communist generals and commissars will be holding a meeting to discuss the future of the war. And a messenger will run in with news that the Americans have knocked out even the bridges at Toko-ri. And that little thing will convince the Reds that we'll never stop . . . never give in . . . never weaken in our purpose."

Again the two men studied each other and the admiral asked, "More coffee?" As Brubaker held his cup the old man said gruffly, "But I didn't call you here to discuss strategy. I'm supposed to chew you out." With the coffee pot he indicated the file of papers.

"They crying because I wrecked that wheel?"

"No. Because of your wife."

The astonishment on Brubaker's face was so real that Tarrant was convinced the young man was unaware his wife and two daughters were in Japan. Nevertheless he had a job to do so he asked, "You knew she was in Japan?"

"She made it!" A look of such triumph and love captured Brubaker's face that the admiral felt he ought to look away. Then quietly the young man said, "This is more than a guy dares hope for, sir."

"You better hope you don't get a court martial."

"I didn't tell her to come," Brubaker protested, but such a huge grin captured his face that he proved himself a liar.

Tarrant kept on being tough. "How'd she get here without your help?"

"Politics. Her father used to be senator from Wyoming."

Brubaker closed his eyes. He didn't care what happened. Nancy had made it. In the jet ready rooms he had known many pilots and their women troubles but he kept out of the bull sessions. He loved one girl. He had loved her with letters all through the last war in New Guinea and Okinawa. The day he got home he married her and she'd never given him any trouble. Now she was in Japan. Quietly he said to the admiral, "If she's broken a dozen rules to get here it's all right by me."

The old man didn't know what to say. "War's no place for women," he grunted.

Then Brubaker explained. "If my wife really is in Japan, I know why. She couldn't take America any longer. Watching people go on as if there were no war. We gave up our home, my job, the kids. Nobody else in Denver gave up anything."

This made the admiral angry. "Rubbish," he growled. "Burdens always fall on a few. You know that. Look at this ship. Every man aboard thinks he's a hero because he's in Korea. But only a few of you ever really bomb the bridges."

"But why my wife and me?"

"Nobody ever knows why he gets the dirty job. But any society is held together by the efforts . . . yes, and the sacrifices of only a few."

Brubaker couldn't accept this, Tarrant realized, and he was getting mad in the way that had characterized the admiral's sons. The old man had learned to respect this attitude, so he waited for the young pilot to speak but Brubaker happened to think of his wife waiting in Japan and his anger left. "Look," he said. "It's sleeting." The two men went to the dark window and looked down upon the silent carrier, her decks fast with ice, her planes locked down by sleet.

"It'll be all right by dawn," the old man said.

"You ever hear what the pilots say about you and the weather? 'At midnight he runs into storms but at take-off the deck's always clear, damn him.' "

The admiral laughed and said, "Three days you'll be in Japan. No more worry about take-offs for a while." He slapped the papers into a basket. "I'll tell Tokyo you had nothing to do with bringing your wife out here."

"Thank you, sir."

Quickly the admiral resumed his austere ways. Shaking Brubaker's hand he said stiffly, "Mighty glad you were rescued promptly. Why don't you see if the surgeon can spare a little extra nightcap."

As soon as Brubaker left, Tarrant thought, "His wife did right. If mine had come to Hawaii when our oldest son was killed, maybe things would have been different." But she had stayed home, as navy wives are expected to, and somewhere between the bombing of Pearl Harbor, where she lost one son, and the battle of Midway, where her second was killed trying to torpedo a Japanese carrier, her mind lost focus and she started to drink a lot and forget people's names until slowly, like petals of apple blossoms in spring, fragments of her gentle personality fell away and she would sit for hours staring at a wall.

Therefore it angered Tarrant when civilians like Brubaker suggested that he, a professional military man, could not understand war. Quite the contrary, he knew no civilian who understood war as thoroughly as he. Two sons and a home he had given to war. He had sacrificed the promotion of his career by insisting that America have the right weapons in case war came. And now in Korea, of the 272 pilots who had initially served with him in his task force, 31 had been killed by communist gunfire. Tonight he had come within two minutes of losing Brubaker, the best of the lot. No one need tell him what war was.

He was therefore doubly distressed when the people of the United States reacted like Brubaker: "Hold back the enemy but let someone else do it." He felt that his nation did not realize it was engaged in an unending war of many generations against resolute foes who were determined to pull it down. Some of the phases of this war would no doubt be fought without military battles. Whole decades might pass in some kind of peace but more likely the desultory battles would stagger on and from each community some young men would be summoned to do the fighting. They would be like Brubaker, unwilling to join up but tough adversaries when there was no alternative. And no matter where they might be sent to serve, Tarrant was positive that they would hate that spot the way he and Brubaker hated Korea. It would always be the wrong place.

As if to demonstrate afresh how ridiculous Korea was, the aerologist appeared with the midnight weather reports from Siberia and China. Since these nations were not officially at war, their weather stations were required to broadcast their customary summaries, just as American and Japanese stations broadcast theirs. But since Korean weather was determined by what had happened in Siberia and China two days before, the admiral always had the tip-off and the enemy gained nothing.

"All wars are stupid," the old man grunted as he filed the Siberian reports. "But we'd better learn to handle the stupidity." He recalled England and France, dragging through their Korean wars for more than two hundred years. They had avoided panicky general mobilization and millions of citizens must have spent their lives without worrying about war until something flared up like Crimea, South Africa or Khartoum.

"And their wars weren't even forced upon them," he growled. Secretly he was frightened. Could America stick it out when dangers multiplied? If Englishmen and Frenchmen, and before them Athenians and the men of Spain, had been willing to support their civilizations through centuries of difficulty when often those difficulties were self-generated, what would happen to the United States if her citizenry abandoned the honorable responsibilities forced upon her by the relentless press of history?

He went up on the bridge to check the rolling sea for the last time. "What would they have us abandon to the enemy?" he asked. "Korea? Then Japan and the Philippines? Sooner or later Hawaii?" He walked back and forth pondering this problem of where abandonment would end, and as the sleet howled upon him he could not fix that line: "Maybe California, Colorado. Perhaps we'd stabilize at the Mississippi." He could not say. Instead he held to one unwavering conviction: "A messenger will run in and tell the commissars, 'They even knocked out the bridges at Toko-ri.' And that's the day they'll quit." Then reason might come into the world.

Upon that hope he ended the long day. He had checked the wind and the weather and the rolling of the sea and the number of planes ready for the dawn strike and the location of those storms that always hovered near his ships. He had posted the night watches and he could do no more.

LAND

IT WAS the greatest liberty port in the world. It had more variety than Marseilles, more beauty than Valparaiso. Its prices were cheaper than New York's, its drinks better than Lisbon's. And there were far more pretty girls than in Tahiti.

It was Yokosuka, known through all the fleets of the world as Yu-*koss*-ka, and almost every man who had been there once had a girl waiting for him when he got back the second time. For in the cities near the port were millions of pretty girls who loved American sailors and their hilarious ways and their big pay checks. It was a great liberty port.

Now as the *Savo* moved cautiously in toward her dock hundreds of these girls waited for their sailors and thousands were on hand for sailors they had not yet seen. Grim-faced guards kept the invaders away from the ship, but the girls did gather outside the gates, and among them on this windy, wintry day was one especially handsome girl of twenty dressed in plaid skirt from Los Angeles, trim coat from Sears Roebuck, and jaunty cap from San Francisco. She wore her jet hair in braids and kept a laugh ready in the corners of her wide, black eyes. Her complexion was of soft gold and seemed to blush as some of the other girls caught a glimpse of the *Savo* and pretended they had seen her sailor.

"There's green hat!" they cried in Japanese.

"You don't worry about green hat," she replied, pressing against the fence.

A comic among the girls put her right hand high above her head and swaggered as she had seen Mike Forney swagger on earlier leaves, and excitement grew as the *Savo* approached her berth. But this morning the girls would have to stand in the cold a long time, for there was a sharp wind off the sea and the lumbering bulk of the carrier presented so much freeboard for the wind to blow against that tugs with limited maneuvering space could not hold her from crashing into the quay, and emergency measures were clearly necessary. Accordingly the bull horn wailed the bad news, "F4U and AD pilots prepare for windmill."

Every propeller pilot cringed with disgust but none showed such outrage as one of the jet men. Stocky, florid faced, with a cigar jutting from his teeth, this forty-year-old Annapolis man whipped his bullet head and underslung jaw toward the bridge to see what stupid fool had ordered another windmill. As "Cag," commander of the air group, he was in charge of all planes and felt sickened as he watched the propeller jobs wheel into position. He was about to storm off the flight deck and raise a real row when Brubaker, standing with him, caught his arm and said, "Take it easy, Cag. You don't have to pay for the burned out engines."

"It's murder," the Cag groaned as his valuable prop planes

were lashed down to the edge of the deck which threatened to crash against the quay. Their noses were pointed into the wind and their unhappy pilots sat in the cockpits and waited.

"Start engines," yowled the bull horn. Sixteen valuable engines revolved and sixteen sets of propeller blades tried to pull the big carrier away from the quay, but the effort was not sufficient, and the *Savo* appeared certain to crash.

"Enginess full speed," moaned the bull horn and the noise on deck became great as the props clawed into the air and magically held the great ship secure against the wind.

This caused no satisfaction among the propeller pilots, for since their planes were stationary on deck, with no wind rushing through to cool them, each engine was burning itself seriously and one plane mechanic rushed up to the Cag with tears in his eyes cursing and crying, "They're wrecking the planes! Look!"

One of the low-slung F4U's had begun to throw smoke and the Cag ran over to study it. He chomped his cigar in anger and said grimly, "They're killing these planes."

"Somebody's got to stop this," the mechanic said.

"I'm going to," Cag replied quietly and started for the admiral's plot, but before he could get there Brubaker hauled him down and the two men watched the propeller planes gradually ease up and allow the *Savo* to inch into her berth as gently as a fragile egg being laid into a basket by an old farm wife.

"Cut engines," rasped the bull horn and the Cag said bitterly, "Burn those engines up now and next trip over Korea the pilot bails out. This lousy captain thinks he has a new toy to play with."

"Save it for the hotel," Brubaker said. "Take it up with the admiral there." So the Cag turned away and as he did so Brubaker looked down from the carrier deck onto the quay and there stood Nancy and the two girls, dressed in winter coats and huddling together to protect one another from the wind. A great lump came into his throat and for a moment he could not wave or call, so that Mike Forney, who was marching up and down, impatient to burst ashore, asked, "That your family, sir?"

"Yes."

"It's worth bein' saved for them, sir." The way Mike said *sir* made Brubaker look to see if the cocky Irishman were kidding him, but Forney was staring raptly at Nancy and the two girls. "Hey, Mrs. Brubaker!" he roared. "Here's your hero."

Jumping up and down on her toes Nancy called excitedly to her daughters, "There's Daddy!" And they all threw him kisses.

Mike, watching with approval, said, "Right beyond that fence, sir, I got the same kind of reception waiting for me."

"You married?" Brubaker asked in astonishment. Somehow he had never thought of Mike as a family man.

"Not yet, but I may be. This shore leave."

"Some girl who came out with the Occupation?"

"Japanese girl," Mike said, adjusting his green hat at a night-club angle, but a messenger from the ship's executive officer arrived to inform Forney that the uniform of the day called for something more traditional and the insulted Irishman went below.

Immediately Brubaker wished that Mike had stayed, for the pain of seeing his women on the quay below was too great. They had come too far, they loved him too much and they reminded him too soon of icy Korea's waters clutching at him, trying to drag him down. For the first time in his life he became desperately afraid and wanted to leave the *Savo* right then, for he saw leading from the deck of the carrier, right above the bodies of his wife and daughters, four bridges stretching far out to sea and they were the bridges of Toko-ri and he was breathlessly afraid of them.

"Nancy," he whispered. "You should have stayed home."

But as soon as the ship's lines were secured, he dashed down the gangplank to embrace his wife and as he did so his young-est daughter caught him by the leg and began to babble furiously and from the way he bent down and listened to the excited little girl—as if he actually wanted to know what she had to say—every married man on the deck of the *Savo* towering above knew that Brubaker really loved his kids.

What the child said was, "I made a long airplane ride and now I know what you do on the ship." But Brubaker remembered the icy water and thought, "Thank God you don't know. And thank God your mummy doesn't, either." Then he laughed and caught the little girl in his arms and kissed her a lot and she said, "I like to fly airplanes like you, Daddy."

For Mike Forney reunions were somewhat less complicated, at first. Attended by silent Nestor Gamidge he strode to the gates of Yokosuka Naval Base, threw the marine on guard a nifty salute and stepped outside to freedom. He was a cocky figure, his fists jammed into his pea coat jacket, his uniform a trifle too tight, and it took him only a moment to find the girls. He stopped dead, thrust his big paw onto Gamidge's chest and cried, "Look at her, Nestor! Best-dressed girl in Japan!" Then he gave a bellow, rushed forward and caught Kimiko in his arms and kissed her lovely little cap right off her head.

"Hey, Kimiko! Fleet's in!"

To his astonishment she pushed him away, sedately picked up her cap and said, "Not so fast, big boy. We got to talk." And she led him to a bar and started patiently to explain the radically new situation, the one which was to cause the two riots.

For the officers of the *Savo* the Tokyo brass had reserved rest and recuperation rooms at the Fuji-san, a meandering Japanese hotel whose exquisite one-storied rooms and gardens hung on a mountain top which commanded a superb view of Fujiyama. In the old days this had been Japan's leading hotel but for the first six years after the war it served Americans only. Now, in the transition period between occupation and sovereignty, it had become a symbol of the strange and satisfying relationship between Japan and America: the choice rooms were still reserved for Americans but Japanese were welcome to use the hotel as before; so its spacious gardens, bent with pine and cherry, held both Japanese families who were enjoying luxury after long years of austerity and American military men savoring the same luxury after long months in Korea.

No one enjoyed the Fuji-san more than Admiral Tarrant. He arrived on the second day of liberty, changed into civilian clothes, gathered about him his younger staff officers and forgot the rigors of Task Force 77. Other admirals, when they reached Japan, were whisked into Tokyo for press conferences where they sat on the edges of their chairs trying to say exactly the right and innocuous thing. They must not, for example, admit that they were fighting Russians, nor must they even indicate that any of our men were being killed. In this special war there were special rules to keep the people back in America from becoming worried.

Admiral Tarrant was not the man for such interviews. The navy tried it once and he had said bluntly, "We're fighting Russian guns, Russian radar, Russian planes and Russian submarines. And a hell of a lot of our men are being killed by this Russian equipment, manned by Russian experts." General Ridgway's headquarters in Tokyo had blown a gasket and the entire interview was made top secret and the navy was advised that whereas Tarrant might be terrific as a task force commander, "Send him to some good hotel when he gets ashore . . . and keep him there."

Now he lounged in the bar and watched a group of pilots pestering Beer Barrel. Ten minutes after the *Savo* docked, the landing-signal officer had grabbed for the bar stool and he had sat there for almost twenty-nine hours, lapping up the wonderful Japanese beer. "Look at him!" one Banshee pilot cried. "He's going crazy. Doesn't know whether to claim Texas has the biggest midgets in the world or the smallest."

Four jet men, themselves pretty well hung over, formed a solemn circle about Beer Barrel and began to chant the carrier pilot's version of the Twenty-third Psalm:

The Beer Barrel is my shepherd
I shall not crash.
He maketh me to land on flat runways: he bringeth me in off
    the rough waters.
He restoreth my confidence.
Yea, though I come stalling into the groove at sixty knots, I
    shall fear no evil: for he is with me; his arm and his paddle,
    they comfort me.
He prepareth a deck before me in the presence of mine ene-
    mies; he attacheth my hook to the wire; my deck space run-
    neth over.

Admiral Tarrant laughed at the nonsense. Since his big operation two years ago he drank only coffee, but he often growled, "Just because I'm a reformed drunk no reason why I should deny pleasure to others." He poured himself some inky black coffee and looked into the gardens, where he saw Harry Brubaker's wonderfully lovely wife and her two daughters and they reminded him of what wars were all about. "You don't fight to protect warships or old men. Like the book says, you fight to save your civilization. And so often it seems that civilization is composed mainly of the things women and children want."

Then the admiral grew glum, for Mrs. Brubaker had told him at lunch, "If the government dared to ask women like me, this stupid war would end tomorrow." There lay the confusion. These bright, lovely women, whose husbands had to do the fighting, wanted to end the war on any terms; but these same women, whose children would have to live through servitude or despair should America ever be occupied, would be the precise ones who would goad their men into revitalization and freedom. So Admiral Tarrant never argued with women because in their own deep way they were invariably right. No more war . . . but no humiliation. He hoped to see the day when this difficult program could be attained.

But a more present problem was at hand, for the Cag stormed

across the garden, his cigar jutting belligerently ahead like a mine sweeper. The tough airman was known throughout the navy as a fireball and this time Tarrant, himself an airman, knew the Cag was right. The *Savo's* use of windmill had been intemperate, a perversion of aircraft engines, but a deeper concern was involved, so the admiral prepared to squelch the likeable hothead.

For the navy high command had secretly asked Tarrant to send in a concurrent report upon this demon flier when his Korean duty ended. It was hinted that a bright and brash young man was needed for rapid promotion to a command of real authority and Tarrant guessed that the Cag was being weighed as an eventual task force commander. "It's a big job," the admiral mused.

He could recall that day in 1945 when Admiral Halsey commanded a supreme force built of five components each twice as large as present Task Force 77. It was so vast it blackened the sea with more than twenty carriers. It stretched for miles and ultimately it sank the entire Japanese fleet. One brain had commanded that incredible force and it behooved the United States to have other men ready for the job, should such a task force ever again be needed.

Long ago Tarrant had begun to argue that some new weapon —rockets perhaps or pilotless planes of vast speed—would inevitably constitute the task force of the future. He had seen so much change, indeed had spurred it on, that he could not rely perpetually on ships or airplanes or any one device. But until America was secure behind the protection of some new agency that could move about the earth with security and apply pressure wherever the enemy chose to assault us, it would be wise to have young officers trained to command a sea burdened with ships and speckled with the shadows of a thousand planes.

Perhaps the Cag was such a man. A lot of navy people thought so but no one knew for sure whether he had those two ultimate requirements for vast command: had he a resolute spirit and had he due regard for human life?

The Cag jammed his cigar through the door and asked, "May I speak with you, sir?"

Tarrant liked the younger man's brusque approach. "Sit down. Whisky?"

"Please."

"What's wrong?"

The Cag sailed right in. Chomping his cigar he snorted, "These lazy carrier captains. They're burning up our engines."

Tarrant thought he'd better let the fireball have it right between the eyes. Staring coldly he asked, "You think you could handle a carrier better?"

This stunned the Cag and he fumbled for a moment. Then, fortunately, the bar boy arrived with his drink and he grabbed for it. "You not having one, sir?" he asked.

"You know the doctor made me lay off," the admiral explained coldly.

Such treatment threw the Cag off balance, for he knew Tarrant's power in the navy. The old man may have queered his own promotion but he was still known as the incorruptible and his judgment on the promotions of others was prized.

In the embarrassing silence Tarrant asked grimly, "What's your major complaint against the carrier captains?"

The veins stood out on the Cag's bullet head, but he stamped his cigar out and said firmly, "They shouldn't burn up our propeller planes."

"How would you berth a big ship against the wind?"

"In the old days I would have waited. But whatever I did I wouldn't run a lashed-down engine at top speed."

Admiral Tarrant stared impersonally at Fujiyama, the wonderful mountain, and although he wanted to agree with Cag, he pondered precisely what question would most completely throw this young hothead off balance. Finally he settled on: "So you'd have a group of complaining F4U pilots dictate naval procedure?"

Again the Cag was staggered. "Sir, I . . . ." He fumbled for words and then blurted out with startling force, "Sir, an engine has only so many good hours. If you burn them up on deck. . . ." He fumbled again and ended weakly, "Why can't they use half-power?"

The admiral turned slowly away from Fujiyama and asked bleakly, "Do you consider an F4U engine more valuable than a carrier?"

The Cag retreated. "What I was trying to say. . . ."

"Another whisky?"

The Cag needed something to restore his confidence but reasoned that if the old man was in an evil mood he'd better not accept two drinks, so he said lamely, "Thank you, sir, but I have a reservation for one of the sulphur baths."

"They're fun," the admiral said mournfully and when the Cag awkwardly excused himself, the old man sagged into a real depression, for he found it ugly to watch a promising young commander back away from what he knew was right. "Well," Tarrant grumbled, "he's popular. He'll be able to wangle a desk job. But he's no good for command. And I'll have to say so when we get home." Grieved, he decided to leave the bar.

But before he could get away, young Brubaker and his pretty wife approached and it was apparent she had been crying. "She wants to talk to you," Brubaker said with the air of a young husband who hopes somebody else can say the magic word which he has been unable to find.

"My husband tells me you can explain why this war is necessary," she said. "I sure wish somebody would."

"It isn't necessary," Tarrant said. Then, seeing the Brubakers' surprise he added, "You two have something to drink?"

"May we join you?" Nancy asked.

"Doctor won't let me." Then, seeing the young people frown, he added humorously, "I have no vices, no ambitions, no family and no home."

"That's what I mean," Nancy said. "I can understand why you get excited about war. But we do have a home and family."

"I'm not excited about war," the admiral contradicted. "And I don't think it's necessary. That is, it wouldn't be in a sensible world. But for the present it is inevitable." He poured himself some coffee and waited.

"If it's inevitable, why should the burden fall on just a few of us?" Nancy pressed.

"I don't know. You take the other night when your husband. . . ." Before he could tell of the ditching he saw Brubaker make an agonized sign indicating that Nancy knew nothing of the crash and the admiral thought, "Like the rest of America, she's being protected."

He salvaged the sentence by concluding, "Your husband bombed a bridge. Because he's one of the best pilots in the navy he knocked out two spans. He didn't have to do it. He could have veered away from the bridge and no one would ever have known. But some men don't veer away. They hammer on in, even though the weight of war has fallen unfairly on them. I always think of such men as the voluntary men."

Nancy fought back her tears and asked, "So until the last bridge is knocked out a few men have to do the fighting? The voluntary men."

"That's right. The world has always depended upon the voluntary men."

Before Nancy could reply, the bar boy hurried up and asked, "Is Lieutenant Brubaker here?" The boy led Harry to a back door of the hotel where Nestor Gamidge stood, bloody and scarred.

"I'm sure glad to see you, lieutenant," he gasped. His blues were ripped and his face was heavily bruised.

"What's up?"

"Mike's been in a terrible fight, sir."

"Where?"

"Tokyo. I came out in a cab."

"What happened?"

"He's in jail."

"A public riot?"

"Yep. His girl's marryin' a bo'sun from the *Essex*."

"You mean his . . . Japanese girl?"

"Yes, and if you don't come in he'll be locked up permanent."

Tokyo was sixty miles away and to rescue Forney in person would consume many hours of leave that he might otherwise spend with his family, so Brubaker said, "I'll phone the M.P.'s."

"Callin' won't help, sir. Mike clobbered two M.P.'s as well as the gang from the *Essex*."

"You two take on the whole town?"

"Yes, sir."

Brubaker had to grin at the vision of these two tough kids on the loose and made up his mind abruptly. "I'll help."

He hurried back to where Nancy and the admiral sat and said quickly, "Admiral Tarrant, will you please see that Nancy gets dinner? There's been trouble in Tokyo and I . . ."

"Oh, no!" Nancy protested.

"Admiral, it's Mike Forney."

"Drunken brawl?"

"Girl threw him over."

Nancy pleaded, "On our second night, why do you have to get mixed up with drunken sailors?"

Brubaker kissed his wife and said tenderly, "Darling, if Mike were in China I'd have to help."

"But, Harry. . . ." It was no use. Already he was running down the long hallway.

When Nancy realized that her husband actually was on his way to Tokyo, she looked beseechingly at Admiral Tarrant and pleaded, "Who's this Mike Forney he thinks more of than his own children?" Her eyes filled with tears and she fumbled for a handkerchief.

The admiral studied her closely and asked, "If you were freezing to death in the sea and a man brought his helicopter right over your head and rescued you, wouldn't you help that man if he got into trouble?"

Nancy stopped crying and asked, "Did Harry crash at sea?"

"Yes."

She looked down at her white knuckles and unclasped her

hands. Very quietly she said, "You know your husband's at war. You know he's brave. But somehow you can't believe that he'll fall into the sea." Her voice trembled.

When she regained control Admiral Tarrant asked, "Has Harry told you about the bridges? At Toko-ri?"

"No. He never talks about the war."

"You must ask him about those bridges."

Weakly she asked, "Is he involved with the bridges?"

"Yes. When we go back to sea, your husband must bomb those bridges."

In a whisper she asked, "Why do you tell me this?"

He replied, "In 1942 I had a daughter as sweet as you. She was my daughter-in-law, really. Then my son was killed at Midway trying to torpedo a Jap carrier. She never recovered. For a while she tried to make love with every man in uniform. Thought he might die one day. Then she grew to loathe herself and attempted suicide. What she's doing now or where she is I don't know, but once she was my daughter."

Nancy Brubaker could hardly force herself to speak but in an ashen voice she asked, "You think that . . . well, if things went wrong at the bridges . . . I'd be like. . . ."

"Perhaps. If we refuse to acknowledge what we're involved in, terrible consequences sometimes follow."

A strange man was telling her that war meant the death of people and that if she were not prepared, her courage might fall apart and instinctively she knew this to be true. "I understand what you mean," she said hoarsely.

"Let's get your little girls and we'll have dinner," Tarrant said.

But Nancy was too agitated to see her daughters just then. She pointed to the end of the bar where Beer Barrel lay at last sprawled upon his arms, his face pressed against the polished wood. "Will he fly against the bridges, too?" she asked.

When the admiral turned to survey the mammoth Texan his lean, Maine face broke into a relaxed smile. "That one?" he said reflectively. "He flies against his bridges every day."

When Brubaker and Gamidge reached Tokyo, night had already fallen and there was slush upon the wintry streets that lined the black moat of the emperor's palace. At the provost marshal's office a major asked sourly, "Why you interested in a troublemaker like Forney?"

"He's from my ship."

"Not any more."

"Major," Brubaker asked directly, "couldn't you please let me handle this?"

"A mad Irishman? Who wrecks a dance hall?"

"But this man has saved the lives of four pilots."

"Look, lieutenant! I got nineteen monsters in the bird cage. Every one of them was a hero in Korea. But in Tokyo they're monsters."

Patiently Brubaker said, "Mike's a helicopter pilot. The other night Mike and this sailor. . . ."

The major got a good look at Nestor and shouted to a sergeant, "Is this the runt who slugged you?"

"Listen, major!" Harry pleaded. "The other night I ditched my plane at sea. These two men saved my life. This runt, as you called him, jumped into the ocean."

The major was completely unimpressed. Staring at Nestor he said scornfully, "I suppose the ocean tore his clothes. Did he get his face all chopped up jumping into a wave?"

"All right, there was a brawl."

"A brawl! A brawl is when maybe six guys throw punches. These two monsters took on all of Tokyo."

It was apparent to Brubaker that pleading along normal lines would get nowhere, so he asked bluntly, "You married, major?"

"Yep."

"Tonight's the second night in eight months that I've seen my wife and kids. I left them at Fuji-san to get Mike out of jail. That's what I think of these two men."

The major stared at the docket listing Mike's behavior. "You willin' to cough up $80 for the damage he did?"

"I'd pay $800."

"He's yours, but you ain't gettin' no prize."

A guard produced Mike Forney, his face a nauseating blue in contrast to the green scarf. "She's marryin' an ape from the *Essex*," he said pitifully.

"I suppose you tried to stop her."

"I would of stopped the ape, but he had helpers."

When they reached the narrow streets where hundreds of Japanese civilians hurried past, Mike begged, "Talk with her, please, lieutenant. She might listen to you."

He led Brubaker to one of the weirdest dance halls in the world. A war profiteer had cornered a bunch of steel girders and had built a Chinese junk in the middle of Tokyo. He called it the Pirates' Den and installed an open elevator which endlessly traveled from the first floor to the fifth bearing an eleven-piece jazz band whose blazing noise supplied five different dance floors. The strangest adornment of the place was a mock airplane, piloted by an almost nude girl who flew from floor to floor delivering cold beer.

The steel ship was so ugly, so noisy and so crammed with chattering girls that Brubaker wondered how anyone had known a riot was under way and then he met Kimiko, Mike's one-time love. She was the first Japanese girl he had ever spoken to and he was unprepared for her dazzling beauty. Her teeth were remarkably white and her smile was warm. He understood at once why Mike wanted her, and when she rose to extend her hand and he saw her slim perfect figure in a princess evening dress which Mike had ordered from New York, he concluded that she warranted a riot.

"I very sorry, lieutenant," she explained softly, "but while Mike at sea I lose my heart to *Essex* man. *Essex* not at sea."

"But Mike's a fine man," Brubaker argued. "No girl could do better than Mike."

Kimiko smiled in a way to make Brubaker dizzy and plaintively insisted, "I know Mike good man. But I lose my heart."

Things started to go black for Mike again and he shouted,

"Not in my dress, you don't lose it!" And he clawed at the dress which represented more than two months' pay.

Kimiko began to scream and the owner of the Pirates' Den blew a shrill whistle and prudent Nestor Gamidge said, "We better start runnin' now."

"Not without this dress!" Mike bellowed.

Nestor handled that by clouting Mike a withering blow to the chin, under which the tough Irishman crumpled. Then Nestor grabbed him by the arms and grunted, "Lieutenant, sir. Ask the girls to push."

In this way they worked Mike out a back door before the M.P.'s could get to him, but in the alley Nestor saw that Mike still clutched part of Kimiko's dress. He pried this loose from the stiff hand and returned it to Kimiko, saying, "You can sew it back on." Upon returning to Brubaker he reported, "Japanese girls are sure pretty." But when Mike woke up, sitting in one of the gutters west of the Ginza, he said mournfully, "Without Kimiko I want to die."

Gently they took him to the enlisted men's quarters, where Gamidge put the rocky Irishman to bed. When this was done, the little Kentuckian laboriously scratched a note and tucked it into the lieutenant's fist: "We owe you $80. Mike and Nestor." Then Brubaker started the long trip back to Fuji-san, where his wife waited.

It was nearly three in the morning when he reached the Fuji-san, but Nancy was awake and when he climbed into bed she clutched him to her and whispered, "I'm ashamed of the way I behaved. Admiral Tarrant told me about Mike Forney."

"I wish he hadn't. But don't worry. Nobody ever crashes twice."

There was a long silence and she kissed him as if to use up all the kisses of a lifetime. Then she controlled her voice to make it sound casual and asked, "What are the bridges at Toko-ri?" She felt him grow tense.

"Where'd you hear about them?"

"The admiral." There was no comment from the darkness so

she added, "He had good reason, Harry. His daughter-in-law had no conception of war and went to shreds. He said if I had the courage to come all the way out here I ought to have the courage to know. Harry, what are the bridges?"

And suddenly, in the dark room, he wanted to share with his wife his exact feelings about the bridges. "I haven't really seen them," he whispered in hurried syllables. "But I've studied pictures. There are four bridges, two for railroads, two for trucks, and they're vital. Big hills protect them and lots of guns. Every hill has lots of Russian guns."

"Are Russians fighting in Korea?"

"Yes. They do all the radar work. We have only two approaches to the bridges. The valley has one opening to the east, another to the west. When we bomb the bridges we must dive in one end and climb out the other." He hesitated and added quickly, "At Toko-ri there is more flak than anywhere in Germany last time. Because the communists know where you have to come in from. And where you have to go out. So they sit and wait for you."

They whispered until dawn, a man and wife in a strange land talking of a war so terrible that for them it equaled any in history. Not the wars of Caesar nor the invasions of Napoleon nor the river bank at Vicksburg nor the sands of Iwo were worse than the Korean war if your husband had to bomb the bridges, and toward morning Nancy could control her courage no longer and began to cry. In her despondency she whispered, "What eats my heart away is that back home there is no war. Harry, do you remember where we were when we decided to get married?"

"Sure I remember. Cheyenne."

"Well, when I was explaining to the girls about the birds and the bees Jackie looked up at me with that quizzical grin of hers and asked, 'Where did all this stuff start?' and I said, 'All right, smarty, I'll take you up and show you.' And I took them to the Frontier Days where you proposed and I almost screamed with agony because everything was exactly the way it was in 1946.

Nobody gave a damn about Korea. In all America nobody gives a damn."

When the morning sun was bright and the girls had risen, Harry Brubaker and his wife still had no explanation of why they had been chosen to bear the burden of the war. Heartsick, they led their daughters down to one of the hotel's private sulphur baths, where they locked the door, undressed and plunged into the bubbling pool. The girls loved it and splashed nakedly back and forth, teasing shy Nancy because she wouldn't take off all her clothes, so she slipped out of her underthings and joined them.

They were cavorting in this manner when the locked door opened and a Japanese man entered. He bowed low to both Nancy and Harry, smiled at the girls and started to undress. "Hey!" Harry cried. "We reserved this!" But the man understood little English and bowed to accept Harry's greeting. When he was quite undressed he opened the door and admitted his wife and two teen-age daughters, who laid aside their kimonos. Soon the Japanese family stood naked by the pool and dipped their toes in. Harry, blushing madly, tried to protest again but the man said with painstaking care, "Number one! Good morning!" and each of his pretty daughters smiled and said musically, "Good morning, sir!"

"*Ohio gozaimasu!*" shouted the Brubaker girls, using a phrase they had acquired from their nurse. This pleased the Japanese family and everyone laughed gaily and then the man bowed again. Ceremoniously, father first, the family entered the pool.

By now Harry and Nancy were more or less numb with astonishment, but the pleasant warmth of the room, the quiet beauty of the surroundings and the charm of the Japanese family were too persuasive to resist. Harry, trying not to stare at the pretty girls, smiled at the Japanese man, who swam leisurely over, pointed to one of the Brubaker girls and asked, "Belong you?"

Harry nodded, whereupon the man called his own daughters who came over to be introduced. "Teiko, Takako," the man said. They smiled and held out their hands and somehow the bitterness of the long night's talking died away. The two families intermingled and the soft waters of the bath united them. In 1944 Harry had hated the Japanese and had fought valiantly against them, destroying their ships and bombing their troops, but the years had passed, the hatreds had dissolved and on this wintry morning he caught some sense in the twisted and conflicting things men are required to do.

Then he sort of cracked his neck, for he saw Nancy. His shy wife had paddled to the other side of the pool and was talking with the Japanese man. "We better hurry or we'll miss breakfast," Harry said, and for the rest of his stay they became like the spectators at the Cheyenne Frontier Days and they enjoyed themselves and never spoke of Korea.

Then shore leave ended in one of those improbable incidents which made everyone proud he served aboard a good ship like the *Savo*. Admiral Tarrant went aboard at noon and toward four Beer Barrel staggered up the gangplank with his two golf bags. Brubaker had obtained permission for Nancy to see his quarters but when she found how astonishingly small the room was and how her husband slept with his face jammed under two steam pipes she said she felt penned in and would rather stay on deck.

In the meantime hundreds of sailors and their Japanese girls had crowded into Yokosuka and in the lead were Mike Forney and Nestor Gamidge, accompanied by seven girls from the dance halls of Tokyo, Yokohama and Yokosuka. "I never knew there were so many girls," Nestor said to one of the plane captains. "Best thing ever happened to Mike was losing Kimiko to that ape from the *Essex*."

Mike agreed. When he had kissed his girls good-bye he swung onto the quay, elbows out, and pointed to the *Savo*: "Greatest flattop in the fleet." Then he stopped dead for he saw that the *Essex* was alongside and there stood beautiful Kimiko, wearing the expensive plaid he had bought her. She was kissing her ape from the *Essex* and things went black. Clenching his fists, Mike lunged toward the lovers but little Nestor grabbed him.

Mike stopped, slapped himself on the head and muttered, "Sure, what's one girl?" With grandiloquent charm he approached Kimiko, kissed her hand and said loudly, "The flower of Japan." Then he grabbed the *Essex* man warmly and proclaimed, "The flower of the fleet. The best man won. Bless you, my children."

Then everything fell apart. For some loud mouth in the *Essex* yelled derisively, "And we could lick you bums in everything else, too."

Mike whirled about, saw no one, then looked back at golden Kimiko and she was beautiful in that special way and she was his girl. Blood surged into his throat and he lunged at the *Essex* man standing with her and slugged him furiously, shouting, "You lousy ape!"

Six *Essex* men leaped to defend their shipmate and stumpy Nestor Gamidge rallied *Savo* men and soon M.P. whistles were screeching like sparrows in spring and there was a growing melee with men in blue dropping all over the place. Mike, seeing himself about to be deluged by *Essex* reinforcements, grabbed a chunk of wood and let the ape have it across the ear, laying him flat. At this Kimiko started to scream in Japanese and Mike grabbed her hat and tried to pull off the pretty plaid jacket, bellowing, "Go ahead and marry him. But not in my clothes." Three *Essex* men, gallant to the end, knocked him silly.

The captain of the *Savo* witnessed this disgraceful riot and determined on the spot to get rid of Mike Forney, but Admiral Tarrant, surveying the brawl from flag bridge, thought, "I'd hate to see the day when men were afraid to mix it up for pretty girls." He called for his glasses and studied Kimiko, who knelt over her *Essex* man and all the sailors aboard the *Savo* and the officers too were a little more proud of their ship.

SKY

THE SUN had to be well up or the photographs wouldn't be any good, so it was nearly 0945 when Harry Brubaker's jet catapulted violently across the prow of the *Savo* and far into the sky toward Korea. Ahead of him streaked a single Banshee with an extraordinary nose containing nine broad windows through which heavy cameras would record the bridges of Toko-ri.

While the *Savo* was in Yokosuka, other carriers were supposed to photograph the target but they had failed. When Cag bent his bullet head over their muddy films he growled, "What's the matter? They afraid to go down low? We'll show 'em how to take pictures," and he assigned himself the dangerous mission, choosing Brubaker to fly protective cover.

Now, as the two Banshees streaked toward higher altitudes Brubaker concerned himself with trivial details: "Lay off those even altitudes. Use 25,300. Makes it just that much tougher for the anti-aircraft crews. And remember that when Cag goes down for the pictures, keep 3,000 feet above him."

Then, in the perpetually mysterious way, when he had climbed into the higher atmosphere, he experienced the singing beauty of a jet as it sped almost silently through the vast upper reaches of the world. Sea and sky fell away and he was aloft in the soaring realm of the human spirit.

It was terrible and supreme to be there, whistling into the morning brilliance, streaking ahead so fast that the overwhelming scream of his engines never quite caught up. In this moment of exhilaration he peered into the limitless reaches of the upper void and felt the surging sensation that overtakes every jet pilot: "I'm out front." Through the silent beauty of this cold February morning he soared through the blue-black upper sky and thought, "I'm out front."

Then, as his eyes swept the empty sky in casual patterns, he uttered a stunned cry, "My God! There it is!" But when he looked directly at what he had seen it vanished, so he returned to scanning and from the powerful corner of his eye he saw it again, tremendous and miraculously lovely, one of the supreme sights of creation: Fujiyama in morning sunlight towering above the islands of Japan. The cone was perfect, crowned in dazzling white, and the sides fell away like the soft ending of a sigh, and somewhere on the nether slope Nancy and the girls were waiting.

He now looked at the majestic volcano with his full eye, but again it was the omniscient corner which startled him, for it detected the mountains of Korea. Dead ahead they lay, bold and blunt and ugly. Tortured and convoluted, they twisted up at the two fleeting jets, the terrible mountains of Korea. They were the mountains of pain, the hills of death. They were the scars of the world's violent birth, the aftermath of upheavals and multitudes of storms. There was no sense to them and they ran in crazy directions. Their crests formed no significant pattern, their valleys led nowhere, and running through them there were no discernible watersheds or spacious plains. Hidden among them, somewhere to the west, cowered the bridges of Toko-ri, gun-rimmed and waiting.

Brubaker knew the guns would be waiting, for as the Banshees crossed the coastline, a signal battery in Wonsan fired and he could follow the course of other gun bursts across Korea, for the communists announced impending danger exactly as the Cheyennes of Colorado had done two hundred years before.

Now the day's hard work began. As soon as the Banshees came in range of communist guns, Cag began to descend in swift jinking dips and dives to confuse ground gunners, never staying on either course or altitude for longer than fifteen seconds. This threw a special responsibility on Brubaker who stayed aloft, weaving back and forth lest some stray MIG try to pounce upon the preoccupied photographic plane. So imperceptible was Cag's silvery slim Banshee as it skimmed across the mountain tops that Brubaker was taxed to keep his eye upon it.

At Yangdok a flurry of ground fire exploded at almost the right altitude to catch the photographic plane, so the jets increased speed to 560, jinking violently. Below them they spotted the ruins of a less important bridge, four spans rusting in the river. Farther on a communist working party strove to rebuild a major bridge, but this morning Cag ignored them, certain that later fights would halt the work. For now on the horizon rose the peaks that guarded Toko-ri.

Each was pock-marked with many circular red depressions in the snow. These were the gun emplacements and in swift estimate Brubaker decided there must be more than sixty. Lower were gaunt walled nests for the huge five-inch guns, a single shell from which could pulverize a plane before it fell to earth. And deep within the hills, hiding along the river, were the four bridges. On this first fleeting glance he noticed that the two historic bridges were on tall stone pillars and decidedly vulnerable, but that the two emergency alternates were extraordinarily low, scarcely clearing the water.

But most significant of all was one solemn fact: to get to the bridges you really did have to fly in one end of a valley, traverse it and fly out the other end. Brubaker swallowed and thought, "They got you lined up going and coming. And when you pull out for rendezvous you're a dead duck." Then he laughed to relieve his tension and whispered, "No wonder they saved this one till last."

At that instant Cag started his bold run into the western entrance to the valley. Pushing his nose down into a 40° dive, he screamed along the shimmering river, held courageously to the hairline railroad tracks, and roared upon the bridges at 580 miles an hour. During each inch of this run more than two hundred communist guns fired at the streaking Banshee, but it howled straight on, its cameras grinding, making no concession to the fire. Cag had one mission only, to bring back photographs, and he ignored everything else. Five-inch guns, three-inchers, machine guns and even carbines blazed at his wailing jet, but at last he pulled away from the mortal pit and with a sickening upward twist sped off to the north.

For a moment Brubaker lost the sleek Banshee as it fled to the hills for rendezvous. In some anxiety he cast his eyes swiftly left and right and thus caught a fleeting glimpse of the plane in the corner of his eye. Quickly rotating his vision in that area he gradually pinpointed the photographic plane, twisting and turning toward the safer hills. He had the sensation of spying upon an animal retreating to some sheltered valley after a wounding fight.

"Drop down and look me over," Cag called. "My tail section OK?"

Brubaker passed under the long-nosed jet and studied the fuselage minutely, for although both planes were doing more than 400 miles, in relation to each other they were nearly motionless. "Nothing visible," he reported.

"Back we go," Cag said.

The photographic jet heeled over in a tight turn, jinked to a lower altitude and went into a paralyzing dive. Out of the sun it streaked with blazing speed, but the communist gunners were waiting and in monomaniac fury they poured their fire upon the wraith-like Banshee as it screamed upon them. It seemed positively impossible that Cag could writhe his way through such fire but he bore on, clicking his shutters at the doomed bridges.

From aloft Brubaker followed this incredible mission and experienced a resolute desire to be there with his commander, but the instant this thought came to mind it was dispelled by the vision he had seen at Yokosuka: four bridges reaching out into space far above the heads of his wife and daughters, and he grew afraid; for he knew that tomorrow as the sun came up he would be pushing his own overloaded Banshee down, down upon the real bridges. It was then that the great fear came upon him, the one he would not be able to dispel.

Then he heard Cag cry, "Well, home we go."

Ecstatically the two jets zoomed to 26,000. Far below them the savage, cheated mountains of Korea began to assume a beautiful countenance. Gone were the tortured profiles and the senseless confusion, for with the bridges of Toko-ri behind him, Brubaker saw Korea with a kindlier eye. To the north sprawling reservoirs glistened like great brooches, holding the hills together. To the south snow hung upon the ridge lines and made the valleys shimmering wonderlands of beauty, while beyond the upcoming range of mountains lay the vast blue sea, bearing somewhere upon its bosom the task force, that fair circle of home, with Beer Barrel waiting on the after deck.

Even Cag was impressed and called, "Real estate sure looks better on the way home."

But when they reached home there was dismal news. "You heard the hot scoop?" Harry's plane captain asked as soon as Brubaker was out of the cockpit.

"We ordered home?"

"Forney and Gamidge are being sent to the barge."

"The barge?" This was a scow stationed near the Korean coast, and helicopter men with that duty lived miserably and engaged in one dangerous land mission after another.

A destroyer moved in and the last the *Savo* saw of Mike Forney was when he climbed into the bo'sun's chair, green top hat, green scarf and Irishman's pipe. "I'll send you the eighty bucks, sir," he yelled, giving the word *sir* its old infuriating touch.

Brubaker didn't care if the captain was watching. He grabbed the disgraced man's hand and said, "Take care of yourself, Mike. Pilots need you."

"I go for rough duty," Mike yelled, clutching his hat as the lines started to draw him over to the destroyer. "Because I really hate communists."

The chair dipped perilously toward the sea but Mike kept his legs clear. Instinctively the pilots cheered but the Irishman yelled derisively, "You apes go into the drink, not me!"

The new helicopter pilot was an officer, a college kid and no doubt competent, but the jet men and propeller crews knew that flying off the *Savo* would be a little tougher now.

The fear that was reborn when Brubaker watched Cag dive into the valley at Toko-ri grew all that day, augmented by the gloom of Mike Forney's dismissal and the briefing. After dinner, in the crowded ready room, the intelligence officer had passed around marked copies of the photographs made that morning and said, "Take-off at 0900. By then the sun will have driven ground fog out of the valley. Keep well south of the guns at Majon-ni. Cag, you tell them about the approach."

Cag, cigar in mouth, said briefly, "On paper it looks like a lot of flak concentrated here." He jabbed at the map with his right forefinger. "But it's not accurate. We'll go in low. We'll go in three times. And we'll go in from the east each time. When we're through, there won't be any more bridges."

There were some questions and then Cag handed them the cold dope. He held his cigar in his left hand and said, "Marty, you take your four men in at 1000 feet to suppress flak. I'll follow with my four at 1200. Brubaker, you mop up."

Tightly Brubaker gripped the arms of his chair and fought back his fear. He couldn't fly this mission. He couldn't take his jet inside that blazing rim of hills. His old bitterness at having been called back into service sneaked up into his throat and corroded his courage. Frantically, as if afraid he might break down before his peers, he rose and hurried out.

Stumbling down the narrow passageways of the carrier, he banked against stanchions and bruised his shin upon the damnable hatches. Seeking out his own room he slammed the door shut and climbed up into his bed under the steam pipes. In uncontrolled panic, there in the dark room, he cast about for some way to avoid the strike against the bridges.

"I'll go see the doc. I'll just walk in and announce, 'I've lost my nerve.'" Impulsively he climbed down and started for the door. Then he stopped and laughed nervously at himself.

For the navy had worked out the perfect way to handle situations like this. Suppose you went in and said you were too jittery to fly, the doc simply said, "OK. Don't fly." It was so easy that a man thought a hundred thousand times before he used that dodge. He stood alone, sweating, in his dark room and recalled the Cag's flight into the valley, and almost without knowing it he uttered the tricky words that bind a man to duty, those simple words that send men in jet planes against overwhelmingly protected bridges: "If Cag can fly that flak, so can I." That was what kept the navy system working. You could weasel out any time, but within the essence of your conscience lived the memory of other men no less afraid than you who were willing to tackle the dirty jobs. So you stuck.

But then a late flight returned and he thought ungraciously, "What mission did they draw? Rail cuts. Up where there are no guns. Why don't they get the bridges? Why does it have to be me?"

He felt ashamed of himself and turned on the light but was appalled by his own gray and ashen face in the mirror. "Get hold of yourself!" he commanded. Methodically, as if attention to some one job would restore his courage, he sat down to write a letter to his wife, but after he had written only a few lines he drew back in disgust. "You stinker!" he whispered at his picture in the mirror. "Scaring Nancy by letting her know you expect to be killed at the bridges."

He began a new letter and with great composure told Nancy how much he loved the children and of how he longed for the days of peace when they could all go camping again in the Rockies back of Denver. He ended with a paragraph in which he described in detail the suit she had worn that day on the quay at Yokosuka. "It looked very expensive," he wrote, "and I was amazed when you said you made it yourself."

But when he crawled back into bed things were worse than before and like a stabbing agony in the darkness he cried, "Why does it have to be me?" He remembered the men he had known in Colorado. Some hated their wives but they stayed home. Others hated their jobs, but they stayed on those jobs. Some of them, he recalled, had always wanted to travel, some had loved airplanes, others were always picking a fight and some good Catholics like Mike Forney hated communism so much they could taste it. Others were poor and needed navy pay. But all of them stayed home.

Through the long night Brubaker wrestled with his fear. Toward morning he was taken with frenzy and leaped from bed, rushing down the passageway to report his loss of nerve, but he never reached the doctor. A shattering sound halted him and in the gloomy darkness he whispered, "They're launching the dawn planes. It won't be long now." Then the catapult fired again and he remembered something Forney had once said and he stumbled down the ladder to the port catapult room, breaking in among the crew and crying, "Where did Mike Forney stand?"

"Here."

"Is that the piston he told me about?"

"Yep."

Before Brubaker could ask more questions the engine fired and from its nest forward eleven tons of gleaming metal roared back with appalling force to stop a few inches from his face. Involuntarily he stumbled backward. The enlisted men laughed.

"Forney stood stock still," they said.

Mike had explained that he came to the catapult room whenever his nerves were getting tight and the explosion of that enormous piston right into his face cured him: "If a guy can take that, he can take anything," Mike had said, but before Brubaker got set the monstrous machine fired again and that tremendous gleaming force sprang at him. He fell back.

"Takes a real idiot to stay put," a crewman shouted.

"You ever tried it?" Brubaker asked.

"I ain't no idiot."

Brubaker rooted himself to a position from which he could not be budged, and like a frightened bullfighter he mumbled to himself, "This time I keep my feet here." While he watched, the mighty piston leaped at him, then stopped with a powerful uuuuush less than four inches from his face.

The catapult crew applauded and said, "Pretty soon now you'll be as crazy as Forney."

"Is that bad?" Brubaker asked. Briskly he returned through the darkened ship and climbed into bed. "Well," he assured himself, "at least I'm not yellow." But immediately he was more afraid: "Because you know the catapult's got to stop. But the guns at Toko-ri never do."

So when the messenger called at 0700 he found Brubaker awake and sweating, staring at the steam pipes. When he reported to the wardroom bleary-eyed, Cag asked, "What were you doing in the catapult room last night?"

There was no use kidding anybody so he replied, "I was jittery."

"Does sticking your face in a piston cure that?"

"Yes."

Cag knew he should have left it at that but this mission was too important so he asked, "You want to ground yourself? Because today we've got to do a first-rate professional job."

"That's what I'm here for."

"Good. I put you in the follow-through spot because I know that if my gang miss the bridges, you'll get 'em."

"I'm going to."

At 0730 the pilots moved into the cold ready room where the worst part of the flight took place. Twelve reasonably trim lithe young athletes began to pile onto themselves such a mass of encumbrances that soon they waddled like pigs, completely muscle bound and sweating from every pore. Sometimes even the bravest pilots felt their nerves shiver when they faced the degrading job of dressing for a winter flight.

Brubaker started in shorts. First he climbed into long-handled woolen underwear, then into a skin-tight g-suit, which applied pressure on vital parts of his body so that when he pulled out of steep dives the enormous drag of gravity, the g's, would not suck all the blood from his head. He covered the g-suit with inch-thick quilted underwear, two pairs of short bulky socks and a third which reached his knees. Then came the rough part, for even though the watertight rubber poopy suit had already saved his life once, getting into it was always murder.

Since the neck band had to be tight to keep out freezing water and since no zippers were allowed, he had to get into the poopy suit in a special way. A long slash ran from the left shoulder across the chest and down to the right hip and he climbed in through this hole, pushing his feet down into the massive boots and his head up through the impossibly tight neck band. Then he grabbed the two flaps of extra rubber along the slash and rolled them together into a bulky, watertight seal which fattened him like a watermelon. And as soon as he closed this final seal he began to sweat like a pig and every minute he wore the poopy suit he was smelly and wet and uncomfortable. From time to time he pulled the neck band out and blew fresh air inside to get some relief. That's why the ready room was kept so cold, to keep the pilots from sweating, but all the same they sweated.

After the poopy suit came the survival vest, the pistol, the bulky Mae West, the hip knife, three cumbersome pairs of gloves, golden crash helmet, oxygen connection, harness straps and heavy goggles. Weighed down like some primeval monster, he waddled to the escalator which lifted him to the flight deck —another trick to keep down sweat—where an enlisted man handed him the board for clamping onto his knee with navigation data, codes, plots and all kinds of miscellaneous papers.

Even when he climbed into his jet there was more gear, so complicated that his plane captain had to crouch behind him and adjust safety belt, shoulder harness, ejection gear, microphone cord and oxygen supply. Harry Brubaker, who was about to soar into space with a freedom no previous men in history had known, was loaded down with such intolerable burdens that at times he felt he must suffocate; just as many citizens of his world, faced with a chance at freedoms never before dreamed of, felt so oppressed by modern problems and requirements that they were sure they must collapse.

As Brubaker adjusted himself to the cockpit he was hemmed in on left and right by more than seventy-five switches and controls. Directly facing him were sixteen instruments and thirteen more switches. He thought, "If there were one more thing to do. . . ." He never finished the sentence for the mighty catapult fired and he was shot into space, where the suffocating paraphernalia and the maze of switches seemed to fall away and he roared into the upper blue, tied down only by his cancerous fear of the bridges at Toko-ri.

But today he would not see those bridges, for at Wonsan the radio crackled and he heard Cag's disappointed voice, "Weather scout reports target closed in. Ground fog. Stand by for alternate instructions."

When Brubaker heard this life-saving news he shouted, "A reprieve! I knew I wasn't meant to tackle the bridges today." He started to sing the chorus of *Cielito Lindo* but stopped in embarrassment when he saw that in his surging joy he had unconsciously lifted his Banshee 400 feet higher than the formation.

But ground fog did not save him, for in the next minute a miracle of modern war occurred. Cag received a radio message from Admiral Tarrant, and instantly the twelve jets stopped in midflight, almost as if they were a flock of pheasant searching for a Colorado grain field. Abruptly they turned south, heading for the mountainous battle front, where in the trenches a new emergency had arisen.

At dawn that morning a battalion of South Korean infantry had been hit by a murderous concentration of communist power and it became apparent that the Koreans would be annihilated unless air support could be provided. So a United States army liaison officer serving at the front phoned a Korean general, who called the United States army command in Seoul, who got hold of an air force general, who said he had no planes but would try to get some from a marine general, who suggested that Admiral Tarrant, far out to sea, might have some to spare. The inquiry arrived in flag plot just as the early-morning weather plane was reporting: "Toko-ri closed in but good. Takusan ground fog. Takusan no see."

Tarrant, who normally would not see such a message, made a note to chew out a pilot who would use Japanese in a battle report, and replied, "One flight of twelve heavily armed jets available. Already air-borne."

Seoul immediately ordered, "Proceed Roundelay. Operate as he directs."

So by means of field telephone, radio, ship-to-shore communication and ship-to-plane, American jets were diverted to rescue South Korean foot soldiers. As the planes swept south Cag called ahead, "Roundelay, twelve jets reporting for orders. We're loaded."

From the bright morning sky came a whispery voice: "This is Roundelay. I'm flying an SNJ."

Each jet pilot was astonished that in today's swift war the out-of-date old SNJ would still be used. It had been ancient before they took basic training, but no one had quite the shock that Harry Brubaker experienced. "An SNJ?" he repeated incredulously and he was back in 1935, a gangling boy stretched out upon the floor, quietly and supremely happy, for he had mailed the box tops and the company had kept its promise.

Here was the highly colored put-together of America's latest plane. "It was an SNJ," he recalled.

Then suddenly from behind a mountain, there was the real SNJ, a rickety, two-bladed propeller job with a high greenhouse, a useless spare seat and six smoke rockets slung precariously under its wings. A slap-happy air force captain was wheeling it slowly around and Harry thought, "What's an SNJ doing here?" Then he learned.

"This is Roundelay. Get the big guns first."

"Can't see 'em," Cag said.

"Follow me."

And to the amazement of the jet pilots Roundelay trundled his slow plane down almost to the treetops and delivered a smoke rocket against the target. "See it now?" he called.

"Will do!" Cag cried, and he led his twelve screaming jets into a howling dive, right onto the gun and it fired no more.

"Strictly wonderful," Roundelay called. "D'you see the other two?"

"Negative."

"Watch this smoke." And the buglike SNJ hopped almost at ground level up a narrow valley to deliver another smoke rocket against another gun. Then, when it seemed the midget plane must follow the rocket against the rocks, the pilot twisted free, skipped over a ridge and ducked down upon a third gun.

"Will do!" Cag reported, and when his swift jets had silenced the guns, Roundelay called cheerily, "You must come back often."

The jets had zoomed so high they could not keep track of the tiny plane, but then sunlight glinted on the ridiculous greenhouse and they heard Roundelay call, "I think I see Red troops beginning a new attack. Follow me." And once more he hurried off like a busy old woman going to market.

Brubaker's division was aloft and he watched Cag's four jets roar low into a column of communists assaulting a hill. With appalling accuracy the Banshees spread their hundred pound bombs, each wound with high-tension steel wire that shattered into small pieces with machine gun fury. The communist advance wavered.

"Next division," Roundelay called. "Keep hitting them while they're confused."

"Will do," Brubaker replied, but as he prepared for his dive, the SNJ wheeled suddenly and Roundelay called, "Do you see what I see?"

Below, in obedience to some order of incredible stupidity, more than one hundred communists had moved out of a woods and onto a frozen road, and as Brubaker's jets came screaming at them they did an even more unbelievable thing. They fell to their knees in the middle of the road, clasped their arms about their heads and made no effort to escape inevitable death. The tactic so astonished Brubaker that he gasped, "They're sitting ducks!" And some ancient boyhood training in the mountains back of Denver restrained him.

But when he had zoomed high into the heavens he heard the unemotional voice of Roundelay: "Clobber those guys. That's their standard trick. Throwing you off balance."

So the jets wheeled and came screaming back down the road. Not a communist moved. Not one hit the ditch. They huddled and waited. "Here it comes," Brubaker whispered grimly, and his finger pressed the trigger. Keeping his eye upon the kneeling troops, he watched his bullets spray a path among them. "You wanted trouble," he said weakly.

Roundelay now spotted another column of attacking communists and called in Cag's division. Brubaker, with sickening detachment, watched the merciless jets and thought, "Those people in Denver who ridicule air force reports of enemy dead ought to see this." And he remembered Admiral Tarrant's words: "If we keep enough planes over them enough hours somebody's got to get hurt. And when they hurt bad enough, they'll quit."

"How's your fuel?" Roundelay asked.

"Can do one more pass," Cag replied, and the jet pilots, who approached the speed of sound, watched as the slow little doodlebug SNJ hopped about in search of fat targets. Brubaker, pulling out of his last bombing run, sped past the prop plane and for an instant of suspended time the two men looked casually at each other. Harry saw that the air force man was very thin and wore a moustache but he saw no more, for a five-inch communist gun, hidden until then, fired one lucky shot and blew the frail little SNJ completely to ribbons.

In terrible fury Brubaker launched his jet at the gun and tried to root it from its cave. He carried his fire almost into the muzzle of the enemy gun. Then, although his fuel was getting tight, he turned and made another run, pushing his jet to a deadly speed. He saw the gun, saw the wounded crew and the shell casings. On he came, firing until his own guns were silent, and the communists fell away. Then he zoomed aloft to overtake the homeward jets, but except for his wingman the planes were far away.

"You ought to tell me when you're going to run wild," the wingman protested.

"I really clobbered that one," Brubaker said grimly, but as the two Banshees soared away from the ravaged battleground with its wrecked artillery and dead bodies huddled along frozen roads, the enemy gun that Brubaker thought he had destroyed resumed firing. Mute with outrage, Brubaker wanted to dive upon it once more but he heard his wingman say, "Their side has guts, too."

Finally, when the roar of battle was past and the jets were far in the wintry sky Brubaker called, "How's your fuel?"

"Thousand five."

His own gauge read just under a thousand and he thought, "I hope Beer Barrel is bringing us in." Then he heard his wingman cry, "There's Cag, up ahead."

The two jets increased speed to rejoin the flight and all pilots began the difficult job of trying to spot the task force. Drifting clouds mottled the sea and made the ships almost invisible, but they had to be within a small area, for to the east hung the permanent snow line and to the north a new storm boxed in the fleet, but no one could see the ships.

It was ridiculous. Twelve highly-trained pilots couldn't find a task force of nineteen ships, including carriers, cruisers and a battleship. For some perverse reason Brubaker took delight in this limitation of human beings and thought, "You never master this business." Then Cag called, "There's home!" and where absolutely nothing had been visible a moment before the jet pilots saw the nineteen ships. And Brubaker, seeing them as big as barns on an open meadow, laughed.

But his relief didn't last because when the jets descended he saw that the carrier deck was pitching rather formidably, and this meant many wave-offs because the landing officer would have to wait until the carrier stabilized itself between lurches, so that you might approach in perfect altitude but find the deck in a momentary trough and have to go round again. That took fuel. Because when you got a wave-off you had to pour it on. And there went your fuel.

Then he had a happy thought: "They probably haven't turned into the wind. The deck'll be better when they do."

But as he watched, a flight of jets took off from the *Hornet* and that proved the carriers were already into the wind, so he looked at the heaving *Savo,* stern leaping high in the air, bow down and said, "There's your deck and you'll like it." Then, although he never prayed, he mumbled, "Beer Barrel, be out there today!" And as if in answer to this plea Cag announced, "Beer Barrel's bringing us in on a pitching deck. Anybody short on fuel?"

Brubaker reported, "1591 reporting over ship with 800."

He listened to Cag forward this news to the *Savo* and then call, "We'll double up. No trouble getting aboard."

So instead of the normal interval which would enable one jet to land each 26 seconds, the twelve Banshees formed a tight little circle yielding 15-second intervals so that whenever the deck stabilized there would be some jet diving right for it. But this also meant that one out of every two planes would have to take automatic wave-offs. "Hope I'm one of the lucky ones," Brubaker said.

He was. On his outward leg the *Savo* pitched so badly that no landing plane got aboard, but by the time Harry's downward leg started, the big ship was shuddering into stabilized position. "It'll hold that position for at least a minute," Brubaker assured himself. "Time to get three of us aboard." Nervously he ticked off the jets ahead of him in the circle. "Seven of them. Just right. First two will have to pass because the deck won't be steady enough, but three, five and seven'll make it. Boy, I'm seven!"

Then he saw Beer Barrel's paddles bringing number three in and the deck crew had the hook disengaged in two and a half seconds and the deck was steady and clear. "What an outfit when the going's tough," Brubaker said admiringly.

Then hell broke loose. The pilot in jet number five did what Beer Barrel had warned his men never to do. As his Banshee neared the cut-off point the deck lurched and the pilot tried to compensate. Instead of flying Beer Barrel he flew the deck and missed every wire. In great panic he managed to pancake into the barriers but he ripped them both away and the crucial barricade as well.

Brubaker, screaming over the wreckage, saw instantly that it would be many minutes before the deck could be cleared and he cried feverishly to himself, "I don't want to go into the sea again."

His fear was unreasonable. He could see the helicopters waiting to rescue him. He saw the alert destroyers, always quick to lift a downed pilot from the waves. But he also saw the gray sea and he'd been down there once. "The second time you crack up. You sink and they never find you." Instinctively he felt to see if his three gloves were watertight at the wrist. That's where the sea crept in and froze you. Then he pulled his hand away in horror and whispered, "Beer Barrel, don't let me go into the drink."

Then he got hold of himself and heard Cag's quiet voice say,

"All nylon torn away. At least ten minutes to repair it. Is that critical for 1591?"

Brubaker breathed deeply to drive down any quiver in his voice and reported evenly, "I'm down to 600."

Cag said to the ship, "1591 low on fuel. Must land on first pass after barrier is fixed."

The radio said, "*Hornet's* deck temporarily fouled. But would landing there in eight minutes be of help?"

Promptly Brubaker said, "I'd waste just as much gas getting in the circle. I'll stick here." What he did not say was that without Beer Barrel's help he might lose his nerve completely.

With mounting fear he noticed that the crashed plane still fouled up the landing space and the broken barriers were not being promptly repaired. What made this especially infuriating was that all this time the carrier remained in stabilized position and all the jets could have been landed. Then he saw something that froze him. The towering black crane called Tilly was being moved into position alongside the wrecked Banshee, right where the missing nylon barricade should have been. Then a quiet, reassuring voice spoke to him, offering a choice. "1591," the impersonal voice said, "*Hornet's* deck still not ready. Impossible to erect barricade in time for you to land but we must protect planes parked forward. Have therefore moved Tilly into position to stop you positively in case you miss wire. Do you wish to attempt deck landing or do you wish to ditch? Advise."

He stared down at the monstrous crane looming up from the middle of the deck. "That'll stop me. Oh boy, will that stop me!" It was a brutal thing to do, to move Tilly out there, but he appreciated why it had been done. Behind the crane were parked $40,000,000 worth of aircraft and they must be protected and he felt no resentment at the maneuver. But before replying he reasoned carefully, "The last guy missed the wires because the deck pitched. I can too," and he was about to elect ditching but a compelling instinct told him that his only hope for safety lay with Beer Barrel.

"I'm coming in," he said.

He made his first turn and prayed, "Beer Barrel, bring me in. I don't care if the deck is going crazy, bring me in."

On the down-wind leg he dropped to correct altitude and avoided looking at the pitching deck. He kept his eyes on the screen that shielded Beer Barrel from the wind but for a moment he became quite sick, for the stern was bouncing about like a derelict rowboat.

"Bring me in, Beer Barrel."

Then as he whipped into the final turn he saw that terrible thing, the crane Tilly filling the end of the landing space and he would have turned aside had he not also seen Beer Barrel. The big man stood on one foot, his paddles up . . . still good . . . still coming . . . oh, Beer Barrel, keep me coming. . . .

Then mercifully the cut sign, the firm hook catching securely, the run of singing wire, the tremendous pull upon his shoulders, and his eyes looking up at the monstrous crane into which he did not crash.

From the flag bridge Admiral Tarrant followed the emergency landing and when he saw Brubaker lunge onto the deck safely he sent an aide to bring the pilot to him as soon as intelligence had checked battle reports. Some minutes later the young man appeared relaxed and smiling in freshly pressed khaki and said, "Somebody told me there were eight hundred ways to get back aboard a carrier. Any one of them's good, if you make it."

Tarrant laughed, jabbed a cup of coffee into the pilot's hands and asked casually, "What were you doing in the catapult room last night?"

Brubaker sat down carefully, sipped his coffee and said, "I lost my nerve last night."

"You looked pretty steady out there just now."

It was very important now that Brubaker say just the right thing, for he knew that something big was eating the admiral but he couldn't guess what, so he looked up over the rim of his cup and said, "Best sedative in the world is Beer Barrel and those paddles."

The admiral remained standing, somewhat annoyed at Brubaker's having presumed to sit. Nevertheless, the bonds of sympathy which bound him to the younger man were at work. He didn't want Brubaker to participate in the attack on the bridges, so in an offhand manner he asked, "Son, do you want me to ground you . . . for tomorrow's flight against Toko-ri?"

Brubaker thought, "If he'd wanted me to stay down he wouldn't have asked. He'd have told me. This way he hopes I won't accept." But of his own will and regardless of the admiral he decided to say no and replied evenly, "If anybody goes, I go."

Admiral Tarrant was at once aware that he had posed his question the wrong way and said, "I think you're jittery, son. I think you ought to stay down."

Again Brubaker thought, "The old man's wrestling with himself. He wants to ground me but he's afraid it would look like favoritism. So he's trying to trick me into asking. That way everything would be OK." But again he said, "I want to fly against the bridges."

Certain, and in some ways pleased, that the young man would refuse the order, Tarrant said, "Harry, I've been watching you. There's nothing shameful in a man's reaching the end of his rope for the time being. You know I consider you our finest pilot . . . after the squadron leaders. But I can't let you fly tomorrow."

And Brubaker said quietly, "Sir, if you'd offered me this chance last night I'd have jumped to accept it. Or half an hour ago when I stared at that big black Tilly. But I think you know how it is, sir. Any time you get back safe, that day's trembling is over. Right now I haven't a nerve. Look." He held out his coffee saucer and it remained rigid.

"You're sure it's passed?"

"Positive. Remember when you told my wife about the voluntary men who save the world? I've seen two of these men. It shakes you to the roots of your heart to see such men in action."

"Who'd you see?" Tarrant asked, the sparring over.

"Yesterday I saw Cag take his photographic plane. . . ."

"Cag?"

"Yes, sir. I saw a man so brave. . . . Admiral, he went in so low that he simply had to get knocked down. Then he went in again . . . lower."

"Cag?" Admiral Tarrant repeated, amazed.

"And this morning. . . . Did anyone tell you about the air force spotter in the SNJ?"

"No."

Brubaker's voice almost broke but he stammered, "He was killed by a gun I might have knocked out . . . if I'd really been on the ball." There was a long silence in which Tarrant poured more coffee. Finally Brubaker said, "Sometimes you look honor right in the face. In the face of another man. It's terrifying." His voice trailed away and he added in a whisper, "So I have no choice. I have to go out tomorrow. If he could fly an SNJ, I can fly a jet." He laughed nervously and thrust his saucer out again. It remained immovable, like the end of a solid stone arm. "No nerves now," he said.

It was 1145 next morning when Cag, his jets poised aloft for their first run against the bridges, cried, "Attack, attack, attack!"

With deadly precision, and ignoring the mortal curtain of communist fire, four Banshees assigned to flak-suppression flung themselves upon the heaviest guns at more than 500 miles an hour. Rendezvousing to the north, they swept back in ghostly blue streaks and raked the principal emplacements a second time, but as they reached the middle of this passage communist fire struck number three plane and with a violence few men have witnessed it smashed into a hill and exploded in an instantaneous orange flash.

Before the eight pilots aloft could realize what had happened Cag called quietly, "Prepare to attack," and the four jets in his division peeled off for swift assault upon the bridges. They descended at an angle steeper than 50° and for the entire final run of two miles no pilot swerved or dodged until his first huge bomb sped free.

From aloft Brubaker saw that Cag had got two of the bridges. Now he must finish the job. He brought his division down in a screaming dive, aware that when he straightened out the pull of gravity upon him would suck the blood away from his head and drag his lips into grotesque positions, but the fascination of those looming bridges of Toko-ri lured him on. Lower and lower he came. When he finally pickled his bomb and pulled away he absorbed so many g's that a heaviness came upon his legs and his face was drawn drowsily down upon his chin. But he knew nothing of this for he experienced only surging elation. He had bombed the bridges.

Then he heard the dismal voice: "No damage to main bridge."

And you had to believe that voice, for it was Roy's, last man through. Tomorrow stateside newspapers might exaggerate the damage. You could kid the intelligence officer. And you could lie like a schoolboy to pilots from another squadron, but last man through told the truth. No damage.

"I'm sure Brubaker got a span," Cag argued.

"Negative," Roy replied flatly.

"How about the truck bridges?"

"Clobbered, clobbered, clobbered."

Cag called, "Stand by for run number two," and eleven jets orbited for position. The three flak-suppression Banshees stampeded for the gun-rimmed valley and as they roared in the leader confirmed Roy's report: "No damage to the main bridge." But the last of the flak jets reported, "We really have the ground fire slowed down."

Then, to the surprise of the communists, Cag brought his men in over the same check points as before and cheated some of the communist gunners, who had been gambling that he would use the other entrance to their valley. Through gray bomb smoke and bursts of flak, through spattering lead and their own fears, the first four pilots bore in upon the bridges.

Roaring straight down the railroad track like demon trains they pickled their heavy freight upon the bridge and pulled away with sickening g's upon them, their mouths gaping wide like idiots, their eyes dulled with war and the pull of gravity.

As Brubaker led his men upon the bridges he saw a magnificent sight. Three spans were down and a fourth was crumbling. The two truck bridges were demolished and the alternate railroad span was in the mud. In triumph he called, "This is Brubaker. All bridges down. Divert to the dump." And with blood perilously withdrawn from his head he swung his Banshee away from the bridges, over a slight rise of ground, and down upon the sprawling military dumps. Strafing, bombing, twisting, igniting, he screamed on, his three teammates following. Somebody's bomb struck ammunition. Consecutive explosions, each keeping the next alive, raced through the stores.

This time Roy, last man through, said, "We hit something big."

Cag, aloft, called, "All planes, all planes. Work over the dump."

Brubaker, now higher than the others, watched the dazzling procession of Banshees. Swooping low, they spun their fragmentation bombs earthward and retired into the lonely distance. Returning, they dodged hills and spread deathly fire. Over snowy ridges they formed for new runs and wherever they moved there was silent beauty and the glint of sunlight on the bronzed helmet of some man riding beneath the plexiglas canopy. It was a fearsome thing to watch jets assume control of this valley where the bridges had been, and it was gloomy, for no matter where any of the pilots looked they could see the scarred hillside against which one of their team had plunged to death a few minutes before.

His ammunition nearly spent, Brubaker nosed down for a final run upon the spattered dumps, but Cag called, "Stay clear of the ammo dumps. We have them popping there." So he twisted his jet to the south, away from the ammo but before he could launch his drive, two jets streaked across his target and jettisoned their bombs so that again he had to pull away. He was tempted to drop his last bomb where he thought he saw a gun emplacement but promptly he discarded this idea as unworthy for it occurred to him, quite clearly in this instant of decision, that even one bomb more might mean significant interdiction of supplies to the front: fewer bullets for communist gunners, fewer blankets for their trenches, less food. He recalled Admiral Tarrant's words: "If we keep the pressure high enough something's got to explode over there."

So in an effort to add that extra degree of pressure which might help to beat back aggression, he turned away from his easy target and picked out a supply dump. He activated his nose guns and watched their heavy bullets rip into valued cargo and set it afire. Then he resolutely pickled his last bomb but as he pulled out of his dive, with heavy g's upon his face, he heard a pinking-thud.

"I've been hit!" he cried and as the jet sped upward chaos took over. He lost control of his mind and of the thundering Banshee and in panic thought only of Wonsan harbor. He felt the irresistible lure of the sea where friendly craft might rescue him and violently he wrenched his nose toward the east and fled homeward like a sea-stricken thing. But as soon as he had made this desperate turn he became aware that panic was flying the plane, not he, and he called quietly, "Joe, Joe. Just took a hit. So far I'm all right."

From the dark sky aloft came the reassuring whisper, "Harry, this is Joe. I have you in sight."

"Joe, drop down and look me over."

Now an ugly vibration identified itself as coming from the port engine but for one fragile second of time it seemed as if the frightening sound might abate. Then, with shattering echoes, the entire engine seemed to fall apart and Brubaker whispered to himself, "I'm not going to get this crate out of Korea."

A communist bullet no bigger than a man's thumb, fired at random by some ground defender of the dump, had blundered haphazardly into the turbine blades, which were then whirring at nearly 13,000 revolutions a minute. So delicately was the jet engine balanced that the loss of only two blade tips had thrown the entire mechanism out of balance, and the grinding noise Brubaker heard was the turbine throwing off dozens of knifelike blades which slashed into the fuselage or out through the dark sky. Like the society which had conceived the engine, the turbine was of such advanced construction that even trivial disruption of one fundamental part endangered the entire structure.

He had, of course, immediately cut fuel to the damaged engine and increased revolutions on the other and as soon as the clatter of the damaged turbines subsided he cut off its air supply and eliminated the destructive vibrations altogether. Then, in fresh silence, he checked the twenty principal indicators on his panel and found things to be in pretty good shape. "I might even make it back to the ship," he said hopefully. But promptly he discarded this for a more practical objective: "Anyway, I'll be able to reach the sea."

He laughed at himself and said, "Look at me! Yesterday I pushed the panic button because I might have to go into the sea. Today I reached for it because I might miss the water."

As he reasoned with himself Joe came lazily out from beneath his wing and waved. "Everything all right now?" Joe asked.

"All under control," he answered.

"Fuel OK?"

"Fine. More than 2,000 pounds."

"Keep checking it," Joe said quietly. "You may be losing a little."

Then the sick panic returned and no more that day would it leave. Impeded by heavy gear he tried to look aft but couldn't. Straining himself he saw fleetingly from the corner of his eye a thin wisp of white vapor trailing in the black sky. Knocking his goggles away he tried to look again and his peripheral vision spied the dusty vapor, no thicker than a pencil.

"Joe," he called quietly. "That looks like a fuel leak."

"Don't your gauges show it?"

"Don't seem to."

"You'll make the sea all right," Joe said, and both men surrendered any idea of the ship.

"I'll make the sea," Harry said.

"I'll trail you," Joe called.

In a few minutes he said, "You're losing fuel pretty fast, Harry."

There was no longer any use to kid himself. "Yeah. Now the instruments show it."

Joe drew his slim blue jet quite close to Harry's and the two men looked at one another as clearly as if they had been across a table in some bar. "I still think you'll make the sea," Joe said.

But Harry knew that merely reaching the sea wasn't enough. "How far out must we go in Wonsan harbor to miss the communist mines?" he asked.

Joe ruffled through some papers clipped to his knee and replied, "You ought to go two miles. But you'll make it, Harry."

The turbine blade that had sliced into the fuel line now broke loose and allowed a heavy spurt of gasoline to erupt so that Joe could clearly see it. "You're losing gas pretty fast now," he said.

There was a sad drop on the fuel gauge and Harry said, "Guess that does it."

To prevent explosion, he immediately killed his good engine and felt the Banshee stutter in midair, as if caught by some enormous hand. Then, at 250 miles an hour, he started the long and agonizing glide which carried him ever nearer to the sea and always lower toward the mountains.

Quickly Joe cut his own speed and said, "We better call the word."

With crisp voice Brubaker announced the strange word which by general consent across the world has come to mean disaster. In Malaya, in China, over Europe or in the jungle airports of the Amazon this word betokens final catastrophe: "Mayday, Mayday."

It was heard by communist monitors and by the officers in Task Force 77. Aloft, Cag heard it and turned his jets back to keep watch upon their stricken member. And aboard the scow the newly reported helicopter team of Mike Forney and Nestor Gamidge heard it.

"Mayday, Mayday."

Silently, through the upper reaches of the sky, the two men flew side by side. They had never been particularly friendly, for their interests and ages varied, nor had they talked much, but now in the dark violet sky with sunlight gleaming beneath them on the hills of Korea they began their last urgent conversation, their faces bright in plexiglas and their voices speaking clear through the vast emptiness of the space.

"We'll make the sea," Joe said reassuringly.

"I'm sure going to try."

They drifted down to the sunny spaces of the sky, into the region of small cloud and laughing shadow and Joe asked, "Now when we reach the sea will you parachute or ditch?"

"I ditched once, I'll do it again."

"I never asked you, how does the Banshee take the water?"

"Fine, if you keep the tail down."

"Remember to jettison your canopy, Harry."

"I don't aim to be penned in."

"Six more minutes will put us there."

So they fought to the sea. As if caught in the grip of some atavistic urge that called them back to the safety of the sea after the millions of years during which men had risen from this element, these two pilots nursed their jets away from inhospitable land and out toward the open sea. They were low now and could spot communist villages and from time to time they saw bursts of communist guns, so they fought to reach the sea.

But they did not make it. For looming ahead of them rose the hills in back of Wonsan harbor. Between the jets and the sea stood these ugly hills and there was no way to pass them. In-

stinctively Harry shoved the throttle forward to zoom higher—
only a couple of hundred feet, even fifty might do—but relentlessly the stricken Banshee settled lower.

From the adjoining plane Joe pointed to the obstructing hills
and Harry said, "I see them. I won't make it."

Joe asked, "Now, Harry, are you going to jump or crash
land!"

"Crash," Harry said promptly. Back in the States he had
decided to stick with his plane no matter what happened. Besides, communists shot at parachutes, whereas the speed of a
crash often took them by surprise and permitted rescue operations.

"Keep your wheels up," Joe said.

"Will do."

"Be sure to hit every item on the check-off list."

"Will do."

"Harry, make sure those shoulder straps are really tight."

"Already they're choking me."

"Good boy. Now, Harry, remember what happened to Lou.
Unhook your oxygen mask and radio before you hit."

"Will do."

"Knife? Gun?"

Harry nodded. Although he was soon going to hit some piece
of Korean ground at a speed of 130 miles, his plane bursting out
of control at impact, in this quiet preparatory moment he could
smile out of his canopy and converse with Joe as if they were
long-time friends reviewing a basketball game.

"Pretty soon now," he said.

"I'll move ahead and try to find a good field," Joe said. Before he pulled away he pointed aloft and said, "Cag's upstairs."

Soon he called, "This field looks fair."

"Isn't that a ditch running down the middle?"

"Only shadows."

"You think I can stop short of the trees?"

"Easy, Harry. Easy."

"Well then, that's our field."

"Listen, Harry. When you do land, no matter what happens, get out fast."

"You bet. I don't like exploding gas."

"Good boy. Remember, fellow. Fast. Fast."

Desperately Brubaker wanted to make one run along the field to check things for himself, but the remorseless glide kept dragging him down and he heard Joe's patient voice calling, "Harry, you better jettison that canopy right now."

"I forgot."

Like a schoolteacher with a child Joe said, "That was first on the check-off list. Did you hit those items, Harry?"

"I got them all," Harry said.

"Field look OK?"

"You pick 'em real good, son."

Those were the last words Harry said to his wingman, for the ground was rushing up too fast and there was much work to do. Dropping his right wing to make the turn onto the field, he selected what looked like the clearest strip and lowered his flaps. Then, kicking off a little altitude by means of a side slip, he headed for the earth. Tensed almost to the shattering point, he held the great Banshee steady, tail down, heard a ripping sound, saw his right wing drop suddenly and tear away, watched a line of trees rush up at him and felt the final tragic collapse of everything. The impact almost tore the harness through his left shoulder socket but without this bracing he would surely have been killed. For an instant he thought the pain might make him faint, but the rich sweet smell of gasoline reached him and with swift planned motions he ripped himself loose from the smoking plane. But when he started to climb down he realized that his oxygen supply tube and his radio were still connected, just as Joe had warned. Laughing at himself he said, "Some guys you can't tell anything." With a powerful lurch he broke the cords and leaped upon Korean soil.

He was in a rice field three miles from a village. Beyond lay other rice fields and many curious U-shaped houses of the Korean countryside, their roofs covered with snow. To the north were mountains, to the south a row of trees, while from the east came a hint of salt air telling him that the sea was not far distant. But even as he surveyed his field he started running clumsily from the plane and before he had run far it burst into flame and exploded with numerous small blasts which sent billows of smoke into the air, informing communists in the village that another American plane had crashed. "They'll be after me soon," he thought and ran faster.

Within a few steps he was soaked with sweat inside his poopy suit and his breath hurt as it fought its way into his lungs. But still he ran, his big boots sticking in snowy mud, his intolerable gear holding him back. Finally he had to rest and sat upon a mound of earth forming the bank of a wide ditch that ran along the western edge of the field, but when one foot went into the center of the ditch he drew back in disgust for the smell he stirred up told him this was used for storing sewage until it was placed upon the rice fields. The stench was great and he started to leave but across the field he saw two communist soldiers approach the burning jet with rifles. So he did not leave the ditch but hid behind the mound of earth and reached for the revolver which he had once fired nine times in practice. He inspected its unfamiliar construction and remembered that it contained six bullets, to which he could add the twelve sewed onto his holster straps. "None to waste," he said.

Then one of the soldiers shouted that he had discovered the American's trail in the snow. The two men stopped, pointed almost directly to where he hid and started for him, their rifles ready.

At first he thought he would try to run down the ditch and hide in the line of trees but he realized the soldiers would intercept him before he could accomplish that. So he decided to stick it out where he was, and he hefted his revolver, for American pilots knew that if they were captured in this part of Korea they were usually shot.

"I'll wait till they reach that spot," he said, indicating a muddy place. "Then I'll let 'em have it." It did not occur to him that he

probably wouldn't be able to hit a man ten feet away and that
the spot he had selected was ridiculously remote, but fortunately he was not called upon to learn this ugly lesson, for as
the two soldiers approached the point at which he was determined to fire, Joe's Banshee whirled out of the noonday sun and
blasted the communists. Then, with a wailing cry, it screamed
to rendezvous with Cag for the flight back to the *Savo*.

From his filthy ditch, Harry watched the mysterious and
lovely jets stream out to sea and cried, "I'd sure like to be going
with you." They were supreme in the sky, these rare, beautiful
things, slim-lined, nose gently dipping, silver canopy shining in
the sun. Once he had been part of those jets and now, huddling
to earth, he was thankful that he had known the sweeping flight,
the penetration of upper space, the roaring dive with g's making
his face heavy like a lion's, and final exultant soaring back to
unlimited reaches of the sky. Then, as they disappeared completely, he pictured them entering the landing circle and he
thought, "It would be fun, heading in toward Beer Barrel right
now." Then he dismissed the jets.

He was determined to find a better refuge before new communists arrived, for the smell in this ditch was becoming too
strong to tolerate, but when he did start to run toward the trees
he saw four people standing there. Quickly he brandished his
revolver at them, but they must have known he could not shoot
them from so far for they stood impassively watching.

They were the family from the nearest farm, a mother, father
and two children, dressed in discarded uniforms and brandish-
ing rakes. He stopped to see if they intended attacking him, but
they remained still and he saw them not as Koreans but as the
Japanese family that had intruded upon his sulphur bath that
morning in the Fuji-san and an unbearable longing for his own
wife and children possessed him and it was then—there in bright
sunlight in the rice field—that he knew he would not see his
family again.

He was driven from this brief reflection by the arrival of
more soldiers. From the very trees to which he was heading ap-

peared eleven guards, shouting in Korean, so he hastily dived back to his stinking ditch where they could not hit him. They launched a methodical encircling attack but before they could bring him under fire four F4U's appeared overhead, called in by Cag to protect the downed pilot until rescue operations could begin.

Using Brubaker as their focus point, the slow propeller planes established a four-leaf clover in which each flew a big figure eight with such perfect timing as to have one plane coming in over Brubaker at all times, with alternate planes commanding different sectors of land so that no enemy dare approach.

The very first run enabled the F4U men to spot the eleven communists, and with sharp fire they tied the soldiers down. In the respite Brubaker thought, "With such cover a helicopter might make it," and he began to hope. Then, thinking to find a better spot from which to dash to the copter if it should arrive, he started to move out, but the Korean family saw him and thought he was moving toward them, so they withdrew. The F4U man responsible for this sector spied the Koreans, saw their tattered uniforms and roared upon them, his guns ablaze.

"No!" Brubaker screamed.

"No! No! No!" He waved his arms, jumped wildly to divert the F4U.

But the pilot could not see him. Focusing his sights grimly at what he knew to be the enemy, he brought his fiery guns a few yards from the faces of the Korean family. For one ghastly moment he thought two of the soldiers might have been children, but by then he was far away, roaring back into the four-leafed clover.

Sick, Harry Brubaker stood in the ditch and thought of his own daughters, and his heavy body was cold with much sweat.

He was standing thus when the helicopter appeared. It had lumbered in from the scow, dodging ground fire and flying so low that a revolver bullet could have destroyed it. Smack in the middle of the rice field it landed and Mike Forney got out. He wore his green top hat, a new Baron von Richtofen scarf of

Japanese silk and a carbine. Behind him stumbled sad-faced Nestor Gamidge, also with a carbine. Leaving Gamidge at the copter, Forney ran across the rice field shouting, "Relax, Harry! Everything's under control."

Brubaker shouted, "Better dodge and duck."

"Why, is there a war goin' on?"

"Look!" He pointed toward the trees and as he did so a volley of machine gun fire spattered the helicopter. Gamidge fell to the ground but rolled over several times and indicated that he was all right, but above his head the helicopter burst into flames.

Forney jumped into the ditch and turned back to watch the fire in silence. No other copter would come onto this field. With flames of noon in their eyes the two men in the ditch looked at each other, unable to speak. Then slowly Mike pulled his right foot up.

"Harry," he asked. "Is this what I think it is?"

"Yep."

Scornfully he said, "You sure picked a wonderful place to fight a war." Then he shrugged his shoulders and growled, "We might as well get Nestor in here. Three of us can stand those apes off for days."

He hefted his carbine nonchalantly and started across the rice field to convoy Gamidge but when the sallow-faced Kentuckian stood up, communist bullets chopped him in the chest and he fell. Mike, still wearing his green hat, blasted the line of trees in pathetic fury, for he must have known his carbine could not carry so far. Then he ran forward to where Nestor lay but soon he crawled back to the stinking ditch and tried not to look at Harry.

"Is he dead?"

"Yep." ·

In silence the two men tried to build protection for their faces, but when they reached into the ditch for stones, an evil smell arose, so that Forney stared back at the ditch and muttered, "I could have picked a better . . ." Then he said bitterly, "They were goin' to give Nestor a medal."

"Why'd you bring the copter in here, Mike?"

"I take care of my men, sir."

"How is it aboard the scow?" Brubaker phrased the question so as to imply that Forney would be returning there when this day was over.

"It's fair, but carrier duty spoils you."

"I liked the *Savo*," Brubaker said, and when referring to himself he used the completed tense, surrendering hope.

Forney caught this and said, "You know what kills me right now? Thinking of Kimiko going to bed with that ape from the *Essex*."

"That would be tough," Brubaker agreed.

The two men looked up at the F4U's and Forney asked, "How much longer will they be able to stay?"

"Not long," Harry replied.

"Well, we got nothin' to worry about. The jets'll be back."

Harry said, "This morning I had a chance to watch jets in action. They're terrific."

"Look at those apes," Mike said, pointing to where communists were starting to move in. From time to time accurate rifle fire pinked the top of the mound and Brubaker thought ruefully of people back in Denver who visualized communists as peasants with pitchforks who overran positions in mass attacks.

"Those guys know what they're doing," he said.

"But they don't know what they're gonna meet!" Mike laughed. Then he suddenly looked at Harry and said, "Why didn't you tell me you didn't have a carbine." And before Brubaker could stop him, he dashed across the rice field, grabbed Nestor Gamidge's carbine and stripped the dead man of ammunition. Two F4U's, seeing what Mike was doing, roared low and held the communists off while the Irishman dodged and ducked his way back to the ditch.

"Boy, now they'll know something hit 'em!" he cried as he jammed the weapon into Harry's hands.

Realization that Mike intended to battle it out here made

Harry shiver and he asked, "You think there's any chance they'd allow us to surrender?"

"Those apes?" Mike asked.

The two Americans piled the last rocks before their faces and Harry asked, "Why do you hate them so much?"

"Simple. One Sunday morning in the cathedral I heard the cardinal explain it all," Mike said. A bullet zinged into the mud behind them and Mike grabbed Brubaker's arm. "You understand, sir, I came out here to save you. I don't want to die. There was a fightin' chance or I wouldn't have come. But now we're here, let's go down really swingin'."

He watched one of the communists creep forward for a better shot. "Don't fire too soon at these apes," he whispered. He kept his hand on Harry's arm for at least two minutes. Then, just as the enemy soldier got into position Mike blasted him right in the face. When Mike looked back he saw that Brubaker was busy with his hip knife, slashing away at his poopy suit.

"What are you doin'?" the Irishman exploded.

"Letting some air in."

"Have you gone nuts, sir?"

"Ever since I climbed into my first poopy suit I've been weighed down. I've been sweating and unable to breathe. Like a zombie. Today I want to feel like a human being." He stripped away large chunks of his burdensome gear and stood reasonably free. "I feel better already," he said.

Mike was sure the lieutenant had gone off his rocker but there wasn't anything he could do about it so he laughed and said, "I'm the same way. I couldn't fight these apes without my green hat."

"Why do you wear that?" Harry asked.

"I want people to know I'm around."

"That's what you told the captain. But what's the real dope?"

Mike stopped, looked frankly at Brubaker and said, "When I was a kid we lived. . . ." He stopped abruptly and asked, "Tell me the truth, sir, wasn't that captain a pathetic ape?"

"The way he used to windmill all the time."

"In about three minutes now," Mike said, pointing to the trees.

The communists moved slowly and with deliberate plan. Four of them came in from the south, three from the mountain quarter. "I'm gonna keep my eye on those four out there," Mike said.

Some minutes passed and there was a flurry of fire from the three soldiers in the mountain quarter but Forney yelled, "Forget them!" and he was right for the other four lunged forward and tried to overrun the ditch. Calmly Mike and Harry waited until the communists were close upon them. Then they started to fire rapidly. The communists fired back but Mike yelled, "They're crumblin'," and he chopped them down.

"That'll take care of the boys," he shouted. "Now bring on the men." But as he turned to congratulate Brubaker an unseen communist who had sneaked in from the sea quarter hurled two grenades into the ditch. One of them Mike managed to throw back but as he lifted the second it exploded and tore him apart. His body, motivated by the driving forces that had occupied his mind, stumbled forward toward the unseen enemy and pitched into the snow.

Now the sky was empty and the helicopter stood burned out in the rice field and in the ditch there was no one beside him. Harry Brubaker, a twenty-nine-year-old lawyer from Denver, Colorado, was alone in a spot he had never intended to defend in a war he had not understood. In his home town at that moment the University of Colorado was playing Denver in their traditional basketball game. The stands were crowded with more than 8,000 people and not one of them gave a damn about Korea. In San Francisco a group of men were finishing dinner and because the Korean war was a vulnerable topic, they laid plans to lambaste it from one end of the country to the other, but none of them really cared about the war or sought to comprehend it. And in New York thousands of Americans were crowding into the night clubs where the food was good and the wine expensive, but hardly anywhere in the city except in a few homes whose men were overseas was there even an echo of Korea.

But Harry Brubaker was in Korea, armed with two carbines. He was no longer afraid nor was he resentful. This was the war he had been handed by his nation and in the noonday sun he had only one thought: he was desperately in love with his wife and kids and he wanted to see them one more time.

The memory of his family was too much to bear and for an instant he pressed his right hand across his eyes and thought, "The girls will be in the garden now. . . ."

He did not complete the picture for the hidden communist who had tossed the grenades had remained close and now with one carefully planned shot sped a bullet directly through the right hand that covered the American's face. In that millionth of a second, while ten slim Banshees roared in from the sea to resume command of the sky, Harry Brubaker understood in some fragmentary way the purpose of his being in Korea. But the brief knowledge served no purpose, for the next instant he plunged face down into the ditch.

Through the long afternoon that followed, Admiral Tarrant haunted his telephone, waiting word of the miracle that would save his son. When Mike Forney left the scow with his helicopter, the admiral had said, "Well, Mike'll get him." Then the leader of the F4U's reported the copter burning.

Now, from the clandestine broadcaster near Wonsan came the facts: "Jet plane crash. Helicopter crash. Three Americans killed by communist troops."

Shaken, the lean, hard-bitten admiral left flag plot and walked gravely to his tiny room, for he knew that he must report these facts to Nancy Brubaker, in Yokosuka. But as he stared at the paper he asked, "How do you explain to a wife that her husband has died for his nation? How do you tell that to a woman with two children?" And he thought of his own wife, sitting somewhere in a dark room knitting a child's garment . . . but it was already more than seven feet long.

The job was too much for him. Later, maybe, he would know

what to write. Then he thought of the Cag, who had led this ill-starred mission. He burned with fury and summoned the Cag to him, lashing at the bullet-headed commander as soon as he appeared.

"Why was Brubaker abandoned?"

Cag's eyes were red and tired from too much flying but he controlled his nerves and said, "We kept an air cap over him."

"If one helicopter crashed, why didn't you send another?"

"Sir, it's not my job to dispatch copters. You ask for volunteers. And there are never enough Mike Forneys."

"How was Brubaker hit in the first place?"

"He was working over the dumps."

The admiral pounced on this. "What was he doing at the dumps?"

Patiently Cag explained. "Before we took off we agreed. If we get the bridges, we expend our ammo on the dumps."

Icily, from the empty bitterness of his bosom, the old man asked, "Was that wise?"

Cag had taken enough. He'd stood this angry old tyrant long enough and there was no promotion in the navy that would make him take any more. "Admiral," he said grimly, "this was a good mission. We did everything just right. I put Brubaker in charge of the third division because I could trust him to fly low and bore in with his bombs. He did just that."

Cag, trembling with anger, rushed on, "Admiral, everybody in the air group knows that you selected Brubaker as your special charge. You do that on every command and we know why you do it. Some kid your own boy's age. So today I led your boy to death. But it was a good mission. We did everything just right. And it was your boy who helped destroy the bridges. Admiral, if my eyes are red it's for that kid. Because he was mine too. And I lost him."

The old man stood there, staring stonily at the shaking commander with the bullet head while Cag shot the works. "I don't care any longer what kind of fitness report you turn in on me because this was a good mission. It was a good mission." Without saluting he stormed from flag country, his fiery steps echoing as he stamped away.

For many hours the admiral remained alone. Then toward morning he heard the anti-submarine patrol go out and as the engines roared he asked, "Why is America lucky enough to have such men? They leave this tiny ship and fly against the enemy. Then they must seek the ship, lost somewhere on the sea. And when they find it, they have to land upon its pitching deck. Where did we get such men?"

He went out to watch the launching of the dawn strike. As streaks of light appeared in the east, pilots came on deck. Bundled like animals awakened from hibernation, they waddled purposefully to their jets. The last to climb aboard was Cag, stocky and round like a snowball. He checked each jet, then studied his own. Finally, as if there were nothing more he could do, he scrambled into his plane and waited. Majestically, the task force turned into the wind, the bull horn jangled and a voice in the gloom cried, "Launch jets."

Admiral Tarrant watched them go, two by two from the lashing catapult, planes of immortal beauty whipping into the air with flame and fury upon them. They did not waste fuel orbiting but screamed to the west, seeking new bridges in Korea.

ABOUT THE AUTHOR
OF "THE BRIDGES AT TOKO-RI"

JAMES A. MICHENER was born in New York City in 1907 and grew up in Doylestown, Pennsylvania. Having, as he says, "an itching foot," he departed at fourteen and bumed his way cross-country. These early hobo-like years gave him a fine appreciation of his country and of the kindness and friendliness of ordinary Americans. He was a sports columnist at fifteen, an amusement-park spotter during the summers. On the Chautauqua circuit he was, in his words, "a frightfully bad actor, much addicted to Italian food."

Feeling that he must have some formal education, Michener entered Swarthmore College on a scholarship and studied in the honors course, developing a tremendous appetite for reading. After graduation he spent two years in Europe, where he studied Sienese paintings and did research in the British Museum, collected rare songs in the Hebrides and shipped as a chart-corrector on a Mediterranean coal carrier.

In America again, he joined the faculty of the George School in Pennsylvania as a social science teacher. He became a specialist in teaching others how to teach and spent time at Colorado State College, the University of Pennsylvania, the University of Virginia and at Harvard. He left teaching in 1941 to take a position as associate editor in the textbook department at Macmillan. His stay there was interrupted by World War II. Waiving his Quaker principles, he enlisted in the Navy.

While atoll-hopping in the South Pacific as a trouble-shooter in aviation maintenance, he visited forty-nine islands from Australia to Tarawa. Out of his wartime experience in the Solomons came *Tales of the South Pacific* (Pulitzer Prize, 1947), which was adapted into the fabulous musical *South Pacific* by Rodgers, Logan and Hammerstein in 1949.

Prior to his enlistment in the Navy, Michener had to his credit some professional educational books with lots of footnotes and an unfinished autobiographical novel, *Fires of Spring*, his first novel, which was published in 1949. *Return to Paradise* and *The Voice of Asia* were both published by Random House in 1951.

THE STORY OF AVIATION

MAN CONQUERS THE AIR

Practical aviation started December 17, 1903, when, in the presence of five spectators, the Wright brothers, Orville and Wilbur, made the first flights in a controllable heavier-than-air machine at Kitty Hawk, North Carolina. At the same time the Wrights were experimenting, Samuel P. Langley was also working on his aërodrome but his machine did not leave the ground till years afterward, and then possibly with some mechanisms not developed by him at the time.

*Copyright by Doubleday & Company, Inc. 1935, 1938, 1940, 1941, 1942, 1944, 1946, 1953

INAUGURATION OF THE AIR MAIL SERVICE

The United States showed the same slowness in carrying the mail by air
despite years of such transportation abroad, that it had in recognizing the
epoch-making invention of the Wright brothers. It was not until May 15
1918, that the first air mail service was begun, a comparatively short
"hop," between New York and Washington. Below is shown President
Wilson greeting the pioneer pilot at Potomac Field. The flight ushered in
the development of the modern air service.

© UNDERWOOD & UNDERWOOD.

FLIGHT OF THE "NC-4" ACROSS THE ATLANTIC

With a string of warships stationed at intervals along their route in case of trouble, the Navy flying-boats NC-1, NC-3, and NC-4 left Rockaway Beach, New York, May 8, 1919, in an attempt to cross the Atlantic by airplane. They reached Trepassey Bay, Newfoundland, and on May 16th headed for the Azores. Of the three, only the NC-4 made the journey by air, the time being a little more than 15 hours. The NC-1 was forced down and sank, a steamer rescuing the crew. The NC-3 also suffered a mishap, but navigated on the surface to Ponta Delgada safely. The NC-4 afterward flew to Spain and England. Crossing the ocean in heavier-than-air machines had been proved feasible. The photograph shows the start of the three planes from Rockaway Beach.

END OF THE FIRST NON-STOP ATLANTIC FLIGHT

Early transatlantic flights by American aviators often obscure the fact that to Britain belongs the credit for the first non-stop transatlantic airplane journey. On June 14-15, 1919, eight years before Lindbergh's achievement, John Alcock and Arthur W. Brown flew their Vickers-Vimy biplane, similar to a wartime bomber, from St. Johns, Newfoundland, to Clifden, Ireland, in safety. The plane sustained damage in landing, as the pilot brought it down in an Irish bog, but 1960 miles had been flown in a little more than 16 hours.

AROUND THE WORLD BY AIR

Though the Navy made the first transatlantic airplane flight, the Army did its part in a round-the-world flight that made history. Four Douglas biplanes started from Santa Monica, California, March 17, 1924, and headed for Seattle, the official starting point. One plane was forced down in Alaska. The remaining three continued on the trip but one of them was wrecked in attempting to reach Iceland, after Asia and Europe had been successfully spanned. Lieutenants Smith and Nelson piloted the remaining two to Seattle, where they landed on September 28th. The photograph shows the welcoming crowd at Mitchel Field, Long Island, N. Y., one of the stops made near the end of the flight.

BYRD FLIES OVER THE NORTH POLE

Another flying achievement was credited to America when Commander Richard E. Byrd and Floyd Bennett, U. S. Navy, took off from King's Bay, near Spitzbergen, on May 9, 1926, and reached the North Pole. They circled it successfully and returned, having covered 1500 miles over the Arctic wastes. Their trip was of geographic value for it showed no new land in the area over which they traveled. The picture shows the Byrd plane returning to Spitzbergen from the flight over the Pole.

The aviation event which most captured popular fancy in the pioneer years of transatlantic flight was the solo trip of Charles A. Lindbergh from New York to Paris in his Ryan monoplane *Spirit of St. Louis*. He hopped off while more pretentious expeditions were in course of preparation, in the early hours of May 20, 1927. Al-though he encountered bad weather, he landed his craft at Paris, 3610 miles away, in 33 hours and 29 minutes. Above, the landing at Le Bourget airdrome near Paris, with soldiers and gendarmes holding back a wildly enthusiastic crowd.

© PACIFIC & ATLANTIC PHOTOS.

UNITED PRESS PHOTO

PEACE TIME'S MOST DRAMATIC FLIGHTS

Characteristic of the widening rift between the West and the Iron Curtain countries, as Russia and her satellites were called, was the Russian blockade of the Allied sectors of Berlin in 1948. With Germany split in two Russia whose relations with the West had been steadily deteriorating ever since the end of hostilities, tried to cut off access to Berlin on a paltry pretext having to do with currency regulations. American and Allied airmen circumvented the move by flying in passengers, food, supplies, and even coal. The success of the flying blockade runners resulted in the calling off of the blockade, though it was 1949 before Russia took official action to end the stoppage. The costly air lift was a striking example of Western resourcefulness and of determination to lose no points in the difficult game of persuading the nations of Europe that democracy was resolved to take a positive stand. The picture shows coal carrying C-54's waiting to be unloaded.

The
SWIMMING POOL

MARY ROBERTS RINEHART

COPYRIGHT, 1952, BY MARY ROBERTS RINEHART AND
PUBLISHED BY RINEHART & COMPANY, INC., NEW YORK

1

One day last fall I ordered the swimming pool destroyed. For we were leaving The Birches, our family summer home for many years, and our asylum after the panic of '29. For various reasons neither my brother Phil nor I myself cared to stay there any longer, and the fear of the atom bomb had at last enabled us to sell it. The family that bought it had small children, so they did not want the pool.

But standing there watching a man at work it seemed incredible that only the spring before, having sold a short story for more than my usual price and received another unexpected check, I had had it put into condition after years of neglect. Had repaired the old diving platform and the bench along the side, and even restored the picnic table under its falling roof.

I must have been very small when it was built, but I could remember my father watching the work and not looking particularly happy. He had liked the small creek that was to feed it, and which had been temporarily detoured. But he had saved the valley above it, below the stables, and had kept it in its wild state, with trilliums and May apples and other humble little plants, even an occasional jack-in-the-pulpit on the bank. None of the gardeners was allowed to touch it.

So the pool was built over his protests, because mother insisted on it. A swimming pool was a sort of cachet in those days, as later it was in Hollywood. But I think it worried him for other reasons too. The water, he said, would be cold, and there was always the danger that I, at five or thereabouts, might fall in. I remember him looking down at me as it began to fill. He was a tall man, usually reserved except with me, and I have wondered since just how he came to marry mother, or whether he was ever really happy with her. They were so different.

Anyhow that day at the pool he was definitely worried.

"You'll have to learn to swim, baby," he said. "We can't have you falling in the thing, unless you know how to get out."

I was always "baby" to him.

As a result it was he who gave me my first swimming lessons that summer, his hand under my skinny tummy and his own lips blue with cold. After that I taught myself, usually with a frightened nurse or governess screaming at me. And the day I jumped in from the diving platform, feet first and holding my nose, the mademoiselle of the moment actually fainted.

Yes, the pool had plenty of memories for me, some good but at least one tragic. I was glad to see it destroyed.

It is hard now to remember the extravagance of those days. True, the stables were no longer used, although the coach house still held a high trap and mother's old surrey, and a case on the wall of the tack room showed the ribbons father had won at horse shows and so on. I think in his mild way he resented the motor age, although he never said so.

But he loved The Birches, so called because of a grove of them on the hill near the house. He was always happy when, each early June, the family hegira from the city house began. The gardeners had been working all spring, the flower borders were beginning to show their colors, and while we were too late for the forsythia and the dogwoods, we still had the peonies and roses. Father always hurried to his wild garden, to which he had added lilies-of-the-valley, and the first time I was allowed to visit his grave I carried a drooping bunch of them and laid them there.

That was later, of course. It was years before I was told how and why he died.

As I watched the man working that day I was thinking of those mornings of the late 1920's. Perhaps children remember more than we realize, and the expedition from town house to country place was certainly impressive: the six or seven servants, including a butler, we four children with nurses and governesses, mother and her personal maid, and usually a dog or two, excited at the prospect of freedom and strange new scents. Inside the big house everything would be in order. Mother would look it over with complacency: the enormous drawing room with the conservatory opening off it—both closed now for years—her morning room, the library, and father's den. She would glance in at the service wing, where Helga and the kitchenmaid were already fussing with the huge coal stove, but she never stayed in the kitchen. That was Helga's realm.

After that she would go up the stairs to her big bedroom over the front veranda—the one where years later my sister Judith was to nail the windows shut—and watch her maid unpacking the trunks. She was a large woman, mother, dominant and, I realize now, very proud of her wealth and social position.

She would stand by while her handsome clothes came out of the trunks to be hung on perfumed hangers, and her jewels went into the wall safe beside the big old walnut bed. If I was lucky she would not notice me, so I could stay. Sometimes, however, she ordered me out.

I think now I understand why

she never really cared for me. She looked after me, of course. No one could say any of the Maynard children was neglected. But it must have shocked her profoundly when, ten years after Judith, she found I was on the way. My sister Anne was fourteen then, Phil was thirteen, and Judith was ten. That was after the first great war, when the world was pretending to be at peace, and we were carrying on as though there was no such thing as taxes, or an approaching end to our sort of living; or even another and more devastating conflict.

I arrived, however, a black-haired squealing baby who remained skinny for years, and a living, breathing embarrassment to mother up to the day of her death.

Outside of that, in summer the Maynard family carried on much as usual for several years. In the mornings the chauffeur and the high Pierce-Arrow carried father five miles to the railroad, where he commuted to New York and his brokerage house, and met him in the evenings. In the afternoons mother either drove about the countryside making calls at the other summer places, or sat at home in state to receive them. I can still remember her, sitting beside her tea table with its glittering expanse of silver and china, and the butler of the moment carrying in trays of thin bread and butter, hot buttered biscuits or scones, and cakes of all sorts.

Perhaps all this background is not necessary to my story, but in a way it is. So much happened at The Birches years later, and so much of it was the outgrowth of those early days. Young as I was —I was only six or so—I remember clearly when Anne was married there in the summer of 1928.

It was a huge wedding, with a marquee on the lawn, a band there for dancing, and an orchestra in the house. And of all things I was a flower girl, in white tulle and a white lace cap! Phil said I looked like a charlotte russe, which I do not doubt. But Anne had married rather poorly, according to mother. Martin Harrison was an unsuccessful architect, and nothing much to look at, but I daresay Anne loved him. At least she stuck to him, which is more than Judith did.

I realize now that father hated ostentation. When I missed him I often found him down by the creek, and we would stay there for hours. But it was rare for him to make any protest. As I have said, he was a quiet man, soft-spoken and gentle, and I adored him. I would slip out of my nursery in order to waylay and hug him on his way out to the incessant dinner parties that were a part of the summer season. But I always disappeared before mother came rustling out.

I could see her, however, by peeping around a corner. She was handsome, as Anne was later, but never the beauty Judith became. And she always wore the pearls in which Laszlo had painted her, and diamond bracelets on her left arm almost to the elbow.

I know now it was Judith who

wanted the pool, Judith to whom mother could refuse nothing. According to Anne, father objected. Not because of the cost. Apparently there was plenty of money, but already in her teens boys gathered around Judith like flies. They broke down his shrubbery and trampled his little wild-flower garden.

"Why turn the place into a picnic ground?" he said. "It's bad enough already, with every young punk in the neighborhood cluttering the house."

Mother got her way, of course. Or rather Judith did. Judith was a curious mixture of beauty and determination. Years later Anne said she was a psychopathic troublemaker and liar from the time she was born. I don't know about that. Perhaps Anne was jealous. However, I do know that either she got what she wanted or would sulk for days until she did.

But how lovely she was! I liked to watch her brush her long beautiful hair, and put on the extravagant dresses mother bought for her. Phil has said since that she was mother's ace in the hole, to offset Anne's unfortunate marriage. I imagine he is right. Judith was to marry money and position, as eventually she did.

No one had any plans for me. I was still the ugly duckling in those days. My straight black hair and ordinary gray eyes, as well as the fact that I was always missing a tooth or two, were probably the reason mother found me a real disappointment. As a result I was allowed more or less to run wild, to climb trees and wade the creek, and—after the pool was finished—to watch the boys swim and to swim myself.

I could dive too. I would climb to the high top of the platform with Judith's crowd below, and yell at them.

"Watch me!" I would shriek in my little girl's voice. "Watch me dive!"

I don't think they ever did. All they saw was Judith, sitting on the cement rim of the pool or on the bench beside it. Even the girls would be watching her, and she was something to see. She had cut her hair sometime or other. I don't remember when, but I do remember mother bursting into tears when she saw her.

"Oh, Judith, your lovely braids!"

It suited her, however. It grew out into small blonde curls all over her head, and she hated wetting it. Then too she swam badly. She could ride well. She could play the piano magnificently, but she hated the water. She was always afraid of the water. Perhaps that excuses her for what happened years later.

I can still see her in her bed at the hospital, with a policeman on guard outside the door, and most of her beauty gone.

"I was afraid, Lois," she said. "I tried, but it wasn't enough."

I was thinking of all this that day last fall as I stood by the pool. The bench had already gone, the bench where the unknown woman had lost her cameo pin, and the dizzy platform from which Anne's boy Bill looked down and saw something in the water. The long picnic table was gone too, where an old snapshot I found one night showed Dawson, our sardonic butler at the time, carving a ham.

Curiously enough, I did not remember seeing Ridgely Chandler there, the man Judith married twenty years ago. For one thing, he was older. The youths around the pool were mostly college boys, while he was well on in his thirties. He must have been there, especially during the summer of 1929. He must have watched Judith, as the others did. But knowing him later I doubt if he joined the rest in the noise or in the surreptitious drinking of those Prohibition days.

Apparently no Chandler ever broke the law.

They drank a lot, Judith's crowd, and I suppose Judith herself did too, although she was careful on account of father. But on Sunday mornings, running through the shrubbery to the pool, I would find bottles and flasks, empty and discarded, and once I cut my foot rather badly on one of them.

I speak of 1929 because that was our last happy year at The Birches. When we went back after the crash, as we were compelled to do, it was to make it our permanent home. All around us the big country places were empty and on the market, with no buyers. The Adrian place, nearest to ours, was closed and on the market for years.

No one had any idea of that, of course, when we moved back to the town house in late September of that year. It was always a blow to me, going back to the city, to school, to dancing class, to all the things I hated. The city house in the East Seventies was a tall one, elegant but dreary, the halls dark, the windows heavily curtained. The nursery—I still rated a nursery, to my disgust—as well as my nurse's room, was on the fifth floor, and instead of the grounds at The Birches I had only Central Park.

It was all behind me, of course, that fall day when I stood by the pool. We had sold the furniture, and a junkman had bought the surrey and cart and some of the old stuff from the attic where I found Judith on her knees one night years later. But in clearing out my desk I had found a scrap of paper which brought back to me a sleepless night when, confused and frightened, I had sat up in bed, and picking up the pad from the stand beside me, had absently found myself drawing the outline of a cat.

I am no artist, but a cat is easy to draw: two circles, just one small and one larger, then add the ears, dot in the eyes, and wrap a tail around it.

Only this cat was a solid black, and the window curtains around it were hanging in rags.

2

It must have been in February of last year when Anne drove out to The Birches. It was a wet day, with rain melting the snow, and Anne was in a rotten humor. She stalked into the living room, which had once been mother's particular habitat, as Phil called it, and looked around her with distaste.

"How you and Phil can stand this shabby old ruin!" she said. "Why at least don't you paint it?"

"What with?" I inquired, less than grammatically. "Can you see Phil on a ladder, with a brief in one hand and a brush in the other?"

Phil was a lawyer, and not a successful one. He had very little help at his office, so he often brought his work home at night. Anne only snorted.

"Do you run to a cup of tea?" she asked. "I suppose there's no use asking for a whisky and soda."

"We're not as bad as all that," I said. "I'll mix you one, if you'll sit down and relax."

She drank her highball, but she did not noticeably relax. I gave her a cigarette and lit one myself, eying her as I did so. Anne at forty-two was still handsome, but stout and matronly, as well she might be, with two children to raise and educate and not too much money.

"Bill and Martha all right?" I asked.

"So far as I know. They're both away, Bill at college and Martha at school." She put down her glass and faced me. "See here, Lois," she said, "what's wrong with Judith?"

"Probably nothing that a rest cure wouldn't help," I said indifferently. "Judging by the columnists she's still the most photogenic as well as one of the ten best dressed women in America. Also she's the leader of what they call café society, whatever that may be. What more can you ask? Or she?"

Anne frowned.

"I know. That awful treasure hunt, with a flower from Woodlawn cemetery and a hair of the mayor's mustache! How she's kept her looks so long I don't know." She put out her cigarette and dropped it into an ashtray. "But I think she's breaking. She's been going to a psychiatrist for a month or two. Ridge told me. And she's changed. My God, Lois, how she's changed!"

"What do you mean, changed?"

"She's thinner, for one thing, and she doesn't run about the way she did. I saw her at the Stork Club one night. She looked like a death's-head."

"What about the psychiatrist? Maybe he's slowed her down."

"I wouldn't know. He's a man named Townsend, on Park Avenue. Of course it's smart to be analyzed these days, but I understand he's good."

"Maybe she's fallen for him," I said lightly. "That's part of it, isn't it? They call it transference or something. Anyhow Judith's almost forty. It's time she settled down."

"Women of forty are not precisely senile," she said stiffly. "Anyhow I'm not thinking of Jude. I'm thinking of Ridge Chandler. She's led him up the garden path for a long time. He's had no sort of life with her. That wild crowd of hers, drinking and staying out all night, and God knows what! He quit it years ago."

I'm afraid I grinned. "He's pretty much of a stuffed shirt. The Chandlers can do no wrong."

"Don't be ridiculous. He has a proper sense of his own dignity and position. He inherited a good name and a lot of money, and Judith's throwing them both away. I might as well tell you. She's going to divorce him."

I was shocked. Although I seldom saw her, for years I had envied Judith. Not only her beauty, I still had the little sister's admiration for that. But I had envied her her marriage: the big apartment, luxurious and with plenty of servants, her cars, her clothes, her jewels. To throw all that over was incomprehensible to me.

"Why?" I said. "What on earth is the reason? She's got everything. I don't think Ridge is any ball of fire, but the Chandlers don't divorce. Or do they?"

Anne lit another cigarette, a sure sign she was upset.

"Of course she never loved him," she said. "Mother made the match. I found her crying the morning she married him. Her wedding dress was on the floor, and she was tramping on it. I had to press it before she could wear it."

"She didn't have to marry him. Mother couldn't have forced her to a thing like that. She adored her."

"I suppose he meant safety," Anne said thoughtfully. "You know how things were after father's death. Selling the town house and moving out here. And Ridge meant security. He was old enough too to know what he wanted. All I can say is he got it, and more."

We were silent for a while. I had tried for years to forget father's death, and only to remember his gentleness and kindness. And as I have said, the stark fact of his suicide had not registered until years later. The crash had ruined him. He had paid as much as he could of the debts he owed, but in January of 1930 he had gone back to his office at night and put a bullet through his head. We had not even known he had a gun.

Anne was remembering too.

"Funny," she said. "Mother never would realize what had happened to the country. She gave a big dinner the night father—died." She glanced up at the Laszlo portrait over the mantel. "Martin and I were living there, you know. We were pretty hard up, so I cut the train off my wedding dress and wore it. She had terrapin, I remember."

"Do you mean to say he had to sit through all that before he . . ." I didn't go on. I could not.

"He was quiet, I remember that. But he was always a great gentleman, Lois. He just got up and went out after the coffee. Nobody missed him."

She saw it was a dangerous topic. She went back to Judith.

"Ridge says she's asked him for a divorce," she said. "She doesn't give him any reason. Just says she wants to live abroad, or in South America. Of all the idiotic things!"

"That doesn't sound like the psychiatrist, does it?"

"Well, you know Judith. She's liable to do anything. She was a brat as a child. She'd lie at the drop of a hat, and she'd either sulk or raise a stink if she didn't get her own way. If Ridge had only turned her over his knee and spanked her it might have helped. But he was too damned well bred. He just gave her her head, and now she's lost it. I've always blamed mother. She practically sold Jude."

Neither of us said anything for a while. I suppose Anne was thinking of mother. I know I was. Phil had once said bitterly that she took father's death as a grievance rather than a grief. It was a cruel thing to say, but I could remember when the town house was sold soon after, and her refusal to part with much of the furniture, as well as the tapestries and her Aubusson carpet, all of which she insisted had to go to The Birches. Along with her portrait, of course.

We had had to sell them later, over her bitter resentment. After all, we had to eat. But neither Phil nor I had the heart to sell the Laszlo. It was still over the mantel in the old library, now our living room, and Anne got up and stood looking at it.

"Why do you think she forced Judith to marry Ridge?" she asked. "I've often wondered about it. Do you think he helped her out in some way? Money, perhaps?"

"I suppose it's possible. He must have been crazy about Jude to—well, to buy her."

"He was, of course. He was mad about her." She looked at her wrist watch and picked up her bag.

"I have to get home," she said. "As usual the maid walked out on me yesterday, so I have to cook Martin's dinner. I thought I'd better warn you about Jude. You certainly don't want her here. And if you pick Phil up at the station be careful. The roads are hellish."

I saw her into her old sedan and watched her down the drive. Then, with a couple of hours to spare, I went back to my typewriter and what I hoped would be a novel someday. I had moved into mother's room after her death, because the light was better and it was easier to heat. But I did no more work that day. The talk about Judith had made me uneasy. Also Anne had said something on the big front porch as she left which set me to thinking. She stopped and looked at me there in the gray winter light.

"Are you always going on like this, Lois?" she said. "You're a very pretty girl, you know. And nobody would guess you're twenty-eight years old. Isn't it time you stopped looking after Phil and began looking after yourself?"

"I'm doing all right. I even earn my keep, in a small way."

"What about men? Do you ever see any?"

"I've had a few passes made at me," I said, and I'm afraid I giggled. "Nobody I wanted."

She left then and I went back into the house. Her news had really startled me. I went into the living room and looked up at mother's picture. Anne had said Judith had never cared for Ridge, that mother had forced the marriage. And perhaps she had. I remembered her before she died. She had hated her new poverty, the skimping and saving of the years after father's death. But somehow she had managed to give Judith a big wedding. Like Anne's, and less than a year after father's death.

I never knew where she got the money, but I was too young in those days to worry about it. I remember that Phil gave Judith away, in our small local church, and that she wore sweeping white

satin and carried white orchids. But Anne said she had had to press the dress that morning, because Judith had thrown it on the floor and tramped on it.

I knew something else too. Until she died five years later mother had had a small income from some unknown source. She never spoke of it, and Phil said it was probably father's pension from the Spanish-American War. But now I wondered if Ridgely Chandler had paid it. Certainly, wherever it came from, it ended with her death.

Yet I don't think mother was ever satisfied about the marriage. Not that Ridge Chandler was not a good husband. He was pretty nearly a perfect one so far as we knew. But a month or two before mother died she asked me to look after Judith, if anything happened to her. I was only thirteen at the time, and I remember staring at her.

"What in the world can happen to her, mother?"

She gave me a long, rather odd look.

"She's not like the rest of you," she said. "She's the kind to get into trouble. And beauty can be a curse, Lois. I'd feel better if you would promise to look after her."

"Of course I will, mother."

"I spoiled her badly, I'm afraid," she said feebly, "and the sins of the fathers *are* visited on the children. I know that now."

"Everybody has always spoiled Judith, mother."

She nodded her poor head. It was queer, but as she failed and depended more and more on me I found myself giving her the affection I had never felt as a child. We could not afford a nurse, so Helga and I looked after her, with Phil giving us a hand when he could. And I was alone with her that day.

"I've made a good many mistakes," she said. "Some I felt were for the best, but I knew she wasn't in love with Ridgely when she married him. But you were a child then. You don't know how things were. I thought Judith needed someone to look after her. She was too attractive to men. And Ridge was older. All those boys . . ."

Just before she died, a few weeks later, I think she tried to tell me something more. But Helga came in just then, and she never finished it. I have wondered since if she meant to tell me the whole story, and if it would have helped me if she had.

So there I was, after Anne's visit that day, bound by that old promise to look after a Judith whom I scarcely ever saw; a Judith in some sort of trouble after twenty years of marriage. A Judith too who, although she was thirty-eight when she went to Reno, could pass for thirty any time. And also —as though she knew of the promise to mother—was to change her plans and decide to come to The Birches. For safety.

We did not want her. Both Phil and I knew from the beginning that trouble was her middle name, but there was nothing we could do. A part of the place was legally hers, and there was plenty of room. There should be a law against families who, in the luxurious years before two world wars, built vast country places and then left them to their descendants. Here we were, with a hundred acres and the big house in Westchester County, and with two maids we could barely afford. As Helga, now an old woman, never put a foot beyond the kitchen, we had to have a general housework girl as well. Her name was Jennie.

I don't want to sound bitter, in view of Judith's tragedy, but she had been the spoiled beauty of the family far too long, and after the way she had lived for twenty years it must have been hard for her to adapt herself. Not that she really tried. It was no help to my work that she chose the times when I was at my typewriter to play the fine old Bechstein piano mother had salvaged from the wreckage of the town house. And I noticed after she came that Phil increasingly took refuge in the library, under pretense of work.

But I have not told how she came to The Birches, or why I went to Reno with her. Nor that at first when we got home she refused even to mention Bernard Townsend, her psychiatrist. We pretended not to know about him, but she was in such nervous shape and sleeping so badly that Phil finally suggested someone of the sort.

Her first reaction was one of sheer fury and, I thought, of suspicion.

"Don't be a fool," she said. "If you think I'm going to spill my guts to one of those peeping Toms you can think again. 'What do you dream about?' 'What is the earliest thing you remember?' It's childish. It's sickening."

She slammed out of the room, and Phil grinned.

"I guess Anne was wrong," he said. "She hasn't fallen for the guy, nor he for her. I don't know why he hasn't. After all she's a damned attractive woman, and I don't suppose her idiosyncrasies would bother a chap like that. He must see a lot of crackpots."

Because by that time we had decided that something was defi-nitely wrong with Judith. I suppose every now and then some family has somebody like her; someone who has gone slightly off the rails psychopathically—if that's the word. Phil thought she had a persecution complex, for certainly she was terrified of something, or somebody. I knew that on the train coming back from Reno, when she fainted in the vestibule of our car.

But that faint was definitely not psychopathic. She *was* terrified, although it was only after long months of what I can only call travail that we learned the reason for it.

3

In a way I have already jumped the gun in this record. To make things clear I must go back to a day or so after Anne's visit, when, looking up from my typewriter, I saw Ridgely's car coming up the drive.

It was Jennie's day out, so I went down and let him in. It was still slushy, and the snowplows had not got around to clearing the roads. He stamped the melting snow off his feet, apologized for the mess, and then remembered to shake hands with me.

Looking at him as he took off his overcoat I thought he looked half sick. I had never cared for him, and so far had our paths di-verged that it was a couple of years since I had even seen him. For one thing, he was thinner, but as always he was immaculately dressed. He was a smallish dapper man in his late fifties, with an arrogant manner and an already balding head.

Some of the arrogance was gone that day, however, as I took him into the library and put a match to the fire there. He looked, I thought, rather desperate.

"Sorry to bother you, in case you were writing," he said. "I see you still have the Laszlo. It's a nice piece of painting." And he added, "She was a strong woman, your mother, and a dominant one. It's very like her."

"Yes," I said. "Nobody has ever taken her for Whistler's mother. Would you like a drink? It must have been a nasty drive."

"Not now. Perhaps later."

He waited until I sat down, and then seated himself. I had an idea that never in his life had he sat while a woman stood. He did not speak at once. He seemed to be wondering how to begin. When he did his voice was dry and hard.

"I'm not going to beat about the bush, Lois," he said. "I suppose you know why I'm here. Or do you?"

I nodded. "Anne told me. It's Judith, isn't it?"

"Yes. It's Judith," he said. "She's not herself. She hasn't been for the past month or so. I'm worried about her."

I hedged a bit. "What do you mean? Isn't she well?"

"Oh, she's well enough, or at least she has been until lately. Good God, she must be as strong as an ox, the way she's been getting around. I'm not feeble myself, but I couldn't take it. Haven't for years. Lois, do you think it's possible she's fallen in love with somebody?"

I wanted to say she was in love with herself and always had been. I couldn't, of course.

"She's always had men around her," I told him. "Like any woman

with her looks. But I think it's unlikely, Ridge. She's—well, she really doesn't care for men. Not the way you mean, anyhow."

"I realize that," he said dryly. "She only cares for herself. I had some hope when she married me, but it didn't work out. I suppose I was a fool. I wasn't married a week before I knew she didn't really give a damn for me."

"You've stuck it out a long time," I said.

He gave me a chilly smile.

"What was I to do? I come of an old conservative family. We have stood for something in the city. Even in the country itself. Much like your own people. I—well, I put up with a lot for that reason. As for divorce . . ."

I found myself feeling sorry for him. He had been twenty years older than Judith when she married him. Now I wondered if it had been twenty years of martyrdom for a proud man.

"I must confess I don't understand it," he went on. "I've never given her any grounds for it." He smiled faintly. "You might say the shoe should be on the other foot! I have stood for a great deal for a good many years. Not that I think she'd commit adultery, but she hasn't been a wife to me for a long time. Years, in fact. She—has she talked to you about it?"

"No. I hardly ever see her, Ridge."

He seemed rather at a loss. He took a cigarette from a gold case and lit it before he spoke.

"She sprung it on me at breakfast a day or two ago. She didn't often get up so early, but that day she did. I was surprised, because she'd been out late the night before. She simply sat down at the table and threw it at me."

"She always did unexpected things," I said. "Her life's full of exclamation points. You hadn't done anything to annoy her, had you?"

"Practically everything I do annoys her." He looked rather grim. "Outside of that, no. There isn't another woman either, although the way things have been between us for years she probably wouldn't have minded that much. No, Lois. I'm well past the stage of extra-marital affairs."

He hesitated.

"Perhaps I'd better tell you about the night before that breakfast when the divorce came up," he said. "I'm not proud of it, but maybe you can make some sense out of it."

What developed was that they had occupied separate rooms for years, and that he seldom even heard her come in. That night, however, he did, and did not go to sleep again. After a while he realized that she was not following her usual bedtime routine of bath, face cream, and so on. Instead she was walking the floor.

"It puzzled me," he said. "It wasn't like her."

I looked at him impatiently. I have no use for men who let their women trample all over them.

"Why on earth didn't you go in and find out?" I said.

He shrugged his padded shoulders.

"I told you. We haven't been on terms like that for a long time. I suppose it was my fault. I work hard and I need my sleep. I couldn't take her routine, and if I looked at the clock when she came in she thought I was checking up on her."

"Well, for heaven's sake, why wouldn't you check up on her?" I said indignantly.

He let that go. He was gazing up at mother's portrait again.

"I don't know exactly why I'm telling you all this," he said. "It's damned unpleasant. After all, she's my wife. But I have to know why she's leaving me, or what has happened to her the past few weeks, and especially the past few days."

Some of what had happened, when he finally got down to it, was queer enough. It seems he lay in his bed, expecting to hear her usual ritual before going to bed. But as it turned out she was not going to bed. So far as he could make out she was walking about the room, her high heels clicking on the hard wood between the rugs. Then she must have decided something, for he heard her working at the safe where she kept her jewels. As she never bothered to put away what she had worn until the next morning, this surprised him.

He must have picked up his courage at that point. Anyhow he got up and went to her door. Her back was to him, and she did not hear him. She had got out everything she owned: the diamond bracelets, the pearls, the emerald earrings and necklace, a dozen or so clips and brooches, and she added to them the huge ten-carat solitaire which was her engagement ring. She was examining them piece by piece.

"As if she was appraising them, by the Lord Harry," he said. "And some of them had been my mother's."

I stared at him incredulously. He had left her there like that, he said. He had returned to his room and finally gone to sleep. But, idiot that I considered him, he was not entirely weak minded. It had looked like blackmail to him. What else could he think of?

"Only apparently it isn't," he said. "When she said she wanted a divorce I asked her if she was in any sort of trouble, and if she was I was willing to help. She could have any money she needed. Do you know what she said to that?"

"What?"

"That all she wanted was to get out of the country! She intended to live somewhere abroad."

"And no reason?"

"No reason whatever. By God, I began to wonder if she'd killed somebody!"

"You don't think so now?"

"No. She's not a passionate woman. She has a temper, of course, but she's pretty well controlled. She would never risk a thing like that. She's played around. She likes admiration, but she'd never get into trouble about a man. Even if she did, why would she want a divorce? You'd think she'd want to stick to me, at least for safety's sake. And she's no child, Lois. She's kept her looks, but she's facing middle age. And there's nothing she can do about it."

I was puzzled. Whatever Judith felt about Ridgely, she had cared passionately for the life he enabled her to live. He had plenty of money, and she liked money. He had position too, and, like mother, that meant a lot to her. To throw everything overboard like this sounded crazy to me.

"Maybe she didn't mean it," I said. "You know Judith. She has erratic spells, when she does crazy, silly things. She's always had them, but they're never serious, and she gets over them in time."

"She's not getting over this," he said, his voice grim. "She's going to Reno as soon as I can get space on a train. Yes, she's let me do that. And she's in a hurry. She wants to get out of town. I left her packing her clothes. I think I'll have that drink after all, Lois. I guess I need it."

I got a bottle of Scotch from the liquor closet and cracked some ice from the refrigerator. We had no ice cubes at The Birches. The big gloomy kitchen was empty but warm, and I went over to the coal range and stood there for a minute, thinking. That Judith was in a jam of some sort was obvious, but what sort of jam? I agreed with Ridge that it was not like an affair of any kind. A more generous woman might let herself go in that fashion, but not Judith, unless she had something to gain by it.

Then what? Or who? Some millionaire who had fallen for her looks and was offering her a yacht or a house at Palm Beach? But the sea made her sick, and she could go to Palm Beach anytime. Then, again, why get out of the country?

I put the question bluntly to Ridge when I gave him his drink, but he only shook his head.

"You tell me," he said heavily. "Tell me why she hasn't been herself for the past few weeks, and why she locks her door at night. She's not afraid I'll bother her. What's she afraid of, Lois?"

"It's not like her to be afraid of anything, Ridge."

"It's possible, of course, that she's afraid of me. But why? We had established a pretty fair *modus vivendi*. I couldn't live her sort of life. She liked gaiety; she wanted crowds around her. Sometimes I felt as though I was running a nightclub. Or she'd be out late and I'd be afraid she had had an accident with her car. You know how she drives. Of course, the very fact that I worried got on her nerves. She wouldn't take the chauffeur unless she couldn't help it."

I knew all that. Judith at the wheel of one of her smart cars—she had a new one every year or so—was enough to set one's teeth on edge. How many times she had been arrested for speeding I didn't know, but Ridge probably did. He must have had to bail her out fairly often.

"You don't think it's a hit-and-run case?" I asked. "If she ever hurt anyone—or killed them—she

would lose her head, probably. Just go and keep on going."

"Why would that make her divorce me?"

I looked at him. Even when he married Jude he could not have been a romantic figure. Now, in father's old leather chair and clutching his highball glass, he looked what he was, an elderly gentleman of what we used to call the old school who was, to use more modern jargon, in one hell of a mess.

"Of course it must be blackmail," I said. "Nothing else would explain the jewels, would it?"

"I'm not blackmailing her, and it's me she's leaving," he said sharply.

I thought of the old woman who left her husband because she had just lost her taste for him, but I said nothing.

"Anyhow, blackmail for what?" he went on. "I know she's seen Anne. Has she told her anything?"

"Anne's as much puzzled as you are, Ridge. She doesn't know what it's all about."

Curiously enough, he seemed to relax at that. He finished his highball and leaned back in his chair.

"Good whisky," he said.

Apparently we were through with Judith for the time, but I still thought him rather a pathetic figure. After all, he had stood by Jude for a good many years, submitted to her crowds, her hectic life, and her vagaries, which had ranged from parties for dogs and other pets—in the apartment!—to taking over the piano in a nightclub and transposing the music so that the soprano burst into tears and left the platform. The treasure hunt was only one of a series, and Ridge showed the wear and tear of those years, although she had been less often in the papers recently.

"Living with her has certainly been an experience," he said with his cool smile. "But in spite of the fact that we've lived separate lives for so long, I still don't believe there is anybody else. She likes admiration. She likes being one of the best dressed women in America. She likes crowds around her. But she prefers notoriety to scandal, if you know what I mean."

He looked rather better after he had finished his drink. The divorce was settled, he said. He had even arranged what alimony he was to pay her, which, oddly enough, was all she asked. Also he had already had his lawyer wire another one out there in Reno to do the dirty work, and I wondered if there wasn't a bit of relief behind all these plans. He was certainly shocked and bewildered, but he was tired and not too young. I wondered too whether he rather looked forward to peace and quiet after what he had endured for so long.

It was, however, what came next that got me up, so to speak, all standing.

"What brought me here," he said, "is that she is frightened about something. It's real. She's not dramatizing herself. Personally I don't believe she's in any sort of danger, but you know her. I've always looked after her as much

as I could, and before we were married your mother did the same thing. I suppose we've spoiled her, but there it is. She's reckless and unstable, and I don't want her to get into trouble out there. I thought, if you went with her, you could—well, keep an eye out for anything which might turn up."

I think my very soul revolted, but at least I managed to keep from shrieking.

"She would hate it, Ridge," I said. "She's never been fond of me. And I'd be useless in any sort of crisis."

"I don't expect a crisis, as you put it," he said grimly. "But I do expect her to behave herself. Also I have a right to know what, if anything, she's afraid of or why she wants to leave this country. And I think she means to take her jewels, and she's careless about them."

"In other words," I said, "what you want is a Saint Bernard dog with a keg of brandy around its neck. No, thank you, Ridge, you can do your own spying."

He was annoyed. He put down his glass and stood up.

"Look, Lois," he said. "Think back and you'll realize you owe me something. The money that took you through college was not from some old stocks you had forgotten. It was mine. And as long as your mother lived I paid her a small annuity. Now I want a little help, and you refuse it."

Well, there it was, take it or leave it.

I thought of the crime book I was writing. The story was just

THE SWIMMING POOL

beginning to jell, and we needed the money for the old house. I have always said that when I died the words "guttering and spouting" would be found written across my heart, like Bloody Mary and Calais. I suppose he saw my face, for he hurried on.

"I'd be prepared to pay for your time, if you'll go with her," he said rather apologetically. "Say a thousand dollars and all expenses. You may be able to work out there too. She won't stay in town. She'll be on a ranch. Horseback riding if you like it, that sort of thing."

The horseback riding didn't interest me. By the time I was old enough to ride anything but my pony the horses were gone from the stables at The Birches. The thousand dollars did, however. In a burst of optimism the previous spring—as in the case of the swimming pool—I had repaired and furnished the lodge at the gates, in the hope of renting it to someone for the summer. But no one had taken it, and Phil called it Maynard's Folly and said it depressed him every time he passed it on the way to the train.

"When is she going?" I said feebly.

"In a day or so. She wanted to go today, but it's not easy to get a drawing room just now. She's afraid to fly."

In a day or so! There must be something badly wrong, I thought, to cause such haste. It could not be Ridgely himself. You don't live all those years with a man and insist on leaving him in hours.

"She won't tell me anything, you know, Ridge. We've never been close. And what will I do if she won't have me?"

"She'll have you," he said, still rather grim. "It's one of the conditions I made, and she didn't object. She hasn't many women friends. Only that crowd of hangers-on and parasites who trail around with her." He put a brotherly hand on my shoulder. "You'll do it, won't you? I'll feel a lot better with you around. She's in a queer mood, Lois. Badly as she's behaving I don't want her taking an overdose of sleeping pills, or something of that sort."

I think that was the first time I really felt the situation was serious. For I realized that Ridge was not only the deserted husband. He was frightened himself. Something was wrong. Under all his urbanity he was suspicious and alarmed. All through our talk he had been tense with strain.

"I suppose I'll have to do it," I agreed finally. "Only I wish I had some idea what to look out for. If you know it you should tell me."

"My dear girl," he said paternally, "if I knew I wouldn't be asking you to go to Reno. Whatever it is it must have happened suddenly. She hadn't been well for a couple of months, but when she went out to dinner the night I speak of she was entirely herself. She was wearing a new evening wrap, ermine and sable, and it suited her. I was at my desk in the library when she passed the door, and I'll swear she was as normal as you are. She even waved goodbye to me."

So she had waved good-bye to him! It seemed as little as any woman could do for a new ermine and sable wrap, and when I thought of my own shabby muskrat I wondered why he had not strangled her.

But I was trapped and I knew it. I knew something else too. As he drove away that day he looked not only relieved. He was a little smug, as though by making me his stoolpigeon he had achieved something important to him. For all his air of ignorance I wondered if he knew more than he admitted about Judith's terror.

I went upstairs feeling that I had sold my birthright for a college education, a small annuity to mother while she lived, and a thousand dollars in cash. And the mood continued while I put away my manuscript and slammed the cover on the typewriter. That annuity to mother worried me too. I sat there in what had been her room and thought about her. Why had she forced Judith to marry Ridge? If she did. And why on earth had Judith agreed? She could be as stubborn as a mule when anything displeased her. Yet she had gone through with the thing, with mother still in black for father pulling out her white satin train and then marching stiffly up the church aisle on an usher's arm. For all the world like a woman who had accomplished something and could now sit back comfortably and let Providence take care of the rest of it.

The roads were horrible as I drove in to town to meet Phil's train, and he looked so tired that I waited until he had put on his old smoking jacket and mixed his evening cocktail before I told him.

"I'm going to Reno in a day or two," I said.

He almost dropped the shaker.

"For God's sake don't tell me you've been married all this time!" he said.

"Don't be an idiot. I'm going with Judith. She's divorcing Ridge."

He stared at me incredulously. "Don't tell me she's letting go of ten million dollars," he said. "I don't believe it. Not our Judy. That's fantastic."

"Ridge was here this afternoon. It's true all right."

He sat down, his jaw dropped, and his long thin body looking collapsed.

"I don't get it," he said. "What's sending her off the rails this time? Got something better in sight?"

"Ridge doesn't think so."

He drank his cocktail thoughtfully.

"Well, it's a break for him," he said. "I don't think our dear sister has been much of a wife. But if you ask me she's not leaving the soft nest she's got unless she has a plush-lined one waiting for her somewhere else."

He couldn't have been more wrong, of course. But when he learned I was serious about going with her—and within a day or so at that—he blew up.

"Don't be a fool," he said. "You never got along with her. Who could? And what's the idea anyhow? A woman thirty-eight years

old! If she can't take care of herself by this time she never will. As
a matter of fact she's always taken
damned good care of herself. And
why all the hurry? What's she running away from? Ridge?"

"He doesn't think so. He believes something has happened to
her," I told him. "That she may
be in trouble of some sort. She
talks about living abroad."

"I'd be for that," he said cal-
lously. "What's she been doing?
Stealing some woman's husband?"

"Not so far as he can find out."

"And why you? Can't she hop a
train by herself?"

"I'm being paid. A thousand
dollars. To act as Ridge's stoolie."

Phil's reading does not consist
of crime fiction, as mine does. He
only looked confused.

"I'm to watch Jude and report to
him," I explained. "It's a dirty job,
but I'd fall still lower for a thousand dollars. Think of the coal it
will buy!"

He grunted and looked de-
pressed. The furnace was his job.
Then Jennie announced the evening meal in her inimitable manner. It consisted of opening the
library door, yelling "Dinner"
loudly, and disappearing. Phil
looked still more down in the
mouth.

"I seem to remember a time,"
he said sadly, "when some impec-
cable individual of the male per-
suasion politely opened that door
and mentioned the fact that food
was ready to be served. If Judith
ever wants to come here—which
God forbid—one week of Jennie
would send her flying."

"That's silly. Why in the world
would she come here?"

"Just out of general cussedness,"
he said, "and our usual bad
luck."

Which again might have been
funny if it had not been so horrible.

We had to drop the discussion
during dinner, with Jennie in and
out of the room, and when she
slammed down the dessert, which
was bread pudding, Phil stared at
it with distaste.

"When I think of the poor little
hungry birds outside in all this
snow," he said sadly, "I wonder
why I have to eat all the stale
crusts. Jennie, can't you convey to
Helga that it's too late for them to
make my hair come in curly?"

But Jennie only giggled and
banged out of the room as usual.
Phil ignored his dessert and lit a
cigarette.

"If I were Ridgely Chandler,"
he said, "I'd be cutting capers all
over the place tonight. Only of
course the Chandlers don't do
things like that. As it is, all I am
grateful for is that Judith's going
abroad after it's over. The very
thought of having her here makes
me shiver."

I left him there with his coffee
and went upstairs to look over my
clothes. They were a skimpy lot
compared with the old days when
mother's handsome silks and bro-
cades hung there. But as it turned
out they did not matter. Nobody
in Reno noticed me when Judith
was in the vicinity.

There were times when I felt
like her shadow, and when I had

to gaze in a mirror to convince myself of my own reality. I did not really feel like myself until we were on our way east, and Judith fainted in the vestibule of our compartment car.

4

The trip west was uneventful, but when I met Judith at the railroad station in New York I realized that something had happened to her. Her face looked thinner, and she seemed to be watching the crowd feverishly. Her "Hello, Lois" was rather less than sisterly, but as I had not seen much of her for years I had not expected anything else.

She was traveling without a maid, to my surprise, and—also to my surprise—she looked almost shabby. She was wearing her hair differently too, as though she had made a feeble effort at disguise.

"What!" I said. "No mink coat?"

"I won't need it out there."

"I thought it was cold in Reno."

She did not answer that. Her eyes continued to stare at the people around us, and not until we were inside the train did she seem to relax. Even then she showed that she did not intend to bother with me, or even that I was particularly welcome. "What's the idea anyhow?" she said peevishly. "If you're spying for Ridge, just forget it. There's nothing wrong. He simply can't understand how anybody can divorce a Chandler."

"Personally," I said, "I don't give a tinker's dam about Reno or your business there, Jude. I'm simply going along for the ride and a substantial check. I need the money."

She looked startled. Then she laughed.

"So Ridge is keeping an eye on me!" she said. "Well, he won't learn much, or you either. You have the compartment next to my drawing room, and I won't need anything. I am going to rest and read. Just amuse yourself."

I took the hint, and she spent almost the entire trip shut in her room and in her berth. I know she ate, for stewards brought trays and took them away, and once or twice the porter brought her ice, which I daresay meant a cocktail. After Chicago, however, the tension lessened. She even had the door opened between our rooms, and once we went to the diner together.

She had abandoned the semi-disguise of the railroad station. Also she looked better, and as we went to our table I saw people looking at her, as they always did. It is hard to describe Judith. She is a blonde—an editor once told me that I must hate blondes, as I always made them obnoxious characters in my fiction—and her eyes have a little uptilt at the outer corners, which is unusual and attractive. But beauty is too hard to define. After all, the human individual universally has two eyes, a nose, a mouth, and a chin. It is the assemblage of those features that counts, and believe me Jude's counted.

It was in the diner that day when she asked me about The Birches.

"I haven't seen it for years," she said. "How is it? Lonely as ever?"

"Pretty much. The village is slowly dying, since so few of the big houses are open. I'm fixing the old pool this spring. We need it in hot weather."

"Do you still have Helga?"

"Yes, by the grace of heaven. But she's getting pretty old. She has arthritis."

I had no idea what she had in her mind that day: that The Birches might be a haven sometime, or even a hiding place. I prattled on in my innocence, while my bad angel patted me on the shoulder for being a good little fool, and Judith ate fresh mountain trout and listened.

We were better friends after that. Not intimate. Certainly not sisterly. But I began to realize that her early coldness had nothing to do with me. She was simply absorbed in herself and her problem, whatever it was. Because there was a problem. She would sit for hours staring out the car window but seeing nothing. And once or twice I saw her shiver, although the train was warm.

"We used to say that meant somebody walking over our graves," I offered once when she had been shaking for some time.

"Oh, for heaven's sake!" she snapped at me. "Why don't you read or pick up some man in the club car? Or does Ridge insist you watch me all the time?"

But she had lost all her color, and for a moment I thought she was going to faint.

Reno was not too bad. We were on a ranch outside of town, and I learned to ride a horse and like it. Judith rode too, but also she spent a lot of time in town, she said at the movies, but I had an idea she was gambling. It wasn't my affair, of course. I saw very little of her. When I did she was usually surrounded by cowboys or the men who were guests at the ranch.

I have the carbon of a letter to Ridge which I wrote on my portable after we had been in Reno a couple of weeks.

"Dear Ridge: We are comfortably settled and getting along nicely. Judith is fine, sleeping well and looking much her old self again. Apparently it was New York which did not agree with her, as she improved steadily all the way west. I do not see much of her, however, and it looks as though I am here under false pretenses. She seems to feel entirely safe, as I am sure she is.

"Personally I wonder whether she was merely tired to the point of exhaustion before we came here, and so got some sort of delusion of persecution. You might ask her psychiatrist that. As things are I am rather like a third leg here so far as she is concerned.

"Better burn this letter, and it's not necessary to reply. She knows you sent me and why, and I think it amuses her, which shows, I think, how normal she is. Yours, Lois."

I gathered that the divorce was being arranged, but she never mentioned it, nor did I. And whatever purpose the shabby disguise had served, it was not resumed after we left Chicago. She broke out in gay little dresses and evening gowns, hired a car and drove it recklessly, and on the proper day and surrounded by assorted males threw her lovely platinum wedding ring into the Truckee River and proceeded to pack for the East.

It was a few days before we left that she came into my room to say she had decided to stay at The Birches until she made up her mind what to do.

"The Birches!" I said with a sinking heart. "Why on earth The Birches? You never liked it there, and you'd go crazy, after what you're accustomed to."

"If you remember, a part of it is mine," she said coldly. "I've never asked any rent from you and Phil,

nor has Anne. But I certainly have the right to live there if I want to."

"I thought you were going abroad," I said in a sort of desperation.

"I need to be quiet for a while," she said. "I can make other plans later. I'm better now. Thank God I don't have to live up to the Chandler virtues any more."

I stared at her, but she apparently meant it, so I let it go.

"How's the Bechstein?" she inquired. "I need to catch up with my music."

"It hasn't been tuned for years," I said. "Now look, Judith," I added desperately, "we simply can't have you at The Birches. Most of it is closed. We only use part of it. And I write. I have to earn money, and I need quiet to do it."

"Aren't you forgetting Ridge's little contribution?" she said nastily. "That ought to help."

But I still didn't believe her. Not until she told me she had wired Phil to have the Bechstein put in order. The immediate result was a telegram to me from Phil.

"Don't understand but strenuously object. Paying small boys in neighborhood to plant a few skunks, etc. Insist this must not happen."

A day or two later there was an air-mail letter from Anne along the same lines:

"What in the world is this idea of Judith coming to The Birches? She was always a troublemaker, and this divorce certainly shows she is still unstable. I am sure

Ridge would let her have the apartment if she wanted it, and I simply cannot see her in the country. You may have servant trouble too. Helga never liked her, and you don't want to lose her.

"I have not talked to Ridge since, but as I told you there is something queer behind this divorce. Do you think she is in trouble? And if so, why Reno? I have asked around among the gang she played with, but they say no other man.

"I have been worried about you too, Lois. How can you write with her around all the time? If she wants the old Bechstein, let her have it. Give her anything else she wants. But for heaven's sake don't have her at The Birches. She will drive you crazy."

Anne was the practical member of the family, as well as the oldest, and I read her letter carefully. A solidly built woman and entirely domestic she was only four years older than Judith, and consequently knew her better than I did. But the divorce came up about that time, and I saw very little of Judith until we started east.

So far as I know, however, she had been perfectly well. As usual she had two or three men see her to the train, and she looked beautiful and barely thirty that day. I remember we had two boxes of flowers, three of candy, and a bottle of Chanel No. 5 to help us survive the trip, as well as innumerable magazines and books. I stood on the platform in an effulgence of reflected glory as the train pulled out, the men waving, Judith smiling, and myself trying to hold the accumulated tribute.

Then, when it was all over, I turned to follow Judith into the car, and saw she was unable to move.

She was standing there, holding to a rail, and no amount of makeup would hide the fact that she was practically fainting. I tried to hold her but she kept sliding out of my grasp. Then a tall man standing behind us realized the situation and together we got her to her drawing room. She really fainted then, passing out in her seat like a light, and the tall man stood in the doorway, looking uneasy.

"Think I'd better get a doctor?" he asked.

"No. She'll be all right. She's done it before. But thank you anyhow."

He disappeared then, and a moment later Judith opened her eyes. I had a glass of water in my hand by that time, but I had been startled enough to be irritable.

"For heaven's sake, what happened to you?" I asked. "One minute you're all smiles, waving to that posse out there, and the next you're going to pieces on me. What was it?"

She sat up then and ran her hands through her hair.

"I just got dizzy," she said shortly. "And take that water away. I'm all right. Stop staring at me with your mouth open. You look like an idiot."

I shall always believe that what Phil called Judith's agoraphobia—

which he explains as fear of the market place, or her idée fixe, to use his own words—began that day. I only know that she behaved very strangely. For one thing, the moment she recovered from her faint she insisted on having the door locked, only permitting me to open it to let the porter bring in fresh linen for her berth, and so far as I know she never left her bed until we were drawing into New York.

Even I was shut out, and I could only get in by rapping twice and then once, and after that first day she never let the porter in at all. The dining-car waiter didn't matter—she ate almost nothing, and I took in her tray. But the porter did. His job devolved on me. He would give me the fresh sheets, with a queer look on his face, and I would have the back-breaking job of making up the berth.

"Lady have a bad scare about something?" he said once.

"She's a nervous case," I explained lamely.

He showed beautiful white teeth in a smile. "Sometimes Reno do that to them," he said. "Other times they act like they very happy. Never can tell."

I was puzzled, but also I was sorry for her. The flowers faded. The candy and magazines were not even opened. She simply lay there, looking like death and refusing to explain anything.

"Why don't you tell me, Judith?" I would say. "You're afraid of something, aren't you?"

She scowled at me. "Can't I be sick without you bothering me?"

"I don't think you *are* sick. You're scared. All this locking yourself in is silly. What on earth can happen to you on a train?"

"People have been murdered on trains," she said, and shivered.

That was as much as I got out of her on the trip. I sat in my compartment next door and tried to puzzle the thing out. Whatever had happened had been as the train was ready to move out. There had been the group of waving, grinning men, piling her arms with tribute, a red-capped porter or two, and the train conductor. A taxi or two had driven up at the last minute, but their passengers were two laughing young women and an elderly one who walked with a cane.

To save my life I could see nothing menacing in that departure of ours. I wondered if the trouble was some passenger on the train, and the second day I began to look it over. It was a long train, and if there was anything sinister about any of the passengers I could not discover it. All I saw was tired and bored people, the women reading or trying to doze, and none of the men with what my detective-story reading told me should be the bulge at the left shoulder that indicated a holster and a gun.

Whatever Judith thought, I could not see Nemesis in wrinkled suits, crying babies, and tired-looking women who had left Reno and their former lives for the unknown future that lay ahead.

I daresay any train east from that Nevada city carries its own load of drama, but I had no idea it was carrying ours.

5

It was not until the second day that I saw again the man who had helped me with Judith. My legs were tired from my search of the train, and so, when I reached the club car, I sat down for a cigarette and a drink.

He was across a table from me, and when I searched for a match he leaned over and offered me a light.

"How is the lady?" he inquired.

"She's better, thanks," I said. And that was all for the moment. He was a big man, broad shouldered and powerful, wearing dark glasses with shell rims, and with heavy hair going gray over his ears. There is something disarming to me about gray hair. It shouts respectability, for one thing, although he was not old; in his early forties, perhaps. And beyond asking about Judith he let me alone until I had had my highball. Then he turned and said something about the scenery. As I had had a bellyful of scenery I merely nodded, but he seemed to be lonely, for he kept on.

"In Reno for the usual reasons?" he inquired.

"I'm not married," I said coldly. He was not easily snubbed, however.

"I've seen you going through the train," he said. "Not looking for someone, are you?"

"I've been looking for Nemesis," I said shortly, and he laughed.

"And why," he said, "should a pretty young woman like yourself be expecting Nemesis?"

It was the first time I realized he was Irish. Probably only Irish descent, but it was there, in the turn of phrase, in the quick uptake and the laughter. But I had an idea he was watching me through those dark glasses, and for just a moment I wondered if it was he who had terrified Judith. It was impossible, of course. He had been behind her and she was staring out when it happened.

"I don't know," I said vaguely. "Something made my sister faint yesterday. I thought perhaps she saw something. Or somebody. She's really quite strong. It bothers me."

He nodded. "I have an idea I've

seen her somewhere," he said. "Either her or her picture."

"Probably her picture," I said, with some bitterness. "The New York columnists use it a lot."

"They would," he agreed. "She's very good-looking. I think I remember now. She's Mrs. Ridgely Chandler, isn't she?"

"Judith Chandler. Yes. You were very kind. I meant to thank you."

He ignored that. He seemed to be thinking.

"What do you think frightened her?" he said. "Or are you imagining something? After all, the strain of getting a divorce must be something."

I didn't tell him that you could have put Judith's strain about her divorce in an eye and not even blinked. It had gone through her like a dose of castor oil. But I did intimate it.

"In this case it was practically painless," I told him. "No, it wasn't that."

"Sure of it, are you?"

"Positive."

He looked thoughtful.

"Then why not let me look over the train for you?" he said. "It's more in my line than yours anyhow. And if you don't object to meeting me in the diner tonight about seven o'clock I'll tell you what I find, if anything."

He did not explain his line, and I did not ask him. But I found myself liking him. Also I was lonely and feeling rather forlorn, so I agreed at once. He took me back to Judith's drawing room, and stood by while I gave the customary raps. He smiled down at me.

"Like something out of a book, isn't it?" he said.

I was annoyed.

"I wouldn't put anything so silly in a book of mine."

He looked startled. "You mean you write books?"

"I've done one or two," I said modestly. But he only stared at me.

"Good God!" he muttered, and left abruptly.

I was in two minds after that about having dinner with him. To say I was annoyed would be a considerable understatement. On the other hand, I couldn't very well go into the diner and show my resentment by sitting by myself, and I ended by putting on fresh make-up and what I hoped was a highly literary expression.

It did not seem to impress him. He was waiting for me at a table for two, with a couple of cocktails ready and a beaming smile. He seated me with considerable manner.

"I hope you like Martinis," he said. "It seems like a good idea to drink to a train as innocent as this one."

"You found nobody?"

"A couple of 'con' boys. I wouldn't worry about them."

In a way it was a relief, but I found myself eying him curiously. He did not look like a policeman. I was sure he was not flatfooted, he was well dressed, and his hands were well cared for. His diction too was good. In a rather rugged way he was good-looking, but his face was strong rather than handsome.

"You seem to know a lot about that sort of thing," I said tentatively.

"I should. I'm a cop myself. Or I was," he added. "I've been in the army. Got knocked about a bit. All right now, however."

Perhaps it was the cocktail. Or perhaps there is something about a train trip which is rather like being on an ocean liner. You make contacts, but because you know they are brief, or perhaps you are bored, you talk rather more than you should. So within an hour or so I knew that my big friend's name was Terrence O'Brien. "With two r's, my mother insisted. God rest her soul." That he was usually called "Irish," that he had been a lieutenant of Homicide in the New York Police Department, had left it for the South Pacific during the war, and having inherited "a little something" was now at a loose end.

"Thinking of getting a small place out of town," he said. "Maybe raise a few chickens. That sort of thing."

I wondered just what he meant by being knocked about a bit. If ever a man looked in the pink of condition he did.

"You'll miss your work, won't you?" I asked.

"Maybe. Maybe not. I have a lot of reading to do. I got thrown out of college." He grinned. "In a moment of exhilaration it seemed like a good thing to take the pants off the campus policeman," he said. "Which is funny, because I went on the force myself later on. I'd always wanted to be a cop,"

he added. "I suppose most kids do."

But he reverted to Judith almost immediately.

"You can tell her for me there's nobody dangerous on this train," he said. "Or, on second thought, just leave me out of it. It won't hurt her to shut herself away for a while. And by the way, I don't know your name. Maybe I should, if you write."

"You don't like writing women, do you?"

"Never knew any," he said promptly.

But he didn't laugh. He looked appalled when I told him my name and that I wrote crime stories.

"Don't tell me," he said. "I know. The guy is a private eye. He keeps a fifth of Scotch in a drawer of his desk, he's blackjacked and then gets up and goes about his business instead of being taken to a hospital where he belongs, and he solves the crime when the regular cops are running in circles."

In spite of myself I had to laugh.

"Not quite," I said. "My detective is a woman."

He looked really disgusted then, but as dinner arrived at that moment we let the subject drop. Nevertheless, I felt during the meal that he was quietly observing me. I had no idea why.

I didn't tell Judith about him when I carried in the tea and toast that night. Policemen to Judith are men who give you tickets when you park a car or hale you up in traffic court for one thing or another. But I felt a little safer having him, so to speak, on call. He looked so reliable.

I saw him only once again during the trip. That was the same night, after I had rubbed Judith's back, given her two sleeping pills, and heard her lock herself in, I wandered back to the club car again. He was where I had seen him first, only he had abandoned the spectacles, which made him look younger. He got up when he saw me.

"I was hoping you'd come," he said. "I've kept this chair for you. Sister any better tonight?"

"She's just about the same," I said. "She's still locked away, if that's what you mean."

"Still no idea why?"

"No idea why."

He dropped the subject, got out a rather handsome cigarette case, and after giving me one took one himself.

"I've been thinking about you," he said abruptly. "Read a book of yours out on the islands. *The Red* something or other, wasn't it?"

"*The Red Urn,*" I said, probably with a lilt in my voice.

"You slipped up in it, you know," he said. "Why don't you crime writers learn something about police work? And that heroine of yours was a dilly. No character. Nothing but looks. As for that woman detective of yours . . . Why for God's sake a woman? Know what I think?"

"I haven't an idea," I said coldly, and with the lilt certainly gone.

"This sister of yours," he said.

"She's a beauty, and so probably you were brought up to believe she was God's gift to the world. It doesn't work out like that. Look at the ugly women some men marry! Not that you're that, God knows," he added magnanimously.

That made me laugh, and before long I was telling him of my childhood, of The Birches and our reasons for living there, to Phil and Helga and Jennie, and even to the rehabilitated swimming pool and the gatekeeper's cottage I had done over and could not rent.

He said it all sounded very pleasant to a tired New Yorker. He was pretty much at a loose end himself. He'd thought of a farm, but he realized that a farm without a woman might be pretty lonely, and he had never married. "Been too busy," he added.

Months later I was to think back over that talk of ours, and to wonder that I had not realized its undercurrents. Except for his helping me when Judith fainted in the train at Reno none of it was accidental. If I had not gone to the club car he would have managed to meet me somehow. Before I told him he knew perfectly well who Judith was, and almost certainly my own identity. And what is more, he knew what she was afraid of.

He had done, I thought resentfully, rather a professional bit of acting!

I had no suspicion of him then. When I finally said good night and went back to my compartment the connecting door into

Judith's drawing room was closed and locked on her side, so I hoped she was settled. At one o'clock in the morning, however, she shook me awake.

"I'm not going to New York at all," she said. "We can take a train from the station as soon as we get there, can't we? I'm going directly to The Birches."

"Well, you can't do it in the state of Illinois, or wherever we are now," I said peevishly. "For goodness' sake go back to bed and let me sleep."

But I didn't sleep much after that. Lying in my berth I could see Phil's face when we arrived, and Helga's. I thought of the quiet days at my desk in mother's room, and the Bechstein underneath. I thought of the salad or sandwich that was my customary lunch, and Judith's ideas on food. And I wondered how in heaven's name we could lock up a great rambling place like that if Judith persisted in behaving as she was doing then.

It was daylight before I slept.

I did not see my policeman again. Apparently he had left the train somewhere, perhaps in Chicago. I missed him, for I could have used a little help. It was Judith, of course. She would not leave the car at Grand Central until the entire train was empty, and even then only the warning that it was going out to the yards finally evicted her. By that time there was not a redcap in sight, and had it not been for a benevolent conductor I might still have been there, surrounded by luggage.

Luckily there was a local ready, and as I had wired Phil he met us at the station with our rattling old car. I expected Judith to make some comment on it, but she did not. She ducked in as though all the fiends of hell were after her, and kept looking behind all the way as though she expected to be followed.

Even Phil, resentful as I knew he was, finally noticed it.

"What the devil's the matter with you, Jude?" he said. "Expecting your ex-husband to follow you?"

"Of course not," she said sharply. "I thought I heard a state trooper behind us."

"They know this heap," Phil said dryly. "When they stop me it's for obstructing traffic." He turned around and eyed her as she sat in the back seat, surrounded by her handsome luggage. "Why don't you relax, Jude? You'll find The Birches a fine cure for the jitters. All we ever get there is an occasional scream in the night. Got any plans for the future?"

"Plans?" she said. "I'm staying at The Birches for a while anyhow. The house is as much mine as yours, isn't it?"

"Such as it is," he said. "The food, including Jello and bread pudding, both of which I detest, is paid for by Lois and me. So are the taxes, the light, the heat, the telephone, and the man who wanders in a few times a year to cut the grass. We count that and upkeep as rent. You'll have to ask Lois if she wants to take a boarder."

There was very nearly a row right then in the car. It ended, however, with her agreeing to pay a part of the expenses while she was there, but by her demanding mother's old room in return. I was furious.

"Sorry, Judith," I said stiffly. "That's mine now. Has been for years. I certainly don't intend to move out."

"If I'm to be a boarder I have a right to it. It's the biggest. Anyhow I have my own reasons for wanting it."

"What reasons?"

She declined to say, so it was a stalemate until we reached the house.

In spite of everything I was glad to be home. As I have said, spring at The Birches is wonderful, with the grass brilliantly green, the forsythia golden yellow, and the trees showing their new young leaves with pride. Like mothers with young babies, father always said. As we drove in I saw the pool was finished and was slowly filling, and Judith looked at it with an odd expression.

"I thought you'd let it go," she said.

"We did. It's just been restored."

I thought she shivered.

"I always hated it," she said, and closed her eyes.

Then the house was sprawling before us. The white elephant, as Phil called it, was no longer white. Even the big pillars of the porch were now scaling and gray. It was still impressive, however: the center three stories high, with the top floor the large attic; and the

two wings, one the service one with the pantry, kitchen, storeroom, and laundry in it and eight or ten servants' rooms above; the other containing what had been the morning room and was now our living room. In the el on that side was the library, what had been father's gun room but was now empty, and beyond the drawing room the unused conservatory, much of the glass gone and looking rather as though it had been bombed.

Judith had not been there for years, and she looked shocked when she saw it.

"What do you mean by upkeep?" she said indignantly. "The place is a ruin!"

"Guttering and spouting," I told her. "New tiles on the roof so we don't sleep under umbrellas. Toilets and bathtubs that work. What did you expect? Buckingham Palace?"

She said very little when she was inside, although her face was a study. The long hall that ran from the front to the rest of the house was carpetless, except for a rug or two, and some impulse on Jennie's part had opened the door to the drawing room, although it had been closed for years.

It stood there, naked and enormous, with what little furniture remained covered with sheets, including the piano, and the glass chandeliers and the mirrors similarly protected. She stood gazing in at it.

"Welcome home," I said. "You can't say I didn't warn you, Jude."

"But it's dreadful. Where's mother's Aubusson carpet? And all the rest of her lovely stuff?"

"Sold," I told her. "Sold long ago when Phil was getting a start. It went for food and doctor bills, and when mother died it buried her."

I think she hesitated then. She looked as though she meant to turn and leave, but some second thought, some secret reason, decided her to stay. At that moment Helga and Jennie appeared, and I saw by Helga's expression that there was going to be trouble.

"You'll have to take us as we are, Miss Jude," she said. "We live pretty plain. Not the way you're used to."

But Judith had pulled herself together by that time.

"I only want to rest," she said plaintively. "I don't expect a great deal, Helga. Just peace and quiet."

"That's all we've got," Helga said, her face grim, and decided to offer a gnarled old hand for Jude to shake. "This is Jennie. She's not what you're used to either, but she can get about, which is more than I can."

All in all it must have been an unpleasant homecoming—if you can call it that—but Judith had apparently made her decision. She may have had some qualms, however. She stood at the front door, gazing down the drive while Phil carried in her luggage.

"I don't remember it like this," she said. "It used to be so gay. And it's frightfully lonely. Aren't there any neighbors?"

Phil put down some bags and mopped his face.

"Quite a lot has happened to the world since your day," he said. "Or perhaps that crowd of yours in town didn't know it. No, there are no neighbors, Judith. Take it or leave it. And my own suggestion is to leave it."

She only shrugged her shoulders, and I left her there to go back to the kitchen and Helga. She was standing by the stove stirring something, and her old shoulders looked bent and depressed.

"I'm having lamb stew for dinner," she said, her voice stubborn. "She can eat it or let it alone. I don't want her here, Lois, and that's flat. I've seen you and Mr. Phil struggling for years while she lived on the fat of the land, and not so much as a visit from her. Now when she's in trouble she's here."

She sat down on the edge of the big kitchen table.

"What do you mean, trouble, Helga?" I said. "I wouldn't call her divorce that."

Helga eyed me dourly. "Maybe you haven't really looked at her," she said. "She's in some sort of jam, and I don't like it. She looks haunted-like. She's thin too. What's she done? Killed somebody?"

"Don't be an old fool," I said, and put an arm around her. "She won't stay long. We'll have to make the best of it. That's all."

I found Judith already ensconced in mother's room, with an entranced Jennie opening bags and taking out the lace-trimmed underwear and nightgowns it contained. A country girl from the village, she had certainly never seen things like that before. Nor anyone like Judith, anxiously examining her face in the mirror of my toilet table. Already my typewriter and table had been moved into the hall, and I was almost speechless with fury.

"You always get your own way, don't you, Jude?" I said, my voice shaking. "If you ask me, this is a pretty dirty trick. There are plenty of other rooms."

"I won't be here long. I've told you that."

"Then why throw me out?"

"I have all my jewels with me. I need the safe, Lois. It's still here, I see."

I was appalled.

"Do you mean to say you took all that stuff to Reno?"

"Why not? I always carry it with me."

"Is that why you locked yourself away in the train?"

She looked at me in the mirror.

"Of course. What do you think?"

I didn't believe her for a moment. She was lying, and I knew it. She had had it on the way west, and never bothered about it. But she followed it up cleverly.

"That's why I want Phil to nail those windows shut over the porch," she said. "The other two will do for ventilation."

I stood staring at her.

"That's ridiculous," I said. "No one knows you have anything valuable with you. Anyhow you have the safe. And we never have burglars. They know we have nothing worth stealing except mother's

Georgian tea set, and that's been on the sideboard in the dining room for twenty years."

She looked stubborn.

"Anyone could climb those porch pillars," she said. "I'm taking no chances."

Jennie had gone out for something by that time, and I confronted Judith with what I daresay was not a particularly sisterly face.

"What are you afraid of?" I demanded. "Don't pretend to me, Jude. You're scared to death. You've done something, haven't you? Something wrong. Maybe something terrible. What is it?"

She did not like it. I thought for a moment she was going to slap me. Then she thought better of it.

"Don't be absurd, Lois," she said. "What could I have done? And if I had, do you think I could get away with it, as well known as I am? That's simply silly. I'm taking normal precautions, like any sensible person. You're building up something that actually doesn't exist."

It was her round. I'll grant you that. She had won mother's room and even Phil's reluctant support. For the last thing I heard that night was the sound of a hammer as he nailed her two windows shut.

I was back in my old nursery by that time, still seething, but in spite of myself I had to smile, remembering dinner that night. Judith had come down to dinner in an exquisite negligee, had waited for the soup course, which did not arrive, and winced when Jennie slammed her plate of stew in front of her. Phil watched her without appearing to until the dessert appeared.

"I'm sorry, Judith," he said, "but we've had to let the butler go. Got into the wine cellar and turned up plastered. But I can recommend this lemon gelatin. Not fattening but full of energy."

Whereupon he ate the stuff, which I knew he detested.

6

Ridgely called me up the next morning. He sounded irritable.

"I didn't expect to have to learn from the papers that you were back," he said. "When did you get in?"

"Late yesterday. She's here at The Birches, Ridge. I don't know why."

"I suppose she has her reasons," he said coldly. "I'll mail you a check today."

He hung up without so much as a good-bye, and as I put down the receiver I wondered again why he had wanted me to go to Reno. It seemed singularly pointless. He was not even interested in why she was where she was.

I had my first chance to talk to Phil when I drove him to the station that morning. I told him the whole story, the fainting at Reno, and the way she had locked herself away on the train. But I did not mention O'Brien. It seemed unnecessary.

Phil was thoughtful, especially after I told him of Ridgely's call.

"Suppose she's afraid of him?" he asked.

"He wasn't in Nevada," I said. "Or on that train. And she's not afraid of him. She never has been."

It was true, of course, and Phil nodded.

"I suppose he's out," he said. "Certainly he's behaved damned decently, but then as a Chandler he would. Think she got mixed up with some man out there?"

"Not seriously. No, Phil, it's not Ridge, and it's nobody else I can think of."

He grunted.

"Well, I wish to God she'd take her troubles somewhere else," he said heavily. "Just as we're beginning to see daylight . . ."

I did some marketing in town after I left him at the station. Town is what we call the bustling small city where the station is situated. The village, a mile or so beyond our gate, is merely a huddle of houses. Thus I buy our food in town, shop for clothes in the city, and get our grass cut—so to speak—by the village. So I bought the groceries in town that morning, and then drove slowly home.

The Birches sits on a low hill, with higher ones behind it, and the drive slopes gradually from the cottage to the house, some five hundred feet or so. The Adrians' neglected entrance was not far beyond ours, and as none of us had money to do any pruning we were practically drowned in shrubbery. I had managed to clear a bit around the pool, which lay halfway to the house on the Adrian side.

I looked at the cottage as I turned in. It was still closed, and I decided to open and clean it soon. I had put it in the hands of an agent again. And I stopped the car by the pool and got out. It must have rained recently, for the water was slightly muddy. It looked cold too, and I wondered if after all it would ever justify its cost. Maybe, when the weather got really warm . . .

I was startled to hear someone behind me, and turned to see a young man with a camera in the drive.

"Any chance of my getting a shot of Mrs. Chandler?" he asked cheerfully. "Famous beauty in bucolic surroundings. Resting after Reno. You know the sort of thing."

"I haven't an idea," I told him. "She's never objected before, so far as I know. You can try anyhow."

He went toward the house, and I walked up to what I called father's garden. The banks of the little stream—it was only a foot or two across—were still pretty bare, but here and there small green things were pushing their way up after their winter's sleep. I could still see him there, holding my hand and calling me baby. And I could still remember the wilted lilies-of-the-valley from those very banks which I had carried to his grave, long after his death.

What would he think of us now? I wondered. Or of the bleak old house? Or of Judith and the mystery that apparently surrounded her? He would be patient, I thought. Patient and understanding. He was always understanding. It was he who had established the small cemetery under the birches where we buried our pets, the dead baby robin I had found and wept over, the kitten one of his hunting dogs had killed. In later years Phil and I still carried it on, and the green mounds were always neat.

As I walked to it I thought drearily how much of the family history was there: the early pets, my turtle, the little alligator Phil bought somewhere and kept in his bathtub, even the cats kept in the stable to catch the mice there. Then the long interval after father's death, with mother at The Birches refusing, as she said, to turn the place into a zoo, without even a dog allowed. And after she was gone Phil's terriers and my own series of Pekes with their small tragedies, usually traffic ones. After Chang died I had had enough heartbreak. I had no other dog but, as I say, we still kept the place in order, although the little wooden crosses had long lost the inscriptions on them.

I was pulling some weeds from one of the mounds when I heard footsteps again, and saw the photographer coming toward me.

"Look," he said. "Do you live here?"

"I do. Why?"

"Well, I want you to take a good look at me. Would you say, just casually, that I am a thug or a gangster? Or that I've got horns and a tail?"

"Not casually," I told him. "I don't know what investigation might disclose."

He managed a grin.

"Thanks," he said. "It's like this. Mrs. Chandler was in the hall when the maid opened the door. She just took a look at me, yelped, and ran up the stairs." He took off his hat and mopped his face and head with a handkerchief. "Darnedest thing you ever saw, or heard."

So Judith was really in hiding. It was the first time I had actually believed it. It was silly, of course. It had already been in the press, as witness Ridgely's call. But as she never looked at a newspaper perhaps she did not know it.

My cameraman left after that, and I wandered slowly up the stream toward the old stables. The birch grove was on my way, and I stopped to stroke the smooth silver-white boles. They were big trees now, and I was a big girl. Too adult at least to be as uneasy as I was beginning to feel. And

the grove quieted me. It had always done that. There is something soothing about a tree. It is so permanent, and in a way so patient.

I was feeling better when I went back to get the car, although Helga was indignant when I carried the groceries into the kitchen.

"You're late," she said snappishly, "and what's all this about some man attacking Judith? Jennie says she's locked in her room and won't come out."

"Nobody attacked her. A newspaperman wanted a candid-camera shot of her. That's all."

"And when did she ever run from a camera?" Helga asked shrewdly. "The attic's full of snapshots of her down at the pool in the old days."

None of it made any sense to me. How on earth did she expect to hide? She had always been the columnists' delight, and while we were out at Reno Anne had sent me an envelope of clippings. To quote one is to quote them all: "The beautiful Judith Chandler is in Reno, ending an apparently happy marriage of twenty years. She and Ridgely had been drifting apart for a long time, Judith preferring the white lights while he stayed at home and read a good book. What Judith plans for the future is unknown, but if there is a romance involved no one seems to know."

I never showed any of them to her, but I think it was the cameraman's visit that put her virtually in a state of siege. For days after it she did not go beyond the front porch in the daytime, although at night she would put on a dark cape and walk up and down the drive. She always left the front door open, however, and if she could induce either Phil or me to go with her she seemed happier.

I made the best of an uncomfortable period. My old nursery was in the wing over the living room and, I hoped, remote enough to enable me to work. It was not too comfortable, of course. Shelves which had been adequate for a little girl's books did not begin to hold mine. Also I had forgotten the piano, and it seemed to me at that time that I never went to my typewriter but Judith simultaneously sat down at the Bechstein.

She did not do it deliberately. I want to be fair. It was simply something for her to do when I was not available. For the curious thing was that she had apparently cut herself off entirely from her old life. She telephoned nobody, and such bits of mail as came for her outside of her alimony checks seemed to be largely advertisements or travel circulars.

Even Phil noticed it.

"What's happened to her old gang?" he asked inelegantly. "Don't they call her up or anything?"

"Out of the papers out of mind," I suggested.

"Well, I suppose there's a difference between alimony and ten million dollars," he said philosophically. "See here, Lois, I haven't said this before, but has it oc-

curred to you that Judith has some sort of persecution complex?"

"Who on earth is persecuting her?"

"How do I know? But I've watched her. I begin to think she's a schizophrenic, although God knows what that means. Can't you sic her back on Townsend—or whatever is the psychiatrist fellow's name?"

But Judith was no schizophrenic, although ultimately she did go back to Doctor Townsend. I must admit, however, that even I was puzzled when she had been back a few weeks—it was early in May then—when one day a locksmith came out from town and asked for her. I was in the hall, and I stared at him.

"A locksmith," I said incredulously. "What are you to do? Or did Mrs. Chandler say?"

"I've got it here." He put down his bag and got out a card. "It says new locks and bolts on main bedroom and bathroom. All right with you?"

I had no chance to answer. Judith appeared on the stairs then and took him up with her. She never explained, nor did I ask, but the next time I heard her at the piano I investigated. In the early days I suppose mother's bathroom had served several of the family, for in addition to opening into the bedroom it also opened into the hall. Later on, of course, other baths were installed. Even my nursery had one. So did Phil's, and several of the guest rooms. Now, however, there were heavy new locks on both Judith's bedroom and bath, and a chain on each of them.

I stood staring at them for some time, and that night I told Phil. He did not seem surprised.

"I told you," he said. "Now maybe you'll listen to me. If she won't go back to Townsend, get her to go to someone else. Suppose she sets fire to herself with a cigarette? We'd never get her out."

I hesitated. We were getting along rather better, Judith and I. She was never sisterly to me, but at least she no longer seemed to regard me as one of the help. The only open warfare in the house was between Helga and herself. It puzzled me. I even wondered sometimes if Helga knew something about her, but if she did she kept it to herself.

Then too something happened a day or so later which took my mind off Judith as having nothing to do with her. Or did it? I was not even sure of that.

The spring was well advanced by that time. One day our itinerant gardener appeared and cut the lawn, and I was reminded of the cottage which I hoped to rent.

It was a pleasant little place, a one-story bungalow-type house, with a shed behind it where in the early days the men at work on the grounds had stored their tools.

I walked down that afternoon armed with the keys and a broom and dustcloth, and wearing an old pair of slacks. As usual I stopped at the pool, which was clear by that time, and I saw a car in the drive next to ours. As the Adrian

house had been closed for years, this rather surprised me. I saw nobody around, however, and promptly forgot it.

The cottage stood close to the main road, with a path from our drive leading to it, and it smelled musty and damp when I went in. The door led directly into the sitting room, and beyond it were two small bedrooms, a bath, and the kitchen: as all were shuttered, the place seemed dark and uninviting.

I stopped as soon as I went into the kitchen. Someone had been smoking there. The ashes apparently from a pipe had been dumped into the sink, I thought rather recently, and the reek of smoke was over everything. I was annoyed rather than startled. After all, the agent had another set of keys, but if he had sent someone to see the place I should have been notified.

Rather indignantly I opened a window and the shutters, and I had just stepped back when I heard a car on the road. As it is not a main artery, there is not much traffic on it. What with most of the summer places closed what usually passes us are delivery trucks to the village a mile or so beyond, an occasional pair of lovers seeking privacy, or a family out for a Sunday jaunt. So I glanced out the window, to see the car I had noticed leaving the Adrian drive and going rapidly toward town.

It was a yellow taxicab from the city. Our local ones are cream colored with blue fenders. But I

had no time to see who was in it.
As I looked around the cottage,
however, it became more and
more clear that someone had been
inside it, perhaps for some time.
There was a glass on the living-
room table where the intruder had
taken a drink of water, and further
investigation showed a defective

shutter and a window not entirely
closed. Whoever it was had not
been sent by any agent.

I did no cleaning that day, although I was angry rather than
frightened. And as that was the
night Phil chose to suggest a psychiatrist to Judith I promptly forgot it.

7

Judith had been more relaxed
since the extra locks had been
placed on her doors, but she still
looked drawn and tired. She must
have realized it too, for at the
dinner table she said she really
needed a shampoo and a facial.
Phil pushed away the tapioca pudding he loathed and looked interested.

"Do you good," he said. "Go to
a beauty parlor and get fixed up.
Can't neglect yourself at your age,
Jude. How about the old nerves?
Sleeping better?"

"My nerves are all right," she
said sharply.

"Then you certainly don't show
it. They can sure play the devil
with a woman's looks." He had
touched on a raw spot, and he
knew it. "You've been ready to
jump out of your skin ever since
you came back from Reno. Why

don't you see somebody about it
when you're in town? A good
psychiatrist might help you."

Which was when, as I have already written, she told him not to
be a fool; that she had no intention of spilling her guts to any
peeping Tom. She was suspicious too. We were not supposed
to have known of the Townsend
visits.

"I suppose you have someone
already picked out for me!" she
said. "If you have, forget it."

"Not me," Phil told her. "Pick
your own, or consult the old girl
Lois writes about. Of course if
you want to lose your looks that's
your business. When I go to bed
I go to sleep. That's how I keep
my beauty."

But if Judith repudiated the
idea of a psychiatrist, I did not.
There was something badly wrong

with her, and in common humanity I felt we should know about it. I resolved that night to see Doctor Townsend, and making the excuse of having to see my publisher, I called at his office the next morning.

I had no appointment, so it was some time before I saw him. Anne had been right. He was a handsome man, and he looked relieved when I said I was not a patient, but I had called about one. He glanced at the clock on his desk.

"I can give you ten minutes or so," he said. "Who is this patient, Miss—Miss Maynard?"

"My sister Judith Chandler, doctor."

He gave me a quick glance.

"Mrs. Chandler left me some months ago. You know that probably."

"Yes. Of course she has been in Reno. Now she is living with us in the country. Do you mind saying why she came to see you, doctor? I'm not merely curious. It may be important."

"What do you mean by important?"

"She's not well. She's—well, she's in a curious state of mind. My brother thinks she has delusions of persecution. I don't agree with him."

"So?" He looked thoughtful. "Well, Miss Maynard, so far as I know she came to me because she was not sleeping. I suppose that's understandable. If she was contemplating divorce . . ."

"I don't think she was really," I said flatly. "I think something scared her, I don't know what,

but she's still scared into panic, and I believe she needs help."

"Yes," he said. "Quite definitely she needed help when I saw her. Only—suppose you tell me what you know."

I did. No halfway measures were any good, and I knew it. Also I felt I could trust him. There was something quieting about him too, as though no depths of the human mind would shock him. I began with the night Ridgely had found her with her jewels, and went on from there to her sudden determination to go to Reno, and what happened at the station there and on the train. He listened absorbedly, as though he was trying to reconcile it with what he knew of Judith.

"Of course," he said, "if this terror is real it is a matter for the police. On the other hand, your brother may be right. I have no idea why she wanted a divorce. Quite frankly she never mentioned it to me. But you have to remember that divorce in itself is often a sort of psychic shock."

He went on. He had to deal with such people quite often. They had reached the end of one road, and unless another opened up they felt lost and confused.

"Especially with divorced women," he said. "Up to that time they've been sheltered. At least there was someone around they could depend on, in case of burglars, for instance!" He smiled at me. "Someone to keep house for, to order food for, even to dress for. If they marry again, all right. At least they are back in a familiar groove. If they do not, what have they? They haunt the movies and the beauty shops, they gamble frantically, and some of them end up in this office, out of sheer loneliness and despair."

"I suppose she does miss her old life," I agreed, "but she's not only lonely. She's sick with fright. If someone like you could find out what it is . . ."

He shrugged.

"She was difficult," he said. "I often wondered why she came at all. She only talked about unimportant things. Of course it's normal for the human mind to protect its privacy, and we don't use medication, Miss Maynard. In this job of mine all we have is words. I get sick of hearing my own voice sometimes," he added. "Your sister did, I know, but she never really came clean. Actually I never knew what she was thinking. And it was deliberate. She didn't want me to know."

"Would you try again, if she came back?"

He hesitated.

"If she came of her own free will," he said. "Otherwise it would be the same story all over again."

"Perhaps if you called her up and talked to her—as a friend," I went on hastily, seeing his face. "You see, it's not only Judith who needs help. We all do. Life isn't really bearable just now. This locked-door business is only a part of it. She hasn't left the house, except at night when no one can see her. She doesn't go far even then, only up and down the drive a short distance. And while she

talks of going abroad I don't believe she really will. She seems to have no initiative."

He nodded.

"That's understandable," he said. "Someone else—her husband, I suppose—always arranged things for her before. But you must realize I can't very well ask her to come back. However—wait a minute." He rang a bell and the nurse appeared. "Miss Robey," he said, "did anyone ever claim that gold compact?"

"Not yet, doctor."

"I see. Thank you." He turned to me as she went out. "I might call her about that," he said. "Ask if it's hers. I rather think it is. She left me pretty abruptly the last day she was here."

He looked at his watch and I got up.

"Don't expect too much, Miss Maynard," he warned. "We may get her over her agoraphobia. The fear of open spaces, if that's what it is. But if she is in real danger I suggest the police."

I was depressed when I left him, but to my astonishment his call that night worked like a charm. Not immediately. At first, as I have said, she was not only suspicious but resentful. But two days later she came down to breakfast, hitherto unknown, and announced she was going with Phil to New York. She was dressed in a thin spring suit, and with careful makeup she looked more like her old self. But she did not mention Bernard Townsend. She was, she said, going to have a shampoo and a facial. But she wore a heavy nose veil and a scarf she could pull up over her chin.

It looked for all the world like an attempt at disguise. I did not mention it, however. And in spite of my growing sympathy for her it was a relief to me to get her out of the house. I did the first real day's work I had managed since she came. Phil reported later that the excursion had taken on all the attributes of high adventure.

"She wouldn't get out of the car at the station until the last minute," he said. "She sat there, eying everybody in sight, until I felt damned conspicuous. Same in the city. Look, Lois, why is she afraid of taxis? She wouldn't take one. Wouldn't go near one, in fact."

"Even in the city?"

"Certainly in the city. She shies off like a frightened horse when she sees one."

I was tempted to tell him about the one in the Adrians' drive, but it seemed rather pointless. After all, there might be a dozen reasons for its being there, or someone breaking into the cottage. Curiosity perhaps, or someone thirsty and needing a drink. As for her phobia about cabs, I had no idea what caused it. Certainly she never explained it, although from that time on she went regularly to New York. It existed. I knew that. When I could not take her, or Phil's train was too early for her, she used Ed Brown's rattling one, which he kept in the village. She was looking better, however. A shampoo and a rinse had brightened her hair, and she was using a new make-up.

I suspected she was seeing Doctor Townsend again, but she never admitted it.

Perhaps I am spending too much time on that interval, before our real mystery began to develop. My only excuse is the change Judith made in our living, with the old peace gone, with Phil growing increasingly irritable and my own work suffering. The servants too were hard to manage. Jennie even threatened to leave, after Jude sent her breakfast down because she maintained the coffee was cold. I found her crying in the pantry.

"How do I know when she's going to ring?" she said. "And that coffee was boiling when I poured it. Only two of us in a house this size, and her acting like she was a duchess or something."

I spoke to Helga that day. It was raining and her arthritis was bothering her. But I knew and she knew that after forty years with us and at her age she could not get work elsewhere. Also she had known Judith since she was born, and apparently nothing she did surprised her.

"She's what she is, Lois," she said. "She was a spoiled child from the day she could walk, and looking like a little angel all the time. She was sly too. Your mother never knew half the things she did. But she's not so young now. She isn't cute any more, or anybody's angel either."

However, she promised to talk to Jennie, and in the end Jennie stayed on.

But I was still uneasy. Judith not

only locked herself in her room at night, but sometimes in the daytime. She was losing weight. As Phil said, if she was fooling herself she was making a good job of it. Then one day I had a brainstorm. I decided to talk to Ridgely.

It was early June by that time, and quite warm. The little wild garden father had planted by the creek was flourishing, and when Phil came home in the evenings he would take a dip in the pool. I used it too, although the water was still cold. And I was sitting on the bench beside it one day after a swim when I thought of him.

I had gone back mentally to the old days, when Judith would be there surrounded by boys of all ages, and I would climb to the top of the platform, an often toothless straight-haired seven-year-old, and yell to them to watch me dive. Just to prove I could still do it I climbed the ladder, and suddenly I remembered the one time I had seen Ridgely there.

He had been standing by the pool watching me, and he said, "That's too high for you. What's the idea? Showing off?"

Funny! I had forgotten that entirely until then. To my childish eyes Ridgely had appeared out of the blue, walking down the church aisle with his bride on his arm!

Judith was in town that day, so I called him on the telephone and asked him to have lunch with me as soon as possible.

His voice sounded apologetic.

"I've been meaning to call you," he said. "If you don't mind the Yale Club, meet me there at one tomorrow. How is everything?"

"I'll tell you when I see you," I said, and hung up.

He was not particularly cordial when I met him. He said he hadn't much time, and to get on with it. He was as dapper as ever, but I didn't think he looked well. I suppose a divorce is as hard on a man as on a woman, although I was sure he had long since ceased to care for Judith. He ordered cocktails and then sat back and surveyed me.

"You look a trifle desperate, Lois," he said. "You're thinner too."

"That makes a pair of us," I said. "Judith is losing weight too. Ridgely, when she left you, you thought she was in some sort of trouble. Did you ever find out what it was?"

"I thought she might be being blackmailed. Why?"

"Because I don't think it's that. She's afraid. Physically afraid. Blackmailers don't kill, do they?"

"Not as a rule," he said dryly. "Who's she afraid of, Lois? Not me surely."

"Not you, of course. I think it's somebody she saw in Reno."

"Reno? For God's sake, why Reno?"

But of course I had no idea. I told him the story, the locks on her doors, her windows over the porch nailed shut, and her attack on the train from Reno and her odd behavior after it. He seemed puzzled rather than uneasy.

"Sure she's not merely dramatizing all this?" he asked. "She was rather good at that sort of thing."

"She's making a real job of it if she is. I wondered . . . Is she really afraid her jewels will be stolen, Ridge? That's the excuse she gives."

He shrugged his well-tailored shoulders.

"She was always fairly casual with them. I can't imagine such extreme measures."

"Well, I'll ask you another," I said. "Was she always afraid of taxicabs?"

"Taxicabs?" He looked astonished. "Not that I know of. Of course she didn't use them often. She had her own cars. What's all this about taxis? It doesn't sound sane."

"Maybe *I'm* crazy," I said. "Only it looks odd to me. Even Phil has noticed it. So have I. I think she's gone back to Doctor Townsend too. But she walks everywhere here in the city, rain or shine. She won't use a cab. Did she ever have any trouble about one? Run into it or something?"

He shook his head. If she had, he said, he had never heard of it, and he almost certainly would if it had been serious.

"I can think of a lot of things," he said grimly. "If the trouble is real—and you know Judith, she imagines a good bit—it may be blackmail. Only the hell of it is I can't learn anything about it. As a matter of fact I put a private inquiry agent on it after she left me. I felt responsible in a way. He worked for six weeks. He went back a dozen years and turned up a lot of dirt about some of the

people she played around with, but nothing about Judith. Absolutely nothing, Lois. She always—to use his own phrase—landed in her own bed, and no mistake about it."

So that was that. No blackmail. No lovers. Probably even no anxiety about her jewels. Then what?

I felt vaguely dissatisfied when I left him. He was too cold, too detached. After all, she had been his wife for a long time. I wondered that day if her life with him had been any bed of roses. He was a gentleman and a Chandler, but he must have known something, or why had he paid me to go to Reno? And why of all things a private detective?

As it happened, it was that same evening that Jennie added her mite, if you can call it that, to our general bewilderment, which led Phil, sweating and exhausted, to drop into a chair and light a cigarette with shaking hands.

"If I've ever made any cracks about having Judith committed," he said, "just forget it. I'm the one who needs it. A cell and a nice strait jacket sound like heaven to me."

Yet the incident itself was not hair-raising. It was simply bewildering.

We were in the living room, and I had been telling him about Ridge. He was listening comfortably, his highball nightcap in his hand, and looking up now and then at mother's portrait over the mantel.

"So what?" he said when I finished. "He doesn't give a good

God damn. After all, since Judith never cared for him, why should he bother?"

Then we heard Jennie. She was running screaming toward the house, and the next moment she was in the room, still shrieking. Phil dropped his glass and catching hold of her shook her.

"Stop that noise!" he shouted. "What the devil's the matter? Stop it, I say."

She began to cry then, and little by little we got it out of her.

She has what she calls a boy friend in the village and, as Helga strongly forbids "followers," their usual meeting place is the bench by the pool. What Jennie said, after she became intelligible, was that she had been waiting there for him when a man came through the shrubbery from the unused Adrian place, and pointed a gun at her from across the pool.

"A gun?" Phil said. "It was dark, wasn't it? How could you see a gun?"

She didn't insist on the gun after that, but she did insist that he spoke to her.

"He spoke to you! What did he say?" Phil asked.

"He said I was to stay there until he could talk to me," she said surprisingly. "And that I knew damned well what it was about."

"And that's all?"

"That was plenty, if you ask me, Mr. Phil. I just yelled and ran."

Luckily Judith had gone to bed, or we might have had trouble. As it was, the two of us, Jennie not voting, made a careful search of the grounds that night. We found nobody, but there were some broken branches among the rhododendrons across the pool, and above it someone had crushed a few of the lilies-of-the-valley father had planted there.

But it seemed incredible that Judith had heard nothing, and later I was to wonder whether she did. Whether she had not lain shivering in her bed that night, listening to those shrieks of Jennie's and realizing that The Birches was no longer a haven.

I think she did, for the next day she began to make inquiries over the telephone about ship sailings. She was too late, as it turned out, for that was the summer of the great hegira to Europe. But those inquiries of hers eventually led to her tragic undoing.

8

Later in the month to my amazement I happened on the O'Brien man again. I had almost forgotten him, but there he was, big and smiling and holding out his hand. I had been to the butcher's in town that morning, and I was clutching a leg of lamb when he confronted me.

"Well, look who's here!" he said. "I thought you lived somewhere in this neck of the woods, Miss Maynard, but I certainly never expected to see you."

He had been smoking a pipe. He emptied it and dropped it in his pocket, and we shook hands like old friends. After which he insisted on taking me into a drugstore and buying me a Coke. Over his glass he inspected me with some care.

"You're thinner," he said. "Anything wrong? Or is your lady detective working you too hard?"

His eyes were keen and very blue. Also he was not wearing his spectacles, although he got them out later and put them on. But I realized he had the trained eyes of a policeman. What he looked at he really saw. They could be cold too. Oh, God, how cold they could be!

"I'm all right," I said. "I'm not working well, but I have those spells. All writers do, I think, especially if their heroines have only looks, no character."

He ignored that. "And your sister? How is she?"

"She's staying with my brother and myself at The Birches, five miles out of town."

"Five miles!" he said. "That's a short ride but the devil of a long walk. I like your neck of the woods," he went on. "I've been looking it over. But I'm not sure I'm cut out to be a farmer. I have no natural affection for cows or even pigs. Chickens are about my limit."

I laughed and his eyes twinkled.

"What I really need is a small place somewhere," he said. "I'd like to sow some seeds and see what comes up, if anything. Maybe keep a few chickens, and get an egg or so at the source, so to speak. What about that little place of yours? Rented it yet?"

It was too casual, too easy, somehow. And there was that pipe of his in his pocket.

"No," I said. "Didn't you like what you saw of it the other day?"

"What's that supposed to mean?"

"You were out there, weren't you? In a taxi? I saw the cab, and I knew someone had been inside the house."

He actually looked startled.

"I've never been near the place," he said. "What's this all about? Been having trouble?"

I told him about Jennie's intruder, and he listened carefully.

"No idea who he was?"

"None whatever."

He was thoughtful, but I still was not trusting him entirely in spite of his disarming manner, and just then he put his hand in his pocket and rather sheepishly threw a bunch of keys onto the drugstore counter.

"I'll be honest," he said. "I've never seen your place, Miss Maynard, but I've been in to see your agent just now, and he gave me those keys. Want them back? Or shall we go out and look it over?"

I hesitated.

"What about your job?" I said. "Does a lieutenant or whatever you were in Homicide simply walk out and raise chickens?"

He looked impatient.

"I've told you all that," he said. "I had some trouble in the Pacific. Not mental. I didn't have to take sitz baths and weave rugs! But enough so I've got what you might call a protracted leave of absence. Got shot in a lung and am supposed to have a good rest and breathe some good country air. Your agent says that's what you have."

Of course his being a wounded veteran made a difference, I told myself, but I thought too that it might be a good idea to have a policeman on the place. What with Jennie's experience and someone breaking into the cottage itself some of my former confidence in the peace and security of The Birches was rapidly vanishing.

"We have the air," I conceded. "I'm not so sure you'll have a rest." Which, as he told me later, was not only prophetic, but an understatement of considerable magnitude.

The clerk behind the counter had disappeared, so sitting there I told him my story: Judith's terror and the extra locks, Jennie's man with or without a gun, even the yellow taxi in the Adrian drive, and the intruder in the cottage. When I finished he was looking grim.

"I don't know what it all adds up to," I said. "It's a sort of Chinese puzzle, isn't it?"

"What it all adds up to," he said soberly, "is that I'm taking the cottage, whether you want me or not. No reflection on brother Phil, but if there's dirty work at the crossroads I don't think it's precisely a lawyer's job. But," he added, "I'd better tie a string to this. I'm not going there as a cop. For one thing, I don't believe your sister would care to have an ex-policeman at her heels. She hasn't been very cooperative about her trouble, has she?"

"She seems deadly afraid we'll learn what it is."

"Good enough. I'm a veteran,

with a hole in my chest and maybe a bit of business to take me into town now and then. How about it? And how about another Coke?"

"Thanks, but it so happens I loathe the stuff."

He reached out solemnly and shook my hand.

"So do I," he said, and we both laughed.

It is hard to remember how cheerful I was that day! Because I liked him, and I thought he liked me. Because there was something dependable about his big strong body and beady eyes. And perhaps because, shut away in the country as I had been, I had been lonely for a long time, and here at last was a good companion and what I suspected would prove a loyal friend.

We made a small procession that day on our way to The Birches, I ahead in our old sedan while he followed in an equally shabby coupé. The place looked beautiful in the sunlight, and he got out and stood looking about him with a pleased smile on his face.

"Wonderful," he said. "And don't tell me that's a swimming pool over there! I can't believe it."

I told him it was and that he could use it whenever he wanted, although the water was still cold. Upon which I had some difficulty getting him into the cottage at all. Once inside, however, with the shutters opened and the windows raised, he stood in the sitting room with his hands in his pockets, gazing about him complacently, although his size dwarfed the small room.

"It's swell," he said. "And that shed back there would be fine for chickens. I'm right handy with tools. And if you don't mind chicken wire, I could make a place for them to run. How about it?"

"Do anything you like," I told him recklessly. "I'll go so far as to buy your eggs too."

"Well, maybe now and then I'll make a present to your cook. There will be no money passing between the lady of The Birches and Terry O'Brien. I can tell you that."

It was a little time before he settled down. Then I found him in the kitchen, inspecting the ashes in the sink.

"Fellow was a pipe smoker like myself," he said thoughtfully. "Where's the glass he drank out of?"

It was still on the sitting-room table, and I was about to pick it up when he yelled at me.

"Haven't you ever heard of fingerprints?" he demanded. "Find me some paper, can you? If there's real trouble afoot, this is as good a start as any."

I found him some newspaper in the woodbox by the fireplace, and he wrapped the glass carefully and put it in his car. He was thoughtful when he came back.

"Any chance your sister will remember me?" he asked. "That might be awkward."

I didn't think she would, and told him so. After all, she had not seen him when he picked her up, and she had really fainted after that. But he thought it best to try before he settled in, so I took him up to the house to lunch.

He need not have worried. Jennie was having her day off, and a disgruntled Helga limped around the table, eying him as she did so. But when Judith wandered in, beautiful in a blue silk house gown, she merely gave him a long stare as I introduced him.

"Mr. O'Brien has taken the cottage for the summer, Judith," I explained. "This is my sister, Mrs. Chandler."

She nodded and sat down.

"I always thought it was a dreary little place," she said, without interest. "Maybe Lois has fixed it up." Then she gave him a double take and scared me almost out of my wits. "Haven't I seen you before, some place?"

He smiled. "It's possible, Mrs. Chandler. But if I had seen you anywhere, be sure I would never forget it."

That is all I remember of the lunch, Helga's smoldering eyes on him and Judith's failure to show any interest whatever, especially in the chickens he insisted on discussing. I know she left the table as soon as the meal was over, and he looked thoughtfully after her.

"She gave me a bad minute or two," he said. "She's seen me, all right. Hit-and-run case, where the woman died. We never proved anything on her, and she denied it, of course. It was years ago."

"Would that be the trouble now?" I asked. "Some relative, or something like that?"

But he shook his head.

"The old girl had no family. The city had to bury her. I have an idea Mr. Chandler suspected his wife at the time, but I don't know."

I remember showing him the lower floor of the house after that, and finding him totally unimpressed, except with mother's portrait. He stood in front of it for some time.

"Looks like a woman who knew her own mind" was his comment. Then suddenly: "What happened to the pearls?"

"I suppose they were sold long ago, like everything else."

"Pity," he said. "They'd look nice on you." He turned and looked at me. "I'm beginning to think you've had the hell of a life, and that it's not getting any better fast. You might just remember that I'll be around in case of trouble. Or in any case," he added.

We walked down to the cottage, and at the pool he stopped and pulled out a small black book. As I had always had the police in my fiction carry just such books I was entranced to see him writing in it.

"You've got some sort of clue already, haven't you?" I asked breathlessly.

"Clue?" he said. "Oh, the book. No, I'll need some bathing trunks. That's all."

After which anticlimax I simply sat down on the running board of his car and laughed until I cried.

He arrived to stay a week later. Jennie and I worked hard over the cottage, and I must say it looked wonderful. The living room-dining room had shelves for books, and I carried down some of my father's and a few recent novels. There were bright rag rugs on the floors, a big center table in the living room, and one easy chair with a lamp beside it which I thought he would like. At least it was large enough for him!

I had not seen him since the day he took the place, although a huge roll of chicken wire had come, and some lumber I supposed was to turn the shed into an adequate chicken house. I had finished my work and was locking the door when he arrived, and my first impulse was to laugh. His car was loaded to the roof with what I gathered were his lares and penates, as well as with cases of provisions; and on top of everything else was a crate with six bedraggled hens in it.

He grinned as he got out.

"Got to get the girls out of there," he said. "They've raised hell all the way."

Then and thereafter those hens were "the girls" to him, and in time I found myself calling them that. He took the crate out and set it tenderly on the ground.

"Now behave yourselves," he admonished them. "Tomorrow you can run all you like. Only remember you have a job to do."

He wanted no help unloading the rest of the car, but he did allow me to arrange his provisions in the kitchen. He seemed to be delighted with the place. Also it was evident he did not mean to starve.

"Someday," he said, "when the girls get going, you must have breakfast with me. I learned to make griddle cakes at Childs' when I was working myself into and out of college, and I like fried ham and cream gravy. I hope you do."

I did, and said so. But when the car was about empty and he was picking up a few last things, I saw him take a gun out of the glove compartment and drop it in his pocket. He didn't think I saw him, but it gave me an uneasy feeling. After all, what did I know of the man? I had not asked him for any references. I was not even certain that he had been hunting a country place. So far as I knew he might have been the man Jennie saw at the pool, and for a panicky moment I wondered if he was a part of Judith's terror.

On the other hand, she had not really recognized him. As a matter of fact she had practically ignored him. But Helga had been suspicious, and I wondered why.

The gun was out of sight when I went back into the house, and O'Brien himself was busily laying out a half dozen bottles. When he saw me he held one up.

"I was thinking of a drink to celebrate," he said. "Does the lady of the manor drink with her tenants? This is all new to me, Miss Maynard. How about it?"

I suppose it was his smile again. Somehow I could not associate it with anything evil. So I sat down in the midst of all the confusion and let him put a drink in my hand. Possibly it was the highball, or possibly it was because I felt I had misjudged him. For before long I was telling him about the early days at The Birches, and about father. He liked the idea of the wild-flower garden.

"You'll have to show it to me someday," he said. "He must have been quite a man."

Perhaps it was the glass in my hand. Perhaps I could not talk any more about father. But I remembered then the glass he had taken to the city with him, and asked about it. At first he affected not to know what I referred to, then he remembered.

"Oh, that!" he said. "Prints all right, but none on record."

I did not think he lied easily, but I was sure he was lying then. He changed the subject too quickly.

"I've been learning a little about your sister," he said. "I hope you don't mind, but with things the way they are . . . Of course you know she's been pretty well known around the night spots for years. Nothing against her," he added rather quickly, "but she was meat and drink to the society editors. Isn't it possible she's tied up with someone in her old crowd?"

"Her husband says not."

"Oh! So you've talked to Chandler about it?"

"He gave me a thousand dollars to go to Reno with her. That's partly how I paid for the pool. That, and a check for a story I sold."

He looked surprised. Then he grunted.

"Thank God for Ridgely Chandler," he said. "And in case you're interested, I bought the trunks. To a guy who learned to swim in the East River that pool is pure temptation."

I was rather thoughtful as I went back to the house. I had installed a policeman at The Birches and told no one I was doing so. Now I was a little frightened. Perhaps the sight of the gun had done it. Certainly I felt guilty, and when I saw Judith's door open I went in. She might feel safer if she knew about him, or again . . .

She was sitting at my toilet table, the one I had substituted for mother's big walnut bureau. It was littered now with elaborate bottles of perfumes, with her gold-backed brushes and mirrors, and the innumerable jars of creams and cosmetics she used. At the moment she was painting her fingernails, and she looked up at me unsmilingly.

"So your chicken man has come!" she said. "I tell you here and now, if he has a rooster to wake me in the mornings, I'll kill the creature."

"No roosters," I said. "Half a dozen hens is all."

"Who on earth is he, Lois?" she asked. "I hope he has references."

"The agent in town attended to that. He's a veteran. He was wounded in the South Pacific. That's good enough for me."

"The war's been over out there for five years. He's had plenty of time to get well."

Luckily for me she dropped the

subject. She sat waving her hands in the air to dry her nails, and wondered if it was true that Paris was wearing shorter skirts. If Jennie could sew she could turn up some hems for her. It was useless to tell her that Jennie had plenty to do without that, or even that her own chances of getting to Paris that summer were negligible.

One thing, however, was clear. She was no longer the terrorized woman she had been not long before, and that day, working on her face after her nails had dried, she told me she was seeing Doctor Townsend again.

"I'm glad, Judith," I said. "Do you think he's helping you?"

She gave me an odd little half-smile.

"I don't need his kind of help," she said. "But he's a darned good-looking man."

"So what? He's married, isn't he?"

She laughed. "What's that got to do with it? Don't be naïve, Lois. Anyhow there is such a thing as divorce."

"You ought to know!" I said, and left her.

Phil stopped in to see our new tenant that evening on his way home. He had used Ed Brown's taxi, as he did occasionally, and when he came to the house he was grinning broadly.

"Nice fellow, your new tenant," he said. "But have you seen his girls?"

"Only in the crate. Why?"

"He's got six different breeds of chickens, including a White Leghorn that won't stay out of the house. He calls her Henrietta, for God's sake! I've asked him up for a cocktail. Get the stuff out, will you, while I wash?"

I knew I should have told him who O'Brien really was. After all, Phil was the understanding sort. But the dove of a new peace had apparently settled down on us just then, and who was to know that it was really a vulture?

9

The alfresco cocktail party was a success, and after it for a few days everything was quiet. As it turned out, O'Brien played bridge, and once or twice in that time he made a fourth and easily won from all of us.

Otherwise he seemed to have settled down comfortably, although the occasional sound of a hammer showed that he was being active. I imagine he used the pool too, although I never met him there. He had no visitors, except that one day looking up from my typewriter I saw a woman knocking at his door. She wore a black hat with what looked like a wreath of bright flowers on it. After a time she gave up and I thought she was dispirited when she left. She stood for a time on the road, evidently hoping to thumb a ride, and someone must eventually have picked her up, for she disappeared.

It was not until after O'Brien had been installed for some time that he asked us all down to supper at the cottage, and gave us a thick steak done to a turn, French fried potatoes and peas, and peaches with what he called a Russian sauce of whipped cream, eggs, and brandy.

The cottage was immaculate. Even the bed where we left our wraps had the corners squared, I suppose military fashion. But to our amusement the little white hen refused to go to roost with the other chickens. She trailed him around the kitchen with alert bright eyes, and he scolded her for getting under his feet.

"You're a nuisance, Henrietta," he would say. "Get out of here. Go where you belong."

In the end he had to pick her up squawking and take her out to the roost with the others. He came back looking apologetic.

"Must have been some kid's pet," he said. "Darned if I know what to do with her."

But I had an idea that he had a good many lonely hours there in the cottage, and that Henrietta at least allowed him to hear his own voice. By tacit agreement I had made no effort to see him, and for that brief period there seemed no reason to do so. There were no more intruders. Judith still locked herself away at night, but she was much less restless, and down at the cottage I gathered that O'Brien had finished his chicken house and now had a dozen girls and boasted of the eggs they produced. He must have been catching up with his reading too, for at night from my old nursery in the wing of the house I could see his light on until all hours.

My book too was moving, slowly but surely, and I had settled down to work and what proved to be a factitious peace, broken only by an occasional swim in the pool. Then one day toward the end of the month Anne called up. She was in a state bordering on tears.

"I'm in a jam," she said. "Martha has been visiting in Boston since school ended, and now she has appendicitis. I'm going there tonight to be near her in the hospital. They're operating in the morning. And Bill's home from college and at a loose end. Can you possibly take care of him for a few days? I have no mind, as usual, and while Martin can go to the club I can't leave Bill here alone."

Of course I was glad to do it. I liked Bill, who had steadfastly refused to believe I was his aunt and had called me Lois since he could talk. He was a tall rangy boy of nineteen, too thin for his height and still given to pimples, but with a cheerful grin and an enormous appetite.

I went back to the kitchen and told Helga, who smiled and looked cheerful for the first time since Judith's arrival.

"We'd better lay in a good stock of food," she said. "That boy's hollow all the way down. And maybe I'll make some gingerbread. Keep him from raiding the icebox at night."

He arrived late that evening during a heavy summer storm, and in a thing on wheels he called the Ark, because he said it pitched within and without. I heard it rattling up the drive, and the next moment he was in the hall.

"Hello!" he shouted. "Bill's here! Come arunning, one and all."

I ran down to meet him, and he grabbed me and lifted me up in the air.

"Getting skinny, aren't you, kid?" he said. "Or maybe I just don't know my own strength. Anything around to eat? I missed my supper."

I took him to the kitchen and watched with sheer amazement while he finished a cold roast of lamb, cold potatoes, some cold string beans, and a whole square of gingerbread. Then, replete for the time, he leaned back and surveyed me.

"Who's the gent at the gatehouse?" he inquired.

"That's our tenant. He's taken the place for the summer, and he's

nice, Bill. We all like him very much. Do be nice to him."

"Like that, is it?" he said. "Maybe you can contemplate him with equanimity. I can't. Gray hair and spectacles! I'll bet he's forty if he's a day! You ought to do better, even at your age."

As I was only nine years older than Bill I treated this with the scorn it deserved, but I was curious to know when he had seen O'Brien. He snorted.

"Seen him!" he said. "I damned near ran over him. As I turned into the drive he shot out his door as if the fiends of hell were after him. He had a flashlight, and he turned it on me before he'd budge out of the way. Then he said, 'Sorry, old man,' and beat it back to his house. I think he had a gun too. It looks crazy to me."

But Bill's statement kept me awake for some time that night after I settled him in the guest room, with another shot of gingerbread in case he got hungry in the night. It looked as though O'Brien was indeed watching us, or watching over us. And I wondered if he still felt he had to protect us.

I was positive he knew something about Judith which he had not told me. He had certainly lied about the fingerprints on the glass, and the night we dined with him I had seen him watching her, as though she puzzled him. He had seen me observing him, and when she and Phil had started home he tried to explain it as he picked up my light summer coat.

"Amazingly beautiful woman, your sister," he said.

I was annoyed, for no particular reason.

"Yes," I said. "She got all the looks in the family."

He looked astonished.

"I don't agree with you, Miss Maynard," he said. "Not for a moment."

Which, I was to learn, was as near to a sentimental speech as he usually came.

There in bed that night I lit a cigarette and lay thinking. What sort of danger threatened Judith, if any? And how did he come into the picture? That he had fully meant to take the cottage, I already knew, and I had a brief thought he might be the man Ridgely Chandler had employed to check on her. I abandoned that, however. Ridge had said that was over, and he thought she was only dramatizing herself anyhow by her locks and bolts.

It was unseasonably hot that night. There was a breeze of sorts, but it was from the south and only made things worse. At one time I thought I heard someone on the stairs, but the old house always creaks and groans in a wind. And still later I heard Ed Brown's ancient village taxi go by the road and a minute or two later pass again on the way to town.

I wondered drowsily if the Adrians had at last decided to open their place to escape the heat of the city. Not of course that they would have escaped much, but there is a pleasant theory that the country is always cooler than

New York. When finally I went to sleep it must have been three o'clock. I must have practically passed out, for I felt as though someone had been shaking me for some time before I wakened.

To my astonishment it was Bill. He was in bathing trunks and dripping wet, and his young face looked pale.

"For God's sake wake up, Lois," he said as I sat up. "Something horrible's happened. There's a woman's body in the pool."

"A body!" I said, shocked. "Whose body, Bill? You don't mean— It couldn't be Judith, could it?"

"It's not Judith. I never saw her before. And Judith's locked away. I tried her door first. It was nearer. Get up, will you? I have to wake Phil."

I got into a pair of slacks and a sweater as being the quickest things I could find, and ran down the stairs. Bill had left the front door open, and it must have been half past six by that time, for the birds were singing and the sun well up. But as nothing rouses either Helga or Jennie until seven, there was no sign of life from the service wing.

It took me a couple of minutes' hard running to get to the pool, and Bill caught up with me as I reached it. I could only stand and stare, for there *was* a woman there, or a woman's body anyhow. Bill grabbed me by the arm.

"Don't you go and faint on me," he said hollowly. "I dived in on top of her. She was at the deep end. I dragged her where she is before I knew she was gone."

Where she was was on the near side at the shallow end of the pool, where the little brook flows in. There were three cement steps there, and the woman was on them. She was still half in the water, with her back toward us. She had no hat, and her black dress and blonde hair eddied in the stream in a horrible parody of life and movement.

I never heard O'Brien until he was there. He was in his bare feet, and he had only a bathrobe over his pajamas. But he looked shocked, if that is the word. Incredulous is better. "Good God!" he said. "Who is it?" He did not wait for an answer. He was down beside her in a few seconds. Then he was raising her head, and I can only say there was pure relief in his face.

He straightened and looked across at us.

"Anybody know who she is?" he called.

"I haven't seen her face yet," I said feebly.

"Don't try just now," he said. "Go back to the house and get some coffee. She can wait. She's not in a hurry."

"But you can't leave her like that," I protested. "Half of her is in the water! It's beastly."

He came back then, moving more deliberately.

"Look, my dear," he said. "She can't be moved yet. Either she fell in, and that's police business, or she was thrown in, and that's the same thing." He looked at Bill. "Suppose you use my phone. It's

nearest. And call the Chief of Police in town. This is county stuff, but the Sheriff's on a vacation. The Chief's name is Fowler. He's in the local book. Just tell him what happened. Don't trim it any. I'll stay here."

Bill looked injured, but he did as he was told, and O'Brien turned to me.

"I suppose you'd better have a look at her," he said dubiously. "You may recognize her. After that go up to the house. If I know Fowler, he'll be here soon, with some of his outfit. And the State Police will be sure to horn in. There will be a photographer too. You don't need your picture in this."

I could only nod, and I held my breath while he turned the dead face for me to see. But I did not know her. The face was singularly peaceful, as though indeed she had gone to sleep where she was. She was not very old, I thought. Perhaps in her forties, rather small and slight, and with her hair bleached a golden yellow.

"Where's her hat?" I said, vaguely feeling she was the sort to wear one.

"It may be in the pool. Her bag too. Look here, Miss Maynard, are you sure you don't know her? She must have had some reason to be here."

"Maybe she meant to kill herself, and the pool was handy. You thought it was someone else, didn't you?"

"I thought it was your sister," he said soberly.

He didn't explain, and Judith chose that minute to arrive, with Phil holding her arm to steady her. It was typical that routed from her bed, with her hair flying, without make-up, and clad only in a dressing gown, Judith should look as lovely as ever. Somehow it irritated me, with that dead woman lying there. Partly of course it was relief, for I too had thought at first it was she in the pool.

"Who is it?" Phil said. "I always claimed that pool was a deathtrap at night."

Unluckily he had released Judith's arm, and she took only one look at the body and crumpled up. It was a real faint. Her nose looked white and pinched, and her lips had no color whatever. All my resentment faded. She looked pitiful and forlorn lying there, and I sat down on the ground and put her head in my lap. Phil was all for throwing water on her, but I stopped him.

"Just let her alone," I said. "She used to do this, years ago, when she was excited. She'll come out of it all right."

She did, of course. She moaned a little and opened her eyes. Then she tried to sit up.

"Get me up to the house," she said. "I don't want to see that— that thing. It's dreadful."

Well, it wasn't nice of course, so when she could walk young Bill and I took her home. She still looked pretty awful, but we poured coffee laced with brandy into her until she could climb the stairs. We got her into her room

and I tried to put her to bed. But she wouldn't have it. She waited until we went out and then locked the door behind us. Young Bill stared at me.

"What goes?" he said. "What the hell does that mean?"

"I don't know. She always does it," I told him. "She's afraid of something or somebody. I don't know who."

"Not old Ridge, by any chance?"

"I think she'd like us to think so. I don't believe it."

Breakfast was late that morning. Both Helga and Jennie were on the fringes of the crowd that had gathered down by the pool. O'Brien had been right. The State Troopers were there as well as the Chief of Police and a half dozen men, uniformed police and detectives. And as I stood on the porch I saw them giving way to Doctor Christy, the Medical Examiner for the county.

The public was being kept out, but the main road was lined with the cars of passers-by who had stopped to see what the excitement was about, and not until an ambulance had carried the body away did the crowd disperse and our household staff return.

They were in a state of wild excitement, having been asked if they could identify the body.

"We told them no," Helga said, "but it might be someone from the summer places around. One or two are opened this year. Maybe she just walked across and never seen the pool. Looks like it. No hat. No bag."

Chief Fowler came up while Bill and I were eating a belated breakfast. Phil had already gone to his train, so I gave the Chief ham and eggs and coffee. He seemed grateful, but rather uneasy.

"Hate to ask you, Miss Maynard," he said, "but I've got to drain that pool of yours. Way it rained a couple of days ago we can't see into it, and there may be something of hers there."

"Of course. Go ahead," I told him. "Only what could be there?"

"Nothing probably, if she came from around here. Point is, nobody seems to know her. So if she came from a distance it stands to reason she'd have a bag. A hat too, at her age. She must be forty or so. But we've looked around the place. No signs of them."

"We would have to get a man from town to open the gate at the lower end," I said. "It's old and pretty rusty. As the pool is fed all the time, we don't have to clean it. We only empty it for the winter."

He nodded and looked at Bill, young and fresh faced in a bathrobe over his trunks.

"Tell me again about it, son," he said. "You didn't see her before you went in?"

"Well, I did and I didn't," Bill said. "Not from the side of the pool, no. But when I climbed the rickety old diving platform I saw something dark. I didn't think it was—well, what it was. It might have been mud from the creek. When I got down though I knew."

"And then?"

"I was kind of scared." Bill grinned. "I came up for air and to see if there was anybody around to help. There wasn't, so I went down again and got hold of her. I dropped her once. I guess I was pretty nervous. But I got her to the steps and left her there."

Fowler nodded and prepared to go.

"Thanks for the breakfast," he said. "I needed it. And I'm sorry about your sister. Kind of a shock, of course. But soon as she's better I want her to look at the body. We need an identification, and she may have seen her somewhere. You're sure you haven't?"

I said I was sure, but there was something in my mind which kept escaping it. Then, just as he was leaving, I remembered.

"There's one thing," I said. "I'm pretty sure I heard Ed Brown's taxi on the main road last night. It seemed to go as far as the Adrian's drive next to ours, then turn around and go back."

"Ed's taxi! What time was it?"

"I haven't an idea. It was hot and I was restless. It sounded like Ed's the way it rattled. That's all I know."

"Sure the Adrian family hasn't decided to move out from town?"

"The maids here say they haven't. You can't see the house from here. It's not near, and there's all that shrubbery. But the gardener's been working there now and then, as he does for us. He may know the woman, if she works for them."

"Doesn't seem as though she

worked very hard for anyone," he said. "Hands don't look like it. Of course the way folks work today that don't mean much."

I watched him down the drive in his car. There was a State Trooper by the pool, and after he stopped and spoke to him the trooper took off through the woods to where the distant sound of a mower showed the gardener at work. The Chief himself turned toward town, and without apparent purpose Bill sauntered down the drive.

I knew what he meant to do, but he was just too late. The moment the trooper disappeared, O'Brien in a pair of bathing trunks made for the pool and dove in. I was curious. It was only too obvious that he had been waiting for the chance, and for some reason I could not understand. I only knew that when at last he reappeared on the surface he was clutching something, and that he looked completely disgusted when he saw Bill there, and me not far behind him.

He forced a grin, however, as he crawled out.

"Got her bag," he said. "Now if you pair of ghouls can keep your mouths shut maybe we'll learn something."

Bill, whose jaw had dropped, managed to close it.

"You're being damned nosy about all this, aren't you?" he said. "The police will want that."

"The police will have it. Don't worry, son. You'll give it to the Chief and tell him you found it. I think her hat's in there too. Better try and find it."

There was a moment when I thought Bill would revolt, but there was something authoritative about O'Brien's voice and his big muscular body. He turned to the pool.

"Keep an eye on that guy, Lois," he said, and dived in.

O'Brien opened the bag and shook its contents out on the grass. It was made of some sort of fabric, and the contents were soaked. There was nothing exciting that I could see: the usual compact and lipstick, a small money purse with five or six dollars in it, a handkerchief, and a scrap of yellow paper. Then he examined the bag itself. There was a zipper pocket which he opened, only to pull out a water-soaked newspaper clipping, yellow either from the pool or with age, and now a sodden mass. Even I could see that it was barely decipherable, and I was surprised when he tucked it into the belt of his trunks.

"That trooper's coming," he said. "Put the stuff back in the bag, will you? I'll have to dry this scrap."

I suppose I was distracted at the moment, for Bill appeared with the soaked remains of what had been a woman's hat. It was of black straw, with a wreath of bright but now woebegone flowers around the crown, and it looked forlorn and pitiable. But it looked more than that. It looked vaguely familiar.

Bill scrambled out with it, to

hear the trooper bellowing at him.

"What are you doing there?" he yelled. "You know goddam well you were told to keep away from here."

"Oh, drop dead!" Bill said. "I got her hat, didn't I? That's more than you did, fancy britches! And this is my family's pool. Try to keep me out of it!"

The trooper leaped the narrow stream at the head of the pool and made for Bill with at least mayhem in his face. Then he saw me, and I gave him as sweet a smile as I could muster at the moment.

"Bill has been fine, lieutenant," I said. "He got her bag too. The Chief said he wanted them found."

Either the smile or the rank I gave him mollified him, or the mention of the Chief did. At least he laid no hands on Bill.

"Sergeant," he said. "I suppose you've looked through that bag," he added disagreeably.

"Certainly not," I said virtuously, and prepared to empty it on the ground again. He yelped in anguish.

"Don't *do* that," he said. "There may be fingerprints, all sorts of things." He looked completely discouraged. "See here," he said. "Thanks for finding the stuff. Now I'd be obliged if you'd both just go back to the house and let well enough alone. Go back and take a nice rest. I'll manage by myself for a while, and I'll do all right. Don't worry."

We did not go at once, however. I stood staring at the hat, and fighting the feeling I had seen it before. After all, there were probably one million black hats with wreaths in circulation in and around New York. And O'Brien had not reappeared. I could not ask him about it.

We were still there when a loud thumping and rattling announced the arrival of Ed Brown's taxi, and it was followed by the Chief's car. Both of them passed our gate and went on a short distance. Then we heard them coming back, and they turned in at our drive.

The Chief got out, but Ed remained in his car. He has always claimed arthritis in his legs, which prevents him from carrying suitcases or even golf clubs, or helping women under any circumstances. Just now he looked surly.

"How do I know she came here?" he said. "I let her out at the other drive. She paid me for it. That's all I know. As for getting a man out of his bed at this hour I ain't standing for it, police or no police."

The Chief eyed him coldly.

"Didn't she say anything? Weren't you to come back and pick her up again?"

"No. Looks like she meant to stay. She said to take her to the first drive beyond the Maynards'. That's what I did."

"Kind of late for you to be out, wasn't it?"

"I seen some folks off on a train to the city. They'd been out to dinner. So she comes up at the station and says am I a taxi, and I says yes."

"Did she get off the train going toward town?"

"I wouldn't know. She just came up like I said."

"Did she have a suitcase, or anything of the sort? Like she was staying somewhere?"

"I didn't see any. I got this trouble in my legs. Folks handle their own bags."

The first car with a couple of reporters and cameraman arrived just then, and Bill and I beat it. O'Brien had still not shown himself, and I had an idea he wouldn't, with the press around. But Bill was grinning to himself.

"Maynard Mansion Scene of Mystery Death," he said. "Picture of swimming pool, center of many gaieties, where body was found. *Social Register* family bewildered. Say, O'Brien ain't so old, is he?"

"I haven't an idea," I said coldly.

He looked at me.

"He was watching for somebody last night when he shot out at my car. Think it was that woman?"

"If you think he murdered her I'd think again, Bill."

"So you like him, eh? All I can say is that one good push from those arms of his and she's gone. And what's the idea, his getting the bag? He was damned anxious about it, if you ask me."

10

Anne was on the phone from Boston when we got back to the house. She said the operation was over and Martha seemed all right. She'd like to stay a few days, however, if we could keep Bill.

"Try and get me away!" Bill said. "Home's nothing like this. Let me talk to her, Lois."

The last I heard as I went upstairs to dress he was telling Anne we were finding bodies all over the place, that he was under suspicion of murder, and that he'd call her from the jail, if and when.

I let it ride. If Anne didn't know her own son by that time she never would.

To my shocked surprise, as I reached the upper hall, I saw a suitcase standing outside Judith's door, and heard her moving rapidly around inside the room. As I had left her in a virtual state of collapse I was bewildered. I lifted the bag, and it was evidently packed. It looked as though she was leaving, and leaving in a hurry.

As usual her door was locked,

and when I knocked all sounds ceased. But when she spoke it was from close by.

"Who is it?" she asked.

"It's Lois. What's all this nonsense out here?"

"Are you alone? Is anyone near you?"

"I'm alone," I said with such patience as I could summon. "Don't be a fool. Open this door and let me in."

Her room was a mess, clothes all over it, on the bed and the chairs. Even the floor. And Judith herself wasn't much better, her hair in all directions and her face without make-up. She was almost as white as she had been at the pool, and her eyes looked almost demented.

"I'm getting out," she said. "I thought I'd be safe here, but I'm not."

"Safe from what, for heaven's sake?"

"Never mind that. I'm leaving. That's all."

"Look, Judith," I said. "Let's get at this thing sensibly. Did you know that woman who came here last night?"

"No, of course not. How should I?"

There was a ring of truth in that. Judith could lie, and do it well, when she wanted to, but I was sure she was telling the truth now.

"You fainted when you saw her," I said. "If you didn't know her why pass out like that? It looks darned funny to me."

She sat down then, as though the strength of desperation had suddenly abandoned her.

"Why wouldn't I faint?" she said. "She was horrible, dreadful. I don't write crime books. I'm not used to dead bodies, or murdered ones."

I eyed her.

"So you think she was murdered? You don't know who she is. You never saw her before, and even the police don't say it was murder. You'd better get a better story than that, Judith, before they begin to question you."

She did not answer at once. She tried to light a cigarette with shaking hands, and when she finally succeeded she took a long puff before she spoke.

"You saw her," she said. "Her hair is like mine, and she's almost my build. I think she was killed because she was mistaken for me."

"Don't be ridiculous! Who on earth wants to kill you? If you think it's Ridgely you're crazy."

"It's not Ridge. I can't talk about it. Let me alone, can't you? I'm not staying here, that's all."

"Now listen, Judith," I said impatiently. "If you're in real trouble you need police protection. I'll get the Chief up here and you can tell him all about it. Or tell me, if you'd rather. Maybe you're wrong. Maybe you're just scaring yourself. In any case let's find out."

She gave me a quite dreadful look.

"If you bring the police into this I'll kill myself," she said. "I mean it. I'll do just that."

I eyed her. Erratic as she was she did mean it, and I knew it.

"But there has to be a reason

for all this," I argued. "What have you done? Have you killed someone? What else am I to think except that you've committed some sort of crime and now it's catching up with you? That's what it looks like. And don't blame me for thinking so, Judith. It's all you allow me to think. And I'm calling Phil on the phone. He'd better come out and talk some sense into you."

"Phil won't change me, unless you both want me murdered."

She got up determinedly, and I had started for the door when a belated thought stopped me.

"Anyhow," I said, "you can't leave yet. The police have a body. Whether they think she was murdered or not, we'll all be interrogated. There will be an inquest and we'll have to be there. You can't just get on a plane or a ship, and you know it. And what are you going to tell them? That she was killed in mistake for you? They'll want to know why."

Nothing, however, was more obvious than that she had no intention of telling anybody anything. I made one more attempt, though.

"What about Doctor Townsend?" I said. "Can't you tell him what's wrong? That's his business, isn't it? Or does he know already?"

"It has nothing to do with him," she said, her face tight. "I don't want him involved."

I left her after that, feeling pretty hopeless. It was lunchtime, and Bill and I ate hash and his favorite popovers. But he was rather quiet, for him. When Jennie had slammed the pantry door for the last time he looked up from his coffee.

"Think all this has anything to do with Aunt Judith?" he asked.

I tried to look merely interested.

"Judith?" I said. "Where on earth did you get that idea?"

"Oh, Jennie talks," he said. "And all this locking herself in looks queer as hell. If she's in a mess why not tell somebody, get help, get the police?"

"I've tried that, Bill. She won't talk about it."

"Not Chandler, is it?"

"Your guess is as good as mine. He had twenty years to kill her, if that's your idea. Why wait until now?"

"I'll bet he pays her a cracking good alimony."

"I never heard of alimony as a reason for murder."

"Well, if he could get away with it," he said, and lapsed into thoughtful silence, as though the idea of Ridgely Chandler threatening Judith because of alimony was not unpleasant.

I suppose the local police were pretty busy at that time of year, and the town was understaffed anyhow. Anyway, it was two State Troopers who came back that afternoon. They stayed around the pool, and they seemed to be looking for something on the ground. At least they went over it inch by inch. Whether they found what they were looking for I did not know, and except for a couple of reporters, who had learned Judith was staying with us and hung around hoping to get a picture of her, the afternoon was quiet.

O'Brien's car, which he left out in all weathers, was missing, so I gathered he was off on some business of his own. I learned later that the Chief and the State Police were not only canvassing the village and surrounding countryside, but were getting in touch by telephone with the crew of the train from which, according to Ed Brown, she might possibly have come.

As it developed, the conductor of the train was pretty sure he had seen her. He remembered her hat. But as it was a local train from up the river he had no idea where she had taken it. A walking party from the city had pretty well filled it. Also his wife was about to have a baby, and I suppose his mind was not exactly on his job.

Phil had a case in court that day, so I could not get in touch with him. But by six o'clock the police were about where they had started. Even the bleached hair was no help. Our local beauty people said it was probably a professional job, and done not too long before. Perhaps a month ago, or less.

I was relieved to see that Judith had taken her suitcase back into her room. Evidently she had decided to stay, for a time at least, and when I met Phil that evening —Bill had rattled off to see a girl, named Janey, having learned her family had arrived for the summer—I told him of my talk with her.

"So she thinks it was murder,"

he said thoughtfully. "Anybody said that to you? When I left they'd about decided it was accidental. If she knows anything she should tell it."

But when I told him of her threat to kill herself if she had to see the police he was annoyed.

"She's still dramatizing herself!" he said. "Don't let her scare you, Lois. She's too fond of herself for that." Then he saw my face. "All right, all right. Maybe she is in trouble, but what? She played around with a pretty wild crowd, but according to the papers they're all still healthy enough. Although God knows why, the drinks they drink and the hours they keep."

"Judith never drank a lot," I protested.

"There are other vices than liquor, my innocent. Drugs and adultery, for example. Have you any idea if she takes drugs, Lois? It might account for a lot of things."

But somehow I did not think so. There was a curious sort of rationality about what appeared to be her vagaries. She was afraid of somebody or something, and she took what steps she could to protect herself. Grant that, and much of it fell into line. As to the adultery Phil mentioned, Ridge himself had apparently cleared her of that.

We had our after-dinner coffee on the big front porch that night. Hot as it was nobody thought of using the pool, but Phil looked tired and I was sorry for him.

"Everything passes, Phil," I said. "This will go too. Judith's going abroad as soon as she can get a ship. As to this dead woman, none of us know her, not even Jude. It can't mean real trouble with the police."

He only shrugged, but I had apparently reminded him of something.

"Speaking of police," he said, "I saw your tenant in town today. He was going into Police Headquarters at Centre Street. What is he, anyhow? Or do you know? He's a pretty close-mouthed customer about himself."

I suppose I colored, for he laughed.

"Him and his girls," he jeered. "If ever I saw a cop, our Irish friend is one. It stands out all over him. Maybe he did go to college. Maybe he's spent four years in the army. Maybe he's off the force now. But I wouldn't be too damned sure even of that."

"He's not on police business here," I said hotly. "He's been in the army and he's tired. You know all that. And if he wants to see his old friends certainly that's *his* business."

"Once a cop always a cop," Phil retorted. "And if he thinks those specs fool me he's gone in the head. Only what's he doing here? Up to now we've been a pretty law-abiding crowd. Think he's keeping an eye on Judith?"

"Why should he?" I said. Nevertheless, I was more than a little troubled. He had had a purpose in getting the dead woman's bag out of the pool, and he had taken something from it before he handed it to me; something he did

not want the local authorities to know about, and which I did not doubt he had taken to Police Headquarters in the city that day.

Perhaps Judith was right and it was murder, after all. There were other things too. What had the State Police been searching for on the grass by the pool that day? Whatever it was, did he have it, as well as that wadded-up and soaking wet roll of newsprint? And did he know who the woman was? Had she been the one I had seen at his door only a few days before?

It was almost dark when I heard his car come in. The girls had apparently gone supperless to roost, and he did not disturb them. By that time I was practically ready to go down and denounce him, for being in Reno not by chance but by design, for picking me up on the train and inducing me to talk, and for concealing information from the local men.

I did not, of course. Judith came downstairs, saying her room was too hot to stay in, and she was barely settled with us on the porch when Chief Fowler arrived. He mounted the steps and took off his cap.

"Evening, folks," he said. "Warm night, isn't it?"

Phil asked him to sit down and offered him a whisky and soda. He refused, however.

"It's still working hours for me," he said. "Looks as though we've got real trouble on our hands. The boy's not here, is he?"

"Bill? No, he's out somewhere," I said. "Why? Do you want him?"

"Only because he found the body. You see, this woman—the deceased—has a bad cut on the back of her head. No fracture but, well, maybe she was knocked out and then dropped in the water. In that case it's murder."

"Sorry to hear it," Phil said, "but since none of us knew her . . ."

The Chief coughed.

"Well, as a matter of fact that's why I'm here," he said. "I know none of you recognized her this morning. But she looks better now. I'd like you all to see her. Nothing to worry anybody. Just peaceful and quiet." Which last I thought was at least supererogatory. "Ten o'clock too early? Inquest's at eleven."

"I suppose not," I said. "Who is she, Chief? Somebody from around here?"

"Not if Ed Brown's story's true. Only it beats me why a woman would drive five miles in a taxi, get out and send it away, and then fall or get pushed into that pool of yours. It doesn't make sense. What about this fellow you rent the cottage to? Know anything about him?"

Nobody had any decided opinions about O'Brien, except that he seemed like a nice person, and at last, after saying that both Bill and myself would be wanted to attend the inquest the next morning, he went away. Not far, however, I heard his car stop at the cottage, and it was some time before it drove away.

I stayed on the porch when the others had gone. The fact that I was wanted at the inquest seemed definitely sinister to me. After all, I had not found the body, but I had had the bag. It worried me considerably, and after the Chief had left the cottage I walked down toward it. I did not like passing the pool. The memory of the dead woman in it was too recent. But the window of O'Brien's sitting room was open, and it gave me courage to go on.

I stopped at the window and glanced inside. O'Brien was sitting in the big chair by the lamp, but he was not catching up with any reading. He was not wearing his spectacles either. He had two long strips of stiff transparent cellophane in his hands, and he was busy binding them together with what looked like Scotch tape. What seemed like a press clipping was between them, and in the lamplight his face was so grim and intent that when I spoke he practically leaped to his feet.

"Oh, it's you!" he said. "What do you mean, scaring a guy out of his wits! The door's not locked. How about using it?"

I heard him open a drawer of the table and slam it shut, and when he let me in whatever he had been working on was out of sight.

"I wasn't spying on you," I said. "But if that's the clipping you took out of that woman's bag, I imagine Fowler would be interested in it."

"It wouldn't have meant a thing to him. And I wish to God, Lois, that you'd keep your pretty nose out of what doesn't concern you."

It was the first time he had called me that, but he was too irritated to notice it.

"I have to be interested," I said. "I have to testify at the inquest tomorrow. What am I to say about the bag? That you took something out of it?"

He flushed. I think for a minute he wanted to throttle me. Then with a jerk he opened the table drawer and pulled out the clipping in its cellophane covers.

"All right," he said. "So I think a clipping twenty years old is worth preserving. And that it wouldn't mean a damn thing to Fowler or the Medical Examiner either. It does happen to be my affair."

"I see," I said. "So Phil's right, after all."

"Right about what?"

"He says once a cop always a cop. And he believes you're here on police business. That you came here to watch us, or maybe Judith. That's true, isn't it?"

"I haven't made any particular secret about that part of it, have I? Only let's play it differently. Let's say I think your sister may need protection. In fact, I'm damned sure she does."

But I was still indignant.

"It was all neatly arranged, wasn't it?" I said. "The pickup on the train, the renting of this place, the whole bag of tricks. Even that woman in the pool! You recognized her, didn't you? I think she was here the other day to see you, but you were out."

"Say that again!"

He was so astonished that I knew he was not acting.

"She was here?"

"I think it was her," I said, un-grammatically. "At least the hat looks the same, and she's about the same size."

"So that's it," he said, and seemed to be thinking over something. Clearly it bothered him. Then abruptly he flung the cellophane arrangement on the table.

"Maybe you'd better read that," he said. "You'll understand a few things. If that woman is who I think she is, I've been hunting her for twenty years."

I picked the thing up. It was neatly done, an ancient yellow strip of newsprint, carefully placed between two sheets of transparent material. I glanced at the date. It was December 10, 1929, and it had to do with the murder of a girl named Mollie Preston in the old slums down by the East River. According to the paper, she had been strangled to death after a quarrel with a youth who had been seen with her a number of times, and he was being held for the murder.

I was completely bewildered as I put it down.

"This hasn't anything to do with us," I said. "I don't understand."

"No," he said. "How old were you then? Seven or so, weren't you? It's ancient history, but the woman today was a witness in that case. And she'd kept this clipping in her bag. Why? What did it mean to her? And why did she bring it here with her? If I knew that I would know why she was killed."

"Killed! You think she was murdered?"

"I do," he said grimly. "Knocked

out and then pushed into the pool. This man your maid Jennie saw—has she any description of him?"

"None at all. She was paralyzed with fright."

He sat down and picking up his pipe proceeded to fill and light it.

"If you have time I'd like to tell you a few things, Lois. But I'm going to ask you something first. Why do you think your sister fainted this morning, at the pool?"

"It wasn't a pretty sight."

"You don't think she recognized her?"

"I don't know," I said uncertainly. "Of course it's possible. I don't think it's likely."

"All right. Maybe she did. Maybe she didn't. But let's think back to that year of 1929. For most of it the country was riding high, wide, and handsome. Everybody was getting rich. This property of yours was still a showplace. So were a lot of big estates. This dead woman may have been employed around here, or even at The Birches itself. But I doubt it."

"I wouldn't remember her if she was," I said. "What happened about the Preston murder?"

"The boy was found guilty," he said. "Better forget it. Just a dirty miserable slice of life in a tenement. Girl probably a prostitute, boy maybe a little better, but not much. What would it have to do with you, the spoiled darling of a wealthy family?"

That was when I laughed, remembering the ugly brat I had been, remembering the gay crowds around the pool in the summer who never saw me, remembering—but this only faintly —Anne's wedding at The Birches, the marquee with its wooden floor for dancing, and Judith one of the bridesmaids. Remembering mother in pale taffeta with a big hat and plumes and father fussing about his morning coat. And still nobody noticing me. But he was right in one way. Riding high we certainly had been, when I was too young even for bands on my teeth.

"You're away before my time," I told him. "I was only seven in 1929 and Judith hadn't even come out. She always had a lot of boys and girls around, but they were the boarding school-prep school sort, with a great deal of excitement when a college man showed up."

"Just the same," he persisted, "that woman—her name was Kate Henry when I knew her—had a reason for being here. She didn't come near this cottage last night. I know that. Then who else? Could it have been your sister?"

I felt a small shiver up and down my spine, remembering as I did the creaking of the stairs the night before. He saw my face and nodded.

"All right," he said. "Let's forget it. Somewhere I think Conan Doyle says it's important in any case to reason backward. Have you talked to Mrs. Chandler?"

"Yes. She says she never saw the woman before, and I think she's telling the truth. But she was really terrified today. She wanted to get out of the country. She was packed this afternoon, but I talked her out of it."

"Where was she going?"

"Anywhere a ship would take her, I imagine."

He was thoughtful.

"It wouldn't be such a bad idea, at that," he said. "But if she makes a move to leave I want to know it, Lois."

He took me up the drive that night. It was still hot, but it had started to rain, a thin summer drizzle which was utterly depressing. He said very little on the way, and I felt that he knew more than he had told me, but less than he liked. Only at the foot of the porch steps he stopped, and with any other man I might have thought he meant to kiss me. After all, I had had more experience than I had intimated to Anne. But not O'Brien. He had to stand there and make what amounted to a speech.

"Every now and then," he said, "even a smart cop can be wrong. I'm beginning to think I've laid an egg here, and it's not one of the girls'. I'm going to ask you a favor," he added. "When you're called at the inquest tomorrow keep me out of it, will you? It may not come up at all, but if it does it's all right to say I found the bag, but don't say I opened it. It may be damned important."

Which, one way and another, was a poor preparation for a good night's sleep.

11

I cannot honestly say that the dead woman worried me greatly that night. After all, I did not know her. Whether she was murdered or merely fell into the pool and drowned seemed to have no relation to any of us. But I was worried about Judith. Her reaction to the situation seemed ridiculously exaggerated, if she had not known Kate Henry, which O'Brien said was her name. Also the mere idea that she had slipped out of the house and gone to the pool in the middle of the night was sufficiently out of character to amount to absurdity.

At eleven o'clock the telephone rang in the lower hall and I slipped on an old bathrobe and went down to answer it. It was Ridge, and he sounded annoyed.

"You seem to have the faculty out there of getting into the

papers," he said. "What's all this about a woman drowning in the pool?"

"Well, she did. That's about all I know."

"Who was she? Any identification yet?"

I thought quickly.

"I don't believe so, Ridge. She had no cards or automobile driver's permit on her. I suppose it's only a matter of time."

"How's Judith taking it?"

"She was shocked, as we all were. The police think it may have been murder, that someone hit her on the head and then threw her in the pool. I don't suppose that's in the papers yet. It may come out at the inquest tomorrow."

"More likely she stumbled and fell in. I always said that place was a deathtrap."

I went back to bed and tried to think back to the fall of 1929. The crash had come, although mother refused to recognize it. Phil once said she maintained she had lived through at least three of them, and nothing serious had ever happened. I had a vague recollection of the last dinner party she gave the night father killed himself; of sitting on the stairs in my night-clothes, watching the men give their arms to the women, the chattering beautifully dressed procession moving toward the dining room, and—although I did not see him—father slipping out to his downtown office when the men were closeted with cigars and liquors, and using the gun no one knew he had.

I felt a deep wave of pity for him. He had been gentle and kind, a quiet undramatic man who loved his children and his home. Why had he done it? Not because he had lost his money. I did not believe money had ever been important to him, and other men had weathered the storm.

One thing I did remember. Mother had not stayed to see the city house dismantled. She had taken Judith and fled to Arizona not long after the funeral. She made the excuse of Judith's cough, but I felt now that she could not bear the loss of the lares and penates that were so important to her. She had protested over the sale, and I had trailed her around as, red eyed and shaken, she had pasted labels on the things that were to go to The Birches.

Someone—the auctioneer probably—followed her, protesting.

"But, madam, those chairs are a part of the assets of the estate. I have no right to let you keep them."

"They are mine, not my husband's. I bought them myself."

And willy-nilly a van had come and taken them away.

After that she went to Arizona. Phil returned to college, the servants with the exception of Helga disappeared, and one day Anne appeared and drove Helga and me out to The Birches. It was still cold. The damp mustiness of the place was disheartening, and the furniture from the town house had been merely stacked in the hall and left. I think Anne got help from the village eventually, but that first night Helga and I had curled up together in mother's big walnut bed, and I had cried myself to sleep.

It was late spring when mother and Judith returned, mother in deep black and looking harassed, and Judith blooming and beautiful. There were no more picnics around the pool, but Ridgely Chandler was there a great deal. One day I saw the huge square-cut solitaire on Judith's finger, and was told she was engaged to him.

They were married in the fall in the small local church. There were no attendants, and as I may have said, Anne found Judith crying bitterly before she put on her white satin dress. I overheard her but when I went to Helga about it she told me to hush up.

"All brides cry," she said. "Just be glad she's getting a man. Maybe now she'll settle down."

Only she never had. I suppose Doctor Townsend would say the extravagance of her life after the marriage was pure escapism. And of course, behind her locked doors, she was still escaping.

I wondered if in those more prosperous days before the crash the drowned woman had been employed at The Birches. In that case she should have known the pool, however, and Judith might have remembered her. She had not, I was sure of that. Nor had Helga, who seldom forgot a face.

Only three of us went to the inquest the next day, Phil, Bill, and myself. For Judith was sick. She had worked herself into a fever, I suppose because she always hated the idea of death. And O'Brien's cottage was closed and his car gone.

Before the inquest they asked Bill and me to identify the body as the one we had found in the pool, and I stood for a minute or so, looking down at the woman. It seemed utterly sad to me that she could lie there among strangers. For someone she must have worn that flower-trimmed hat and bleached her hair. And at one time she must have been a pretty girl. Even now she was not wholly unattractive. They say drowning is an easy death. I don't know. I don't want to know, but her face was peaceful.

But, as we waited for the inquest to begin, I wondered about her. Why had she carried that clipping in her bag? What connection could she have had with the murder more than twenty years ago of a prostitute in the New York slums? She must have been young then herself. She was not much over forty now. If she was Kate Henry she had evidently known this Mollie Preston. There must have been some reason for her keeping the account of that murder all this time, and having it with her when she died.

And why had she disappeared for all those years? What did she know? Or why again had O'Brien been trying to find her?

At the inquest later it was evident that considerable local interest had been aroused. The room was crowded, and Phil leaned over and told me the District Attorney for the county was present.

"They're not sure," he said. "Maybe a murder, but they've got to prove it."

It took a little time to get organized, and to call the proceedings to order. But I was still calm, merely interested, until my own turn came. Doctor Christy was presiding, and there was some medical evidence by one of his assistants about the nature of the wound in the back of the woman's head. It had been inflicted with a sharpish instrument, but probably not a hatchet or anything of that sort.

"What do you mean by not a hatchet, doctor?"

"I only used the word in a general sense. For instance, a hatchet makes a sharp clean cut. The edges of this injury are contused, broken down. The deceased had a thick skull, or there would probably have been a fracture. Considerable force was used."

"Could it have been self-inflicted? Or caused by a fall?"

"Absolutely not."

"You cannot state the weapon used?"

"Not of my own knowledge."

"Was it the blow that killed her, doctor?"

"No. There was no fracture. She died in the pool, but she was almost certainly unconscious, or semiconscious, when she hit the water. Actually she died by drowning."

"Can you give an estimate as to the time of the death?"

"I can only say some hours before the body was discovered."

"But approximately?"

"The water in the pool was pretty cool. I would guess five or six hours. It's purely a guess. Rigor was well established."

But it was Bill who was the star witness, and I think he rather enjoyed it. He identified photographs of the pool and the old diving platform at the deep end from which he had seen the body.

"Not that I thought it was a body then," he said. "It was just something dark. But when I got down to it, I knew what it was."

"What did you do then, Mr. Harrison?" Doctor Christy inquired.

"I got up for air as fast as I could. Then I yelled for help. I thought she might still be alive. But there was nobody around. So I went in again and pulled her to the shallow end of the pool, so her head was out of the water. Then I ran up to the house and wakened my aunt, Lois Maynard."

"You still thought she might be alive?"

"Well, no," Bill admitted. "But I couldn't just leave her there and go swimming, could I?"

"It didn't occur to you to call the police?"

"I guess I was pretty excited. By the time we got back the man who lives in the old gardener's cottage came running over. His name's O'Brien. He sent me to telephone the Chief of Police."

Doctor Christy looked around the room.

"Is Mr. O'Brien present?" he asked.

Fowler, the Chief of Police, stood up.

"Mr. O'Brien was called away," he said. "I have his deposition here. The body was already found when he reached the pool. He dove in and recovered the deceased's bag, but that's all."

Ed Brown came next. He limped to the chair and sat down with the air of a martyr.

"All I did was take her out from town," he said, looking outraged. "That's my job. I never seen her before, and she didn't talk. Some folks rattle on as if I had nothing to do but listen to them. Only time she spoke was to ask if I was a taxi, and when she got out how much she owed me. I said did she want me to wait and she said no. When I turned around she was still standing there by the road to the Adrian place, like she sort of wanted me out of the way."

He didn't know whether she had got out of the train or not. It was his bedtime. He didn't like to work late. He had bad arthritis. But as soon as she knew he had a taxi she was inside the car.

"You mean she got in in a hurry?"

"I'll say she did."

"As though perhaps she did not want to be seen?"

"Maybe. Maybe not."

I had no idea I was going to be called until, after the usual preliminaries, I heard my name and saw that wretched bag on the table.

"You were present, I believe, Miss Maynard, when this bag was taken out of the pool."

"Yes. I watched Mr. O'Brien take it out."

"Did you by any chance happen to open it?"

"No," I said. "Why should I?" He looked at me.

"It would be natural, wouldn't it?" he said. "After all, you might want to find out who she was, provided you didn't know her."

"But I didn't open it," I insisted. It was the truth, of course. O'Brien had done it. But the Medical Examiner leaned forward and, picking up the awful thing, opened it and dumped its contents on the table.

"This may be a case of accident or suicide, Miss Maynard. Or it may be one of murder. I want you to be careful what you say. This woman got off a local train here late at night. She is unknown in the town. She did not bring anything with her to indicate she meant to stay. Now what would that indicate?"

"I haven't an idea," I said truthfully enough.

"Isn't it possible she would have a return-trip ticket with her?"

The question was unexpected, and it left me practically paralyzed. What had happened to that yellow scrap I had seen on the grass? Did O'Brien have it too? And if so was that why I was not to say he had opened the bag? I couldn't speak. I could only hear Doctor Christy's voice, cold and severe.

"As a matter of fact," he said, "the conductor of the train believes she did have a return-trip ticket. In that case it has disappeared. Perhaps I'd better rephrase the question. Did you at any time touch the contents of the bag? For example, the compact?"

"I—I may have," I said, feeling like an utter fool. "The thing fell open and the stuff spilled out on the grounds. I put it all back."

"Then that would account for your fingerprints on the compact?"

I wanted to sink through the floor, and a small titter showed the crowd was amused. I was not. But the doctor banged on the table with a gavel and went on inexorably.

"During this—er—accident," he said, "did you or did you not see the return-trip half of a railroad ticket?"

"There might have been one. I don't remember."

It must have sounded honest, or at least moronic, for at last they excused me. Not without reservations, I realize now, but the inquest was not over. There was a stir in the back of the room as a newcomer entered, and someone announced that a Mr. Kirk had arrived.

I had never seen him before. He was a tall sandy-haired man with spectacles, and Doctor Christy got up and shook hands with him. He apologized for being late and took the witness chair. The doctor turned to the jury.

"In view of certain developments in this case," he said, "I took the liberty of asking for assistance from the New York Police Laboratory, which is better equipped than the one in this country. Now, Mr. Kirk, will you state just what you received from us?"

"One item was an envelope, marked as containing scrapings from under the deceased's nails. The other was a small scrap of soft leather found, I believe, beside the pool where the body was discovered."

There was a stir through the room. This was what they had come for. Doctor Christy rapped for order.

"You examined these?" he inquired.

"Yes. Under the microscope. There was a filament of this same leather in the envelope containing the scrapings."

"Will you tell us what you then did?"

"I compared both with various types of the leather used for gloves, as they showed salt from human perspiration. In view of the nature of the wound I considered other possibilities."

"Such as?"

"The grip of a golf club was one. A golf club is an excellent weapon, and on investigation I found that the leather so used corresponded with the sample I had."

"Would you say that a golf club was used?"

"I cannot answer that. It is a possibility, of course."

Phil had the nerve to grin and punch me with his elbow, and I knew what he meant. His own clubs stood in their bag in the main hall of The Birches, and had done so for years.

"Good-bye, Lois," he said. "Write me now and then, won't

you? And a bottle of Scotch would come in handy."

"Oh, shut up," I said savagely.

To my surprise the inquest was adjourned almost immediately, but only after the District Attorney had a low-voiced colloquy with Doctor Christy.

Phil looked serious as we left.

"I'm afraid it's murder," he said. "The police must want more time. What the hell made you say you didn't open that bag?"

"I didn't," I said indignantly. "O'Brien did. He dumped the stuff out on the grass. All I did was to put it back."

"Why on earth didn't you say so?"

"He asked me not to, but if I ever lay hands on him he'll be sorry. He made a fool out of me, and I fell for it."

"I told you he was a cop," Phil said smugly.

I was in a cold fury by that time, and Bill suggested a Coke at the drugstore near by.

"You look as though you need something," he observed. "So O'Brien's still a cop. Hot diggety dog! Ain't that something? And don't let that deposition stuff get you. They knew darned well where he was, and why. Only what about that clipping he snitched? Did he give it to Fowler?"

"Why don't you ask him?" I said bitterly. "I never want to see the man again. He got me into this mess, and he can damn well get me out of it."

"Such language! And I thought you'd fallen for the guy!"

Phil had not come in with us, so I sat there at a small table with a lot of school kids shouting and the usual drugstore smell of scented soaps, drugs, and soda fountain around me, and tried to think. Bill had wandered off to the juke box and of course had somehow picked up a pretty girl on the way. But I was worried as well as angry. Not about the dead woman. After all, I could not see how she concerned me, except that I had made a fool of myself at the inquest. But about the clipping O'Brien had taken. What had a murder twenty years old to do with us? Phil had been away at college at that time, Anne was already married, and Judith not yet even eighteen.

Yet somehow it did concern us. Angry as I was at O'Brien he had been sure the presence of the dead woman had something to do with us. Actually of course with Judith. He had said she might be in danger, and there was no question her terror was real. She had been deadly afraid since Reno. Now she insisted the woman had been mistaken for her and deliberately drowned, and while I knew she was a good actress there had been no acting when she packed her bags and tried to leave that day. She had been as near desperation as no matter.

Bill was still at the juke box when I went to the telephone booth and looked up Doctor Townsend's number in New York. His nurse answered. She said the doctor was out and who was speaking.

"It's Lois Maynard," I said. "Mrs. Chandler's sister. Could I see the doctor sometime tomorrow?"

"Mrs. Chandler has her regular appointment tomorrow."

"I don't think she'll be coming. She's not well."

"Just a moment. I'll look at the book."

She came back in a minute or two, said I could come at eleven-thirty, and seemed relieved when I said I didn't want Judith to know about it. She said she thought the doctor would be glad to see me, and hung up as though she had said too much.

I don't know how Phil felt when we got home that day, but I drew a long breath of relief when I saw his golf bag in the hall. The clubs were all there. I counted them.

12

As usual I made my publisher the excuse for going into town the next morning, although I had practically abandoned work. As no one in the house ever considered me seriously as a writer this brought no comment from Phil. But Bill spoke up briskly.

"How about taking me along?" he asked. "I'll tell him you're a prime suspect in a murder case. That ought to be good publicity. 'Novelist Detained In Mysterious Death. Writer Of Crime Fiction Involved In Murder Herself.' How's that?"

"I'm not involved, and it isn't funny. You're not coming."

He was persistent, however. He needed new bathing trunks. Did I want to see his derriére through the old ones? I retorted that as I had watched diapers put on him as a baby he was no treat to me. But his Janey, whoever she was, saved the day for me. She called him up and asked him to lunch, so I was able to draw a free breath again.

I saw Judith before I left. As usual she was locked in her room, but after some grumbling she admitted me. I saw at once something had happened. She looked worse than the day before, if possible, and her hands shook as she crawled back into bed and tried to light a cigarette.

"You'll burn yourself to death someday doing that," I told her. "How are you? Fever gone?"

She did not answer. She took a

puff or two and then put down
the cigarette.

"What's this Jennie tells me?"
she said. "About a man at the pool
with a gun?"

I could have strangled Jennie
at that moment, but I was for it,
and I knew it.

"Apparently some tramp wandered in, but he had no gun," I
said as cheerfully as I could.
"That's pure imagination on
Jennie's part."

"How do you know it was
imagination?"

"Well, look, Jude. It doesn't
make sense. Jennie waiting for
boy friend on bench. Man appears
across pool, points gun and dis-
appears. Jennie screams and runs.
The end."

"What do you mean, the end?"
she asked peevishly. "She saw
someone, didn't she? And Phil
found the place all trampled. I
wish you'd stop treating me like a
child or a lunatic. I'm neither."

I did not argue with her. I had
a train to catch, but it only struck
me later that she had not asked
about the inquest. However, for
once she had a morning paper, so
perhaps she had read about it.

On the way out I saw that
O'Brien's cottage door was still
closed and his car gone. Not only
that, but his girls were raising
a terrific racket, as though they
needed feeding. I made a mental
note to do so when I came back,
but personally I never wanted to
see him again. Whatever he had
meant by vitally important, he had
gone away and left me literally

holding the bag, and I was fed to
the teeth.

The train was crowded, but I
got a seat, and sat there thinking
about a number of things. The
newspaper clipping, for example.
It was dated 1929, and I tried to
remember that period. I had
learned some things about it as I
grew up, that it was the time of
the boyish form, of rolled stockings, and I think the Charleston.
Of the short skirt too. The photograph of Anne on a table in the
living room showed her in her
wedding dress, the skirt to her
knees showing her rather sturdy
legs, the waistline down around
her hips, and the long satin train
which only made the whole outfit
grotesque.

From Anne to Judith was only a
step. She said she was neither a
child nor a lunatic, and in spite of
Phil I began to believe her. Nevertheless, I was determined to see
Doctor Townsend. Somewhere
there was a key to what he termed
the privacy of the human mind,
and I hoped he had found one for
Judith.

He had not, however, although
he seemed pleased to see me.

"I'm glad you came," he said. "I
read the papers, and this death
must be a real shock to your sister.
How is she taking it?"

I told him: her fainting at the
pool, her impulse to escape, her
fever and inability to attend the
inquest. He listened attentively.
He had her file in front of him, as
though he had been going through
it, but he shook his head when I
finished.

"All pretty bad for her," he said. "I don't know how long she can carry on. As you know, she's been coming back to me, but I've not really been able to help her. As I told you before, she doesn't co-operate. When you were here you told me of the jewel episode and of her leaving her husband. Also that she had fainted on the train platform at Reno and seemed to be terrified. Have you anything to add to that?"

"Only that she's still terrified. I'm quite sure she thinks someone intends to murder her."

He took that in his stride. I daresay it was nothing new to him. But he asked me to give him her early history, and I told him what I knew: how she had been spoiled as a child by mother, had been taken to Arizona for several months, and been married the fall after her return. I said too that I did not think she had been in love with Ridge, but apparently they got along well enough. Only she liked to go out and he didn't, and in the end they were merely living in the same apartment.

He nodded, as though he already knew much of it. When I had finished he went back to what I had told him before, about the night she came home and Ridge found her with her jewels, as though she were appraising them.

"Rather a startling thing, of course," he said. "Has he ever said what he thought of it?"

"He wondered if she was being blackmailed. He went into that later after she left him. Apparently there was no reason for it.

She still has the jewels, or so she says. And she had never had a lover, or anything of the sort."

"I see. Also he probably knows that as a rule blackmailers don't murder, or even make the attempt," and he added, rather dryly, "Why should they?"

He knew her side, of course, about the divorce and Reno. She had been willing to talk about it, but apparently she had told him she left because Ridgely had another woman. Trust Judith to say that, and perhaps even make herself believe it.

"I don't know whether Mr. Chandler had an extramarital arrangement or not," he said delicately, to spare my virginal sensitivity. "It's possible, of course. He and his wife had not lived together for a long time. You don't think this dead woman . . ."

"Was his mistress? I don't think so, doctor. She wasn't young, or even beautiful. She looked and dressed like—well, like a housewife."

He abandoned Kate Henry then, if that is who she was, and took me back to Reno again. "You say you saw nothing to induce that fainting attack. But she must have seen something, Miss Maynard."

"I can't imagine what it was. I searched the train after it happened, and there wasn't a large crowd at the station. Just porters and a chauffeur or two and a few taxis. Taxis!" I said excitedly. "That's queer, doctor. She won't use a taxicab. She walks or takes a bus. Does that mean anything?"

"Possibly. It seems carrying

things rather far. It may be an *idée fixe*. We get a good many of those here. It is carried to extremes sometimes. I had a young man here yesterday, perfectly sane in other respects, who believes he is an adopted son. He is not, according to his mother. I have seen his birth certificate."

"Listen, doctor," I said urgently. "I know all that. It happens, of course. Only you can't measure Judith by the usual yardstick. She sleeps in a locked room, with the windows over the porch nailed shut. She won't go into the grounds if she can avoid it. When she does it's at night, in a long black cape. She looks spooky. And I still don't know why she came to The Birches. She would be better off in a good hotel."

"Perhaps The Birches means sanctuary to her, Miss Maynard. She must have been happy there as a girl. She's not entirely normal, of course, but The Birches is easy to explain. It's like—" he decided to disregard my virgin status—"it's like going back to the mother womb."

"Well, the mother womb in this case is having a lot of birth pains," I said. "Judith fainted when she saw the body. That could happen to anybody. But the real reason it worries her is because she thinks this woman was mistaken for her."

"That's curious," he said. "Why would she think that?"

"They were the same build in a way, they were nearly of an age, and they both had blonde hair. The other woman's was bleached,

I understand, but on a dark night —well, it's possible, I suppose."

He sat thinking for a few minutes, his head on his chest. When he looked up his expression was grave.

"Of course it's possible she's really in danger," he said. "We both know she is a psychiatric case, or we believe she is. But we must not let that close our eyes to other things." And when I nodded he went on: "I'd better talk to you rather frankly. I can say this. Usually after this lapse of time I can read a patient's mind pretty well. I'm only a listening post, you know. They talk. I ask questions and listen to the answers. With Mrs. Chandler it's different. I can go so far. Then, as I told you before, there's a wall, and I can't either break it down or get over it. You can't remember anything in her past that would cause— well, let's say a shock, a psychic shock."

"No," I told him. "She's had an unusually easy life until now. She's had plenty of money, she's had the looks of the family, and for years she had a good husband. I can't think of anything."

He smiled.

"What do we mean by a good husband?" he inquired. "A good provider, who stays home and is at least technically faithful?"

"I wouldn't know. I've never had one."

"As to Mr. Chandler, I don't know him. There was certainly incompatibility, and he may be a hard man to live with. It's not unusual for me to have a woman here and after a time discover it is the husband who should be my patient. Do you think Mr. Chandler would talk to me?"

"Not on this couch of yours! He may come. He'll sit where I am, offer you a dollar cigar, and ask if you think Judith ought to be committed."

He grinned.

"I may try to see him," he said. "I like a good cigar. Now I'm afraid I'll have to let you go. I have rather a heavy day. But I suggest you think over what I have said. This danger may be real."

I was out on the hot street before I realized I hadn't asked him about Judith's idea of going abroad. But there was one thing he had said which I found thought-provoking. That was the idea that sometime, somewhere, she had had a psychic shock, and the inference that after years of normal living whatever it was had caught up to her.

Anne might know, I thought, so I found a telephone pay booth and called her up. Her voice was not too amiable. She had got in from Boston that morning, and the apartment was a mess. She wanted to know if I would keep Bill a little longer, and was he actually suspected of drowning the woman.

"No," I said, "but he's enjoying it. Of course he can stay. We're glad to have him. He has a sort of heavy date here with a girl called Janey. She doesn't seem to have any other name."

"They never do," Anne said resignedly. "Any more deaths? And how's Judith?"

"Not so well. Look, Anne, may I have a bite of lunch with you today? I'm in town."

"If you'll take potluck," she said. "Can't you wait until I've got my breath?"

"No," I told her firmly. "I want to talk to you, and it's important."

She agreed unwillingly, and I found her in the kitchen, savagely attacking a pile of dirty dishes. She had the harassed air I always associated with her. She had been a pretty girl, and in a way she was still a handsome woman. But Martin Harrison had been a disappointment. The crash had practically ruined him, and I could faintly remember those days when their house on Seventy-ninth Street had been sold, and they had come to stay with us. There was a night, I believe, when Anne found him with a gun and had to take it from him by force.

Things gradually improved, of course, in the building line, but he was never an ambitious man, and for years she had had to struggle. It had left its mark on her, and I always suspected her of being jealous of Judith's prosperity.

That morning she eyed me grimly after she admitted me.

"Don't tell me I look like the wrath of God," she said. "I know it. You look like the devil yourself. Judith wearing you down?"

"We have had some trouble, such as a murder."

"A murder! I thought it was an accident."

"The police seem to have discovered something," I said vaguely. "I'd rather not talk about it. We don't even know who she is—or was."

She sat down heavily and kicked off her shoes.

"My feet are killing me," she said. "I suppose my poor Bill had the shock of his life when he found her."

"He's had the time of his life ever since! He was the star performer at the inquest yesterday, or don't you read the papers?"

"I've had a fat chance to see a newspaper this morning."

I asked about Martha, who was coming home before long, and in due time I suggested lunch. She shrugged.

"There's practically nothing in the place," she said. "I can fix some scrambled eggs, I suppose, and there is a hambone. It looks as though Martin's been living on ham. I saw it in the refrigerator. It doesn't look too moldy."

As a result I made a ham omelet, and over the kitchen table I had a better look at Anne. Washed and with her hair brushed she looked more like her old self. But as usual she was curious about Judith.

"How are the psychiatric treatments going?" she inquired. "Are they helping her any?"

"I don't think the doctor is satisfied. I saw him this morning. Anne, did Judith take father's death very hard?"

"I don't think I noticed. Why?"

"The doctor thinks she's had a shock sometime or other."

"You have to remember how things were at that time." She poured herself another cup of coffee. "Martin and I were completely broke. He'd been in the market too. I had to ask mother for money even to take a bus! I think she resented it. After all, I had married and she had every reason to think I was off her hands. Then we landed back on her like a pair of parasites! It was sickening. No wonder she got out from under."

"Then it wasn't because of Judith's health they went to Arizona?"

"Listen to me," Anne said. "She's my own sister, and in some ways I'm fond of her. But Judith never had a sick day in her life."

"But it took money, Anne. Where did it come from?"

"I always thought Ridge Chandler financed them. I know he and mother had some long conferences at that time. He'd gone completely overboard about Judith, poor devil. I meant to ask you something, Lois. What about Doctor Townsend? Has she fallen for him?"

"I don't know. She said something once that sounded like it."

She shrugged, and began picking up the dishes.

"They often get that idea, don't they?" she said vaguely. "I gather that's part of the treatment. Don't worry about it, Lois. She'll get over it."

"You don't have to live with her," I retorted. "Look, Anne, you remember her as a kid, and I don't. Was she in any trouble?"

She laughed.

"She didn't have a baby when mother took her west if that's what you mean. She was too busy taking care of her pretty little self. She's never had one since either. I think Ridge has always resented that. The Chandler women always had them, to carry on the name."

"Then what or who is she afraid of? Because she's good and scared now," I said. "Phil thinks it's all in her mind, but she insists someone is threatening to kill her."

"I've felt like that myself sometimes."

"It isn't funny," I said indignantly. "I've wondered. That woman in the pool. Do you think she came to The Birches to see Judith? She fainted, you know, when she saw the body. And Phil's clubs were in the hall at The Birches."

"What about Phil's golf clubs?"

"They say a weapon of that sort was probably used. Not necessarily a club. Something like it."

Anne laughed.

"So you're suggesting that our dear sister took one of Phil's golf clubs and brained her! You know that's funny, if nothing else is. Judith, who wouldn't break a fingernail to raise a window, marching down to the pool in the dead of night, with a club over her shoulder and murder in her heart! Don't be fantastic, Lois."

I dried the dishes for her, and we let Judith alone for a while. Anne, however, was thoughtful.

"I saw Ridgely the other day,"

she said. "The poor old boy looks dreadful. He's aged ten years. Why did she leave him, Lois? Has she ever said anything?"

"It's not Ridge she's afraid of. I'm sure of that. She thinks the woman who was killed was mistaken for her. Anyhow why would he do such a thing?"

"It would save alimony," she said curtly. "But he's as puzzled as we are. He has an idea she was being blackmailed, and I suppose you know he put a private investigator on the case. But it was no soap. He says she always landed in her own bed."

"She would," I said. "I imagine it takes a generous sort of woman to get into that kind of mess."

She laughed at that, and we finished cleaning up before I left. Anne was still in the kitchen mopping the linoleum when I was ready to go, and I realized she had already practically forgotten Judith and even myself.

"Well, thanks for the lunch," I said. "I'd better be going. I have to catch the train and get home."

She looked as though she had just remembered I was still there.

"Glad to have you," she said absently. "And if Helga decides she can't take Judith, send her to me, will you?"

"Judith?"

"No, for heaven's sake! Helga."

I glanced around the apartment on my way out. It looked small to have raised two children in, and the furniture showed abuse. Phil and I had sent her some of mother's stuff after her death when we closed off part of The

Birches. It had helped, but now it looked shabby and neglected. Seeing the place I could understand her resentment of Judith, who had had everything and apparently thrown it away.

13

As I passed the cottage on my way home I saw that O'Brien was back. His car was outside, looking dusty—usually he kept it very clean—and the girls were clucking contentedly. I did not stop. I merely stepped on the gas and sailed by, my head high with sheer fury.

It did not help my morale to see a town policeman and a State Trooper near the pool. Each of them had a rake, and they were combing the grass and even crawling under the shrubbery. So the case was not closed, and this was verified when Jennie said Fowler had been there that afternoon.

"He took Mr. Phil's golf clubs when he left," she said. "He asked Mrs. Chandler if he could, so I guess it's all right. He said he'd bring them back tomorrow."

"Then he saw Mrs. Chandler?"

"Oh, yes. He was here a long time."

Phil was not yet home, and Jennie said Bill was meeting his train with the Ark. I felt practically dazed as I went upstairs. Judith's door was shut, so I did not speak to her. I went on to take a bath and change, but what I call my brain was past all reasonable thinking. The case was not closed. It had only moved from the swimming pool to the house itself.

Rather to my surprise Judith came down to dinner that night. She looked better, and she even took a cocktail.

"I hope it was all right to give the police your golf clubs, Phil," she said. "But I can't imagine why they wanted them. Can you?"

"Very definitely," Phil said. "The idea is to give me free room and board for a time, and maybe a meal I can select before they shave my head. Or do they shave heads? I can't seem to remember."

She fixed him with those curiously tilted eyes of hers and looked puzzled.

"Do you mean those clubs are important?"

"Important! Do you know what they cost? Oh, well, maybe we'll have an atom bomb in time. One can always hope!"

Bill choked over his drink, and I sat down because my legs were shaking.

"Fowler was really very nice," she went on. "He asked a lot of questions, and one of them was funny, Phil. He seemed to think you'd know the woman in the pool. He didn't use the word 'mistress' but that's what he meant. I said I was sure you hadn't had one. Your morals . . ."

"Not morals. Money, my dear. Such ladies are expensive."

"But he was really very pleasant. He said I was not to worry about anything. Just to leave it to him."

Phil looked at me and winked. "It's not limited to birds," he said. "A little salt on anything male and it's all over."

Judith looked blank, but as just then Jennie opened the living-room door, yelled "Dinner," and slammed it shut again, the discussion ended.

I ate very little that night, as did Phil. Not only was he worried about the clubs. I found myself watching Judith and wondered what Doctor Townsend meant by a psychic shock. So far as I knew her life had been one grand sweet song until a few months ago. And if leaving Ridgely and going to Reno was a shock she had certainly recovered fast; playing roulette and the slot machines and shooting craps, always with her entourage of men trailing her. She called them her boys, and they loved it.

It was possible, I thought, that the shock—whatever it was—had come, not in her earlier days, but on the train the day she fainted.

We had coffee as usual on the porch that night, but as the late summer evening turned to night I found myself there alone, Bill announcing that he had to see Janey and would probably propose to her.

"At your age, Bill!" I said. "Don't be absurd."

He grinned at me.

"It's just part of the game," he explained. "Keeps other fellows away, gives me the right to do a little necking, and lets me in to dinner now and then. They have a damned good cook." He saw my face and laughed. "Anyhow, I'd better get some influences behind me, such as her father. You see, I've been using Phil's clubs."

After he had rattled off, Phil took his brief case into the library, and with Judith gone to bed I found myself alone.

I couldn't decide what to do. O'Brien's lamp was lighted, and I had plenty to say to him. On the other hand, things seemed to be breaking too fast even for imagination. Sometime too during that interval I heard a car pass on the road and stop somewhere beyond. It must have been eleven o'clock by that time, the moon was rising over the trunks of the birch grove, and I was about to light the final cigarette of the day when I saw someone standing there.

It was a man, and at first I thought it was O'Brien. Then I realized he was not tall enough. Whoever it was he stood gazing up at the house, his hands apparently in his pockets. One hand was not, however. It was clutching something, and to my shocked surprise it seemed to be a rock.

It was a rock! After seemingly assuring himself that no one was around, he stepped out of the grove onto the drive that led to the stable, and with an easy pitch lobbed it up at one of Judith's open windows. I heard the distant crash as it hit the floor, and Judith's faint scream, both almost simultaneous.

He was gone before I realized it, fading among the trees, and before I could recover from my astonishment I heard a car start up on the main road. As though that was not sufficient I saw O'Brien running up from his cottage. As the car started, however, he slowed down to a walk, but he kept on coming. He was almost on the porch when he saw me.

"Who is it?" he said, peering up.

"It's Lois," I told him. "I'm afraid your friend's gone. After he heaved a rock through Judith's window, of course. That's not mayhem, is it? Mayhem is an attack on the person. But it seems a rather lethal form of amusement."

I doubt if he heard my last sentence or two. He was in the house and upstairs banging on Judith's door almost before I finished. I followed him up as fast as I could, to see him stop at Judith's door, and to hear him calling her name.

"Mrs. Chandler!" he said. "Are you all right?"

She did not answer him at once. When she did her voice was sharp.

"Of course I'm all right," she said. "What on earth is the matter?"

"The rock didn't hurt you?"

"What rock? I don't know what you're talking about."

"Didn't one come through your window just now?"

"I was taking a bath. I'll look around." There was a short silence, while she ostensibly made her search. O'Brien did not look at me. He put a sizable ear close to the door, and I saw he was wearing an army overcoat over his pajamas.

There was a short silence.

"There's no rock here," she said. "I can't imagine what all the excitement is about."

"Won't you let me in to look?"

Then she laughed, the light artificial laugh I knew so well.

"Really I can't do it," she said, her voice close to the door. "I'm just out of the tub. If Lois is around she would call it *in puris naturalibus*. College, you know. Good night, Mr. O'Brien, and thanks for looking after me."

O'Brien turned and looked at me.

"All right," I said in a whisper. "I'm a liar. There was no man and no rock, and everything's nice and friendly in this best of all possible worlds."

He grinned.

"She jumped that hurdle pretty fast," he said in a low cautious voice. "Had a lot of practice probably. Want to come down and talk about it?"

I did. I even wanted a drink to settle my nerves. I got two highballs and carried them to the porch. He evidently had his pipe with him—he had dozens all over the place—for when I went out he was smoking. He looked almost complacent. He sampled his drink, stated it was what the doctor ordered, and then told me to go ahead and—as he put it—add a bit.

Nevertheless, he was serious enough as I told him what had happened: the man's approach by way of the grove, the crash of the rock, Judith's scream, and then the car and the unknown's flight presumably in it. He did not speak until I had finished. Then he told me to stay where I was, and went down the steps and around the corner of the house.

When he came back he was holding a sizable stone in his hand.

"She threw it out the window after we got there," he said. "Notice anything about it?"

"It's just a piece of rock, isn't it?"

"It's rough, and it's squarish. You can tie things to a shape like this. I'm not psychic, but I can tell you what your sister is doing right now. She's either burning the note this carried, or she's flushing it down the toilet." He thrust a big hand into a pocket. "She's pretty thorough, you know, but she slipped up in one thing. She threw the cord too."

He produced it and handed it to me. It was an ordinary piece of white string, not too clean, and O'Brien took it back and put it in the pocket of his overcoat again.

"People get excited and slip up on some little thing," he said.

"That's where the police step in. They're looking for the slip."

"I still don't understand," I said blankly. "Why not write her a letter?"

He smiled.

"Well, there's a bit of drama in this sort of delivery," he said indulgently. "Makes her read it, for one thing. No human being could resist a note tied to a rock and flung, so to speak, at one's feet."

He was not so complacent as he sounded, however. He had been taking a shower when the car drove past and he had not heard it. He had seen it later in the Adrians' drive, and started at once for the house, only to be too late.

"But what's it all about?" I wailed. "Who is he? It wasn't Ridge Chandler. He was bigger than Ridge. If he has to see her or communicate with her why not simply ring the doorbell?"

"Maybe he has his own reasons," he said evasively. "I told you once even a smart cop could lay an egg now and then. Maybe I'm not smart, for I think I may have laid one here. Only, damn it all, I can't get in touch with the fellow."

"You know who it is, don't you?"

"Look, sister," he said. "A lot of things have been going on around here. Some I understand, some I don't. The hell of a lot I don't. And I won't have you involved. Think that over, my dear."

He got up abruptly, stood undecided for a minute, and then stooped quickly and kissed me.

"Been wanting to do that for a long time," he said, and departed.

I was still sitting there in stunned amazement when Phil came out. O'Brien had taken the stone with him, so I could not show it, but he listened to my story with only a mild interest.

"She denied it, did she?" he asked when I had finished.

"Yes. Absolutely. She even laughed. Through the door, of course. She wouldn't open it."

"Well, don't let her get you, kid. She's doing all right. They say lunatics are always happy—in their own way, of course."

"Doctor Townsend says she's sane enough. He thinks she's had a psychic shock of some sort. And certainly she didn't stand out there and sling a stone at herself, Phil."

"Probably another lunatic," he said, and yawned. "Maybe they like company."

Perhaps I was on the verge of a good crying spell or perhaps he merely realized I was considerably unstrung. He lit a cigarette and leaned back in his chair.

"All right," he said, "I'm sorry. Only I don't like to see you losing weight and worrying. Let's look at this thing. If ever a woman was petted and coddled all her life it's Judith. She's what she's always been, spoiled and a trifle off center. Probably the shock was when someone took her rattle away when she was a baby!"

"That wouldn't make her terri-fied now. And she is. She's really afraid. That man tonight . . ."

He moved impatiently.

"I don't know anything about her private affairs. Maybe she has a lover. Who knows? Only remember this, Lois. You say she thinks someone wants to kill her. Well, maybe so, but look at the facts. She's been the beautiful Judith Chandler for twenty years, and she's still something to look at. Maybe when she left Ridge she meant to marry someone else, but he hasn't come through. Or maybe she changed her mind. She doesn't want him, after all. So she not only hides from him, she dramatizes the affair. Either she's his or nobody's. He may even be desperate enough to kill her. Second act curtain."

He yawned again and got up.

"That poor creature in the pool played right into her hands," he said. "Same color of hair and same build, so she insists the fellow meant to kill her and got the wrong woman. Better get to bed, Lois, and stop fussing. She's having the time of her life."

I did not believe him. I was sure he did not believe himself. And when later events proved how wrong he had been I was too busy to remind him. I was, at different times of course, to be visiting both O'Brien and Judith, and of all places in the world, in the local hospital.

14

Bill had not come in by midnight. As he seldom did, I was not uneasy. But I was not Phil, with his humor and his factual mind. I knew I would not sleep until O'Brien had explained just why he had run up the drive, or what warning he had had of trouble. He could not have heard Judith's scream, yet he had come pelting along as though all the fiends of hell were after him.

I wasn't a child, to be put off with a pat and a kiss, I thought indignantly. Or to be shown up as a liar at the inquest. He owed me something, and I intended to collect it.

His light was still on, and after an uneasy moment when I remembered the man with the rock, I decided to go down to the cottage. As an afterthought I took one of father's old canes from the umbrella stand in the hall, and cautiously made my way down the drive.

I think the cane amused him.

"All armed for an attack, aren't you?" he said. "Well, come in. I'm not going to apologize for that impulsive act on the porch, if that's what you're after."

I took a leaf from Judith's bag of tricks.

"What impulsive act?" I said coolly.

He stared at me. Then he laughed.

"All right," he said. "Just the way no stone was fired through your sister's window, isn't it? Only you might remember there was a stone, and I found it."

"I didn't come down for double-talk. I want to know how that man got to the house tonight."

"Easy. His car was parked in the Adrian drive. I saw it there."

"Then you know who it was, don't you?"

"Let's say I have a theory about it. Remember Jennie's man, and a few other things. All I want is to lay hands on the fellow."

"You know that woman was murdered, don't you?"

He did not answer at once. He closed the two windows and drew my chintz curtains across them, picked up a pipe, and gave me a cigarette and lit it before he sat down.

"She was, yes," he said. "But I wasn't thinking only of her. Someone else may be in danger."

"You mean Judith?"

"Possibly. Certainly *she* believes it. I'm not sure."

"Doctor Townsend explains her state of mind as the result of a psychic shock, perhaps years ago. I can't think of anything of the sort. I can only remember how carefully she was raised. Until she made her debut she hardly moved without mother or a nurse, or a governess. She went to a private school in town but the car took her and called for her. Mother had a sort of fixation about her, and when she was dying, although I was only a youngster, she made me promise to look after her. Judith knows that. I think that's why she came here to The Birches."

"Any idea what your mother was afraid of?"

"She wasn't afraid exactly, but Judith was the family beauty. Then too she had been a difficult child. Mother might have been afraid she'd go off the rails somehow. As she has."

"The divorce, you mean?"

"That didn't bother Jude. She never really cared for Ridge Chandler. No. I think she was glad to be free. She was practically normal until we started east. She was going abroad as soon as she could book passage."

He thought that over for a moment or two, knocking out his pipe and refilling it. When he spoke again it was about the inquest.

"Sorry I let you in for that. Of course I didn't know they had your prints. How did that happen?"

"I was an air-raid warden during the war. The police took all our fingerprints."

He nodded. It was very quiet. The only sounds were when once a sleepy hen gave a faint cluck in the chicken house or when now and then a car passed along the road. For there were a few cars now. Summer had come, and here and there a summer place had been opened. But O'Brien was not listening. He was still fiddling with his pipe, and his face looked unhappy.

"I've about reached the end of my rope," he said finally. "I need some help, and I think perhaps you can give it to me. Only I'll have to tell you a story, and go back a long way to do it."

He reached into the drawer and pulled out the clipping from the dead woman's bag, in its cellophane frame.

"It has to do with this," he said. "It doesn't sound important, does it? Yet it may be. It may mean not only this Madam X of ours was murdered. It may explain why. I've tried to trace her and failed. But I need help. In the first place, look at this."

He reached into the drawer again and pulled out a yellow scrap of paper. It was the return-trip half of a railroad ticket to a small town up the Hudson! I suppose I looked jolted, for he spoke quickly.

"Don't judge me yet, Lois," he said. "I had a reason, and a damned good one."

He gave me no chance to speak. He went right on.

"I've told you I'd always wanted to be a policeman," he said. "Maybe you think that's funny, but a lot of kids are like that. Anyhow I stuck. I flunked out of college to do it, and my family was furious, but in the end I got on the force.

"I guess I was a pretty obnoxious young punk at first. Because my people had some money I had the idea that God had made me a little better than the other men. Then one day a Homicide man twice my age took me around the corner and knocked hell out of me. I was laying for him after that. I had a Lower East Side district, and I was prepared to shove him into the river whenever I got a chance. His name was Flaherty. Inspector Flaherty.

"He knew it too, but he didn't let it bother him, and when there was an opening he got me transferred to Centre Street in his department. He grinned when he sent for me.

" 'I'll feel safer when I have you where I can see you,' he said. 'And you have the brains to make you a good cop, as well as the build of one. That's why you're here, O'Brien. I asked for you.'

"Well, you don't shove a man into the East River after a thing like that, and after the first few months I guess I would have let Flaherty tramp all over me. Most of what I know he taught me. He was hard as nails outside, but—oh, hell, I don't want to talk about him. He had only one ambition. He wanted to have a chicken farm when he retired. I guess that's the reason for the girls out there.

"I was still with him a year or so later when they found that girl in the clipping you've read. It wasn't my first murder, but it was bad enough. She'd been a pretty kid, and she had three or four younger sisters and brothers to support. She worked in a cheap store down there, and maybe she made some money on the side. You couldn't blame her. They had to eat.

"The district's changed since then. Not so many pushcarts on the street, for one thing. They sold everything from hot baked potatoes to men's pants and shoes. Now the traffic men have moved them back to the pavements or even into small stores. But it's still a messy place, washing and beddings hanging on fire escapes, and the kids staying out until all hours.

"The Preston kids—you've read that clipping: her name was Mollie Preston—were out until midnight that night. And when they came home she was dead on the floor, strangled. We had the hell of a time getting any story at all, what with the screams and all that. But a girl on the floor below said she saw a young fellow going up the stairs to the Preston flat that night, and that she heard a noisy quarrel. Her name was Kate Henry, and unless I'm crazy she's the woman your Bill found in the pool.

"It was Flaherty's case. I came into it because I'd learned shorthand. And Flaherty took it pretty hard. He'd known the girl since she was a baby.

"Well, it looked like an open-and-shut case. She'd been seeing a young law student from Columbia named Shannon—Johnny Shannon—and Kate Henry identified him in the line-up and before the grand jury. He admitted he'd been there that night, but only for a few minutes to call off a date. The girl was angry because he wouldn't stay, and she was pretty noisy about it. He said there was no quarrel and he claimed an alibi, but it didn't stand up, so he got a life sentence.

"It killed his mother. Only the funny thing is that Flaherty never believed he was guilty. Up to the time of the trial he kept working on the case. He found homes for the Preston children, but even after the trial he was convinced Kate Henry had lied.

"Kate had disappeared by that time. Then one day he told me he thought he had located her in a small town up the Hudson. He didn't tell me its name, except that it wasn't far from Poughkeepsie, and that he was going there the next day. Only he never got there. He was shot and killed on his way home that night."

He stopped, as though he did not want to go on.

"A good Joe," he said heavily. "The best ever. They don't make many like him. But the way it looks someone knew he was getting too close, so he was murdered."

He drew a long breath.

"Sorry. It's a long story, isn't it? But you had a right to understand. I don't want these local guys to gum things up. This is my case. In a way I've been on it ever since he died.

"I wanted to know who killed Flaherty. Maybe it's an obsession with me now. It was a long time ago," he added. "You never knew him, or heard of him. But he was like a father to me, only more than most fathers. People knew he was fair, even the ones he sent up. He was shot because the next day he was going to that town up the Hudson, the town the dead woman came from.

"That's why I kept the ticket stub as well as the clipping," he said. "Flaherty is my case. So was Shannon, if he was innocent. I didn't want Fowler or any of the state cops going up there and spilling the beans. You'll notice nobody from there has claimed the body. That's suspicious in itself."

I sat gazing at the return-trip ticket in my hand. The town was probably thirty miles or more away, and I was bewildered. I was seeing him the day I had met him in town, when he had insisted on buying me a Coke at the drugstore.

"Why did you come here?" I asked. "What have we to do with all this? None of us knew her, or Flaherty. Certainly not this Preston girl. I don't understand it."

"No," he said, "you wouldn't. You were pretty young at that time. Anyhow what would you or your family know about a girl murdered in a tenement down on the East Side? Anyone could have killed the girl. She was that sort. All kinds of men visited her. As I said, Flaherty was out to prove the Shannon boy was innocent. Beyond that I think he didn't care."

"You still haven't said why you're here," I persisted.

He hesitated.

"It doesn't clear anything, Lois, but I'll tell you. I got an anonymous letter after I came back from Reno. It said Mrs. Chandler was in danger. She may have had one too. It would account for a lot if she did. But the postmark was from Kate Henry's town, and I think she sent it."

"But why?" I asked. "Didn't it give any reason? Judith may have enemies. Lots of people don't like her. But to threaten her . . ."

"The letter wasn't a threat. It was a warning. Whoever sent it was trying to prevent trouble, not make it. You see, it's pretty well known I never gave up the Flaherty case. Let's say Kate knew something about it. Maybe she was scared. Maybe she needed protection herself. I don't even know how she located me here, but it looks as though she had. She probably knew I had a car too. She didn't ask Ed Brown to come back for her. But I never saw her that night. Personally I think she was followed here, attacked, and thrown into the pool."

I felt slightly dizzy and certainly confused.

"Who would have followed her? She came by train. That's pretty fast."

"She came on a local. Anybody in a car could beat her time. There's a damn good highway most of the distance too."

"Then it has nothing to do with us," I said flatly. "Or at least with Judith. It doesn't explain her at all. Yet you think she may be in danger. You came here to watch her, didn't you? Why? Don't tell me she killed the Preston girl, or Flaherty. That's ridiculous. She was only seventeen."

"Kids that age do commit murder. But I don't think she ever killed anyone. No, this woman had some dangerous knowledge. Maybe her conscience troubled her, maybe she was afraid. That's as far as I go."

He got up and put the clipping into the drawer. Then he came over and put a hand on my shoulder.

"I'm wondering if a girl like you would be caring to help a bit," he said, lapsing into the brogue I had noticed on the train. "I'll tell you now it's beyond me. I've been to that town and all around it since I saw you last. No woman has disappeared, according to the police there. It's a dead end, in more ways than one."

"And I suppose," I said rather feebly, "that this town is where I come in?"

"That's where you come in, my girl. And only God knows how I need you."

15

I suppose all those small towns up the Hudson River have a basic resemblance. There is a shabby and usually dirty railroad station, a warehouse or two and perhaps a factory by the tracks, and one business street with a movie house, a drugstore, a couple of groceries and nearly always a beauty parlor, a doctor and a lawyer, and possibly a dentist, usually the offices upstairs over a shop.

This one was a little better. It had two such streets, including a woman's dress shop, a milliner, and a tobacconist, as well as a dozen or so small businesses, including a garage.

But it improved beyond the business section. There were houses neatly set in well-kept lawns, and I imagined that beyond them and up the hill there were some large estates. But I did not drive there. Whoever the woman was she almost certainly did not belong there.

I had our old car. I had left Phil at the station as usual, but I did not go home. It was Judith's day to see Doctor Townsend and I suppose she was raving, but I knew Bill and the Ark would look after her. Nevertheless, the whole excursion looked like a wild-goose chase to me. As I told O'Brien I had only one clue, the bleached hair, he only laughed at me.

"For a girl who writes fiction you show a lamentable lack of imagination. What's the matter with her leaving her purse on the train and you finding it?"

"And keeping it all this time?"

"You were afraid to turn it in at the station. Somebody might take the money. So you watched the ads in the paper instead. You knew she came from here. There's the return ticket."

It sounded absurdly easy, put like that, but I was nervous nevertheless. Even the drive did not help much. I kept seeing that dreadful body at the end of the pool, the State Police as well as Fowler and his men, and the crowd being held back along the road. I felt annoyed too at having let myself in for such an excursion. O'Brien's story about Flaherty had moved me the night before. He had been on the case for twenty years, which in itself was touching. But what had I to do with Flaherty, or for that matter the dead woman?

Perhaps it was suspicious that

no one had claimed her, but how did I know it was? Maybe no one had missed her, or nobody cared. Or, again, she was supposed to be away on a visit. She could still have had the return ticket.

One thing was sure. If she lived in that neighborhood she had no car. I stopped at the garage for gas, and I went into my spiel at once. It was easy, for the pleasant young man who waited on me was curious about me.

"Don't live around here, do you?" he asked.

"No. I was just going through, but I meant to stop anyhow."

"Know some folks?"

"Not exactly. You see, I found a woman's purse in the train the other day. No name in it and no papers, but it had a return ticket here."

"Lot of money in it?"

"Just a few dollars. She hasn't advertised it, so I kept it. I don't know her name, you see." I went on: "She was sitting across the aisle from me, a bleached blonde, maybe forty or so, in a black dress and a hat with a sort of wreath of flowers on it."

He had lost interest, however, either because of her age or the amount.

"I wouldn't know," he said vaguely. "Half the women in this town could answer that description. Why don't you just forget it? If she wanted it she'd have advertised. Did you try the Lost and Found Department at Grand Central? She may have reported the loss there."

"Thanks. I hadn't thought of that."

He looked at me as though he thought my I. Q. was pretty low, and as he stood in the doorway watching me I had to drive around for some time before I tried elsewhere. The conversation at both grocery stores followed practically the same lines, but I had kept my ace up my sleeve. That was the bleached hair and the beauty parlor. And there I struck pay dirt.

Gertrude—that was the name on the window, Gertrude's Beauty Shop—was busy when I went in. She was giving a permanent, but her young assistant was free. With inward qualms I asked her for a manicure, and seated at a small table received the usual disapproving query.

"Keep them pretty short, don't you?"

"I use a typewriter," I explained.

She glanced up at me quickly.

"Stenographer, eh?" she observed. "Well, the cuticle's pretty good anyhow. I'll see what I can do."

And it was there, to the rasp of an emery board, that I got my first clue.

"Bleached hair?" she said. "Well, if she's from here, you can bet we did it. And that hat—! Say, Gert," she called, "remember that bleach job you did last week. Old girl in the funny hat? Remember her name?"

"I should remember all the jobs like that I do. What's the idea?"

"Girl here says she left her purse on the train and she found it. Wants to give it back, only don't know who she is. Says the return ticket says she comes from here."

Gertrude however was convinced that the woman in question never left her purse anywhere. "Nor a half dollar either," she added with some bitterness. But she was completely uninterested. "You might look in the appointment book, Edna," she said. "Not that I give a damn."

The manicure was better than I expected. I paid for it, added a tip, and suggested that Edna follow Gert's suggestion. She got a dog-eared small ledger from a desk drawer and with a long nail ran down lists of names for the past week. On a Monday she stopped.

"Listen, Gert," she said, "wasn't it Benjamin? Seems like that rings a bell. Didn't he run that tobacco shop before he died?"

Gert nodded indifferently.

"Guess that's right," Gert agreed. "Lives somewhere around here. Hair was a mess. She'd been doing it herself."

They had no address for her, however. I got it finally from one of the grocery stores I had visited previously. But the clerk observed that she was probably not at home.

"Didn't come in Saturday," he said. "Regular as clockwork, she was. Lost her husband a few months back. He left her plenty, but if that's her purse you found she's probably having a fit. She'd squeeze a quarter until the eagle screamed. Funny she didn't advertise."

He gave me her address. It was up the hill a half mile or so, a small white-frame house set back from the road, with a gate in a picket fence and a path to the front door. It sat alone, with the next houses some distance away, and screened by shrubbery, and as I got out of the car and opened the gate I saw a curtain moving at a window. I began to feel rather awkward. If someone lived there with her, my story was no good and I would have to get out as best I could.

No one answered the bell, however, and as I stepped back and looked at the window I saw the reason. A huge black cat was on the sill, scratching at the glass and meowing wildly. And behind it the curtain was torn almost into shreds, as though by its claws. That the poor thing was desperate was obvious. Possibly it had been shut in when the Benjamin woman left, and it must have been starving, or dying of thirst.

Up to that time I had merely done what O'Brien wanted, managed to identify her and locate where she lived. The rest was up to him. The cat, however, changed things. I couldn't leave it there to die. It was scratching at the glass again, its big eyes fixed on me appealingly, and when I tried the front door I could hear it in the hall, still yowling.

The door was locked, of course. I went around the house to the rear, where there was a small porch, but that door was locked too, and I felt fairly discouraged, especially since the cat had followed through the house and was scratching frenziedly at the back door. I looked around, but there was no one in sight, so I tried a kitchen window. It was fastened but rather shaky, and I needed something with which to pry it open. There was nothing in sight but a garbage can, so at last I went back to the car, got a tire iron from the heterogeneous mass I call the tools and, praying I had not been seen, went back to the window.

The cat was there, on the sink. It seemed to know what I was doing too, for now it was quiet and watchful. I had expected it to rush out once the window was open, but it did not. Instead it ran to an empty pan and equally empty water bowl on the floor by the stove, and waited for me to cooperate. I filled the bowl from the cold-water faucet, and it drank delicately, after the manner of all cats, but steadily and for a long time, giving me time to look around.

The Benjamin woman had been a good housekeeper. The kitchen was neat, the linoleum on the floor worn but clean, and a row of tea towels had been washed and hung up to dry. There was a door to a small dining room, with a drooping fern on the table, four chairs, and a china closet rather sparsely furnished with dishes. I did not go to the front room at once. The cat was brushing against my feet, and I knew it was hungry, so I went back to the kitchen. I found a can of salmon in a cupboard and opened it. The cat was on the table before I could put it in the pan, so I emptied it onto a plate,

and it was half gone before I could rinse out the can.

I was increasingly uneasy. Not only had I broken into the house, but my inquiries in the town might have aroused interest in the missing woman. And not only that. My car was sitting at the gate. I thought resentfully that O'Brien would never have left it there. He would have parked it elsewhere and walked unobtrusively to the house. Well, let him do it, then. I had attended to the cat. Now all I wanted was to get out and away from there.

But black cats are bad luck. When I looked out the front window a half dozen school kids were standing around it and eying the house.

"She's back!" one of them yelled. "The cat's gone."

"How do you know it's her? She hasn't got a car."

"Well, somebody brought her. That's easy."

In time, however, they wandered on, and I stiffened my shaky knees and prepared to leave. It is due to what Bill calls my gluttonous curiosity that I did not. For, after all, the woman whose home this was was dead. I had been sure of that as soon I saw the cat. She had left her house expecting to return either that night or the next morning.

Instead she had died in our pool.

The front room was a parlor. It had the unused look of such rooms in small houses, with a fan of paper in the empty fireplace, a suite of overstuffed furniture, a sofa and three or four chairs, and an old-fashioned marble-topped table. There was only one incongruity, a roll-topped desk, closed but not locked. I don't know why I opened it. I was tired and hungry. I had a long drive back, and no business whatever being where I was. But I walked to it and rolled up the front as though no black cat, fed and grateful, had been rubbing against my ankles.

It looked innocent enough at first. Certainly it was tidy. A block of unused billheads announcing "Walter Benjamin, Tobaccos" had been stuck in one of the pigeon-holes, and there was a photograph of an elderly and bearded gentleman who was, I presumed, the said Walter beside them. Loosely in another compartment were a few receipted bills, one for a black dress from the village shop, several bankbooks, and two or three clippings. I glanced into the bankbooks. To my amazement they showed a balance of well over thirty thousand dollars in a New York savings bank, the deposits made almost twenty years ago, and with apparently no withdrawals since that time.

I stood staring at it. Sometime, somewhere, Mr. Walter Benjamin had had a windfall. In any event he had left his widow a considerable estate. If she owned the house and had sold the tobacco business she was comfortably off. I thought O'Brien would be interested in the bankbooks as well as the unframed photograph, and I slid all of them into my purse.

The clippings seemed unim-portant. They were largely local and New York notices of his death, the latter merely announcements in the obituary columns. I was standing with them in my hand when the doorbell rang, and it so jolted me that I dropped them also in my bag. I knew I was trapped. I had only time to close the desk before it rang again, and I had to open the front door.

There was a woman on the steps. She was in a house dress, a middle-aged stoutish person who eyed me with considerable suspicion.

"Oh!" she said. "I—has Mrs. Benjamin come home? My boy says she has."

"I'm afraid not," I said, recovering as best I could. "There's no one here but the cat and me. Why? Has she been away?"

"She's been gone for days. I got sort of worried. Not that we were ever friendly. If you know her you know she doesn't make friends easy. But the milkman said no one was taking in the bottles, so I stopped them. She may not like it, but it seemed such a waste."

"I'm sure it's all right," I told her, and once again went into the story about the purse and the return ticket.

"So I stopped in to get a manicure, and when I said I thought her hair was newly bleached they sent me here. They thought they remembered her."

She was still suspicious, however, until I told her about the cat and showed her the torn curtain.

"I declare," she said. "I forgot all about him. She thought the world of that Tom of hers. Maybe the children saw him, but you know what kids are. That curtain's ruined. She'll have a fit."

"You say she isn't very neighborly. Do you mean she is quarrelsome?"

"Not exactly, but she and that old husband of hers were no mixers. He did pretty well with his business—tobacco, it was—but he had all sorts of things on the side. Pipes and cigarette cases and lighters. Magazines too. But he had a bad heart, and he was too stingy to buy a car. I always said this hill would kill him, and it did."

"She's a widow then? I wouldn't have thought so. She wore a flowered hat."

"She doesn't believe in mourning. They were out in Indiana, visiting his sister, and he just fell over. I don't believe she's grieving much, wherever she is."

"Then you have no idea where she went when she left?"

"Didn't even know she was gone until the milkman told me."

I showed her the kitchen window and she said her husband would fix it. Also she would take the cat until Mrs. Benjamin came home, and at last I was free to get into the car and start home. I had eaten nothing since breakfast, but somehow I was not hungry. I was seeing Mrs. Benjamin at the end of our pool, her newly bleached hair about her face, and her thirty thousand-odd dollars in a New York savings bank.

They could not help her now. Nothing could help her. But why had she come to The Birches? What did she know that caused someone to kill her?

16

It was, however, merely the beginning of what was to be an unpleasant day: my job of housebreaking, my near discovery by the woman next door, and the long tiresome trip home. For Judith was in a furious temper when I got there.

There had been no sign of O'Brien at his cottage, and as his car was gone I drove straight to the house.

Helga and Jennie were having tea and toasted muffins at the kitchen table, and I sat down with them. I was still there, eating ravenously, when Judith stormed in. "So here you are!" she said nastily. "Perhaps you'll tell me why you chose to go off and leave me this morning. You knew I was going to the city."

"You had Bill," I said. "And anyhow the car is Phil's and mine. I don't have to account to you for where I go."

"That rattletrap of Bill's! And he drives like a lunatic."

"Well, he got you there and got you back, apparently."

"No thanks to you. And I'll remind you I'm paying my way here, including the gasoline for the car. I have a right to expect decent treatment, and what do I get? Rotten food, everyone spying on me, pretending people throw rocks at me at night! I was a damn fool ever to come here."

"The food's as good as you'll get anywhere," Helga said indignantly.

"I notice you do all right by yourselves!"

Both of the women had risen when she came in, something they never did for me, but she ignored them completely. For the first time since my childhood I saw her in what Helga called one of her tantrums. She picked up the plate of muffins from the table and flung it, cakes and all, at the stove. Then she turned on me.

"What were you doing today? You were out with O'Brien, weren't you?"

"Certainly not. I haven't even seen him."

Under her make-up she was white with anger.

"You're plotting something against me. Oh, I'm not blind. I've seen you slipping in and out of his cottage. You were there until all hours last night, and God knows how many others. An Irish cop! And don't tell me he isn't a cop. It's written all over him. A cop!" she repeated shrilly. "You sicked the police on me, and I won't have it."

She picked up another plate and was about to throw it at me when Helga went into action. She caught the plate with one hand, and with the other she slapped Judith in the face. It was a real slap too. It almost knocked her down. Certainly it surprised her. She stared hard at Helga and then at me, and suddenly the wild look was gone.

"I'm sorry," she said, and dropping into a chair put her head down on the table and began to cry, deep choking sobs which shook her whole body.

Helga looked at me.

"I had to do it," she said. "I did it when she was a child too." Then she moved over and put a calloused old hand on Judith's lovely hair. "It's all right, Judy. Don't cry, darling. Don't cry."

I belong to a different generation, I suppose. The old soothing methods do not occur to us. We don't like our bruises patted or kissed. And our usual answer to any emergency is a drink. At any rate I shot out of the kitchen, got Phil's decanter of brandy, and brought it in with a glass. Judith was still crying, but more quietly.

"Here's some brandy, Judy," Helga said. "Just take a sip of it. It'll help. You're worn out, darling, and scared too. Just a little taste now, for old Helga's sake. And, Lois, if you'll fix her bed, Jennie and I will get her upstairs."

I knew it was a sign-off. Helga wanted to get rid of me, and I was glad to go. I went up to Judith's room and after turning down her bed I filled a hot-water bottle—a relic of my air-warden lessons—and put it between the sheets. Then I retreated to my nursery, and to my utter amazement burst into tears myself. I was still crying, face down on the bed, when Helga came in.

She came over and stood beside me.

"No use crying over spilled milk, Lois," she said. "She probably won't even remember what happened."

I managed to sit up. Helga got some tissues from my bed table and handed them to me.

"I'm not crying about what she said," I told her. "I'm crying because I'm so damned sorry for her."

"You'd be sorrier if you'd taken off her clothes," she retorted. "She's nothing but skin and bones. She's been padding her breasts and hips so she could wear her things and we'd not notice. I'll bet she don't weigh more than a hundred pounds."

"What is it, Helga? Haven't you any idea what's scaring her?"

"I can think of a lot of things," she said evasively. "From the day she was a baby. I wouldn't try to see her yet, Lois. I gave her one of her sleeping pills, and she's best let alone."

She stood looking across the room, with the geese and frolicking lambs on the walls and my typewriter covered on its table.

"How's the book coming?"

"Book?" I said bitterly. "You don't write books in a lunatic asylum."

"She's not crazy, Lois."

"Then I'm about to be."

I doubt if she even heard me. She turned and went out, and I could hear her creaking down the stairs.

I lay back on my bed. It had been a long day and a wretched one: the long drive, the breaking into the Benjamin house and being caught there, and Judith's strange outburst. All, I thought resentfully, because of a newspaper clipping and a man named Flaherty.

What did Flaherty matter to me? Or the fact that O'Brien had loved him like a father? I had got myself out on a limb for no good reason whatever. Even O'Brien was not sure the Benjamin woman had anything to do with that dead-and-gone case. Yet she had been murdered. Murdered and then thrown helplessly into our pool.

Why had she come there? To see O'Brien after her previous failure? Why then have Ed Brown leave her at the Adrians' drive and have to break through dense shrubbery on a dark night?

I wondered what my woman detective, yclept Sara Winters, would have done under the same circumstances. Probably made fun of the regular police and at the end triumphantly produced the real criminal, someone like Phil, for instance, whom nobody had ever suspected.

For some reason that apocryphal case cheered me. I got up and dressed for dinner, putting on the new pale-blue silk I had paid for with part of Ridgely's check, and was rewarded when, over cocktails in the living room, Bill burst in and gave a loud wolf call.

"Who's the family beauty now?" he inquired. "You're a knockout, Lois."

But he was full of Judith's excursion to the station in the Ark, and at the table he related it with gusto.

"She said it would probably fall to pieces on the way, and she made me dust the seat before she got in. As to speed, I could have kicked a barrel faster." He glanced at Phil, who was surveying with disgust the tapioca pudding in front of him. "See here," he said after Jennie left the room, "who's she afraid of? Don't tell me she isn't. She watched one man for ten minutes before she'd get out of the car. Then he turned around, and I guess she saw it was all right. Anyhow she began to breath again. So did I."

He wolfed down his dessert, lit a cigarette, and sat back.

"I don't get it," he said. "Locking herself in her room, sticking in the house this hot weather, and making someone go with her when she walks out at night. It doesn't make sense. What's the idea, if any?"

Phil had apparently forgotten the tapioca, for he grinned.

"You don't know your Aunt Judith very well," he said. "I imagine she's dramatizing something or other. A sort of play, with herself as the star. Maybe Ridgely Chandler is the villain. I wouldn't know. Man at the station look like Ridge?"

"No, Ridge is short. This fellow was tall."

"That wouldn't make any difference to her. She has to have a villain. That's all."

He glanced at me complacently, but Bill was not having any.

"Look here," he said, "do you mean she has a persecution complex? That's not so good, is it?"

"Whatever she has I imagine she's enjoying it," Phil said cheerfully. "Gives her the center of the stage again. She's used to it, you see. She's been the society editors' baby for years."

I can look back on that evening now with a certain amount of perspective: Judith locked in her room and shaken by terrors we did not understand, Phil's easy acceptance of her fears, and young Bill's bewilderment.

I got up and blew out the candles.

"Let's talk about something else," I said. "I'm fed to the teeth, if either one of you cares. Only don't let Phil fool you, Bill, Judith is scared, and plenty."

Phil was free that night, and Bill's Janey was otherwise occupied. To my annoyance I found myself with two men on my hands, and no chance to go to the cottage. The result was canasta, at which I lost three dollars before Bill began to yawn. It was half past eleven by that time, but from the porch I saw that O'Brien's light was on, and by midnight when the house finally settled down I got my bag and started down the drive.

The night had turned cool, so I took Judith's black cape from the powder room where she kept it and wrapped it around me. It was very dark, no moon and no stars, but as I knew every foot of the way I was walking fast when I heard a movement among the rhododendrons by the pool. The next moment someone caught hold of me and held a hand over my mouth.

"Don't try to yell," he said roughly. "If you do I'll drop you in the pool. We're going to have this out if it's the last thing you ever do."

He jerked off my cape and to my utter amazement picked me up like a child, ducked into the shrubbery and toward the pool. I did not dare to scream. He was strong and muscular, and I realized he had meant what he said. At the bench, however, he paused.

"You she-devil!" he said. "I ought to drown you, but I need you first. And you're going to talk. Believe me, you're going to talk and talk fast. You know what I want. You got my note all right."

I had got my breath by that time.

"What note?" I gasped. "I don't know what you mean."

He was certainly startled. His hold on me relaxed, although I was still in his arms.

"Good God!" he said. "Who are you?"

"Lois Maynard," I said, "and if you don't put me down I'll scream my head off."

He seemed as stunned as I was, but he still held onto me. Then unexpectedly he laughed.

"All right, scream!" he said, and pitched me into the pool.

It was the deep end, and I went in with my mouth wide open. I swallowed a lot of water before I fought my way to the surface and could swim enough to get out. Even that was not easy. The skirt of my new dress wrapped itself around my legs, and I was still coughing and choking. I stood there, dripping and shocked as well as outraged, until I heard a car starting and moving off, and I realized he was gone.

Somehow I staggered to O'Brien's cottage and knocked at the door. His face was a study as he saw me, and I must have almost fallen, for he caught me up and carried me to a chair. He gave me a drink and put a match to his fire before he let me speak. Then he said:

"Don't tell me you fell into that pool. I don't believe it."

"I was pitched in."

"I see. Bill playing tricks, or what?"

"No. I suppose it was the man who threw the stone through Judith's window. He picked me up from the drive and carried me through the shrubbery to the bench by the pool. He said I had got his note all right, and I was to talk. To talk a lot. So I asked him what he meant. I guess my voice scared him. He asked who I was, and when I told him he pitched me into the pool."

"Rather drastic, wasn't it?" He was being calm, but he didn't fool me. His face was set as he filled his pipe. "I suppose he escaped again?"

"He had a car. I heard him start it."

And then he said something which almost brought me out of my chair.

"The crazy bastard!" he muttered. "The poor crazy bastard!"

I stared at him.

"You know who it was don't you?"

"I have an idea. I could be wrong."

He had been standing on the hearth, with a dressing gown over a pair of slacks, and for all the attention I got after that I might have been a stuffed codfish.

"How long ago was all this?"

"I don't know. I swallowed a lot of water, and I had to swim the length of the pool. Ten minutes maybe, or more."

He did not say anything. He went to the telephone and called a number in town. When he got it he lost no time.

"Try road into town from here," he said, "and be quick about it. Put somebody by the reservoir, too. Better block the road . . . Oh, hell, put your own car across it, man! Just see that you get him."

Then for the first time he really looked at me. I was not a pretty sight, with my hair in dank strings, one of my white pumps missing,

and my new dress a complete wreck.

"Of course I had to wear the best thing I own," I said sourly. "I don't think the damned thing was meant to wash."

He roused at that. He pulled my chair closer to the fire and threw another log on it.

"You'll have to get out of it," he said. "Better strip off everything. No use your taking pneumonia. What else have you got on?"

In case he expected a maidenly blush from me he was disappointed.

"I'm wearing exactly one slip, one bra, and one pair of panties," I said. "I'll keep the slip and let the others go."

If he recognized the paraphrase he did not show it. Instead he simply pulled my dress off over my head and wrung it out over the hearth.

"Get out of the rest," he said. "I'll turn my back if you're too modest. Better hang them on the fire screen to dry."

We made quite a picture when I finished, I in my low-cut white slip, with my dress, panties and bra draped on the screen. I'm afraid I giggled, thinking of Judith that afternoon. O'Brien saw nothing funny in the situation.

"I suppose you didn't get a good look at this fellow?"

"I never really saw him at all. He seemed pretty strong."

"You think he mistook you for your sister?"

"He mistook me for somebody. Not necessarily for Judith. Anyhow, what has Jude to do with all this? Don't tell me at the age of eighteen or so she shot and killed your Flaherty! I don't think she's ever owned a gun in her life, or fired one."

He smiled, for the first time.

"Still the loyal little sister!" he said. "Of course she hasn't. In fact I think it might be as well if she did have one. I don't like this thing tonight."

"Maybe you think I do!" I said.

He only nodded, which annoyed me.

"Why do you think he thought I was Judith?" I asked. "You do, don't you? Something's really threatening her, and that's why you're watching the grounds. It's this man, isn't it? Why don't you tell me who he is? What is the danger? I have a right to know. After all, she's my sister."

"Of course," he said. "Only I'm not certain. There are things I still don't understand. When I get those straightened out . . . The man tonight wasn't Chandler, was it?"

"No," I said. "Absolutely not."

"What about today?" he said, as if he had suddenly thought of it. "Did you learn anything?"

I nodded. Suddenly I remembered.

"My bag! It must be in the pool. I know I had it when he threw me in."

"Anything in it?"

"Everything," I said despairingly. "A bankbook, her husband's picture, the works! And they're gone."

"Who was she?"

"She's a widow. Her name was Benjamin, Selina Benjamin. There was a cat in the window. That's how I found her."

"Of course. A cat. That explains everything," he said. "When you've stopped scaring me to death you might tell me about it. What did you find out from her house? And are you sure it's the woman from the pool? We can't afford to make a mistake there."

It had never occurred to me that I might have been mistaken; that a bleached-blonde woman named Benjamin might have left her home and her cat and been killed by a taxicab in the city. Or had merely chosen to disappear, leaving thirty thousand dollars in the bank. And as I told my story I could see he agreed with me.

"We'll have to get an identification, of course," he said. "The cat woman may be anybody. But what's this about all that money?"

"It was deposited a long time ago. That's all I know."

"And the name of the bank?"

"I didn't notice."

He looked rather disgusted.

"You'd better stay here and dry out," he said. "Take your stockings off. They're soaking. I'd better make a try for the bag, although there's only a remote chance I can find it in the dark. Where did you go in?"

I told him it was the deep end, and he grunted. But he disappeared into his bedroom and when he came back he wore only his bathing trunks. Annoyed as I still was I had to admit he was the fine figure of a man, broad shouldered and narrow hipped. He was muscular too. Not muscle bound. Just strong. But he had a scar on his chest I had not noticed the morning at the pool. He almost dared me to mention it now.

"If the telephone rings, get the message," he said. "And lock the door behind me. I may be some time. Only for God's sake be sure who it is before you open it."

He put another log on the fire. Then he was gone and I was alone. I smoked one of his cigarettes and tried to think. Nothing was clear, however, except that he considered Judith's danger was real. But I had a long day, and the fire was warm and comforting. I put my head back and was about to go comfortably asleep when a noise in the kitchen aroused me.

I had not dreamed it. As I jerked my hand up, it was repeated, and for all the world it sounded like a chicken shaking its feathers.

It *was* a chicken shaking its feathers. Sitting on a nice small roost in a corner, with a newspaper spread beneath it as a sanitary measure, was Henrietta. I stood in the doorway and laughed, while Henrietta inspected me, first with one eye and then with the other. I had no idea then that the determined little lady was to play her own part in our mystery. As it was, she went back to sleep, and it was not long before I followed her example.

It was two o'clock in the morning before a rap on the door roused me. It was O'Brien, and big and strong as he was he looked exhausted as well as blue with cold. He did not say anything. He threw my other pump on the hearth to dry, flung my sodden bag on the table, poured himself a huge slug of Scotch and drank it straight, asked if the telephone had rung, and when I said no disappeared into his room. When he came back he was wearing his old dressing gown over his pajamas, and he looked better.

"Sorry," he said, "but I'm no fish. I'd about given up when I found the thing. How about some coffee? You probably need it. I know I do. And leave the bag. I want to open it myself."

The coffee tasted wonderful, strong and black. It stimulated me as no whisky could have done, but as a result of waiting for it, it was half past two before at last he carefully opened the bag. As it was leather the contents were wet but not sodden. And to my surprise it contained not only the bankbooks and the photograph but a half dozen or so newspaper clippings. Then I remembered the woman pounding at the door, and having my hands full of things.

"They were in the desk," I said. "I must have picked them up, and when that woman rang the doorbell I dropped them in my bag. I haven't looked at them since. I just forgot I had them."

"Mrs. Benjamin evidently had the clipping habit," he said. "People do, you know. Like collecting stamps. Let's dry them out, and the bankbooks too."

He did so carefully in front of the fire, and it was the bankbooks he inspected first. He made a note of the amount of the deposits, and their dates, but when he glanced at the clippings the first one he saw was about the woman herself, and there was no doubt of her identity. It was from a local newspaper. It showed her picture, and according to it she had won a prize at a charity card party. O'Brien showed it to me.

"Our woman all right," he said. "Good job, Lois. You'd make a pretty good detective yourself."

"It was easy," I said modestly. "I just thought what Sara Winters would have done, and did it."

"Winters? Who the hell is Sara Winters?"

"She's the woman detective I write about."

He snorted and went back to the clippings.

Among the others there was the obituary notice of a Walter Benjamin, aged sixty-four. It was brief, and dated some months before. It did not give the place of death. And there was one which O'Brien held for a time and then reluctantly handed to me. It was one of the articles about Judith's divorce and her return to The Birches, and a picture of her, evidently taken previously, with a gay party at the Stork Club.

I sat staring at it.

"Rather interesting, isn't it?" he said. "Your sister says she didn't know her, never saw her. But this Benjamin woman cuts her picture out of the paper and keeps it. What do you make of it?"

I was trying to think.

"I think it's very unlikely Judith would know her," I said. "She's

lived for years in that little town."

The telephone rang just then and he answered it. Someone was speaking at length.

"I see," he said finally. "Well, better luck next time."

As usual, he refused to explain further, and when I had put on my dress and my shrunken pumps and gathered up the rest, he took me back to the house. I was fairly confident that he had his gun in his pocket. He carried a flashlight too, and when he reached the shrubbery he stopped and examined it. There were some broken branches and a few fresh leaves on the ground, which bore out my story but told nothing else. He seemed reluctant to leave me at the porch, however.

"Who locks this huge barn of a place at night?" he said.

"The last one to go to bed, although we don't bother much about the windows. We've never had any trouble."

"It might be a good idea to take a few elementary precautions," he said rather dryly. "It's more than possible that your Mrs. Benjamin was pretty deliberately murdered. It's not a nice thought."

There was a moment then when he stood looking down at me, and there was a softer tone to his voice.

"You see," he said, "I don't want anything to happen to you, Lois. You're—well, you're a damned nice girl."

He waited until he heard me lock the front door before I heard him going down the drive. He walked lightly for so big a man, but I felt certain that he was not going back to the cottage.

He did not. I was barely up the stairs when I heard his car start and drive furiously toward town. I forgot about him immediately, however, for Judith's door was open and her room empty.

17

She had been in bed. It was mussed, the sheet thrown back, and the book she had been reading lay on the floor. I went panicky for a second or so. If that man was still in the grounds and he found her . . .

Judith, however, was not out in the grounds. As I stood there I heard faint sounds overhead, and realized where she was. The house has only two stories, but above them are the huge attics where ever since the place was built everything was stored: the usual old trunks, broken furniture, and even ancient toys. It was years since I had been there, since the time when I was getting out Phil's battered hobbyhorse for young Bill, and I doubted if Judith had ever been up there at all.

She was there now. There was a candle on top of a box, and she was kneeling on the floor before a small old-fashioned trunk. Its lid was up, and I shall never forget her face when she turned her head and saw me. I don't think she could speak at first. Then:

"What do you mean, following me around?" she demanded irritably.

"I heard you, and your room's empty. If you're looking for something maybe I can help you."

She slammed the trunk lid and got up.

"It was hot and I couldn't sleep," she said, more quietly. "Mother had a lot of my wedding pictures, so I thought I'd look for them."

I remembered what she had said about Doctor Townsend not so long before, and I wanted to say something about setting forth the funeral baked meats for the marriage feast, or whatever it is. I did not, of course. She was still pale, but whatever she was looking for it was not the huge expensive photographs of her wedding. The trunk in front of her I knew was filled with old snapshots taken hither and yon, but nothing else.

"I think there are a few in the library somewhere," I told her. "I'll look in the morning."

She got to her feet and picked up the candle. Without make-up and with a glaze of cold cream on her face and neck she looked her full age that night, and older. But I let her get back to her room and wash her hands, which were filthy with the dust of years, before I asked her what I felt I had to ask. She was rubbing some sort of lotion on her hands when I spoke.

"There was a man in the grounds tonight, Judith," I said. "I'm sure he thought I was you. He grabbed me and started to carry me off. When he found he'd made a mistake he pitched me into the pool. Do you know who he is?"

She stared at me. My hair and my wrinkled dress told her I was telling the truth, and at first I thought she was going to faint. She did not, however.

She simply sat down on the bench in front of her dressing table. The bottle of lotion fell and spilled all over the place, but she paid no attention to it.

"Yes, I know who it was," she said, in a dead voice. "It's someone who intends to kill me."

"Why? Why should anyone want to kill you?" I insisted. "What did you do, Judith? It must have been something."

And then, sick as she looked, she gave me a queer ironic smile.

"What did I do?" she said. "Well, for one thing I married Ridgely Chandler."

"It wasn't Ridge, Judith," I said.

"Of course not," she snapped. "He wouldn't have the guts."

It made no sense. Even now it does not make a great deal. But I got nothing more from her that night, nor did I get much sleep when I finally went to bed. Again and again I went over what I knew. What O'Brien had said about her danger, and her own fears ever since Reno. But why would anyone intend to kill her? What had she done, petted and cared for all her life as she had been? And what had she meant about marrying Ridgely?

There had certainly been no murder in the man who had stopped me in the drive, although his voice had been hard, almost fierce. But if it was Judith he was after he had not meant to kill her. They were to have something out. She was to talk, but about what? And why had he killed the Benjamin woman, if he did?

Sitting up in bed with a cigarette and getting more and more wakeful every minute, I could not see how she belonged, or even why she had come to the pool. To whom could she have been a menace, that middle-aged woman with her clean kitchen, her big black cat, and her small fortune in the bank?

I watched the sun come up that morning. My room faced the east, and finally I got up and drew the shade, to try and get a few hours' sleep. I could see the edge of the pool from the window, and after a moment or so I saw O'Brien there. He was sitting quiet on the bench, smoking his pipe, and I was pretty sure he had been there —or near there—all night.

I had my second talk with Doctor Townsend that afternoon. I had no appointment, and the Robey woman looked annoyed. However, he seemed to be free and, I thought, even glad to see me.

"I've been worried about your sister," he said. "She was rather strange yesterday. Has anything happened?"

"That depends on how you look at it, doctor. She blew up when she got home. I wondered if anything here upset her."

"I don't know," he said thoughtfully. "Perhaps I probed a bit too deep. You have to remember what my work is. Not to use too many technical terms, the theory is to bring any subconscious worries to the conscious mind; in other words, to make the patient dig up the buried anxiety and face it. Mrs. Chandler refuses to do it."

"But it's there—the worry, or whatever you call it?"

"It's there, yes."

"Would that account for her hysterical spell yesterday?"

He didn't answer immediately. He pushed a cigarette box at me, and over the desk lit one for me. When he sat back he smiled.

"I'm sorry it happened to you," he said. "You've been having a bad time for months, haven't you? As to yesterday, let's say a neurotic temperament under strain will occasionally blow up. It's a sort of mental explosion. Usually when it's over it's over."

"Our cook, Helga, has been with us for years. She thinks Judith doesn't remember much about them afterwards."

"That's possible. It relates to something we call the censor, the thing that works while we sleep, and raises hell with our dreams. Has it ever occurred to you that she regrets her divorce?"

"Never," I said definitely. "She detests him. I don't know just why. He's behaved very well. And," I added, "you have to remember he's a Chandler. They always behave well, the Chandlers, summer and winter, cold or hot, up and down and sideways."

He laughed a little, but when I told him about my experience of the night before his expression changed.

"I see," he said. "Well, it's been apparent all along she is afraid of something or somebody. This man wanted her to talk. That's it, isn't it?"

"It's what he said. She'd talk or he'd kill her."

He sighed and put out his cigarette.

"We're not infallible, you know," he said. "A shock or long-continued strain is often mistaken for a neurosis, and I gather this man is a fact, not a delusion."

"He is, unless you think I went swimming in my best summer outfit."

"Then it changes things considerably, doesn't it? You see, it's easy to say people have delusions, of persecution or what have you. A paranoid psychosis, if you like. I was inclined to think that of your sister. But now she has produced what looks like a real neurosis and is actually a fact. You say she won't explain him. Who he is? Why he wants her to talk, and what about?"

"Only to say he means to kill her. Period."

He opened her file and examined it. Then he slapped it shut.

"Just how much do you remember about her marriage?" he asked. "You were—what? Seven or eight, weren't you? Children often have surprisingly good memories."

"I don't remember much, but my sister Anne says she found her that morning kicking her wedding dress on the floor. It doesn't sound particularly ecstatic, does it?"

"Yet she stayed married for twenty years."

"If you call it that. Personally I don't think she was really married after the first week."

"And you're still sure her husband has nothing to do with this terror of hers?"

"Not directly, although she said a curious thing last night, after I found her in the attic and she said someone meant to kill her. I asked her what she had done to be so afraid, and she smiled and said, 'For one thing, I married Ridgely Chandler.'"

"That's interesting," he said. "Did she intimate that he killed the woman in the pool?"

"Absolutely not. After all, why should he? Even if he thought she was Judith? He had had a good many years with her, plenty of time for a murder it he wanted it.

So he waits until he's free of her and then knocks her out with a golf club!"

He was very thoughtful when I left. He seemed puzzled, and I wondered what his science did for him against a problem like this. I daresay he went home and ate a hearty dinner with a wife he was fond of, saw his children, if any, and played bridge or went to the movies later. But I carried a heavy load back with me.

It was on the train I considered father's suicide, and wondered if it could have been the psychic shock he had mentioned. It seemed impossible. Judith was only seventeen or so at the time, and not a particularly devoted daughter; and I at seven had been shut in the nursery of the city house and knew nothing about it. I had missed him, of course.

My nurse would not talk about it, so I would slip down to Helga in the kitchen.

"Where's daddy, Helga?"

"He's gone away, darling. Don't you worry about him."

"But I want him. He didn't say good-bye to me."

"He doesn't like saying good-byes. You know that. Here's some cookies. You'd better eat them here, so you don't get scolded."

There had been a butler at that time. I remembered him only as a rather dark sardonic person. He and Helga did not get along, and my only real picture of him was when mother was going to Arizona, and he was carrying her bags and Judith's to a taxicab. I did not remember him after that.

I suppose he left with the rest when the house was closed.

O'Brien's car was gone when I drove in past the cottage, so was Bill's jalopy, and Phil and I ate dinner alone. With Judith still in seclusion, it was my first chance to talk to Phil in several days and I asked him what he remembered about father's death.

"Why bring that up?" he said. "It just happened, like plenty of others that year. The poor old boy was broke. That's all."

"Doctor Townsend spoke about some sort of psychic shock for Judith," I persisted. "I wondered if that was it."

"It was a shock for everybody. I think Judith fainted when they told her, but as I remember she was going through one of her queer spells at the time anyhow; having a hysterical fit one minute and the next shut in her room and looking lost and forlorn. I think that's why mother whisked her off to Arizona."

"She wasn't engaged to Ridgely then?"

"No. At least I don't think so. Not until they came back."

"Look, Phil, did she want to marry Ridge?"

"She married him, didn't she? Nobody pushed her to the altar—although mother might have given her a shove. She was pretty keen about the match."

With some difficulty I got him back to father's death. He seemed surprised how little I knew about it.

"Of course you were only a kid, but I suppose you know when he did it?"

"After a dinner party, wasn't it?"

He nodded, gave a look at the canned peaches Jennie offered him, and waved her away.

"I was there," he said after she had disappeared. "I hadn't gone back to college. It was the Christmas holidays, you know. The party was over and I had started to undress when the butler of the moment—I forget his name—rapped at my door. He said there was a police officer downstairs, so I put on a dressing gown and went down. It seems the night watchman had been making his rounds and heard the shot. Anne and Martin were living with us at the time. Martin had gone broke after the crash, and I seem to remember Anne was pregnant. Anyhow I got Martin and we went down in the police car. There was nothing to do, of course."

"You're sure he killed himself?"

He stared at me.

"Certainly I'm sure. He left a note for mother on his desk. That was queer too," he said reminiscently. "I opened it, with the police all around, but it wasn't just what you'd expect. All he said was that he could not and would not do anything against his conscience, even to save her pride. I told Martin about it, and we tore it up. Mother was up against enough without that."

"It doesn't sound like him, Phil. He was never cruel. And what did he mean? Why his conscience?"

"Well, he was broke. Maybe she had some not-too-honest idea for getting money, like robbing a bank! But you didn't live through those times," he added patronizingly. "Plenty of men were doing the same thing."

It was not until we were having coffee on the porch that I told him of my experience of the night before. It startled him out of his usual equanimity.

"For God's sake!" he said. "Why didn't you call the police?"

"He was gone by the time I got out of the pool. I heard his car start."

"What's this about his mistaking you for Judith?"

"She says so. She says he means to kill her."

He took a minute or so to think about that, placing his empty cup in its saucer, and then putting them both on the table.

"Then you don't think she's inventing it?" he asked.

"She didn't invent the man. He was real enough. And Doctor Townsend thinks her trouble is real too. I've seen him."

"This is the hell of a place for her in that case," he said. "Anyone can break in. See here, Lois, I'm going to the police. We need protection, or she does. I'll get Fowler out here, or some of the State Police. You might even get that good-looking big guy of yours in the cottage too. Unless he's the fellow himself." He looked at me with sudden suspicion. "Maybe he is, at that!"

"No," I told him. "It wasn't O'Brien. And don't call him my guy. I wish he were."

I don't think he even heard me, for as if Phil's mention of him

had summoned him we saw Fowler's car coming up the drive. He climbed the steps, wiping his face with a large white handkerchief, and greeting us politely.

"Glad you've had your dinner," he said, seeing our coffee cups. "Always hate to disturb people at their meals. But I have some news for you. We have identified the woman in your pool."

Phil asked him to sit down and offered him coffee, which he refused. He sat down, however, seeming, I thought, rather pleased with himself. He did not glance at me, which was fortunate. I must have looked shaken.

"Yes," he said. "Her name's Benjamin. Selina Benjamin. Any of you know her?"

Phil said no, and I chimed in thinly.

"She's a widow," Fowler went on. "Comes from a small town up the river. Well off, too, or at least comfortably fixed. Funny thing, her coming here. She didn't expect to be gone long. Left her cat in the house. No reason for suicide apparently. Anyhow if she wanted to drown herself she had the whole Hudson River almost within spitting distance."

Phil was smoking calmly, but my hands were shaking too much to light a cigarette. Curiously too Fowler was still not looking at me.

"I'm glad you identified her," Phil said. "But I'd like to know myself what she was doing here."

"That's the question," Fowler said, and settled himself in his chair. "You see, we've got a funny story about her. Seems she'd been missing for some days. Nobody noticed it. Apparently she lived pretty much to herself. But a neighbor of hers got suspicious when she didn't come home, and she called up the local police. That was only yesterday, but she tells a sort of queer tale."

He looked at me then for the first time.

"Seems like the house had been broken into. She thought it was all right at first. The girl—it was a girl—said she'd seen the woman's cat tearing the curtains of the front room, so she broke in a kitchen window to see what was wrong.

"This neighbor—her name's Hunnewell—said it seemed all right to her at first. Then she told her husband, and he didn't like it. Said the girl had no business breaking in. She ought to have talked to the neighbors first, or even called the police. Anyhow he took her to the local authorities last night, and they went to the place.

"The woman was gone all right, and they knew what we had here in town. They brought the two of them down here today and they identified the body at the mortuary. Full name was Katherine Selina Benjamin. She used the Selina. This afternoon they got some fingerprints in the house. Hers were all over the place, but there were some others too. I guess, Miss Maynard, you know whose they are."

Phil's jaw had dropped. He stared at me incredulously.

"What's all this, Lois?" he said. "What's it got to do with you?"

I think if at that moment I had had O'Brien near by I would have strangled him with my bare hands. Him and his Flaherty, I thought bitterly. The case that was never closed! And here I was, on the verge of arrest.

"It's not very difficult to understand," I said, as calmly as I could. "I saw the cat in the window. It looked desperate, so I tried to save it. It was almost dying of thirst. I fed it some salmon too, if that's suspicious."

"You didn't feed it at the desk in the parlor, did you?"

"I don't know what you mean. Anyone who would leave a cat like that to die . . ."

"Look, Lois," Phil said. "Of course you're not mixed up in any real trouble. That's preposterous. But what the hell were you doing there at all? That's the dickens of a way from here."

"Can't I take a drive?" I demanded. "I haven't been able to work for days. When I get a spell like that I often drive around. You know it, Phil."

Fowler was having none of that, however.

"You knew her," he said. "You knew where she lived. And she died in your pool. She didn't commit suicide. She was struck with something before she fell in, which makes it murder, Miss Maynard. Now her bankbooks are missing. Mrs. Hunnewell says she often saw them in the desk, but the Benjamin woman didn't have them with her the night she died. They weren't in her bag."

Phil got up. His usual bland

cheerful face was set and hard.

"Are you trying to arrest my sister?" he said. "If you do, I warn you that I'll have you turned out of office if it's the last thing I do. It's absurd. She didn't even know the woman. None of us did."

"I haven't said I'm arresting her," Fowler said with dignity. "I am saying she was in the Benjamin house that day. And I'll go this far. The District Attorney wants to see her tomorrow. Maybe he'll believe in black cats. I don't."

He went away, jamming his hat on his head as he went down the steps and slamming the door of his car as he gave me a last suspicious glance. Phil watched him out of sight. Then he turned to me.

"All right," he said. "Let's have it. Of all the lame-brain stories I ever heard yours was the worst."

"I'm sorry, Phil," I said feebly. "I just can't tell you. But I didn't kill her."

He gave me a long hard look.

"I'll accept that," he said. "You didn't kill her. I merely wondered why Chief Fowler came here and took away my golf clubs."

I regret to say I laughed.

"I'll write often, Phil," I said. "And if I send you a cake look out for a file in it."

18

I don't know what he would have done, outside of throttling me, had Judith not chosen to come out at that moment. She looked really ill, and she had not bothered to use any make-up. She dropped into a chair and when she took the cigarette Phil gave her I saw her hands were trembling. Which made two of us.

"Wasn't that the Chief's car?" she asked.

"It was," Phil said gruffly.

"What on earth did he want?"

"Don't ask me. Ask Lois. It seems she's been saving black cats, or something of the sort."

She looked relieved. What I did or did not do evidently did not interest her just then. She only looked somewhat blank.

"Did you tell him about the man in the grounds last night?" he asked.

"No. I clean forgot." Phil looked uncomfortable. "What's a man to do with a pair of lunatics gumming up the works? Suppose you come clean, Judith. What do you know about this man? First Lois tells me he dumped her into the pool. Then the Chief of Police comes and threatens to arrest her because a woman named Benjamin left a black cat when she died in our pool. Now it's a strange man in the grounds who wants to kill you, Judith. I must have missed part of this movie. It doesn't make sense."

Judith said nothing. She sat very still, as though she had not heard him, but she was still shaking. It seemed a good time to attack her.

"What Phil hasn't said," I told her, "is that I'm likely to be arrested for murder tomorrow."

"Murder!" She looked appalled. "What murder?"

"The woman in the pool. I'm supposed to have killed her with one of Phil's golf clubs."

"But you didn't do it. Why on earth would you?"

"That's the sixty-four-dollar question, Jude, and I have an idea you know the answer."

When she didn't speak I turned to Phil.

"I'm not in Judith's confidence," I said stiffly, "but if she won't talk I will. As I've told you before, she's been afraid of her life for months. I don't know when it started, but I believe it was before she left Ridgely. If she would tell us about it, we could protect her. As it is, one man is trying to do it for us. His name's O'Brien, and I think that's why he rented our cottage."

Judith stared at me.

"O'Brien?" she said. "What does

he know? Or what has he told you, Lois?"

"So far the shoe's been on the other foot," I said curtly. "What I know is his. What he knows is his too. But it may interest you both to know he didn't go to bed at all last night after Judith's friend attacked me and then ran. He stayed up and watched this house until daylight. I saw him."

"What the hell does he say it's about?" This was Phil, looking completely confused.

"He doesn't say. Perhaps he doesn't know. Only he does believe Judith's in danger."

"Why?" Phil said sharply. "Don't tell me you don't know, Judith. And don't sit there like a damned fool and let an ex-cop look after you. You have a family, even if you chose to forget it for a good many years. It's up to us to protect you, and I wouldn't say The Birches is the place to do it in."

"It wouldn't matter where I went," Judith said dully. "I know that now. Unless I get out of the country."

I suppose it was idiotic to feel sorry for a woman who seemed bent on her own destruction. I did, however. I didn't think she was merely stubborn either. She was concealing something because she felt she had to do so.

She got up before I could speak, said a brief good night and went into the house, leaving Phil cursing under his breath and me in a state of pretty complete helplessness. It began to look as though I was going to be held for the murder of a woman I had probably never seen until she was dead. And also as though Judith would let me go to the chair before she revealed what she was hiding.

All in all, it wasn't the end of a perfect day, and I noticed that Phil locked up with extreme care before he went up to bed that night. When I told him Bill was still out he merely grunted.

"He's got a car," he said. "He's got a home too. It wouldn't hurt him to go there once in a while. I'll let him in. You look as though you could stand some sleep."

In spite of that I slept very badly. Quite obviously the police were not accepting my explanation of why I had been in the Benjamin house. And equally obviously Judith would die or be killed before she explained her own terror.

The strangeness of that attitude kept me turning restlessly in my bed. It was certainly abnormal. Or was it? Was she afraid to tell the truth, and if so why? She was a grown woman, not an adolescent pushed into a marriage she loathed. She knew the man she said meant to kill her. It was she he had expected at the pool. Hadn't he said she had the note he had thrown through the window? And she was to talk. Only talk.

It didn't sound like any prelude to murder to me. Or to Sara Winters either.

I thought of Phil's story about father, about the incredible note he had left for mother. It was brutal, as only a man in a brutal

situation could be. But what *was* the situation? Why had mother made her frenzied escape to Arizona, taking a sulky Judith with her? There had been no pregnancy, Anne said. There might have been something else, however. There was the time in the summer of 1929 when father had a ruptured appendix and had to leave the three of us at The Birches.

Suppose Judith had slipped over the Connecticut border and married one of the boys who always surrounded her? There might have been a divorce or an annulment, or—knowing mother—there might have been neither. She was quite capable of ignoring such a complication and marrying Judith to Ridgely Chandler without benefit of the law.

The fact that Judith might possibly have an unknown husband throwing notes attached to rocks through her window was intriguing, to say the least.

But I had my own problem to face that night. The next morning I was going to be interrogated by the District Attorney, and I had no real answers. Mrs. Hunnewell would be there to identify me. Gertrude of the beauty shop could say I had asked where the Benjamin woman lived, and my story to her about a lost purse would blow up with a bang. Also—unless O'Brien told about the return-trip ticket—they would believe I had known all along what town she came from. He would have to talk now, I thought sourly; have to admit he had sent me to locate her, and why.

And he was going to do it, or else . . . !

All evening his cottage had been dark, but now there was a light in it, and at last I put on a pair of slacks and a shirt and went carefully down the stairs. As I opened the front door, however, I had to choke back a scream. Someone was standing on the porch with a handkerchief to his face, and it was a moment or so before I realized it was Bill.

He staggered into the hall and dropped into a big Italian chair there which was a part of mother's loot.

"Sorry, Lois," he gasped. "Suppose I could have a drink? I've had the hell of a time."

I got him some brandy from Phil's decanter in the dining room, and while I have never considered brandy the miracle worker most writers do, he did begin to look a little better. Evidently he had been in a fight of some sort. His black dinner tie was somewhere under his collar and hanging loose, his coat was torn, there was a large welt over his right eye, and his lip was cut and bleeding. He managed to grin at me, however, as he handed back the glass.

"Chased a fellow and caught up with him," he said. "Only he was stronger than I was. He got me down and banged me with a flashlight. Or maybe it was a gun," he added. "I didn't have time to examine it."

I felt weak and shaky.

"Where was all this?" I asked sharply.

"Down the drive near the pool. I saw him skulking there, and I didn't like the idea. When I asked him what he was doing there he tried to get away. Only like a damn fool I could run faster than he could. He—I guess he knocked me out. When I came to I was flat, anyhow, and he was gone."

He seemed apologetic rather than worried. He would have done better in the scrimmage, he said, only he was tired. His car had run out of gas a mile or two from The Birches, and he'd had to walk home.

"That's how I came to see him. My feet were sore, so I came up on the grass. He almost jumped out of his skin when he saw me."

"Did he drive off in a car?"

"He may have gone up in a balloon for all I know. I was having a nice little nap. I don't think he's still around, if that's what you mean. I imagine he wasn't feeling any too good himself."

"Did you get a good look at him, Bill?" I managed to ask. "Was he big or small?"

"Quite a hunk of man," he said. "All muscle too. The minute I grabbed him I knew it was an error and the side was out."

So Mr. X was still around, or had been. Whoever he was he was certainly tenacious, and something had to be done.

"Look, Bill," I said, "can you walk?"

"Walk where?" he asked suspiciously. "If you mean up to bed I guess I can make it."

"Down to the cottage," I said. "It's important, Bill. I'm—I think I'm to be arrested in the morning, and I'm not going along that drive alone."

His young jaw dropped.

"Arrested? You?"

"They think I killed the woman in the pool. Don't ask me why. Just get me to the cottage. Then you can leave. O'Brien will bring me back."

"So that's the way it is!" he said, yawning. "Well, I can only try. If I drop I trust you to carry me back to ole Virginny."

He staggered to his feet, still rather glassy eyed and certainly no protection. But I was too weary to explain anything to him as we more or less weaved down the drive, and although he asked innumerable questions he was not in too good shape himself. Luckily O'Brien was still up and dressed. I suspected he was about to look around the grounds, for he had a gun in his hand when he opened the door. He slid it in a pocket when he recognized us, but I am sure Bill saw it.

"What's this?" he said. "A late call?"

Then he saw Bill's battered face and pulled him inside and into a chair.

"What happened?" he asked. "Been in a fight?"

"It turned into that," Bill grinned. "I chased a fellow, only I'm too good. I caught up with him."

"Where?"

"Here. On the other side of the pool."

O'Brien examined the bruise and the cut lip while Bill explained about his car. The injuries were not serious, O'Brien said, but Bill would look a trifle odd for a day or two. Then at last he looked at me.

"Was Fowler at the house to-night?" he asked.

"He was," I said. "It is now known that I murdered the Benjamin woman and stole her bankbooks. I've been identified, and my fingerprints are all over the house. I did it with one of Phil's golf clubs, and I'm to be interrogated tomorrow—this morning, rather. The District Attorney expects to have quite a day."

He straightened. For the first time since I knew him he looked uncertain. Then apparently he made up his mind.

"Afraid you'll have to go back to the house and put yourself to bed," he told Bill. "I'll see Lois gets in all right. And"—he hesitated, then he pulled the gun out of his pocket—"if you see this fellow again take a shot or two at him. I won't cry if you get him."

Bill looked highly gratified. He took the gun and pushed down the safety catch, then shoved it in his pocket.

"One if by land and two if by sea," he said, and considering it a good exit line cheerfully took himself off.

O'Brien shut the door behind him and turned to me.

"Now," he said, "what's all this?"

He listened carefully while I told him what the police probably knew: Gert's beauty shop where I learned where the Benjamin woman lived, the fingerprints in the house, both Gert and Mrs. Hunnewell to identify me—the works, as Bill would say. When I finished he shook his head.

"They can't arrest you," he said. "Where's your motive? But this plays hell with my own plans. There's only one answer, of course. You found the return-trip ticket and kept it. So you thought you'd play detective and find out who she was."

"And kept my mouth shut after I did!" I said furiously. "You have a lot of nerve, Terry O'Brien. I do your dirty work and you go calmly about your business and let me go to jail. I have no intention of doing any such thing. You and your Flaherty, who's been dead for years!"

I saw him really angry then for the first time.

"I suppose you think I like what I'm doing," he said with cold fury. "I like watching these grounds of yours instead of getting a decent night's sleep. I like trying to save your sister's life when maybe it isn't worth saving. And I suppose I like hiding behind a girl's skirts, or pants, or whatever she's wearing! A few days in jail wouldn't hurt you. At least you'd be safe and I could stop worrying my fool head off about you."

"Nobody asked you to do any of those things," I said. "And don't bother to deny you came here under false pretenses. As if you really wanted to raise chickens! If you ask me you hate them."

Then unexpectedly he laughed.

"As a matter of fact," he said, "they grow on you. They're pretty good girls, you know. They've been contributing quite a bit to your breakfast."

"Are you still going to insist on that ticket thing?" I demanded.

"I'll change the story, if you like. There *was* a slip in the bag, but the wind blew it away. A day or two later you found it. How's that?"

He got it out of the desk and held it out to me. After its immersion in the pool it looked crumpled enough to have been out in the weather. I took it reluctantly.

"Just where does Judith come in in all this?" I asked. "Don't tell me she killed Flaherty, or the Preston girl."

He closed the desk drawer with a snap.

"No," he said. "Someday before long I'll tell you her story. It goes back a long time, and it isn't pretty, Lois. But I don't want her killed. I want her kept alive and well. It's important. In fact it's vital."

"Don't tell me it has anything to do with Flaherty!"

"Not necessarily, no," he said.

He clammed up then, got his car and drove me to the house. Evidently he was taking no chances without his gun. The key was under the porch matting as he had ordered, and I got his gun from the hall table and held it out to him.

He didn't take it. Not immediately, that is. He simply wrapped me in a pair of arms that could have squeezed a bear to death and kissed me hard. Then he released me.

"Sorry," he said. "Just an impulse. Don't think anything of it."

He was off the porch before I could slam the door.

19

When I reached my room I was astonished to find it was only two o'clock. I had thought it was almost morning. I was not sleepy, naturally. Too much had happened, or was going to happen, including O'Brien himself.

Not the kiss. A girl these days who lays any emphasis on a thing like that must have been raised on a desert island. But what he had said about Judith puzzled as well as alarmed me. All those years of marriage, when the press always referred to her as the beautiful Mrs. Chandler. Her music. Her parties. Her big apartment, done by a good decorator as a setting for her. And all this time something hanging over her; perhaps something dangerous.

I found myself going back to the early days when Judith had been my big sister, to whom I looked up with a mixture of jealousy and admiration. Even then she had been popular. And now and then she had gone to subdeb parties, with mother or my governess to chaperon her, much to her disgust.

I was allowed to stay up and see her off when that happened. She would stand in the lower hall, in white chiffon, or rose taffeta, and turn around for my benefit.

"Like it, Lois?"

"It's wonderful. You're wonderful, Judith."

And mother standing by, her pride in her eyes, as though she could not believe she had given birth to so much beauty.

Compared with Judith I had been allowed to run wild in those early days, to ride my bicycle, to play even with the East Side kids whenever I got a chance, to roller-skate and ice-skate while nurse or governess talked scandal with others of her kind on the park benches. And at The Birches I learned to swim like an otter. I had an idea that Anne had had the same upbringing as mine. Judith was different, however. Looking back I think mother was hardly normal about her. She watched her like a hawk, but Judith could have walked all over her had she wanted to do so.

The one time Judith had a certain amount of freedom had been in the summers at The Birches. Then a crowd of girls and college boys would motor out or gather from the vicinity, especially over weekends. The drive would be filled with cars, some sporty and expensive, others rather like Bill's, and to my childish mind fascinating with the chalked designs and words on them. One of them said "Charleston Charlie," because those were the days of the Charleston.

Rolled stockings, very short skirts, girdles surreptitiously removed for dances, and the Charleston! I remembered trying to do it with my knock-kneed little-girl legs, and father catching me up and laughing.

"Stop it, skinny!" he said. "You're still my baby. Let the big girls make fools of themselves. Not you."

But outside of Judith it was the pool that was the center of attraction, and an alfresco lunch was always set out there on Saturdays. There was Prohibition then and no drinks were served, but most of the boys carried flasks, and many a Coke or ginger ale was needled in the shrubbery. I used to watch them, and they would yell at me:

"Get out of here, Lois, you little snoop."

I never told on them, of course.

As I have said, it was the day of big expensive summer places, plenty of servants, plenty of everything. Now most of the houses were gone, either torn down for taxes or abandoned, and try as I would I could not remember the names of any of the young crowd I tried so hard to join, and which so completely ignored me.

O'Brien said Judith's story went back a long time, and was not a pretty one. Whatever it was I felt certain it dated back to those weekends at the pool, and to one of the boys who surrounded her there. Whether she had eloped with him or not he had some sort of hold on her, which her curious egocentrism had built into a deadly menace.

I did not believe he was a menace. I did not believe he had killed Selina Benjamin thinking she was Judith. The note through the window, what he had said when he picked me up and on discovering his mistake dropped me into the pool, were not the acts of a man with murder in his heart. Something else occurred to me too.

He had not waited to get me out of the water. He seemed to know I could swim. Perhaps, after all, he remembered the little Lois Maynard who had been practically amphibious in those days.

With all that, and my approaching interview with the District Attorney the next day, it was early summer dawn when I finally went to sleep, and in no time at all Jennie was pounding on my door.

"You better come down," she called. "The Chief's here for you."

It had come, then. I was about to be arrested, and to be arrested, of all things, on an empty stomach!

I dressed as carefully as I could, although my morning mood before coffee is distinctly sinister. But the plain fact is that what with apprehension and lack of sleep my hands scarcely obeyed me. I dropped my hairbrush, put on too much make-up and had to wipe it off and start again. And of course I pulled a button off the white sports dress I was wearing —as a symbol of innocence—and had to stop to sew it on again.

Chief Fowler was scowling over a cup of coffee when I entered the dining room. There was no sign of Judith, but Bill was there, looking horrible and explaining that he had chased a strange man in the grounds and fallen, a fact which Fowler obviously did not believe. And of course Phil decided to cheer me by being facetious.

"Very nice," he said, inspecting me. "Not that it will save you from the chair, but a good try."

I could not eat. Not with Jennie ogling me with suspicion, and Helga peeping from the pantry door. Not with the story O'Brien had given me to tell, and my own feeling of guilt about it. I did get down a cup of black coffee, however. It steadied me somewhat, as did the announcement that both Phil and Bill intended to go with me to the District Attorney's office. Not with me, exactly. I went in the Chief's car. But there was a certain amount of comfort in knowing they were behind me.

The cottage was closed as we passed it. But O'Brien's car was standing outside, and I felt a wave of fury which actually shook me.

He could sleep, I thought, while I lied myself black in the face with a tale no one was going to believe. And for what? So he could solve the murder years ago of a man I had never heard of and cared nothing about. Why hadn't I come out with the truth? That the ticket had been in the bag, that he had taken it, and that at his behest I had looked up the Benjamin woman.

I still do not know why I had not done it. There had been something in his face when he talked about Flaherty that moved me deeply. He had been like a son speaking of a beloved father. But at least he could have been around, I thought furiously. He could at least say he had suggested I locate Mrs. Benjamin, and that I had given him her bankbooks. Although why they thought I had taken them was beyond me. I certainly could not cash in on them.

Yet my first impression of the District Attorney was rather favorable. A smallish man, thin and with gray hair and a pair of keen blue eyes, when I was ushered in to him he smiled and got up from behind a desk. His name he said as he shook hands was Tarbell.

"I'm afraid this is rather early for you," he said politely. "Sit down, please. That chair isn't bad. Would you like a cigarette?"

He came around the desk to light it, and I found myself relaxing. Somewhere outside were my menfolks, Phil and Bill. And Fowler, who had merely admitted me to the presence, had disappeared. I stiffened, however, when I saw a golf club lying on the desk.

But the District Attorney did not mention it. He went back to his seat and surveyed me benignly.

"You know," he said, "you look like a nice girl. A very pretty one too, if I may say so. I'm wondering just how you got involved in this mess."

"I didn't kill that woman," I said, "if that's what you mean."

"Possibly not, but someone did. And certainly you have done some odd things since, Miss Maynard. Let me tell you what I know. In the first place, you have maintained you did not know her. I accept part of that, for certainly you did not know exactly where she lived. Also your behavior shows it. You described her to certain people in that town of hers, and you located her house.

"You know what happened after that. You broke in and you searched her desk. Your prints are all over it. You took her bankbooks, for some unknown reason, but so far as I know nothing else. Why? She was dead. The bankbooks were of no use to you. I would say she had been blackmailing you, but for one reason."

"I suppose because you can't get blood out of a turnip," I said, attempting to be facetious but inwardly shaking.

He did not smile.

"No," he said. "Because Mrs. Benjamin did not need money. Blackmail is a risky business, so why would she try it? She knew about the money, and it was hers by the will he left. That in itself is curious. Why wouldn't she touch it?"

I didn't know and said so. He went on:

"You say you have no money. What about your sister? Ridgely Chandler is a very wealthy man."

"She has her alimony. That's all. He was smart about that. He made a trust fund for her. The interest is all she gets. On her death it goes to charity. As for my brother and myself, Phil worked his way through college, and I imagine he got Ridgely Chandler to send me."

"I see," he said thoughtfully. "Mr. Chandler has been trying to hush this thing up, Miss Maynard. He has even been in touch with the Governor. But the Governor is a pretty stout fellow. He won't interfere. In fact he can't. Only I don't like that sort of thing."

"Then you don't know the Chandlers!"

He let that pass.

"This is the picture as I see it, Miss Maynard," he went on. "Here's a woman who is well provided for. Her husband had left her some insurance, she had sold the business, and she owned her home. She had adequate means to live as she did, which was very simply. Besides she was a quiet retiring sort of woman, and a churchgoer; not, I think, the blackmailing type.

"Yet she had some reason for being in your grounds the night she was killed. Do you know what that was?"

"I think she was meeting someone there," I told him. "There had been a strange man in the grounds two or three times at night. Once he frightened one of the maids. Another time he threw a rock through my sister's window, and only two nights ago he caught me in the drive, picked me up and threw me into our swimming pool."

He looked completely incredulous.

"Into the pool? Why? Do you mean he tried to drown you?"

"I don't know what he meant. He didn't stop to explain."

"Still, it seems an extraordinary thing to do. Did you recognize him?"

"No. It was dark, of course. I didn't know his voice."

"Oh, he spoke, did he?"

"He told me I was going to talk, or he'd kill me."

The District Attorney was staring at me with what amounted to fascination.

"I don't suppose," he said slowly, "that anyone could invent a story like that. It's too preposterous."

"All right," I said. "If you don't believe it call in my nephew, Bill Harrison, and look at his face."

"I presume it is a nice honest face, but why should I look at it? Especially when I can look at yours."

He was smiling, but I wasn't having any humor at that moment, or any compliments either.

"Because he chased the same man last night," I told him. "He caught him too. He's young and he's fast. Only the other man was stronger. I gather he won the round. At least he knocked Bill out and escaped. If you'll call him in . . ."

He looked a trifle uncertain, which I imagine was unusual. Also he said nothing when I lit a cigarette which, so far as I knew, might be my last one.

"I'll see your Bill later," he said. "Just now I want to talk to you. There are certain other curious angles about this case. For one thing, the Benjamin woman sent the taxi away. Why? Did she expect someone to motor her back to the railroad station? Or—did she mean to stay all night?"

"How could she expect that? None of us even knew her."

"You knew where she lived. The town, anyhow. You went there like a homing pigeon. Don't you think that needs some explanation?"

It was a bad moment. Inwardly I was cursing O'Brien and all his works, but I had to go through with it.

"It wasn't hard to do," I said. "You see, I had this." And reaching into my bag brought out the crumpled water-soaked return ticket. He took it and examined it.

"This was in her purse?" he inquired.

"It must have been. I emptied it, you know. I told them so at the inquest."

"You denied it at first."

"I hated to admit I'd been snooping."

"An inquest is a serious matter," he said, eying me. "So is murder. Now why did you keep this ticket?

What possible reason could you have?"

"I didn't keep it," I said with complete truth. "It just turned up later. As a matter of fact the tenant in our cottage found it and gave it to me. If you don't believe me ask him. His name's O'Brien."

He looked at me.

"So O'Brien found it," he said. "The queer thing about this case is the way Terry O'Brien turns up in it. He's a smart cop, but this isn't a New York case, Miss Maynard. Why is a detective lieutenant of the City Homicide Department involved in it?"

"He's retired, isn't he?"

"No," he said grimly. "Apparently he's on a protracted leave of absence, or something of the sort. I wish to God he'd let us attend to our own business in this county, and keep his nose out of it. What kind of game is he playing anyhow? He's inherited a lot of money, but he doesn't retire. Instead he rents a small cottage from you, pretends to be something he isn't, and for God's sake raises chickens!"

"Maybe he likes them."

He had lost his urbanity by that time. He drew a long exasperated breath.

"All right," he said. "Let's forget O'Brien. I'll keep his ticket, of course. Whether you took it out of the bag or got it some other way, it should have been given to the local police at once. As it is we've wasted a lot of time. What interests me just now is why you broke into the Benjamin house."

"It was the cat," I said, with more assurance. "I couldn't leave it there to die."

"There were neighbors. There was this Mrs. Hunnewell, for instance, the woman who identified her. Why not have called her? Why break a window to get in?"

"I didn't want to be seen there. After all, she had been killed in our pool. But I wanted to know why it had been *our* pool. There must be plenty of others nearer where she lived."

"I suppose your brother and sister did not know of this excursion of yours to the Benjamin house?"

I shook my head. The mention of Judith, however, reminded me of something.

"My sister is convinced someone has been trying to kill her," I told him. "She's psychotic, of course, if that's the word for it. Or is it psychosomatic? But she really means it."

"And she thinks it was this woman?"

"No, of course not. She didn't even know her. I'm sure of that. She thinks whoever did it mistook the Benjamin woman for her. Anyhow she's dead, and Judith's still afraid. More than ever, as a matter of fact."

"Why? Doesn't she say?"

"No. She won't talk about it, but she thinks it's the man who has been haunting our grounds."

"Why for God's sake haven't you notified the police?"

"We did. O'Brien knows all about it."

He looked practically apoplectic, but he managed to control himself.

"What does this fellow look like?" he asked.

"I don't know. Nobody does, unless it's my sister. He's strong. I think he's about medium height. And he has a car, or gets one somehow. I heard him drive off while I was in the pool."

"Your sister refuses to identify him?"

"She says he means to kill her. That's all."

"Have you any idea why? Or why she won't talk?"

I daresay I was pretty well wrought up by that time. I realized too that much I had said sounded like complete nonsense without some sort of background. So almost before I knew it I was telling him of Judith's sudden intention to get a divorce, after twenty years of marriage; of our trip to Reno and her fright at the railroad station; of the locks and nailed windows at The Birches; and of Doctor Townsend's conviction that her terror had a real basis. He listened carefully, making no notes, and part of the time with his eyes closed, until I finished.

"Do you think she's afraid of her husband?"

"No," I said positively. "I don't think she ever was in love with him, as I look back, but they got on well enough. Anyhow he's not that sort of person."

"How can we say what sort of person any individual is? Even children commit murder, and pious women with innocence written all over them. But it wasn't Chandler in the grounds? You are sure of that?"

"Absolutely. Ridge is short. This man is bigger and with a deeper voice. I couldn't be mistaken."

"Do you think she would talk to me?"

"I think she'd faint if she so much as saw you."

He smiled at that. Not much of a smile, but a good try. It was a moment or two before he spoke.

"Had you any reason to associate this Benjamin woman with your sister?" he asked finally. "Or with her divorce? After all, that's a curious story of yours. A woman suddenly decided to leave her husband. She goes to Reno and seems contented there. Then at the railroad station something happens. She faints, and she has been terrified ever since. She won't use taxis, for one thing. That mean anything to you?"

It did not. I said so.

"Any taxi drivers around when this happened? At Reno?"

"One or two, maybe more. I didn't notice."

"Yet a taxi figures in this," he said. "Let's take a purely hypothetical situation. Suppose one night last winter your sister is in a cab with a man and something happens. She's a good-looking woman, I understand. So he makes a pass at her and she—let's say she opens the door and pushes him out. He's killed, and the driver gets out and accuses her of murder. So she's at his mercy. There's blackmail right off, and I've been smelling blackmail in this case right along."

"I don't believe it."

He smiled again.

"I'm only guessing," he said. "She has to be afraid of something or somebody, and according to you it happened suddenly. She wasn't prepared for it, so all she could do was cut and run. She chose Reno, and she was followed there."

"What about this Benjamin woman?" I asked. "Where does she come in?"

"I'm supposed to be asking you that. What about her? Why did O'Brien put you on her tail? Because I think he did."

I didn't deny it. How could I?

"I haven't the remotest idea," I said honestly, and rather to my surprise he seemed to agree with me. He said he thought that was about all, and shook hands with me.

"But," he added, "the next time you find a piece of paper the po-lice are breaking their necks to locate, I suggest you give it to them. You'd be surprised how well they know their business."

Phil and Bill were in the ante-room, waiting anxiously, and when he saw Bill's face the District Attorney grinned.

"Quite a shiner you've got there, son. Want to come in and tell me about it?"

He kept Bill only five minutes or so. And he was not smiling when he let him go. He looked very sober.

"I'd better have a man or two around your place for a while," he said. "Looks as though this fellow has a gun. No fist ever made a bruise like that." He looked at Phil. "And now, Mr. Maynard, I think it's time you and I had a talk."

I shall never forget Phil's face as he went into that room and the District Attorney closed the door behind him.

20

It was an hour before he ap-peared again. He looked as though he had been run through a wringer, and this time the District Attorney did not see him out. But he said nothing, merely nodding when Bill insisted that we have lunch in town to celebrate what he called my escape from the chair. Bill's face called for lively interest in the restaurant, but as usual he ate stolidly from soup to nuts, only to stop now and then with what the newspapers would say that night:

" 'Socialites quizzed in murder case,' " he offered. Or: " 'Woman novelist involved in crime she writes about.' "

As a result we were still there when the Hunnewell woman came in.

She was accompanied by what I learned later was a local detective, a youngish good-looking man who appeared slightly bored, and I knew what was coming the moment I saw her. I would have to pass her table going out, and I hadn't a hope she would not recognize me.

She did, at the top of her voice. "That's her!" she yelled. "That's the girl who broke into the house."

I stopped beside her. There was nothing else to do.

"I've just been telling the District Attorney about it," I said with a forced smile. The whole restaurant was listening, and one or two people stood up to see me better. "How's the cat? And I hope your husband fixed the window."

Apparently it took most of the wind out of her sails. But not all. She stared at me.

"The cat's all right. I wouldn't say the same for you."

"No?"

"Not with Selina Benjamin gone to her grave, and dead in your pool."

Here the detective handed her a menu and said something in a low voice. She flushed angrily.

"All right," she said. "I'll shut up, but if that girl thinks she's putting something over on me she can think again."

It was three o'clock when we reached our drive, and as Phil turned in I saw that the O'Brien cottage was still closed. A window was open, however, and his car was there. As he had been up most of the night I supposed he was sleeping. But his girls were still in the chicken house, announcing feverishly that they wanted to be let out and fed.

That was when I saw Henrietta.

The little hen was strutting about alone in the front yard, and I knew O'Brien never allowed her there. It was a small thing, of course, but Henrietta where she did not belong, plus the indignation in the hen house, made me uneasy.

As a result I made Phil stop the car and got out, with Bill at my heels. The front door of the cottage was locked but a window was open, and when no one answered my knocks and calls I made Bill crawl through the window. It was some time before he opened the door. When he did he stood blocking it with his solid young body.

"Get out of the way, Lois," he said. "Phil, come here, will you?"

I didn't get out of the way, of course. I ducked under Bill's arm and got inside, to see O'Brien in his big chair, unconscious and with blood all over the place. He was in pajamas and a dressing gown, but evidently he had been shot somewhere outside, for there was a trail of blood across the floor from a wound in his right leg. Equally evident was the fact that he had made an attempt to telephone, for the instrument had fallen beside him on the floor.

Not that I noticed any of this at the time. I was screaming for a doctor, Bill says, and that I jerked off his—Bill's—necktie to use as a ligature.

"My best tie too," he said. "You simply yanked it. It didn't help either. The leg had stopped bleeding hours before, but there you were, blubbering at the top of your lungs and wrecking a three-dollar tie, all at the same time."

The real wound of course was in his chest, but the fact is I do not remember much what followed. I recall the ambulance coming, the care with which they carried O'Brien's big body out to it, and Phil going with it when it left. But I do not remember stripping the chair of its bloody chintz cover and carrying it carefully to the house.

Bill said I was making no sense whatever, that I wailed over it all the way, because I had made it and it had been damned hard to make, and now it was stained and would not wash! And Jennie maintains I handed it to her in the hall and told her to take it out to the incinerator and burn it, which the idiot proceeded to do.

I must have been making quite a fuss, for Judith heard me and came down the stairs.

"What on earth!" she said. "Jennie said Fowler had arrested you."

I glared at her.

"Your friend out in the grounds has killed O'Brien," I said frantically. "Now maybe you'll tell us about him. If you don't I warn you I'll choke it out of you. I mean it."

She did not faint. I was still standing with that bloody cover in my hands, and I knew the sight of blood upset her. All she did, however, was to sit down on the stairs and look blank. She didn't even speak. If ever I saw a human being appear sick and frightened it was Judith that day.

"What do you mean, my friend?" she gasped. "I don't understand, Lois."

"The taxi driver," I said. "That's what he is, isn't it? That's why you won't take taxis. The District Attorney knows all about you, the blackmail and everything."

"Blackmail?" she said strangely. "Who on earth is being blackmailed?"

Bill had been standing by, puzzled. He came over and put an arm around me.

"I don't know what all this is about," he said. "But O'Brien isn't dead, Lois. Not yet anyhow. What's this about Judith's friend in the grounds? The fellow I had the fight with?"

"Ask her," I said. "Maybe she'll talk to you. She knows a lot she's not telling."

Then my knees gave way suddenly and Bill caught me and eased me into a chair. I suppose it was the sudden understanding of what he had said, that O'Brien was not dead. In any event I shut my eyes. When I opened them Judith had disappeared, and Bill was standing by me with a glass of whisky. Later he helped to get me up to bed, where Helga undressed me, her old face grim.

"Now you go to sleep, child," she said, tucking the covers around me. "That O'Brien will be all right. Phil promised to telephone from the hospital. But he's strong. Don't you worry about him."

"You know him, don't you, Helga?"

"We've had one or two talks," she said evasively. "When he brought me some eggs. That's all."

"What about?"

"Just about the old days. Nothing important. Now you go to sleep and stop worrying. It takes a lot to kill an Irish cop."

So Helga knew who and what he was. I wondered just why he had talked to her, or what he had hoped to learn. But in one way she had reassured me. O'Brien was strong. I remembered the night when he dived into the pool for my bag, and his big muscular body in his trunks. And—because I was trying to forget that scene in the cottage—I thought over what Helga had said. The old days! What about the old days, when father had killed himself and a police officer named Flaherty had been murdered because he had apparently located a Selina Benjamin, wife of a respected tobacconist! But she might not have been Selina Benjamin twenty years ago. She might have been Kate Henry. Katherine Selina Henry, whose testimony before a grand jury had indicted a boy for murder, and who had disappeared before his trial.

It was nine o'clock that night before we had any word from the hospital. Helga, who would not let Jennie into my room, had brought me a cup of soup and some crackers at seven, but I could not touch them. When the phone rang I was out of bed in a second. Bill, however, was answering it in the lower hall. He listened for some time. Then:

"Good. I'll tell Lois. But listen, Phil, what about Aunt Judith? She's locked in and won't speak to anybody. I'm kind of worried. Think Christy ought to see her?" And after a pause: "No, I suppose not. Well, I'll try it."

He came up to my room. I had put on a dressing gown over my pajamas by that time, and as my door was open he came in. He still showed the marks of battle. In fact the lurid purple was even deeper, but his mouth looked better.

"They think O'Brien will be all right," he said cheerfully. "Take time, of course. They got one bullet. According to Phil, it was in the apex of a lung, and believe it or not it missed the subclavian artery, whatever that might be. The other wound isn't serious. It went through his leg. But he lost a lot of blood, so they're giving him transfusions. Phil says the hospital is lousy with New York cops. Seems the guy is popular."

I sat down, because my knees had given way with relief.

"Does he know who did it?" I asked.

"Didn't see anybody. Of course he isn't talking much. Too weak.

He was by the pool when he got it. That's all he knows."

I must have looked better, for he lit a cigarette and offered me one.

"What makes with him anyhow?" he said. "Phil says those city cops look fighting mad; that they all insisted on being tapped for blood, and it was flowing by the quart, so far as he could tell."

"He's one of them," I said weakly. "Homicide."

He whistled.

"Homicide? For God's sake what's he been doing here?"

"I don't know. It's something about an old murder. An officer named Flaherty was killed, and lately something came up that revived it. I don't know what it is, Bill."

"What's it got to do with The Birches?"

"A woman was killed here. Don't forget."

"He was here before that happened," he said, looking mystified. Then he apparently abandoned the puzzle. "I suppose you know there are cops all over the grounds."

All over the cottage too, I realized. It meant they already had seen the bankbooks and photograph, as well as the clippings. What would they make of the one about Judith? Would they connect her with Selina Benjamin's death? And would they be right? If the golf club on the District Attorney's desk was one of Phil's, and they could prove it had been the murder weapon . . .

Bill's next words penetrated the haze that was my mind at that moment.

"Those guys make it damned inconvenient when a fellow wants to try a job of breaking and entering," he said. "What's the penalty for that, anyhow?"

"Breaking and entering?"

"Look," he said, his bantering tone gone. "I'd better tell you. I'm anxious about Judith. There hasn't been a sound out of her since she learned about the shooting. I've called to her off and on ever since. I've even thrown pebbles at her windows. She won't speak and I can't hear a sound in the place."

I rallied as best I could.

"She's upset, that's all, Bill. And you can't break into her room. That door's too solid. Anyhow it's silly. She has spells like this sometimes. Phil says she did the same thing after father died. I wouldn't worry."

"You didn't see her face when she heard about O'Brien," he said grimly. "She looked like death. Either's she scared into a fit or she knows a lot she's not telling. I think she's scared."

"She's been scared for weeks."

"This was different," he insisted. "How about a window? I'm not fooling, Lois. She may be unconscious or even worse."

"Don't be a young idiot," I said. "She's frightened about something, but she likes to dramatize herself too. You know how she is."

"I know she's as nutty as a fruit cake," he said, with the brutality of youth. "Just the same I think someone needs to look after her.

Where can I get hold of a ladder?"

"I thought you said there were police all over the place."

"They're mostly around the cottage and the pool. Anyhow, what can they do? I'm locked out and trying to get into my room. Apologies and all that. Come on. What are we waiting for?"

"Helga may come in, Bill. If she finds me gone—"

"The hell with Helga. Turn out your lights and lock your door. She'll think you're asleep."

If it were not so horrible I could laugh over that excursion of ours. With Phil away, the lower floor was empty and dark. I did not think Helga was asleep, so we avoided the service wing. We groped our way out the rear-hall door, to find it was raining, a hard summer shower which almost sent me back into the house. But Bill took my arm, and we crept around the back of the old conservatory and toward the stables.

"I used to see a ladder there," he said. "Climbed trees with it when I was a kid. Suppose it's still there?"

I was not sure. I seldom visited the stables. Also I was already soaked and considerably irritated.

"Of all the fool things!" I said. "If you think I'm going to climb a ladder and scare Judith to death you can think again."

"Who asked you to climb? You're the lookout, that's all."

There was a brilliant flash of lightning just then, followed by a clap of thunder. We stuck out like a pair of sore thumbs but, as Bill observed, the glory boys—his name

for the State Police—didn't like to get their pretty uniforms wet.

"They're all cozy in the cottage," he said, "or back in their barracks. What's the matter with you? You're not easy scared."

We reached the stables at last, and once inside Bill produced a flashlight. He caught a glimpse of me then, and serious as he had been he laughed.

"I wish O'Brien could see you now," he said. "You look as though you'd been dumped in the pool."

"He has seen me exactly like that," I said sourly.

He was not listening. He had located a ladder; not the one he remembered but a heavy pruning one, with an extension to reach the upper branches of trees or to clear the gutters on the roof when falling leaves cluttered them in the autumn. But somehow we got hold of it and started back to the house. It seemed miles to me. I lost a bedroom slipper and could not stop to find it, and once Bill fell and the whole end cracked down on him.

The rain was slackening by that time. I could see a flashlight or two in the shrubbery by the pool, but Bill kept doggedly on and I had no choice but to follow him. The expedition seemed more and more absurd as we reached the house.

The two windows at the side of Judith's room were almost dark, except for a faint light from somewhere which outlined them, and since one of them was open, it was there we placed the ladder. It made a small scraping sound, but nothing followed. No Judith appeared, no light went on, and Bill suddenly went shy on me.

"You'd better go first," he whispered. "She'd have a fit if she saw a man in her room after what she says about one trying to kill her. Or maybe she sleeps raw. Not afraid, are you?"

I looked up. The ceilings at The Birches are high, and the windows looked fifty feet above me. Nevertheless, the fact that she had not heard the ladder worried me. I tucked up my dressing gown and having lost my bedroom slipper, put a bare foot on the lowest round.

"Hold it steady," I said, "and don't you dare leave. If she's all right I'll come down in a hurry."

No police had shown any interest in us so far, and the climb was easier than I expected. At the top I stopped and looked into the room. The faint light was coming from the bathroom, the door of which was partly open. There was enough for me to see that Judith was not in her bed, but it was mussed as though she had been, and her dressing gown was thrown over a chair.

I threw a leg over the sill, and immediately a tin tray, balanced lightly on the upturned legs of a chair, fell with a deadly racket. I realized I had walked into a booby trap of no mean proportions, and I waited for Judith to scream. But nothing happened. There was no sound, not even any movement, and I think that was when I became alarmed. The racket had been enough to wake the dead, but no Judith had appeared at the bathroom door. At first I thought she might be out somewhere, and not until I had seen the bolt shot on her door and the chain on did I realize she must be where I found her.

I found her in the bathtub. She had cut both her wrists, and I was certain she was dead. Not that there was much blood in the tub, but because she felt cold when I bent over and touched her. She was wearing a thin nightdress, and her lips without make-up looked blue and thin.

I was still staring at her, unable to move, when I heard a man's voice behind me. I jumped and turned, to find Fowler in the middle of her room, his eyes hard and a gun in his hand.

"What's all this about?" he demanded. "Why the hell are you breaking into your own house?"

I moved then and he saw Judith. He simply stared, as if he could not believe it.

"It's—your sister, isn't it? Is she dead?"

"I'm afraid so," I stammered. "She feels cold."

He pushed me aside and bent over the tub. Then he strode out of the bathroom and to the window.

"Get Jenkins up here," he called, "and bring that boy up too. Then someone get a doctor. Break in the house if you have to, but hurry. Find a telephone."

A uniformed state policeman came up the ladder. He almost fell over Judith's booby trap and looked unhappy as Fowler gave him a nasty look.

"Help me get this woman out of the tub here and put her to bed," he said sharply. "Then wake the servants and tell them to find some hot-water bottles and some bandages. All right. Take her feet."

I was shaking all over, but I managed to speak.

"Is she dead?" I asked.

"I don't know. Pretty close to it anyhow. Who is your family doctor? Or maybe she'd better go to the hospital."

"She'd rather stay here. I'm sure of that. Of course it's up to you, but Doctor Christy . . ."

He nodded and together they carried Judith to her bed and covered her.

"Get Christy," he said to the trooper. "Tell him it's an emergency. Then tell the fellows down the drive to pass him." He looked at me, wet and bedraggled as I was, and he almost smiled.

"If some of these would-be suicides would fill the tub first with warm water they might get away with it. This way the blood coagulates. That's not what's wrong with her. She's taken something."

"What? What do you think she took?"

"Sleeping pills, at a guess," he said dryly. "Why did you break in? You made a pretty poor job of it, you know. That racket . . ."

They brought Bill up the ladder just then. He took one look at Judith and collapsed.

"O God!" he said. "So I was right, after all."

Fowler sent us both out of the room. The house downstairs was already crowded with the local police and a couple of State Troopers who had been in the grounds and who, until they saw me, were smoking surreptitious cigarettes. The screaming of tires announced Doctor Christy and his nurse, who disappeared up the stairs, and after a time Fowler came down. He found us in the hall. I had pinned back my hair, but Bill still looked completely demoralized. It was Bill that Fowler spoke to.

"You say this was your idea?" he said. "Why? How did you know she was going to try to kill herself?"

"It was just a hunch. She wouldn't open her door, or speak to me. I got scared."

"Why did she have a booby trap under her window? What was *she* afraid of?"

"Wouldn't you be afraid?" I said, putting in my two cents' worth. "She says—she has said all along that someone wanted to kill her. You know we've had a man around the place at night trying to get in touch with her. I told the District Attorney about him. She believed he mistook the Benjamin woman for her."

He gave me a not-unfriendly grin.

"So she tries to kill herself!" he said. "That's jumping out of the frying pan into the fire with a vengeance. I've been in this business a long time, Miss Maynard. I've seen a lot of death and some suicides. But I never heard of killing yourself to avoid being killed."

21

Doctor Christy was still in Judith's room when Phil arrived, looking half dead. He found me in the kitchen helping Helga make huge amounts of coffee. I was still in my pajamas and the old dressing gown, with one foot bare.

"You're a sight," he said. "What in the name of heaven is going on? What are all these police doing here?"

"Swilling coffee," I told him. "And if you can stand another shock—and I mean shock—Judith tried to kill herself tonight."

He looked at me incredulously.

"Kill herself!" he said. "They only told me she was hurt. I don't believe it, Lois. Not Judith."

"I've told you all along there was something wrong with her," I said tiredly. "She tried it all right, Phil, believe it or not. I found her."

I told him my story as best I could, with police wandering in and out for coffee, with Helga listening and Jennie having hysterics in the pantry. He still looked stunned.

"But why?" he said. "She's been taking precious good care that nobody got at her. Then all at once this! I don't get it."

Well, of course nobody did. Not then anyhow. I got him some whisky, after which he looked better. He reported that O'Brien was badly hurt but not fatally, and as by that time the police had gradually drifted away we went into the living room and Phil lit a fire.

He stood in front of it, looking up at mother's portrait and evidently making up his mind about something. Then he lit a cigarette and turned to face me.

"It's a bad time to come out with this, Lois," he said tiredly. "You've had enough today. More than enough. But you'll have to know sooner or later."

"It's the golf club, isn't it?"

"Yes. It's mine. It hadn't even been cleaned. Only wiped off on the grass and stuck back in the bag. They didn't need a microscope to know it killed the Benjamin woman. Even the scrap of leather fits the grip."

"It didn't kill her, Phil. Remember, she was drowned."

"Why quibble?" he said. "Someone from this house took it and used it. It isn't hard to guess who, unless you think I did it myself."

It was fortunate Doctor Christy

appeared just then. He wore the smug expression of a man who has just delivered a nine-pound baby, which was as well under the circumstances.

"Glad to say we've got the stuff licked," he said. "The cuts didn't amount to much. It was the barbiturate that gave the real trouble. She'd had quite a dose of it."

"Enough to kill her?" Phil asked.

"Well, it's hard to say. Enough to give her a good long sleep, anyhow." The Chief had come in with him. Now he poured a couple of drinks from the Scotch on a table, and eyed Phil as he gave the doctor one.

"Don't you believe it was a genuine attempt at suicide?" he asked.

I knew what he meant. Someone from the house had taken Phil's golf club and used it on the Benjamin woman, which made our story about the man in the grounds look pretty sick. Phil realized it too. If Judith had been the one she might have been remorseful enough, or frightened enough, to try suicide or at least to fake it. Phil, however, only looked resentful.

"It wasn't guilt that made her try what she did tonight," he said stubbornly. "It might be fear. Ever since she came here she has been afraid someone was trying to kill her. She's been scared for months. That doesn't spell murder, in my language."

"You've admitted the golf club is yours."

"What else could I do? My initials are stamped on it."

"That rather leaves it up to someone here in the house, doesn't it? And in my language suicide is often a confession of guilt."

But Phil only looked weary and impatient.

"A long time ago," he said, "I gave up trying to understand my sister Judith. She never made sense to me, even as a child. My mother spoiled her, of course. She married a good husband, and he spoiled her too. She's always had everything she wanted, even a divorce. I'm sorry," he added. "It's no way to talk about a sister, but I've had about all I can take. The point is that she had no reason to kill that woman. None whatever."

"What about tonight?"

"If death was something she wanted . . ."

"We still have the club, Mr. Maynard. If we leave out the servants, only the three of you are likely to have known where it was kept. You must recognize that."

"Not necessarily," Phil said irritably. "Anyone could have taken it. The house is open except at night. As for me, I am as much in the dark as you are. I haven't played golf for weeks. Any time in the last two months that club could have been taken and never missed."

Fowler threw up his hands.

"If that's your story . . ." he said, and turning on his heel left us abruptly.

By six o'clock when Helga called us to breakfast the house looked as though a cyclone had struck it, but the police had gone. Even Doctor Christy, after a final look at Judith, had departed, although his nurse remained for a few hours.

"Let her sleep it out," he said. "She's all right now. Those cuts will heal in a hurry. Perhaps you'd better not talk to her about it. Let her explain if she wants to."

I had an idea Judith would do no explaining, but I let that go. Helga was a different matter, however. She stood in the kitchen and surveyed the place: cups all over it, the heel of a loaf of bread, the disconsolate bone of what had been a baked ham, and her clean linoleum covered with muddy footprints. Jennie had retired to her room with a headache, so she was alone when I went in.

"Are you trying to tell me Judith meant to kill herself tonight?" she said aggressively. "Because I won't believe it. Not Judith. Never."

"I'm afraid she did, Helga. It wasn't an act. Her door was locked. So was the one from the bathroom into the hall."

Helga sat down, as though her old legs would no longer hold her.

"It doesn't sound like her," she said slowly. "She was no angel. Heaven knows there were a good many times in the early days when I wanted to smack her good. But what would drive her to a thing like that?"

"I have an idea she thought O'Brien was dead, or dying. It may have been the last straw. I'm sure she felt guilty."

"The real guilt was years ago," Helga said somberly. "There is such a thing as the sins of the

fathers catching up with the children."

I must have looked aghast. Certainly she knew she had gone too far, for when I asked her what she meant she clamped her lips shut.

"You must mean something," I persisted. "What did my father do?"

"I didn't say it was your father."

"All right. If you meant mother, say so," I said impatiently.

But Helga was on the defensive now.

"I don't hold anything against her," she said. "But she was a proud woman, Lois, and pride was her downfall."

She would not explain. She went doggedly about cleaning her kitchen, and at last I left her there. I was sure she knew or suspected a great many things, but I knew too she meant to keep them to herself.

It was afternoon when Anne arrived. To my surprise Ridge was with her, as dapper as ever, and Anne looked like a mourner at a funeral.

"Bill telephoned," she said. "I can't believe it, Lois. She'd never do a thing like that. What got into her?"

I had no time to answer. Ridge had brought a huge box of flowers, and after leaving them in the hall he followed us into the living room. He shook hands with me with his usual formality.

"How is she?" he inquired. "It was an idiotic thing to do. Suppose she hadn't been found in time!"

"What do you mean?" I said

sharply. "She didn't intend to be found at all."

He shrugged.

"I hope you don't mind if I question that, Lois. She's threatened it before. You might say it's her way of keeping in the limelight. But she may be disappointed this time. There will be nothing in the gossip columns. I've seen to it."

"So that's the idea!" I said. "She was putting on an act, was she? Well, she didn't stage this, Ridge. It was real, and it was damned near fatal."

Anne was looking bewildered, as well she might, but Ridge was—as usual—the complete gentleman.

"It's possible, of course," he said politely. "I've suspected for a long time she was manic-depressive. Why don't you sit down, Lois? I've had a long drive. Why keep me standing?"

I was, however, too angry to sit.

"I see," I said. "On the upcurve for twenty years and on the down one for the last few months! That's crazy, Ridge."

Anne had said nothing so far. She had dropped into a chair, and lit a cigarette. Now she spoke.

"I don't know what you are talking about," she said querulously. "Why would she try to kill herself? I thought she wanted to go abroad."

"Don't ask me. Ask Ridge. He can explain it!"

"And where's Bill? I told him I was coming out."

"Bill's sleeping," I said shortly. "He was up all night, like the rest of us."

"I'm going to take him home, Lois. This is no place for him: a murder, a shooting, and now this thing about Judith! It's just too much."

"Personally," I said, "I think he's having the time of his life. Anyhow I don't believe the police will let him go—not yet."

"The police! Don't tell me they suspect him!"

I had no time to answer. The nurse appeared in the doorway. She wore a coat over her uniform, and she said Judith was awake and had told her she could go.

Anne bounced out of her chair.

"That's simply idiotic," she said. "I'll go up and talk to her."

"I don't think I would," said the nurse. "She's all right, but she's still very nervous. I couldn't stay anyhow. Doctor Christy needs me. He took me off another case last night."

I don't think Anne even heard her. She bolted out and up the stairs, leaving the young woman staring after her.

"I hope she doesn't tell Mrs. Chandler about the police," she said. "She doesn't know they were here. It might upset her."

Ridge eyed her thoughtfully.

"Has she said why she did it?" he inquired. "She must have given some reason."

The nurse looked uncertain, as though she had been told not to talk.

"She says she doesn't remember much," she said. "She admits she took too many pills, but only because she needed sleep." She glanced at me. "She'll be all right, you know, Miss Maynard. She's not sick. Only the wrists may bother her for a while. Not for long. The cuts aren't deep."

She left then, saying she had brought her own car, and I was alone with Ridge. He sat down and stretched his legs out.

"Sorry if I annoyed you, Lois," he said. "I thought it was merely another bit of self-dramatization on Judith's part. God knows I've had plenty of them. That's why I brought the flowers, to add my bit to the stage setting."

I nodded. There wasn't much I could say, but I could and did mix him a whisky and soda. He watched me while I did it, as though he was making up his mind to something. It came when I handed him the glass.

"I've been thinking, Lois," he said. "We've known each other a long time. You were only a baby when I used to see you down at the pool. You may not like me, but I think you respect my judgment."

"I suppose I do, Ridge. I never thought about it."

"All right. Let's say you trust me anyhow. I'll admit I've been in touch with the police ever since that woman was killed at the pool. Has it occurred to you that Judith might have been the one who carried Phil's golf club there?"

"Of course not. Why would she?"

"Suppose she was meeting some-one—the Benjamin woman per-haps—and was afraid. After all, it was midnight. She might have carried it for her own defense."

"And killed her with it?"

"Not necessarily. The blow was not fatal. The woman may have been dazed by it, and later fell into the pool."

"The police don't think that."

"They're not saying what they think," he said irascibly. "I'm ask-ing you. Did she know the woman? Had she made an appointment to meet her, by letter or telephone?"

"Not that I know of, Ridge. Anyhow I can't see Judith, ter-rified as she was, going down to the pool in the middle of the night. You know we've had a man loitering about the place, don't you?"

"So I understand. Have you no idea who it is?"

"No. I think the police believe we invented him."

He made no comment on that. Instead he wandered over to the fireplace, and stood looking at the Laszlo portrait of mother. It re-minded me of something Anne had once said, and of my talk with Helga that morning.

"I've been wanting to ask you a rather personal question, Ridge," I said. "Anne has always believed you financed the Arizona trip after father's death and the crash. If you did, and Judith resented it . . ."

"Judith never resented anything to do with money, my dear."

"I am only trying to account for why she left you," I said uncom-fortably. "It was kind of you, of course. Mother had no money sense either."

"On the contrary," he said, his voice low and slightly acid, "she had an excellent money sense. I was younger than I am now, and very much in love. So when she came to me after your father's death and said she was in trouble I helped her." He hesitated, then he smiled. "I helped her to the tune of fifty thousand dollars in cash."

They left soon after, Anne in a bad humor because Judith would not answer any of her questions, Ridge almost certainly regretting what he had told me. We had had only a moment or so before Anne came in, and I was too stunned to think clearly.

"I can't believe it, Ridge," I managed at last. "What sort of trouble? Surely mother told you."

He cocked his head on one side, after a habit he had which always annoyed me.

"If I told you I didn't know you wouldn't believe me, would you?"

"I don't think you'd give her all that money without a pretty good reason."

"There might have been a quid pro quo, you know, my dear."

"You mean—Judith?"

"That's rather a crude way of putting it, isn't it?"

"Did she know about it?"

"Not then. She may have learned it later. You might give me credit for sticking to my bargain too. It hasn't always been easy."

Then Anne came in and soon they were gone. I was still somewhat dazed when I went upstairs. Judith's door was closed and Helga was sitting in the hall, in case she needed anything.

She looked at me sharply.

"You'd better get some sleep, child," she said. "What was Ridge Chandler doing here? It's no place for him."

"He thought Judith was putting on an act."

She sniffed indignantly and I left her there. But I did not go to bed. I wanted to get out of the house and think. Too much had happened in the last few hours. Not only Judith's attempt at suicide and the attack on O'Brien. Both Phil and I were under suspicion of murder, and this time I had no one to help me. Up to then I had never felt entirely alone. I had carried my problems to the cottage, and had come away with renewed courage. Even the last time I had seen O'Brien before he was shot, and when he kissed me . . .

From the porch I could hear water running upstairs, and knew the men were awake. But I did not want to talk to them, or to anybody.

Instead I went down to the cottage. The police had left the key on the hall table after they had finished with it. I took it and went down the drive. Someone had released the chickens and apparently fed them, for they were clucking contentedly. But I found myself trembling as I unlocked the door and went in.

With the exception of the stained rug, which had been taken away, the place was orderly enough. The telephone was in place, and except for a dusting of powder here and there for fingerprints and the shabby look of the big chair without its cover it looked much as usual. Rather to my surprise the contents of the table drawer were still there, clippings and all, although they had certainly been examined. And, realizing how some of them related to the Benjamin woman, I knew O'Brien would eventually be in for a stiff grilling about them.

I did not touch them, but picked up the photograph of Walter Benjamin and held it under the lamp. With my hand over the beard the face looked vaguely familiar, especially the eyes. Otherwise I did not recognize it, but I took it with me when I went back to the house.

The men were eating a belated breakfast in the dining room, or rather Bill was. Phil was having only coffee. He looked half sick, as well he might, but he attempted a smile.

"Don't tell me condemned men eat large meals before they go to the chair," he said. "The very sight of Bill and four eggs makes me shudder."

I took the chair beside him and put the photograph in front of him. He gazed at it without interest.

"Who is the hairy ape?" he inquired. "Friend of yours?"

"Put your hand over the beard and see if you know him, Phil."

He tried it, but he shook his head.

"Reminds me of somebody," he said, "only I don't know who. Don't tell me that's Judith's persistent lover. She doesn't go for whiskers."

It was still on the table when Helga came in with the grocery list. She gave it a long careful look and suddenly dropped the pencil and pad she was holding. I thought she was going to faint.

22

The next two or three days passed with maddening slowness. O'Brien was in the hospital in town and gradually improving. I believe Phil saw him at least once, but only for a few minutes. He had apparently no idea who had shot him, or why. According to Fowler, he had been unable to sleep because of the heat and had gone out to the bench by the pool. He had been lighting a cigarette when it happened.

The shots had come from the shrubbery across the pool, he thought, but he had been unconscious for some time. It was daylight when he managed to reach the cottage. He had tried to telephone for help, but the phone fell, and he passed out again. He had had intervals of consciousness after that. During one he had tried to get up and find a ligature of some sort for his leg, but by that time he was too weak to move.

I listened, trying to conceal my suprise. He had not once mentioned the man who had been haunting The Birches. Whatever his reason was I could not imagine, but that he had one I did not doubt. They had recovered one bullet. The other had gone through his leg and was never found. He had been right, however, about the shrubbery. The police found the shell among the rhododendrons where an automatic pistol had ejected it. But Fowler came to the house one morning and asked for me. Phil had gone, and I had just hung up after calling the hospital. He must have heard me from the porch, for there was an odd glint in his eyes.

"You and O'Brien are pretty good friends, aren't you?" he observed.

"We get along," I said cautiously.

"That all? They tell me he's asking to see you."

I felt absurdly cheered, but Fowler hadn't finished.

"I have an idea," he went on, watching me, "you knew who he was when he came here. Knew why too. I think it's time we had a little talk, Miss Maynard. Don't you?"

"I can't think why," I said. We were both standing and I didn't ask him to sit down. I had no idea what he wanted, but I felt myself stiffening.

"No?" he said. "Well, tell me this. O'Brien goes out sometime in the night because it's hot and he can't sleep. That's all right. It could be. But why should a man only hunting a breeze carry his gun with him? Because that's what he did. It was under the bench."

"Are you trying to say he shot himself?" I said, startled.

"No. It hadn't been fired. I'm saying he was out there gunning for somebody, only the other fellow got him first."

I made a feeble protest.

"I've told you," I said. "We've had a man lurking about the place for weeks. Only you don't believe me."

"So O'Brien sets out to shoot him! That's pretty drastic, Miss Maynard, even for a New York cop."

He left on that. It was no use telling him O'Brien was merely trying to protect us. He had had the story of our nightly visitor over and over. But I was thoughtful as I went up to Judith.

She did not notice. Ever since we had found her she had simply lain in her bed, with her poor wrists bandaged and her doors locked most of the time. She offered no explanation of what she had done, but she was gentler than I had ever seen her, and grateful for what little I could do for her. She had lost most of her beauty too. Her face looked pinched and white, and without make-up she was almost plain.

I was trying to induce her to eat some lunch that day when I heard the telephone. I answered it myself, fearful as I had been all along that the press would get the story. It was not a reporter, however. It was O'Brien!

I almost dropped the receiver when I heard his voice, remote but clear.

"Is that you, Lois?"

"Yes. For heaven's sake what are you doing on the phone?"

"Never mind that, and get this quick, while the goddam nurse is out of the room. Got a pad there?"

"Yes. What is it?"

"Take this down. 'A. Morrison. Insist stop further efforts immediately, and contact me.' Sign it 'T. O.' Get it?"

"What am I to do with it?"

"Put it in all the New York papers, under *Public Notices* or the *Personal* column. How soon can you do it?"

"This afternoon, if you're in a hurry. But what's it all about? I don't understand."

His voice was flagging, however. He said to keep it to myself. Then he muttered something about the nurse coming in, and hung up abruptly. I stood there looking at the pad in my hand. Whatever it meant to someone it meant nothing to me. But it was important. There had been urgency in his voice, in the very effort he had made to call me.

With Helga looking after Judith I caught the next train to town

and left the notices as he had instructed. None of the people receiving them did more than count the words. I suppose they are accustomed to cryptic messages, but I felt self-conscious as I handed them in.

It was four o'clock when I finished, which left me an hour and a half until Phil's train. I had time to see Doctor Townsend if he was still in his office. I was lucky. He was there, and Miss Robey, his nurse, was even agreeable.

"We have been wondering about Mrs. Chandler," she said. "We haven't heard anything from her for some time."

"She hasn't been very well. Is there a chance I can see the doctor?"

She said I could, although I would have to wait awhile, and eyed me with considerable curiosity.

"I see by the papers you have had a shooting at your place," she said. "Not serious, I hope."

"It was probably accidental," I said mendaciously. "The man was a tenant. He rented a small cottage of ours. But there is always somebody shooting in our part of the country. Of course it's not deer season, but the natives don't bother about that."

I smiled. So did she. I don't think she believed me, but at least it ended the conversation. She went back to the desk in her small office, and before long a buzzer rang and she disappeared. By the usual system the previous patient had gone out by a different door, so I found the doctor alone. He got up, waved me to a chair, and sat down again.

"I'm glad to see you," he said. "Quite frankly I don't like the way things look. How is your sister?"

"You know about it, then?"

"Your brother called me soon after it happened. He couldn't say much over the telephone, but I got the general idea. Have you any idea what drove her to what she did? Did anything happen to cause any sudden depression?"

"Not to her, at least not that I know of. She's been very nervous, of course, and when Mr. O'Brien was shot we were all pretty much upset. But I think she related the shooting to herself; as though it was part of the plan to murder her. It sounds silly, but I'm sure that's what she believes."

"I don't see the connection."

"It's not easy," I said. "But this O'Brien is a police officer from Homicide here in town. I think he was there to protect her, or partly so anyhow. Then when she thought he'd been killed—"

"What do you mean by 'partly so'? Was there another reason?"

"I don't know, doctor. It's a long story, if you have time for it."

He glanced at his watch. "I'll make time, Miss Maynard," he decided. "I've failed in your sister's case, and I don't like failure. Does this story relate to her?"

"Only in part," I said. "It began a long time ago, when a Homicide inspector here in New York was shot and killed. His name was Flaherty, and Lieutenant O'Brien was fond of him. He's never given up the case entirely, and lately I think he felt he was making some progress."

I told him what I knew. It took some time, as I had said, but he listened carefully: from Judith's sudden intention to divorce her husband to her fainting on the train; from the Benjamin woman's death to O'Brien's asking me to locate her home and my breaking into it, including the bankbooks and clippings I had found; and from the strange man who threw me into the pool to Judith's attempt at suicide.

Carefully schooled as he was he looked more and more astonished.

"It's certainly puzzling," he said. "And you've had quite a time yourself. The wonder is that it isn't you who cut your wrists! I gather you think your sister really made a serious attempt at suicide."

"She had locked herself off from any help. I only found her by climbing a ladder and going in through a window."

He smiled for the first time.

"You are rather an amazing young woman," he said. "I don't have many like you here." Then he became professional again. "Was there enough of the barbiturate to have killed her?"

"The doctor thinks so. I suppose the idea was to put herself to sleep while the—the other thing went on."

"To sleep away," he said thoughtfully. "Well, that's not unusual."

"And to do it as comfortably as possible," I observed, and saw him nod in agreement.

"Yes," he said. "Suicides do that sometimes. They go to bed rather than fall on a hard floor, for instance. What about this shooting of Lieutenant O'Brien, Miss Maynard? Have the police any theories about it?"

"None that I know of, unless they suspect me. I think the police believe I pushed the Benjamin woman into the pool. Or that my brother did it. It was his golf club that knocked her out, you know. It doesn't matter to them that we never saw her until she was dead."

He did not smile. He got up instead and went to a window, although I didn't think he saw anything outside. When he turned his face was grave.

"Has it occurred to you that Mrs. Chandler may have done it? The woman came there to see someone. It might have been your sister. That's why you're here, isn't it?"

"I want to know if you think she's capable of a thing like that. Her former husband thinks she is a manic-depressive."

"So?" he said. "Well, in a way aren't we all? We have our ups and downs, but we're not necessarily off balance. One thing strikes me as odd, Miss Maynard. Your sister never told me the circumstances of her leaving Mr. Chandler. Most women do. They go to all lengths to expatiate on such things, to present their reasons, in other words, to defend themselves. She never has."

"She was never in love with him. He knows that himself. I think my mother rather forced the marriage. Judith was very young at the time, you know."

"The sow is not the only creature that kills her young," he said cryptically. "As you know, I've had your sister for some time. I have never thought she was really paranoid. Sensitive and egocentric she was. She had plenty of personal conflicts, but no particular hostility, although I realized she was not fond of her former husband. Nevertheless, as I told you before, she never gave me a real chance. I could go only so far. Then she blocked me. In fact I've been blaming myself for what she did. The last time she was here I told her she was wasting my time, and hers."

I could not think of anything to say. He went back to his desk and sat down, looking unhappy. He opened her file and glanced down at it.

"You see, Miss Maynard," he said, "the picture is somewhat altered. I gather that The Birches was a peaceful place until recently. Then all at once, or close together, we have a death, a shooting, and an attempted suicide. I don't know anything about the Benjamin woman, but I do know about O'Brien. The police have been here, you see. O'Brien was and is a member of the Homicide Squad here in town. He has a fine reputation. But he went into the army, and was invalided out of the South Pacific. Recently he asked for a leave of absence. But he is still a police officer, Miss Maynard, and I think you are right when you say he had a reason for being at The Birches."

I managed to steady my voice. I felt sure what was coming.

"Do you know what that reason was?" I asked.

He shrugged.

"Your local Chief of Police is a shrewd man," he said. "He has been here. He doesn't think the three events are unrelated. Your brother told him your sister had been consulting me, so he came to see me. What he asked me was if your sister was capable of murder. Or of one murder and the shooting of this man O'Brien."

I had known it was coming, but I felt faint and dizzy. When I did not speak he went on:

"I suppose all of us are capable of it, more or less. Greed, envy, jealousy, rage, fear, self-protection, or sheer desperation—who knows what the human animal will do? And of course there is always what we call original sin. Whatever it is it may be the matter of a momentary impulse or the result of a long train of unconscious preparation. But we do kill."

"I don't believe Judith would kill anybody," I said stubbornly. "And she's really afraid. She was so afraid that she preferred to kill herself rather than be killed. And there is someone after her. I think he mistook the Benjamin woman for her. He certainly did me when he caught me that night. When he found he'd made a mistake he dropped me into the pool and escaped."

"You're sure you don't know who he is?"

"No. I haven't an idea. If the police have been here you know they've been watching for him."

"They don't entirely believe in him. Nor did I, until you told me all this."

"He exists," I said. "Judith knows who he is too, but she won't tell. Not anyone. Not me. Not even you, I suppose."

"No," he agreed. "Of course there is one particular psychosis which seldom accepts treatment. Let's call it guilt."

"Yet she comes here."

"She may want absolution without confession." He glanced through his notes. "You are insistent that she never took a lover?"

"Her husband says so."

"Husbands are usually the last to know," he said dryly. "She may have had affairs, Miss Maynard. Take a woman of her type and the situation between herself and Mr. Chandler, and what can you expect? It might account for a number of things."

Owing probably to my virginal status, he abandoned Judith's sex life, however. I wanted to tell him that I was twenty-eight years old and had lost my belief in the stork at the age of twelve. He gave me no chance.

"Has it occurred to you that her reaction to the sight of this dead woman was rather extreme?" he asked. "She must have seen death before."

"It wasn't a pretty sight, doctor."

He took a turn or two about the room, looking deeply troubled.

"It's just possible," he said finally, "that it was your sister Mrs. Benjamin came to meet the night she was killed. After all, this woman expected to go home. She must have expected someone with a car to take her back to the station. Mrs. Chandler drives, of course?"

"Yes. But the whole idea is ridiculous, doctor."

He sat down at last and giving me a cigarette took one himself and lit them both.

"Perhaps. Perhaps not," he said. "I'm out of my field, of course. I'm no detective. But just when did this Homicide man, O'Brien, ask for protracted leave, or whatever they call it? And why did he take your cottage? To watch your sister or to watch over her?"

"I think he was worried about her. He practically told me she was in danger."

"Why? Didn't he say? Your unknown man couldn't have been Walter Benjamin, unless he is still living and had his own reasons for disappearing. You didn't recognize his picture?"

"No. Of course a beard changes a man."

He looked thoughtful.

"A beard? Would he have a reason for wearing a beard? Unless he had a weak chin or wanted to disguise himself?"

"I don't know why any man wears one," I said. "I think they're horrible."

He laughed at that, and soon after he got up.

"Sorry," he said. "I've given you more time than I should. But I may call you up someday, if that's all right."

"You don't think you should see Judith?"

"At the moment," he said dryly, "I imagine I'm the last person in the world she wants to see." I picked up my bag and prepared to go, but he stopped me. "I hope you don't mind this question," he said. "I think it's necessary. Have you any idea why your sister hated your mother?"

"Hated her? I don't understand!"

He modified it when he saw my face.

"Perhaps the word is too strong. Let's say disliked her," he said. "That has been evident all along. She won't discuss her. She won't even mention her name. I told you once there was a point I could never pass. That is at least a part of it."

"But mother idolized her," I protested. "The rest of us simply grew up, but Judith was the hothouse plant. Nothing was too good for her."

"Not every hothouse plant flourishes," he said dryly, and prepared to leave.

I had plenty to think of on my way home that day, and it did not help matters to find Anne waiting for me at The Birches. She had come by train and Ed Brown's taxi, and she was still indignant.

"What does Ed mean about my Bill climbing a ladder the night Judith tried to kill herself? And the police arresting him?"

"Your Bill wasn't arrested," I said. "He was helping with what he calls a bit of breaking and entering. As a matter of fact, he was holding the ladder while I climbed it. Only the police grabbed him."

"I suppose that explains everything," she said nastily.

"Sit down," I said. "I'll get you a cup of tea or a highball, whichever you wish. And as soon as you're calm I'll tell you the story. Your Bill's all right. He's probably with his Janey this minute. As for the ladder, we needed it to get into Jude's room. I didn't say too much when Ridgely was here, but if it hadn't been for Bill she'd be dead this minute."

Anne chose tea, and I waited until Jennie had brought in the tray, dropped the sugar tongs on the floor, and reluctantly departed before I began. Then I told her, as briefly as I could. She was, like Phil, completely incredulous.

"Then she really meant it after all!" she said. "She's the last person in the world I'd expect to do a thing like that. I thought she was simply playing for sympathy. Or maybe she wanted Ridgely back."

"She doesn't," I said flatly. "But look here, Anne, she really *is* afraid of someone. Not Ridge. This man is a good bit taller than he is, and strong. I only saw him in the dark. But he's been around since. I think he knocked Mrs. Benjamin out and then threw her in the pool, and I believe he shot O'Brien."

She put down her cup.

"It's a pity," she said icily, "that no one ever tells me anything. I send Bill out here to get some good country air while I have to be away, and all at once there's a killer around. I'm taking him back with me, Lois."

I smiled.

"You'd better wait until his face looks better," I said. "He's still not very pretty."

"His face? Did those policemen attack him?"

"No. Bill chased this killer—as we gaily refer to him—a night or two ago and came out second best when he caught up with him. The man got away, but Bill is somewhat battered."

Her face was a mask of horror.

"And you allowed a thing like that!" she said. "My own son, in peril of his life, and you do nothing about it."

"What could I do?" I asked reasonably. "I wasn't there. It was all over when I knew about it. And his lip is healed by this time."

"So they haven't got this—killer?"

"No."

She lay back in her chair and closed her eyes. I knew how she felt. Her quiet domestic life of poor servants, or none at all, of struggling to send her children to good schools, of pot roasts and the price of coffee, of getting Martin off in the morning and seeing him come home tired at night—none of this had prepared her for the drama she was facing.

"I'll be all right after a while," she said. "Let me just rest here a few minutes. I left a note for Martin. He can go out for his supper."

I sat there looking at her. She
was older than Judith. She must
remember things I had forgotten,
or as a child never knew, and I
was remembering what Helga had
said that morning in the kitchen
about the sins of the fathers.

"Do you mind if I ask you something, Anne?" I said.

She opened her eyes.

"What about?"

"About the family. Years ago.
Was father ever in any sort of
trouble? I don't mean financial.
Anything else?"

"Father? Of course not."

"He and mother, they were
happy together, weren't they?"

"They didn't fall all over each
other, if that's what you mean. I
don't think they quarreled much.
But—I've never told this to anybody, Lois; not even Martin—they
had a fearful row the day he shot
himself."

She hadn't heard anything, just
the loud voices and mother crying
hysterically. She had been staying
in the house, as I knew, and she
heard father bang out the front
door in a fury. It wasn't like him,
she said.

"I don't suppose it really meant
anything," she went on. "Only it
was strange that night at the dinner, father in full dress and mother
in the black velvet of the Laszlo
painting there and all her pearls.
I remember wondering at how
well they carried on, although I
don't think they were even on
speaking terms. It was the same
night of course that he shot himself."

Her voice trailed off, as though
she had lost herself in the past.

"Did you know of any trouble
mother was having at that time?
She wasn't in any sort of jam, was
she?"

"What do you mean by a jam?
She was in debt all over town. She
refused to recognize the crash,
you know."

But she couldn't have owed
fifty thousand dollars, I thought.
Anne poured herself another cup
of tea and set down the pot.

"Of course she got out as soon
as she could after father's death.
She took Judith and went to Arizona. I often wonder if she didn't
blame herself. If that was the
reason she left. As though she
couldn't stand the house any
longer. Judith's cough was only an
excuse."

I was remembering myself. The
hasty exodus, and my standing
around child-like to watch the hurried packing of trunks, mother's
face white and strained, and my
nurse grabbing me by the arm
and shutting me in the day
nursery. Curiously enough, I did
not remember seeing Judith at all.
I daresay she was around, coughing, as Anne said, but I did not
remember her.

But, with one of those curious
flashbacks of memory that occur
sometimes, I was remembering a
tall saturnine-looking man, carrying down the bags to the car.

"We had a butler then, didn't
we?" I asked.

"I suppose so. We always did
have, didn't we?" she said
vaguely. "I'd better see Judith, I

suppose. She practically threw me out the last time. What on earth will I say?"

"Don't ask her any questions. Just say you're sorry she's not well. Tell her about Martha, or the high cost of living. Talk to her about going abroad. She intends to, as soon as she can get the space. Just any darn thing, but ignore the bandages."

She did pretty well, although I could see she was shocked at Judith's appearance. I think Judith tried too, although she wasn't successful. They did better over the *Queen Mary*, on which Judith wanted to travel. But she and Anne had never got along, and I was relieved when Anne said she did not want to tire her and got up.

She stayed to dinner that night.

Bill, for a wonder, turned up but he instantly vetoed going back to New York.

"I've got a thing for this Janey girl," he said, "and I'm having the time of my life into the bargain. I'm staying awhile, if Phil and Lois will keep me."

Anne eyed him. His face had improved, but the black shadow around one eye made him a little pathetic. In the end he got his way and, Anne refusing to ride in his jalopy, he drove her to the station in our car. I think she was reassured by the sight of a State Trooper on a motorcycle who followed them into town. It annoyed Bill, however, and on returning he stated he had meant to take Janey for a drive that night, but the idea of a policeman making a third did not appeal to him.

23

I found Helga with Walter Benjamin's picture that night. She had gone into my room ostensibly to turn down my bed, but she had not done so. Instead she was standing holding the photograph, and her hand was shaking.

"Found this on the floor," she said. "Not very pretty, is he?"

"Do you know who it is?"

"Me?" she said indignantly. "Of course not."

I did not believe her. She was both shocked and frightened, and she scurried out of the room as fast as her legs would take her. I gave her time to get to her room and settle down before I followed her, carrying the picture with me.

She had not gone to bed. Apparently she had been sitting beside the window in the dark, as though she were watching the grounds, and I saw she was careful to draw the shade before she switched on a light. For the first time I wondered if she was afraid, and if so, of what. When I asked her, however, she merely said it was a hot night and she liked the air.

But she eyed the photograph with angry suspicion.

"I told you about that," she said. "It's my bedtime, Lois, and what with company and trays and what not I've earned my sleep."

"Of course you have," I agreed. "This won't take a minute. Just who is this man? You recognized him, didn't you?"

"With all that hair? It might be the angel Gabriel for all of me."

I gave up. Helga could be stubborn, and the way her jaw was set over her false teeth a Missouri mule had nothing on her. Yet I felt she wanted to tell me something and was afraid to do so. I tried another tack.

"All right," I said. "You didn't know him and he didn't know you. But perhaps you remember what employment agency mother used, Helga. She must have changed help now and then."

"Not me. I went there as kitchenmaid, and I've stayed ever since."

"But the others. I seem to remember a lot of butlers, for one thing. Where did she get her servants? What agency, I mean."

She threw me a sharp glance.

"She didn't consult me," she said. "My job was my kitchen and I stayed there. Every morning I got my orders. I wrote them down too, so your mother couldn't say I'd changed anything. And every week I added up my slips, so she knew I wasn't getting a percentage like most cooks. Butlers too. They get a cut on all the liquor they buy. That Dawson got rich on it."

Dawson! It was the name I had forgotten, and Helga had managed to tell me after all.

"He was there when father died, wasn't he?" I said casually. "How could he get rich, Helga? We had lost everything."

"Don't ask me," she said. "All I know is he was going to buy a business of his own. That takes money. He was a bad man, Lois. A wicked man. Mind, I don't know anything, but he got that money somewhere that wasn't honest."

"What sort of business, Helga?"

"How would I know?" she said. "And it's no use showing me that picture!" she added. "I haven't got my specs. Left them downstairs. I wouldn't remember anyhow. Now clear out of here. I want to go to bed."

But I held it out to her, and she had to take it. She didn't want to. Her old hands were shaking again, and she gave it the briefest possible glance.

"Never saw him before," she said. "Don't like hairy men. Never did. Who's it supposed to be?"

She knew him all right. But for some reason she wasn't going to tell me who he was, and I knew my whole excursion was a failure. She didn't know anything. She insisted she did not know what agency mother used to find domestic help, and I left her standing in the center of the room, her mouth stubbornly set. But she said one significant thing as I was closing the door.

"You better let sleeping dogs lie, Lois," she said. "We got trouble enough now. Don't you be stirring up more."

I made Judith comfortable before I went to bed that night. I rubbed her back, realizing that she was thinner than I had ever seen her, and I laid out the two sleeping pills she was allowed out of the bottle I kept hidden in my room. She hardly spoke at all, but when I had finished she looked up at me.

"Does Doctor Townsend know about me?" she asked.

"I believe Phil called him up," I said evasively. "Would you like to see him?"

She shook her head.

"I was just tired," she said slowly. "Tired and sort of desperate. I didn't kill that woman, Lois."

"I never thought you did, darling."

"And I didn't shoot O'Brien either." She gave me a thin smile. "Jennie told me he's in the hospital. I hope he's better. I rather liked him. He's improving, isn't he?"

"Yes," I said. "They say he'll pull through."

"And—have they any idea who shot him?"

"I suppose all cops make enemies. Nobody knows who did it, unless you know something yourself, Judith. If you do you ought to tell it."

But she only gave a slight shudder and closed her eyes.

"What I know wouldn't help," she said flatly. Then she did an unusual thing, for her. She reached up a thin hand and patted my arm.

"I've played hell with your work, haven't I?" she said. "Ever since I came."

I grinned at her.

"My agent says the magazines are going all out for sweetness and love," I said. "That rather lets my Sara Winters out, doesn't it!"

She let me go then, as though she was settled for the night. As soon as I had closed the door, however, I heard her beyond it, locking it and shoving the bolt in place. So, whatever the terror was, it was not over for her.

Phil says that out of the mouths of babes and sucklings what issues is usually a lot of burps. Yet as it happened it was young Bill who solved at least one problem for me. For by that time I was practically convinced that Walter Benjamin had been Arthur Dawson, and that he had been involved in some dirty business in the past which concerned us. It would account for the money in the bank, the change of name, the beard, and most important of all, why his widow had come to The Birches.

It was at breakfast the next morning that I asked Phil if he had any idea from what employment agency mother had got her household servants. He gave me his usual morning glare—of wanting to read his paper, of to hell with commuting, and of resentment that anybody could expect him to speak until after his second cup of coffee.

"How the devil would I know?" he said sourly. "And why should you care?"

Bill, however, looked up from a four-inch pile of hot cakes soaked with butter and syrup.

"Ludwig's," he said.

"Ludwig's what?"

"Grandmother always went to Ludwig's, according to mother. So does mother herself, for all the good it does her."

I went into New York late that morning, but as I sat in the train I became more and more uncertain. I had a lot of unrelated facts and some guesses. What had Ridge Chandler's fifty thousand dollars to do with Dawson, alias Benjamin? Could a man, say of fifty and not too honest, have accumulated the sum he had deposited in the bank so long ago? Or had he been the "jam" Ridge had spoken about? In that case what did he know in order to blackmail mother?

She hadn't killed father, of course. There was the note he left, and the dinner party was still going on when it happened. Also Judith was only in her teens in those days, not even allowed to drive a car. Not allowed to do much of anything, for that matter. She had not even made her debut, that winter of 1929–30 and, if she was involved, Dawson had apparently let many years lapse, years when he probably knew she had married well, without bothering her.

It was not Dawson then—or Benjamin, if it was he—who had sent her scurrying to Reno, and I felt rather foolish when I located the Ludwig Employment Agency on a second floor on Madison Avenue. It was a shabby place which showed its age. Old Mrs. Ludwig was dead, the girl at the desk told me, but her daughter was running the business. She was out to lunch, but would be back soon. I sat down to wait in the depressing atmosphere of all such places: the line of women in the adjoining room, the detached young woman at the desk, the occasional telephone calls.

"I sent her over. Didn't she come?" Or: "Well, I'm sorry. Her references are fine. Maybe if you try her a little longer."

I longed for a cigarette or even a sandwich. I had not stopped to eat. And I could feel the eyes of the women on me, suspicious or hopeful as it might be; hope that I might offer a summer place, cool and with grass. Suspicion because all employers were suspect. They made me feel like an interloper. Things picked up, however, when Miss Ludwig appeared. She was a brisk middle-aged woman, neatly dressed, and as she took off her hat she asked me what she could do for me.

"I'm afraid I'm here under false pretenses," I said. "I don't want to employ anyone. I'm really after information, although after all this time . . ."

She listened while I explained. I was trying to trace a butler my mother, Mrs. James Maynard, had employed a good many years ago. He was dead now, but his widow had died too not long ago and there was some money involved. Rather a large sum, in fact. His name had been Arthur Dawson.

She shook her head. The name meant nothing to her. But she said they still had her mother's old ledgers. She herself used a card index system, but the ledgers were around somewhere.

"If Dawson was on her list, mother would have it," she said. "She was most particular."

She got the approximate date from me, raised her eyebrows, and then disappeared into a third room which from the glimpse I had of it was used largely for the storage of broken chairs and a chest or two. When she came back some minutes later she had two dusty volumes in her arms and a smudge of dirt across her nose.

"Mother had her own methods," she said, placing them on the desk. "She had one for what she called the ladies, and I'm glad some of them never saw those books! The other is for the applicants. If you'll

give me your mother's name again I'll take her first."

She found it, and she looked at me with some respect.

"I see you kept eight servants for a good many years," she said. "And—I hope you don't mind this —your mother is listed as hard to suit but fair. She paid well and expected a good bit."

I didn't mind, so she turned to the other ledger. Dawson was there. At the age of forty he had been in a good many situations apparently, but there was no entry for him after mother had employed him. Not even the date he had left. She closed the book and glanced at me.

"I'm afraid that's not very useful," she said. "But you have to remember the times. Most people cut down because of the crash, and very few continued to keep butlers, or indeed much help at all. You were too young to remember, I suppose."

I said I was, thanked her, and left. All I had was a sort of negative proof that Dawson had not used the Ludwig agency after he left us. He might have been anywhere, doing anything. The one thing I was sure of was that he was too old to have dumped me into the pool or banged poor Bill into unconsciousness.

24

It was rather a shock to find Chief Fowler on the porch when I got home. I had come out with Phil, and Bill met us at the train. Phil groaned when he saw Fowler.

"Well, here it comes," he said. "Two to one I go first, Lois."

Apparently, however, no one was arrested. It was a hot day, and the Chief had made himself comfortable. His collar and part of his shirt were open, and his Panama hat lay beside him on the chair. Beside him too on a table was a pitcher of lemonade and a glass. He got up as we climbed the steps, looking rather embarrassed.

"I took the liberty of asking for something cool," he said. "Hope you don't mind."

"Just so you don't pull out a pair of handcuffs," Phil said.

The Chief laughed merrily, or so Phil maintained later.

"Now, now, Mr. Maynard," he said. "You will have your little joke."

"Even in the shadow of the gallows," Phil said. "It is a far, far better thing I do, and so forth."

The Chief looked mystified, having never apparently heard of Charles Dickens and Sydney Carton, and Phil turned sour.

"Just what's the idea of the visit?" he said. "Unless you've decided I shot O'Brien."

"O'Brien's a cop," Fowler said comfortably. "A fellow like that makes enemies, and he knows it. He sends them up the river, and when they get out sometimes they go for him. He's had narrow escapes before this."

So that was O'Brien's story! I almost smiled, but Phil was still irritable.

"Are you here because some gun-happy punk shot O'Brien?" he demanded. "If so, I want a bath and a highball. Then I want my dinner. Unless there is something urgent . . ."

"Well, I don't know whether you would call it urgent or not," Fowler said complacently. "But we haven't forgotten a little matter of a murder here, Mr. Maynard. And since the state boys have pulled out . . ."

"Oh, so they've pulled out, have they?"

"I guess they got word from Albany to quit playing. Or maybe they've decided somebody dreamed up this fellow you all talked about."

Phil snorted.

"You can look at Bill's face here if you want a sign. He'd have a hard time dreaming that up."

Fowler, however, was still in high good humor.

"Funny thing," he said. "These state fellows think they're the cat's whiskers, but now and then they slip up. Take it like this, Mr. Maynard. This Benjamin woman wasn't expecting trouble when she came here that night. Not a bit of it. She was sitting nice and comfortable on that bench down there, waiting for somebody. Smoking a cigarette too. You didn't know that, did you?"

Phil grinned.

"I don't think it would have interested me," he said. "Not to the point of murder, anyhow."

Fowler's smile faded.

"Well, that's as may be," he said. "At least let's say I have eyes and know how to use them."

He reached into his pocket and pulled out a thin old-fashioned gold chain, with a black-and-white locket as a pendant, and held it out for us to see.

"As I said, those state guys are all right for traffic. Give them a bunch of parking tickets and they're happy. But they missed this, and how! It's hers, all right. The Hunnewell woman says she knows it well. Now guess where I found it."

I was not guessing, nor was Phil. We did not even touch the thing.

"All right," Phil said impatiently.

"You found it and it's hers? So what?"

The Chief was slightly deflated, but not much, and he refused to be hurried. He had not been satisfied, he said, with the idea that the blow had stunned the Benjamin woman and she had tumbled into the pool.

"It looked more deliberate to me," he said. "That blow she got didn't knock her out. There was no fracture. Made her head ache maybe, maybe not. But she knew the pool was there. So how did she get into it?"

Nobody said anything, and he went on. He had come back to The Birches that morning and gone over the neighborhood of the pool. He had examined the diving platform, with no results, and at first too the old bench offered nothing. Finally, however, he turned it over and shook it, and the locket dropped out from between the boards.

"You get the idea," he said, returning it carefully to his pocket. "She's sitting there peaceably, and waiting for someone she's expecting. It's a long trip, but she's made it. Maybe she's tired. Maybe she even dozes off. She was a little hard of hearing too. So she doesn't even know there's someone near her until it's too late. Then wham! she gets hit on the head.

"But it doesn't knock her out. She puts up some sort of fight, not much but enough to break the necklace. Maybe she tries to scream. Maybe she does scream. The inside of one of her lips was cut, as though whoever it was tried to gag her with a hand. But she still isn't dead. So she's picked up and thrown into the pool. No woman did all that, Mr. Maynard."

"Look," Phil said. "If you lived in a house full of women, as I do for my sins, you'd know there's very little they can't do. They can move pianos and lift carpets. They break things too; watch crystals, chains, eggbeaters, toasters, even chairs, by God!"

I glared at him.

"Just in case my brother is suggesting the wham came from me," I said, "I had a similar experience myself one night not long ago. A man picked me up and threw me into the pool. If you don't believe me you can ask O'Brien at the hospital. He dried me out."

Fowler looked astonished. Then he smiled.

"Didn't just dive in yourself, did you?" he said. "I gather you're a fine little swimmer."

"If you think I did it to throw you off the track," I said angrily, "you're even more of an idiot than I think you are, and that's plenty. Over and over we have told you about this man, but you still think we've made him up out of whole cloth. Who shot O'Brien? Who threw a rock through my sister's window, or don't you know about that? Who frightened Jennie into hysterics? Who knocked Bill here senseless? And who dumped me into the pool? I say it's the same man who killed Mrs. Benjamin, and if we didn't have a lot of lame-brained police he'd be in jail this minute."

Fowler got up. He even managed to achieve a certain amount of dignity.

"Maybe not," he said. "But lame-brained or not, that golf club came from here. Just remember that, Miss Maynard. You talk a lot. So does your brother. But you don't say very much. And don't think I'm through. Maybe for the shadow of the gallows—whatever that means—you might substitute chair, and not one of those your brother mentioned, either."

He left us then driving away with a look of determination on his face. Bill grinned.

"Made a nice comeback, the blabbermouth, didn't he?" he said cheerfully. "But the big hunk of cheese doesn't know which end of him is up."

"I wouldn't bet on that," Phil said. Then he turned on me. "For God's sake, Lois, what goes on around here?" He stood stiffly, eying me with something less than brotherly affection.

"What is O'Brien's game?" he inquired. "And why did you go to him, as you so nicely put it, to dry you out?"

"His place was nearer, Phil. Anyhow it was over. The man was gone, and I didn't see what I could do."

"That's a fine state of mind!" he said bitterly. "We have a maniac about this place. He throws all sorts of capers, and he even probably commits a murder. But I'm not to know. It's supposed to take brains to be a lawyer, but no. A tuppeny policeman named O'Brien calls the shots."

"O'Brien tried to catch him that night, but he got away. He's after Judith, Phil. Not me. That's why O'Brien was here. To protect her."

"That I don't believe," he said, and turning abruptly went into the house.

Dinner that night was a quiet one. Phil was taciturn. He didn't even bother to look with distaste at the dried apricots which were Helga's attempt to economize while Bill was out. And when it was over he carried his coffee into the library, closing the door behind him, which was his signal to keep out.

Nevertheless, I followed him soon after. He was at his desk, but he had not started to work. He had not even touched his coffee. He was holding his head in his hands, and the face he turned to me was without expression.

"I'm sorry to bother you, Phil," I said. "But it's time we had a talk. I've been holding out on you, but with things as they are . . ."

"Without O'Brien, you mean."

"Partly that. Not all."

"So now I'm to be let into the arcanum! Thanks. Many thanks," he said. "I began to gather that quite a lot's been going on without my knowing it. O'Brien turns out to be a Homicide man. Bill gets his comeuppance. Somebody throws you in that damned pool of yours. Judith tries to kill herself. Just possibly you or I or both of us are about to be arrested for murder, and God knows what else. What do you think I am? A moron?"

"You're always so tired, Phil.

Besides, I don't really know anything. I'm as mystified as you are."

He laughed cynically.

"So you accidentally take a ride, see a black cat in a window, discover the Benjamin house, make a liar out of yourself at the inquest, and get dumped—I believe that's your word—into the pool. What else?"

"Do you want me to tell you? Or are you going to think the whole thing's funny? It's damned unfunny, Phil."

He drew a long breath.

"Go ahead," he said. "I'll try to control my sense of humor."

Sitting there, with Phil at the desk and me in a chair, I began with the death of Flaherty, and went on to the train at Reno and O'Brien. I ended with Helga and the picture of Walter Benjamin. Some of it he knew, some of it he did not. He remembered Dawson, but he saw nothing unusual in his disappearance, even if he had changed his name.

"They wander about, these fellows," he said. "Change places often, and if they lack good references they may change their names. Some of them make quite a bit on the side too, tips from guests, commissions on liquor bills, and so on. If that was his picture you showed me the other night he's changed a lot. Of course twenty years . . ."

"And thirty thousand dollars," I reminded him. "Phil, do you think mother gave it to him?"

He stared at me.

"Mother?" he said. "By the time the estate was settled she didn't have thirty thousand cents. What do you mean? Even if she had it, why give it to Dawson?"

"If he was Walter Benjamin he got it somewhere. She wasn't in trouble of some sort, was she?"

"We were all in trouble," he said shortly. "I was back in college, shoveling snow and washing dishes to finish my last year, and Anne was trying to find a place where she and Harrison could starve to death."

"Yet mother took Judith and went to Arizona, Phil. I think she was running away from something. Could she have owed a lot of money you didn't know about?"

"She owed plenty," he said, his face grim. "The executors had to stop her credit everywhere. She never had any money sense. It was just something to spend. But real money, no."

I might have told him then about Ridge's fifty thousand dollars. I wish now I had. But he reverted to my story as if he did not care to discuss mother's lack of financial acumen. He has a clear legal mind, and as he sat back with a cigarette he reviewed briefly what I had told him.

It looked to him, he said, as though I was confusing two different things. One, he said, didn't concern us. That was the murder of Flaherty.

"That's O'Brien's business," he said shortly, "and if you ask me it's a trifle sentimental after all this time. But the other is Judith's, and knowing her capacity for getting herself in a mess it might be anything from mayhem to bigamy."

"I've thought of that, Phil. Could she have run away and married someone before she married Ridge?"

"And the groom has kept his mouth shut ever since? Talk sense, Lois. How about these clippings? You say they're still in the cottage? I might have a look at them."

It was still twilight as we started down the drive. Phil was silent, apparently thinking over our talk and not liking much of it. But when we were fifty feet or so away I heard Henrietta give a loud squawk and flutter her wings wildly.

"That chicken still roost in the cottage?" Phil asked.

"I think Helga puts her there at night. She sounds frightened."

She *was* frightened. The cottage door was wide open and she was on her way out when we reached it. It took only a glance to see that someone had been there before us. The place had been pretty thoroughly ransacked. The table drawer was open and empty, and the books had been moved about on the shelves. There was no great confusion, however. It had been done in an orderly way, as if someone had hoped it would go unnoticed.

It took only a moment to see all this, and I shot into the kitchen, with that ridiculous chicken practically under my feet. The window there was open, although it had been kept closed and locked since O'Brien had left. I called to Phil.

"He's somewhere outside," I said. "He got out this window

when he heard us coming. He can't be far away. Perhaps you can catch him."

I don't think he relished the suggestion. Nevertheless, he took the poker from the fireplace and started for the door. He stopped there to glance at me with a sickly grin.

"God help me if Fowler sees me with this!" he said, and disappeared.

I stood listening. Darkness had fallen suddenly, and I could hear him beating through the shrubbery. Nothing happened, however, no car started up, as I had expected, and Phil found no one. He came back, covered with burs and looking disgusted.

"Why the brainstorm?" he asked. "How do you know whoever it was went out that window?"

"Because it was open. And Henrietta was scared off her perch. You heard her squawk yourself."

He damned all chickens while he picked the burs off his trouser legs. But he was impressed, nevertheless.

"If there was anyone here how did he get in?" he asked. "Who has a key to this place?"

There were only two, I told him, O'Brien's and the one we kept at the house, on the hall table.

"Helga uses it to get the chicken feed from the kitchen," I said, "but she always puts it back. Phil, did you look in the chicken house?"

"No, and I don't intend to," he said grumpily. "I need a vacuum cleaner and a drink. Or reverse it. A drink, then the vacuum."

As a result it was I who went out to the chicken house, taking O'Brien's flashlight with me. It was too late, of course. The hens were stirring unhappily, but the shed was empty. The doors were open, however. Someone had been there, listening and waiting for a chance to escape.

It did nothing to soothe my feelings to find the key in its usual place when we went back to the house.

I was still upset when I prepared Judith for bed later on. She was up and about by that time. Her wrists had healed with only small scars, but she continued to stick to her room and her locked doors. The terror, whatever it was, still obsessed her. She had tried to escape it by dying, but when that failed it remained with her.

Yet in a way I thought she was less desperate. Certainly she was easier to get along with. Perhaps when one has deliberately faced eternity as she had one's perspective must be altered, and even death may have lost some of its horror. She was still weak, however. I fixed her bed and got her into it before she noticed chicken feathers in my hair and asked about them.

I could not tell her our invader was back again. It would have destroyed what little equanimity she had recovered. I invented something about a fox after O'Brien's girls, and let it go at that.

She turned over as usual to let me rub her back, not interested in chickens, not interested in much, actually, except to get away from all of us and start a new life elsewhere.

"I've been thinking," she said. "I'll be sure to get a sailing soon, with the rush almost over. And a lot of my clothes are still in the apartment. If Ridge lets you in, would you pack them for me? The trunks are in the storeroom."

"Of course," I told her.

"If you can find Clarice, she might help you. She's a wonderful packer."

Clarice had been her personal maid for several years, but thinking of the raft of servants she always employed for some reason reminded me of Dawson.

"I'll try," I said. "Ridge probably gave her a reference. Speaking of her, I wonder if you remember a butler we used to have?"

"What butler?" she asked idly. "We had dozens."

"His name was Dawson."

To my surprise I could feel her stiffen under my hands. Every muscle went rigid, and at first she did not speak. Then, "What about him?" she asked. "I think I remember him. It must have been years ago. Why?"

"Only that he was there when father died," I said. "Phil and I were going over old times tonight. What became of him? Do you know?"

"I haven't the remotest idea," she said.

I was confident she was lying, but I could not be sure. Certainly it was some time before she relaxed. Also certainly she did not revert to him again, and I did not dare to pursue the subject.

But the name had meant something to her, something unpleasant, perhaps even something dreadful, for she was very pale when I went out and she locked and bolted the door behind me.

Clearly whatever her secret was she meant to keep it to herself if it killed her. And as things turned out it almost did.

25

I resolutely put Judith's problem behind me when I went to my room that night. I had two reasons for thankfulness. One—an important one—was that sometime during the evening Phil had told me O'Brien was out of bed. The other of course was the prospect of Judith's going abroad.

I tried to visualize what it

would mean, a return to peace and safety, time to work at my neglected novel, and a move back to mother's room, warm in winter and with a sunny window for my typewriter. I even played with the idea, if I finished the book, of buying a station wagon instead of our old car. Which shows my state of mind, as well as how little I knew.

But it was dampening to realize that O'Brien would probably leave when Judith did. He liked me. I knew that. He even kissed me in an impulsive moment. Yet I knew instinctively that he was a man's man. He had been a tower of strength to me, and he was as masculine as they come. But he had no illusions about women. It might, I thought, be very difficult for him to love one.

So discouraging was the idea that I crawled out of bed, washed my hair, and after a disconsolate look at my nails, ignored largely since Gertrude's, filed and painted them.

This last was not a good idea. I had to wait for them to dry, which gave me time to think: about the chicken house that night, about Fowler and Selina Benjamin's necklace, even about Doctor Townsend's suggestion that Judith might have carried Phil's golf club to the pool.

Even when my hair and nails were dry I was not sleepy, and I remember that was when I drew the black cat on the pencil pad beside the bed. I always kept the pad there, in the vain hope that some fugitive idea about my work would come in the night.

So far as I know none ever did. All there was on the pad when I looked at it were a list of words with which at some time I had evidently intended to enrich Sara Winters's skimpy vocabulary. I remember "functional" and "integration" were among them, as well as "photogenic," which Walter Benjamin definitely was not.

I drew the cat absently, thinking about the Benjamin-Dawson puzzle, and about the cottage and what had happened there. Not only the theft of the clippings that night. There was the shooting of O'Brien, and before it there was the other time when I wandered in from the pool, soaking wet and furious, and he had used the telephone to order the road block.

Because he knew something I did not. Probably a great deal, for that matter. For I could still see him, able and competent, and annoyed rather than alarmed as I stood dripping before him. He had even known who the man was. It was in his voice when he said, "The poor crazy bastard." And then his poor crazy bastard had come back and tried to kill him. Or had he?

I came of course and inevitably to Dawson, and to Judith's reaction that night while I rubbed her back. She was not only shocked. She was instantly on the defensive. Why? If Walter Benjamin was Dawson, he was most certainly dead. I had no doubt O'Brien had verified this. And Helga had recognized the photograph. I knew it, and she knew I knew it.

That was when I remembered

Judith in the attic, with the old-fashioned square trunk before her. She had not been looking for her wedding pictures in it, and whatever she was searching for she had not found. Her hands were empty when she left; empty and shaking, as though she had been caught in some nefarious enterprise.

There was no use trying to sleep after that. I got up and putting on a dressing gown and slippers I went out into the hall. It was dark, the only light a dim reflection from the bulb left on downstairs for Bill, if and when he came home. But I knew the house too well to need any assistance.

The attic, however, was slightly daunting until I found the cord for the ceiling lamp. Then it sprang into life, a vast repository of the family's history, with its broken furniture, its trunks, some of them with foreign labels, even the old toys Helga refused to throw away. They were on a shelf, and I could see my old doll's house, its contents neatly arranged. It gave me a faintly nostalgic feeling for the old days. For father, and a small girl standing by a Christmas tree and staring incredulously at what was beneath it.

"Like it, baby?"

"Oh, daddy, it's wonderful. It's wonderful."

Poor father. The church had decided he was of unsound mind, so he had received a Christian burial. I had not seen his grave for years, but the last time there had been a potted geranium on it. Helga had not forgotten him.

The trunk of snapshots was where it had been before, under the light, and as I raised the lid I was almost appalled. It contained the accumulated snapshots of years, from Phil's boyish efforts to my own with a Brownie later and others probably donated from other sources. But after an hour's hard work I had half a dozen or so clear ones of Judith and her crowd around the pool. In spite of their best efforts I had managed to edge into one or two of them, grinning toothlessly at the camera. Then, when I had almost given up, I found one of a man in a white coat, standing by the picnic table and looking up from slicing a large baked ham.

He was Dawson, right enough, the man I remembered helping mother and Judith downstairs with their bags on their way to Arizona, and I did not need Phil's cynical writing on the back to identify it. It said: "Dawson catering to the locusts!"

He was clean shaven, of course, a man of forty or thereabouts, and I tried to imagine him at sixty or more and with a beard. Except for the eyes I could not be certain. Nevertheless, I took it, along with half a dozen of the groups around the pool, and putting out the light felt my way down the stairs.

I was in the hall when I saw the man. He was hardly more than a shadow, and he had heard me, for he was flattened against Judith's door as though to escape observation. I must have taken two or three steps forward before I screamed, for the next thing I knew my head struck the newel post and he leaped over me and made for the stairs.

According to the best fiction I should then have passed out. I did nothing of the sort. I simply lay there and yelled until Phil bent over me and shook me.

"Stop it!" he shouted. "What the hell's wrong with you?"

"The man," I gasped. "He was there, outside Judith's room. He knocked me down."

"Get up and talk sense. What man, and where did he go?"

I got up indignantly. My head hurt and I was sick at my stomach.

"There was a man," I said slowly and distinctly—and furiously. "He was at Judith's door. When he saw me he knocked me down, so I hit that post and may have a concussion. He then ran down the stairs and by this time has escaped. Let go of me, Phil. I'm going to lose my dinner."

He released me in a hurry, and I made my bathroom without a minute to spare. When I wobbled back to the hall Bill had evidently come home, the search below was in full cry, and Judith was standing in her doorway. Or rather she was leaning against the frame, as though she needed support.

"Did you see him?" she asked.

"Only an outline, Jude. I think he was wearing a cap."

She made a queer little gesture of despair, and turning sharply went back into her room. I could hear her sliding the bolt on her door and putting up the chain.

I was in bed when the men came upstairs again. There was a sizable bump on the back of my head, but I got little sympathy for it. They said he had cut a neat hole in the pantry window so he could get at the lock, and the window was still up when they got there.

Phil had already called the police in town. He said a prowl car was on the way out, but the sergeant or whoever took his message thought too much time had elapsed.

"Fellow could lose himself in two minutes among those trees out there," he said.

He proved to be correct. When, an hour or so later, two big boys in blue examined the pantry window and came upstairs to examine me, they found me with a wet compress on my head and slightly gaga from the whisky Bill had poured into me.

"Come in and sit down," I said cheerfully. "How about a drink?"

The idea appealed to them, but they said they were on duty. Maybe another time . . . And did the fellow who attacked me have a weapon?

"Certainly," I said. "The newel post out there in the hall. Only I hope you don't have to take it away. We really need it."

Phil gave me a nasty look and took them away. It developed that if our man had a car he had not gone toward town. The only car they had seen was a New York taxicab, which had left some people beyond us and was heading back to the city.

The driver, they reported, had seen nobody.

The house settled down at last,

Bill having adopted Judith's idea of a booby trap under the broken window and using most of Helga's tinware to do it. I locked myself in my room, however, and having hidden the snapshots behind some books on my shelves, crawled back into bed. I did not expect to sleep, but Bill's whisky must have been operating, for I remember no more of the night.

Of course there was trouble in the morning, with Jennie as usual threatening to leave and Phil having to raise her wages to induce her to stay. But the effect on Helga was appalling.

She sought me out in the storeroom, where I was making a list of needed supplies, and closed the door behind her.

"Bill says you saw this man," she said. "What did he look like? Was he young or old?"

"I haven't an idea. Not very old, I think, by the way he ran."

"Look, Lois," she said, "can't you get Judith out of here? She's not safe. Nobody's safe either while she's around."

I confronted her, pad in hand.

"Does it occur to you," I said, "that if you told everything you know we might all be safer? What do you know about it, Helga? You must know something."

She drew a long breath.

"I'm not sure of anything," she said slowly. "I only know it has something to do with Judith when she was a slip of a girl. They had to get her out of town, Lois. Your mother was about frantic. Maybe she killed somebody with a car, or maybe she was going to have a baby. And that Dawson—"

"What about Dawson?"

"He knew all about it, whatever it was. He and the madam were shut up in her room for hours one day talking and talking. It wasn't him last night, was it?"

"I think he's dead, Helga," I told her. "Anyhow he would be pretty old now, wouldn't he?"

"It's got to do with him just the same," she said, her face set obstinately. "You get rid of Miss Judith, Lois. Her middle name's trouble."

But I did not have to get rid of Judith. I found her packing her bags again, and she said she was leaving as soon as I'd packed her trunks in the apartment.

"I'm going to a hotel," she said feverishly. "And I'll sail on anything that floats. I should have gone long ago."

As it turned out, however, she did not go. Only a few days later she was in bed in the hospital in town, being held for murder.

26

I never did see O'Brien in the hospital. To my astonishment he came back that afternoon, against the doctor's orders and refusing the ambulance as though it had been a hearse.

He looked much the same, except for the sling that supported his right arm. Perhaps a little thinner and with a slight limp, but his grin was as engaging as ever. When I saw him from the house he was outside in the chicken yard carrying on a one-sided conversation with Henrietta, who gave every evidence of hen hysteria, and when I ran down the drive he looked pleased.

"Somebody's been taking good care of the girls," he said, eying me. "Which is more than I can say of you, mavourneen. But O'Brien's back. We'll have no more of these shenanigans. Do you think I could sit on my rump in that hospital and let fellows bang you on the head with a newel post?"

"He didn't, you know," I said. "He was only pushing me out of his way."

"Well, you gave the town police a good story anyhow. Fowler says how was she injured, and they state 'she was struck by a newel post!' Come inside. I don't stand so good on this leg."

It was what I had learned to call one of his Irish days, which I discovered later only came when he was deeply moved. And once inside I suddenly felt shy. He seemed younger than I remembered, for some reason; and for the first time it occurred to me that he was very good-looking. He was no Adonis. His features were too irregular for that. But any man would have considered him handsome, and a good many women too.

To my surprise he looked embarrassed. After I sat down he stood on the hearth filling his pipe, and it was some time before he spoke.

"I suppose you wouldn't know why I didn't ask you to come to the hospital," he said at last. "I suppose it's because no man wants his girl to see him laid out and helpless. That's a man's pride, and he has a right to it. But I had another reason too. I used to lie in that damned bed and figure what I was going to say to you when I got out and we were here together like this. I had it all fixed, words and music," he said. "Only I can't rememberer any of it."

I'm afraid I blushed, as I had not done for years, but I kept my voice even.

"Personally," I said, "I keep a pad and pencil to jot down fugitive thoughts. You might try it."

"Fugitive!" he exploded. "What's so damn fugitive about it? It's funk, my girl. I'm scared witless, that's all. Only I've changed my mind. I propose to no woman while I have a game leg and an arm in a sling. Besides, I've got a job to do. I may stop another bullet before it's over and not get off so easy. Because this is big-time stuff, my darling."

I managed a smile.

"So I'm to consider the motion passed as read," I said. "Is that the idea?"

He nodded. It was characteristic of him, I thought, to put me aside and get back to his job again without even a break.

"Passed as read," he agreed, and dropped down heavily in his big chair. "Now, what goes on out here? Not last night. I know about that. What have they been doing to you? You look as though you haven't been sleeping for weeks. Has Fowler been bothering you?"

"Only now and then. Of course he is quite sure either Phil or I killed Mrs. Benjamin. He's looking for a motive now. And your clippings and the photograph are gone, just in case you're looking for them."

He was not worried, I saw. Hardly even interested.

"Police take them?" he asked.

"No. Somebody last night. He escaped through the kitchen window while I was bringing Phil to see them."

"Likes windows, doesn't he?" he commented. "Two the same night. Although I can't imagine . . ." He broke off then, as though he was thinking. "What good are they to anyone? Even the bankbooks, I've got the facts on them."

"Not all of them," I said rather smugly. "I don't suppose you know Ridgely Chandler gave mother fifty thousand dollars in cash about the time Walter Benjamin made that deposit. Or do you know that too?"

"I knew it," he said briefly. "At least I knew he'd made a large withdrawal about that time. Did he come out flatfooted and tell you?"

"Not flatfooted. No Chandler is ever flatfooted. He told me, yes."

"Why? Not why did he pay your mother. That's pretty clear. He wanted your sister. But why tell you?"

"I think he was annoyed. Judith had tried to kill herself, and he'd been busy keeping it out of the papers. I think he regretted it later. But maybe a psychiatrist would say it was a part of his buildup; that he had an inferiority complex about his height and this showed him big and generous."

He grinned over his pipe.

"I'll be getting a smart wife someday, God willing," he said. "With a head like that pretty one of yours we could go places. I suppose you know by this time that Dawson was Benjamin."

I gaped at him.

"You knew it all along, didn't you?"

"Well, I had a theory, and I was lucky. I managed to trace him. You see, we're getting along, aren't we?"

"If you mean back to Flaherty . . ."

"Precisely," he said. "Back to Flaherty is right. It wasn't very long after your father's death that Flaherty was killed. And two weeks later an impecunious butler named Dawson went to a downtown savings bank and made deposits of thirty thousand dollars there."

I got up. All the peace was gone from the cottage, or for that matter all that held us together.

"Are you saying," I asked furiously, "that my own mother had Flaherty murdered?"

"I haven't said anything of the sort," he said patiently. "I think your mother was blackmailed out of fifty thousand dollars. Dawson spent some of it. He bought a tobacco business, remember, and he still had thirty thousand left. That was a sizable sum for those days, my dear. For any days, for that matter."

Slowly it dawned on me what he meant.

"The Preston girl!" I said. "You can't think any of us were involved in that, unless you think my father knew a little cheap East Side prostitute and murdered her."

"Dawson murdered her."

"Dawson!"

"He was in love with her. We never had enough to take to a jury.

But Flaherty was sure the Henry woman was lying about young Johnny Shannon. They both disappeared before the trial, and Flaherty was trying to trace them when he was shot."

"You mean," I said incredulously, "someone paid him to kill Flaherty?"

"He was paid for something. Maybe to keep his mouth shut."

"And mother paid him?"

"I think she did, yes."

"But why?" I said bleakly. "What had she done? She had her faults, but she was never the sort to run around. She had a family too. We were only kids, except Anne, and she kept a sharp watch on us. Oh, I forgot, our friend the prowler was here again last night."

He looked annoyed rather than surprised.

"How do you know it was Morrison?" he asked sharply.

"Because he was at Judith's door in the upper hall when I saw him. He knocked me down trying to escape."

If I expected him to leap from his chair in any wild expression of sympathy I was certainly disappointed. He only looked tired and angry.

"The damned fool!" he said. "Did you get a good look at him?"

"I wasn't in any position to inspect him," I said. "I was flat on the floor when he leaped over me. And I was good and sick afterwards, if that means anything to you."

I was still getting no pity, however.

"You must have some idea about him," he said thoughtfully. "Was he big or little, young or old? And what was he doing at your sister's door?"

"I didn't inquire," I said. "We merely met, so to speak, and parted."

He came over then and put his good arm around me.

"I'm sorry, my poor darling," he said softly. "I'd hoped he wouldn't come back."

"But why?" I said. "What does he want? Why is he trying to kill Judith?"

"I'm not sure he is," he said slowly. "I told you once I might be off on the wrong foot in this case. I still wonder. What does Mrs. Chandler say about all this?"

"He was a burglar after her jewelry. Period."

"Not the tea set in the dining room?"

"Definitely not the tea set. And don't try to be funny. I have a bump on the back of my head so I couldn't wear a hat, if I ever wore one. You know who this man is. Why don't you turn him in? Or don't you think he killed Selina Benjamin? Maybe you suspect one of us, as Fowler does."

"Don't forget that's still a possibility, my darling," he said. "A woman with a golf club can be pretty formidable, and Judith's attempt at suicide hasn't helped matters any. As a matter of fact we may find it was Judith Chandler who took the golf club to the pool that night. Whether she used it or not is another question. But Selina was there to meet someone, and I think it was your sister."

I sat back and closed my eyes.

"I don't believe it," I said huskily. "Why would she?"

"Look, my dear," he said gently. "A long time ago someone paid Walter Benjamin—or Dawson, if you like—fifty thousand dollars for some purpose. Maybe to kill Flaherty, maybe not. But Selina Benjamin knows about it. She marries the man, and may have had twenty years of hell with him. Then he dies—he is dead, I've verified that—and she is free. So one of several things may happen. Perhaps her conscience bothers her. Perhaps she sees a chance for more blackmail. Or perhaps, if she wrote the anonymous letter I got, she intends to warn Mrs. Chandler she is in danger."

"So she has to be silenced?"

"She had to be killed."

I got up dizzily.

"I can't bear it," I said. "Judith never killed anybody."

"No," he said, to my surprise. "I don't think she did. Only it's going to be hard to prove."

He let me go then. It was the policeman, not the lover, who showed me out the door of the cottage, and I went home in a bad humor and a mental state of chaos.

I had another sleepless night after that, and at two in the morning I got the pad from my table and tried to make some sort of outline of what I knew. As I kept it, along with the drawing of the cat, I copy it here to show my mental confusion at the time.

The murder of Selina Benjamin.

My visit to her house $\begin{cases} \text{cat} \\ \text{bankbooks} \\ \text{clippings.} \end{cases}$

The inquest and Phil's golf club.

The story of Flaherty.

The rock through Judith's window. Was there a note?

The man who dumped me in the pool.

Bill's fight with him, or with someone, and his breaking into the house.

The shooting of O'Brien.

The theft of the clippings and so on from the cottage.

Helga and Dawson's picture. What does she know?

Judith's attempt at suicide.

They made no sense, of course. There were even none of the clues Sara Winters always sprinkles about, no lost buttons or cuff links, no handy fragments of cloth or fingerprints. Nothing much except Selina's necklace, which only proved she had been at the pool—a fact we certainly knew anyhow—and the golf club, which might have been missing for days without anyone's noticing it.

If I dreamed about O'Brien that night I do not remember it. But I did realize that I was in love with two men; one was big, gentle and loving; the other was a policeman —and I wondered drearily if the two ever met.

27

I packed Judith's trunks in town the next day. She was up and about that morning, and determined to leave The Birches as soon as possible. She even went down to the telephone and tried to make a reservation at the Plaza for the next day. They could not take her until the day after, which infuriated her, and when I left for the city she was calling the various travel agencies. So far as I could hear the news was still bad. All

they could offer was a possible cancellation at the last minute, and she looked rather daunted as she dropped into a hall chair.

"Get my trunks packed anyhow, will you, Lois?" she said feverishly. "They can be forwarded abroad to me if I get a ship."

She sat there, the small dressings still on her wrists and her color bad, but her mouth set determinedly. She was not able to travel. She was not even fit to be where she was, out of bed and downstairs. But there was a sort of desperation about her that morning which left me without protest.

I lunched at the Waldorf with Ridge that day. He had the keys to the apartment and to various closets there, and he had located Clarice, who agreed to help me. He himself was not going back.

"I've turned that particular page," he said, his face set. "I don't want to reopen it."

He did not look well. He was nervous too, although a couple of Martinis relaxed him. He listened to my story of what Judith maintained was a burglar after her jewels, and said she was a fool not to keep them in the bank. But he thought The Birches was no place for her, and said so.

Not until the meal was over and his demitasse was in front of him did he refer to our last meeting and then, I felt, unwillingly.

"About the money I gave your mother," he said, "that was strictly between us, Lois. No need of having it talked about."

"It's nothing I'm very proud of, Ridge. I still can't imagine mother getting into a jam. Didn't she tell you what it was?"

"I gathered it was serious. That's all I know."

I was tempted to tell him about Dawson, and I have wondered since if things would have been different if I had. But he had paid the check and was ready to go, so I said nothing.

He dropped me at the apartment on Fifth Avenue, but he did not go in. Clarice was waiting in the foyer, and we went up in the elevator together. Her face was alive with curiosity, although she said nothing until we had raised the shades and opened the windows. The huge apartment smelled of moth preventives. It had the moldy odor of places shut up for a long time, and with the furniture and even the paintings covered it was dismal and dark.

Clarice called the houseman to bring up the trunks from the basement, and while we waited for them and I lit a cigarette she eyed me.

"Mr. Chandler says the madam is going abroad," she said. "Surely she's not going alone?"

"If you mean a maid, she is having enough trouble getting passage for herself."

She sighed.

"I have missed her," she said. "I have a lady now, of course, but she is old and ugly. It was a pleasure to dress Mrs. Chandler. She was always a picture. And such lovely clothes! I do not understand it," she went on when I said nothing. "So gay she was, and then all at once everything is wrong. She does not go out, she has no parties, even some days she stays in bed. In bed all day," she added. "Not even eating! And Mr. Chandler is bewildered, poor man. Why not?"

"She hasn't been well, Clarice. Perhaps that explains it."

She tossed her head.

"She was not sick, Miss Maynard. I have thought—perhaps Mr. Chandler has a pretty lady somewhere and she finds it out. But then I think that is silly. Mr.

Chandler is not that sort of man. He is too well bred."

I might have enlightened her on what Bill would have called the capers of some well-bred people I knew, but the trunks arrived just then and we set to work.

Even I had not realized the breadth and depth of Judith's wardrobe as Clarice lovingly took dress after dress out of their protective bags. She lingered over the ermine evening wrap.

"I always thought that was the reason she had the row the first night she wore it," she said. "It had just come home, and it must have cost a fortune. Not that he said anything when she showed it to him, except that she looked fine in it. I was there, so he couldn't. But after she came home—wow! He must have given her hell."

"I think we won't discuss Mrs. Chandler," I said briefly. "Let's get on with this packing."

She turned sulky after that, but I paid no attention. I was trying to reconcile Ridge's story about that night with what I had just heard. Somehow it made better sense if they had quarreled, Judith's taking out her jewels and more or less appraising them, and her decision to leave them. He must have said some unforgivable thing. Perhaps that she had been bought and paid for with the money he gave mother and, as he had told me, he felt there had been no value received.

I let Clarice finish the packing and went into the drawing room and stood looking out at the park. Small boys were sailing yachts on the lake almost under the window and, as I watched, one of them turned over and sank. I could hear the boy's wails from where I stood. It made me think of Judith, whose small craft had so nearly sunk.

Her bags were in the hall when I got home that afternoon, so I gathered she really meant to leave us. I found her in bed, however, looking exhausted.

"Well," I said cheerfully, "your trunks are packed and ready. Ridge let me in and Clarice helped me."

"That snoop!" she said. "Are you sure you got everything? She's quite capable of holding out something she liked."

"She didn't hold out your ermine and sable coat, although she drooled over it. It looks as though it had never been worn."

"I only wore it once," she said. "Do you mind sending me a tray? I'm weaker than I realized."

Obviously the coat was out, as were so many things. If she and Ridge quarreled over it she had no intention of telling me. I saw too that her jewel case was beside the bed, and the safe was open and empty.

"Aren't you afraid of our burglar again?" I said. "What's the idea, Jude? They were all right where they were."

"I'll need them, if I get a late cancellation on the *Queen Mary*. There's a chance I may, at the last minute."

I told Phil at the dinner table that night that she was really leaving, and he drew a long breath.

"It's about time," he said, pushing aside the junket Jennie had served him. "She's my sister, but look at the record! She married a good guy who let her run wild for years. Too much drinking, too late hours, and a lot of parasites around her, picking up the crumbs. Then she leaves him. No reason. Just shucked him like an ear of corn."

"So she tries to kill herself," I said. "That's silly, Phil."

"Well, she's at an uncertain age," he said. "She's been a beauty too. Now she's fading, and knows it. That's probably the reason."

"Why did she marry Ridge, Phil? She wasn't in love with him. He isn't even attractive."

"Money," he said tersely. "Ten millions of it. I'm not mercenary, but I'd marry a girl with two heads for less than that."

He got up, after giving the junket a look of pure loathing, and lit a cigarette.

"Think I'll go down and see our cop," he said. "The damn fool ought to be in bed. Maybe I can get him there."

Bill was out, so I was alone after he left, and when the phone rang I thought rather hopefully it would be a travel agency with a room for Judith. To my astonishment it was Doctor Townsend.

"I wonder if you will do an errand for me tomorrow?" he said. "It may be a considerable job, but I've been thinking over that last talk of ours. After all, a still young-ish and beautiful woman doesn't try to kill herself without good reason. And the impulse may still be there."

"She's leaving here the day after tomorrow," I told him.

"For where?"

"The Plaza first, Europe eventually. What do you want me to do, doctor?"

What he wanted was rather curious. He sounded apologetic as he explained. Briefly, and if I was willing, I was to go the next morning to the Public Library, where the various newspapers kept their back files, and look over the winter of 1929–30.

"Look for any mention of your family," he said. "Your father's death, if you don't mind, and the society pages too. It will give you a date or two anyhow. And see if any of you were involved in any trouble at that time. Outside of the panic, of course. Just see what you can pick up."

I don't think he liked the idea himself. The ethics of it must have bothered him. On the other hand, he was trying to help Judith in the only way he knew, and I understood.

"I'll do anything you think will be useful," I told him. "But I doubt if the society news will be helpful. We were in mourning, you know."

"When did your father die?"

"In January, 1930."

"Why not look before that? In November or December. I think what happened to Mrs. Chandler happened that winter. That's what she blocks off, if you know what I mean."

As a result I went in to the city with Phil the next morning. He was not curious, fortunately. He read the paper all the way, and accepted my statement about needing stockings with no comment whatever.

I had no difficulty at the Library, but it was a tough job. The back issues were kept on microfilm, and looking at them through a viewer was troublesome. Also, except for an account of father's death, which I did not read, and a brief notice that mother and Judith had gone to Tucson early in February, there was no mention of the family. But purely by chance I happened on the story of the Preston girl's murder.

The story, when I read it, was about the trial. The date was February, 1930. A boy named Shannon, a student at Columbia at the time, had been on friendly terms with a girl of indifferent reputation who worked in one of the five-and-ten-cent stores. She lived in a tenement on the East Side, and one evening in November, 1929, she was heard quarreling with Shannon. Late that night her strangled body was found in her room, Shannon had been arrested, and in February went on trial.

He protested his innocence but the evidence was all against him. One of the witnesses who identified him before the grand jury was a young woman whose picture was shown.

I sat back and studied it. Given almost twenty-one years and the blankness of a dead face, it was Selina Benjamin. It was her testimony before the grand jury that indicted Shannon, and although she had disappeared by that time

had helped convict him. Flaherty had believed she was lying, had probably traced her to the town up the Hudson, and been killed before he had seen her.

None of this related to my own family, of course, except for Dawson, whose name was never mentioned. But apparently the jury recognized Shannon's youth, for on its recommendation he was given life instead of the chair.

I found a picture of him after he had been sentenced, but he had turned his face away as if to avoid the camera. All I could see was a well-built youth with heavy hair and broad shoulders. And the young uniformed man beside him and manacled to him, according to the caption underneath, was one Sergeant O'Brien.

I called the doctor, reporting I had found nothing, and later I lunched with Anne. She had a maid again, so we ate, as she said, like Christians. But I did not tell her what I had been doing. Instead I asked her if she had ever heard of a Mollie Preston or a Johnny Shannon. She only looked blank.

"Who are they? I never heard of them."

"I only wondered if they were friends of Judith's years ago. I came across the names somewhere."

"Oh, Judith! If they were a part of the gang around the swimming pool every summer, I wouldn't know them. The amount of riffraff she collected . . . !"

She said Ridgely was selling the

apartment and had offered her Judith's huge grand piano.

"As if I had room for it," she said sourly. "Martha wants it, but I told her if she brought it in her father and I would have to move out on the street."

Her real interest, however, was in the fact that Judith was leaving The Birches for the Plaza, and the reason she gave for it.

"A burglar," she said, "and in the house! What on earth did you do?"

"I lost my dinner, for one thing."

I had to explain it, of course, and she looked appalled.

"I suppose he was after that jewelry of hers," she said. "She's acting like a fool about it. Why not put it in the bank? Ridge says it's actually dangerous to carry it about as she does."

I left her soon after, but I did not want to go home. Call it intuition. Call it a hunch if you like, but I was depressed and not a little sad. I could still see O'Brien handcuffed to Johnny Shannon. He had been looking straight at the camera, and there was nothing in his face to show that the boy beside him was going to something worse than death. He looked like a man doing his duty. Nothing more.

Was that what it meant to be a policeman? I thought. To be in Homicide, sending people to the chair or up for life? To build cases against them, stubbornly and doggedly, to grow hard in so doing, and yet to care for some woman, love her and marry her. Even have children and love them too.

Because O'Brien could be hard, and I knew it. I did not want to see him that day. Instead I went to a double-feature movie which I hardly saw, ate a hamburger supper, and took a late train home. As both Phil and Bill were out to dinner, nobody met me.

The only taxi at the station was Ed Brown's, and he drove me to The Birches that night. He sat grumpily in the front seat of the rattletrap he called his car, and at the entrance to our drive he stopped.

"Guess you can walk the rest of the way," he said. "I got to get home. Missed my supper already."

"It won't take you two minutes to go on, Ed. I'm tired. Go ahead. Don't be stubborn."

He turned around in the seat and glared at me.

"Too many bullets flying around this place," he said. "Too much sudden death, if you ask me. Either you walk or you stay in the car and I'll take you back to the station. All the same to me."

I was furious, but I knew Ed. I got out grumbling and I did not tip him, which made him clash his gears with indignation. But I need not have worried about seeing O'Brien. The cottage was dark and his car gone.

I was hardly in the house when the telephone rang, and a man's voice asked for Judith. She must have been listening, for she was down the stairs in a hurry. As I stood by I could see she was wildly excited.

"Of course I can make it," she said. "I'll make it if I have to walk.

Oh, you're sending a car for me? That's splendid. We have none here. My brother is out to dinner somewhere, and so is my nephew. . . . Another passenger, you say? Where do I pick him up?"

Later on, with police all around, I tried to tell them of her real excitement, her real happiness that night. She was not acting. She was almost the young Judith I had admired and loved years ago. But they did not believe me.

She turned to me from the telephone, her eyes shining.

"What incredible luck!" she said. "A really good cabin on the *Queen Mary*. It's a late cancellation. They're sending a car out to pick up someone or other, so they are having it come for me first, and I'll pick the man up on my way in." She was already halfway up the stairs. "We'll have to hurry," she said. "The ship's sailing at midnight, and I have to get there in time. It's lucky I'm partly packed. You'll have to send my trunks later, Lois. I'll cable you where."

She shot up to her room and I followed her. It was after nine by that time, and the two maids were in bed. I did not wake them. While Judith started to dress I finished her packing, and carried the bags down the stairs. After that there was a considerable wait, with Judith consulting her wrist watch every five minutes. When at last we heard the car grinding up the drive I was in what might be called a state. It was almost ten by that time, a starless, moonless night, and I remember piling the bags into the big black car without any attempt at order.

Then Judith was kissing me good-bye, and with her jewel case on her lap was waving as the car started.

28

I waited until the car reached the main road, then with a curious sense of deflation I went back into the house. She was gone, and I realized unexpectedly that I was going to miss her. I went up to her room, which was a chaos of tissue paper, discarded stockings, and all sorts of odds and ends, and for something to do set to work to put it at least partly in order.

There was no need any longer of the bolts on her door or on her bathroom, I thought as I worked.

The terror, whatever it had been, was gone. Or was it? The big quiet house seemed full of ghosts: of mother dying in the walnut bed beside me, of Judith unconscious in it, of the unknown man lurking outside in the hall. I felt somewhat better when, an hour or so later, I saw the lights come on in the cottage and knew O'Brien had come back.

I needed to see him. Not only to tell him Judith had gone, so he no longer felt he had to watch the place at night, but for reasons of my own. I had been badly shaken that day, and my confidence had not yet returned. I needed to see him, not as the man shackled to Johnny Shannon but as the O'Brien I knew, the big kindly man who tolerated Henrietta and even built a roost for her in the kitchen, the man who liked his girls and said he loved me.

The house was still empty when I left it. Neither Phil nor Bill had come back, although it was after one o'clock. And the darkness was appalling. Well as I knew the drive I had more or less to feel my way. Yet darkness meant safety, I thought, in case our intruder was still about. He might not know that Judith was gone, and in fact it was only when I was near the pool that I heard any sound at all.

Someone was in the shrubbery. Whoever it was was moving slowly, as if with a cool deliberation which was worse than any sort of haste. It sent me running madly for the cottage and safety, and fortunately O'Brien heard me coming. He opened the door for me, and it was at that instant a shot rang out. It struck the wall of the cottage beside me as he dragged me inside and shoved me down on the floor as he slammed the door.

"For God's sake!" he said. "What are you doing here?"

He didn't wait for an answer. He left me there and shut off the lights, but not before I had seen his face. He was all policeman at that moment. What's more, he was furious at me.

"Don't move," he said sharply. "He may try again. Where is he?"

"Where he always is," I said hysterically. "Near the pool."

I could hear him getting his gun, and the next moment he was quietly opening the door. It was more than I could bear. Probably I screamed. I know I begged him not to go out, that the intruder was still there.

"He'll kill you!" I yelled. "He's tried once. He'll try again."

"Not now he won't," he said grimly. "That voice of yours was a warning all right. He's gone."

It was some time before I let him go out. I was still crying like a fool, and I knew he was furiously impatient with me when at last he took his gun and a flashlight and went out. I was sitting up drying my eyes when he came back.

"You certainly have a faculty for spilling the beans," he said coldly. "Can't you ever learn to keep your pretty mouth shut?"

Somehow I managed to get on my feet.

"I'm sorry," I said. "I didn't want you shot again. That's all. And I don't like policemen. They're hard. They're not like other people. They have no feelings."

And then I was sobbing on his breast, and his arms were around me, sling and all.

"It isn't cruel to try to get a killer," he said. "It makes the world a better place to live in, mavourneen."

He let me cry it out, my fright and shock, and when I was quieter he offered me a large, very clean white handkerchief. Then he put me into his own chair, and drew up one for himself.

"Let's have this out," he said. "If you ever marry me I'll still be a cop, my darling. It's all I know to be. It's in me, as it was in Flaherty. But I'll be on the side of the law. That ought to mean something."

He was wearing his other face now, the one I knew and loved, and when Henrietta came in, eying us in her crooked manner, he put down a hand and stroked her absently.

"Something's happened to you," he said. "You've known all along what my job is. What is it?"

"I saw your picture today," I told him. "It was an old one. You were taking the Shannon boy to prison for life, and you didn't seem to care."

"I cared all right," he said. "What did you expect me to do? Burst into tears?" And when I only shook my head he went on. "Maybe I'd better tell you about Johnny," he said. "Perhaps I should have done it sooner. You see, he was by way of being a friend of mine. I visited him all the time he was shut away and last winter I got him out. He wasn't even on parole. He was free."

"*You* did that?"

"Don't give me too much credit. He'd been a model prisoner, and the case had been purely circumstantial anyhow. But there he was, free, and with no place to go. You'll have to know his problem, Lois, to understand him. It's not easy to get work for a man like that. He was forty, and his hair had turned white, so he looked even older.

"He lived with me for a while. He was fine. He knew a lot too. He'd read about everything in the prison library. He was the librarian for a long time. But he had one obsession. He hadn't killed the Preston girl, and he wanted his name cleared.

"I think he located the Benjamin woman about that time, although he never told me. Possibly he scared her too, for she and her husband closed the shop and went away, ostensibly to visit her sister, and Walter Benjamin died there.

"But Selina had to come back eventually. There was the estate to settle, the shop to sell. She must have been afraid at first, but as time went on and Johnny let her alone she gained confidence. There was something else too. She had joined the church, and her conscience was bothering her badly. I think too she began to worry about your sister."

"Judith!" I said, bewildered. "What had she to do with him?"

"I'm coming to her, my dear. She knew Johnny was free. The papers played it up when he was released, and it was she, far more than Selina Benjamin, who had let him go up for life. No wonder she was terrified, or wanted to get out of the country."

"Are you saying Judith killed the Preston girl? That's crazy. It's insane. Judith at eighteen! How could she even know her? Mother watched over her day and night."

"That's as it may be, my dear. Let's say after Reno Shannon meant to see her, and had a reason for it. Perhaps he wasn't normal. The big house does things to men, and he'd been there a long time. I began to worry about him, so I wrote to a friend of mine, the police chief in Reno, and told him the facts. He arranged for Johnny to get a license there to drive a taxicab, under the name of Alec Morrison. He did pretty well out there. Reno is a free-and-easy town. But when I read in the papers that Judith Chandler had gone there to divorce her husband I didn't like it. I got some leave and went out. Johnny was all right. Apparently he didn't even know she was there, and I didn't tell him.

"He seemed contented, now that he had a job. He even had a girl, although he said he wouldn't marry her until he was cleared of the murder charge. Then, on the day you were leaving, he saw Mrs.

Chandler on the train, and she saw him. He hadn't changed much, except for his hair, and his cap hid that. But I didn't like the way he stared at her. There was twenty years of pure hatred in it. She saw it too, and fainted."

My lips were dry and my whole face felt tight.

"Why did she faint?" I said. "You know, don't you? You knew all the time, didn't you? It was no accident you were on that train."

"No, it was no accident." He reached over and took both my hands. "Look, Lois, this isn't going to be easy. I hate like hell to do it, but just bear with me, that's all. I'm going to begin with your mother. I'm Irish, and the Irish love their children but, as Doctor Townsend would say, we're not cannibals. We don't eat them alive.

"In a way, that is what your mother did with your sister Judith. It's hard to understand why a cat will pick one out of a litter of kittens to prefer, or a hen a chicken. It happens. I've seen it happen. In this case your mother picked on Judith. Why? She had other children, but for one thing Judith was the beauty of the outfit. She had great hopes for her. She was to make a wonderful marriage and restore the family fortunes, and eventually she did make what looked like a good one. To see that happen your mother was willing to go to any lengths outside of murder.

"But Judith herself almost ruined her prospects. Young as she was, Ridgely Chandler was deeply in love with her but she wasn't in love with him. I don't think she ever had been. In fact she had a sort of adolescent crush on a good-looking boy who used to come out here to the pool on Saturdays.

"The boy was Johnny Shannon."

I didn't speak. I couldn't.

"I think Dawson knew about it. He probably let her in when she came back. But one night she went to Johnny's room on Morningside Heights and was there until almost morning. That was the night the Preston girl was murdered. He had seen Mollie earlier, to tell her he was through, but when she was killed he was with Judith Maynard, as she was then.

"You see how it was, darling. She was his alibi, and his only one. Apparently no one else had seen him. But he told Flaherty, and Flaherty went to see her. Your mother was there, and Flaherty called in Dawson. They both lied. So did Judith. She sat there in your big city house, Flaherty told me, looking like an angel, and lied her head off. He had left me outside, I was his sergeant, and he came out swearing. 'She was in Shannon's room all right,' he said, 'but she's afraid to admit it. She sat there, knowing that boy may go to the chair, and as much as sent him there.'

"Johnny didn't get the chair. He was young and the evidence was circumstantial. He got twenty years to life. But Judith Maynard knew what she had done. In a way I suppose that accounts for the life she led after she married

Chandler. She was safe, as safe as churches, but there must have been times when she remembered the man up the river, with the best years of his life gone. It killed Johnny's mother too, but she may not have known that.

"It was some time until the case came up for trial, and before it did your mother whisked Judith off to Arizona. And Kate Henry disappeared. So did Dawson. But other people had seen Johnny go to the Preston girl's place. I've always thought there was malice in their testimony. He wasn't a part of them. They called him Mollie's dude, just as they protected Dawson, who was raised among them.

"Flaherty got all that, and something more which came from your Helga. She knew Dawson was crazy about Mollie, and she thought he was the one who strangled her. She only thought, which is no good in a murder trial, and before Kate Henry disappeared the police got a deposition from her. It wasn't used at the trial, but it existed and the District Attorney's office knew about it.

"Only Flaherty thought she was lying. She was in love with Dawson, it stood out all over her. And somehow he got on her trail. One evening he told me he was sure he had located her, in a small town up the Hudson. He said he was going there the next day, and if he was right Johnny would go free. But he wouldn't tell me what he knew, or even the name of the town, and that night he was shot and killed.

"He was on his way home when it happened. He had driven his car into the garage beside his house when he got it. His wife was waiting for him. She was having a steak for him. People could buy steak in 1930. Steak and onions. When I got there you could smell onions all over the place.

"She didn't last long after his death. Just didn't want to live. But I promised her I'd find his killer if it took me a lifetime, and for twenty years I've carried the bullet that killed him."

He looked at my frozen face.

"I'm sorry, darling, but now you understand what Judith was afraid of. It was Shannon. I don't think he meant to hurt her. He was no killer. But he did want the alibi she could give him. The worst of it was I had lost him after he left Reno. Even his girl didn't know where he was, or if he had changed his name. I suspected he had come to New York and taken a chauffeur's job, or managed to get a license to drive a taxi. It's not easy, but his Reno license would help. But I was sure of one thing. He would try to see your sister. That's why I took this place.

"He did try. You know that. He picked you up, thinking you were Judith Chandler, and remember what he said. You were to talk. That's all he wanted, for Judith to talk and clear him. He threw a note tied to a rock through her window. He even broke into the house and got upstairs."

"He shot you, didn't he?" I said. "And he fired at you or me to-

night. If that's not being a killer, what is?"

He shook his head.

"Maybe he's changed," he admitted. "But look at my position. When Selina Benjamin was killed here at your pool I was frantic. She as well as Judith was responsible for those lost twenty years. And I couldn't catch him. He was as slippery as an eel, and I began to think—after I was shot—the hell of a lot more dangerous. That's why I asked you to put those ads in the papers, so he would know I was watching him.

"Then, a day or so ago, I had a glimmer of the sense God gave me. I went over to the Adrian house and broke in. He hadn't been living there all the time. He must have had some sort of job. But there was a cot in the kitchen and some canned food, and behind the garage there was an oil slick, where he had hidden his car."

He released my hands, picked up Henrietta gently and carried her to her roost. When he came back he bent down and kissed me. I must have been unresponsive, for he straightened.

"I'm a cop, Lois," he said. "And once a cop always a cop. Johnny didn't kill Flaherty. He was locked away by that time. And Dawson is dead and beyond my reach. I verified it. But someone has tried twice to kill me. That shot tonight was for me, not you. I mean to get him, or her, whoever it was."

Yes, I thought drearily, he would never change. He was wearing his policeman's face again, standing there on the hearth, and when I saw it I looked away.

"How can you say he's not a killer?" I protested. "He murdered Selina Benjamin, and threw her into the pool."

"Why?" he said. "Why would he, Lois? He must have been counting on her to help him. Why kill her?"

There was no time for more. Bill's Ark roared and rattled into the drive and the next minute he was pounding on the door.

"Hiya," he said when O'Brien opened it. "You people know what time it is? What will Judith say?"

"Judith won't say anything, Bill. She's gone."

He grinned.

"What sort of gone? Departed this life or merely The Birches? In any case I shall be brave. I shall bear it like a man."

What with the shot and O'Brien's story, I suddenly realized I had forgotten to tell O'Brien. He stared at me incredulously.

"You mean she's left The Birches?" he said. "Don't you think you might have told me?"

"There was nothing really to tell. At the last minute one of her travel agencies got a cancellation on the *Queen Mary* and sent a car for her."

"You're sure of that?"

"What else could it be?" I said. "After all, she's been hoping for weeks to get such a break."

Perhaps it is hindsight, but I thought O'Brien looked worried. However, at Bill's suggestion—it appeared that Janey's family was opposed to the demon rum—he mixed highballs for all of us, and it was with glasses in our hands and a general appearance of revelry that Phil found us.

He stood in the doorway in his dinner clothes, unsmiling and indignant.

"What the hell goes on here?" he said. "Do you know what time it is?"

"We're celebrating the fact that our dear Judith is now on her way to England," Bill explained. "She's gone, lock, stock, and barrel, with the emphasis on the lock."

Phil relaxed after I told him what had happened. He sat down, explaining that he had won three dollars at bridge that night, and that something should be done about people who didn't watch their partner's discards. But he did not stay. He said firmly that he was not leaving his sister to any orgy, and insisted on driving me home.

He asked a question or two about Judith's departure, and I sensed considerable relief in him.

"I'm fond of her," he said. "At least I suppose so. But she could certainly raise hell around a house. You can have mother's room again too. You'll like that."

I have written this and then re-read it. For the plain truth is that I never moved into mother's room at all. I couldn't face it.

Not until I was in the house did I realize how carefully O'Brien had avoided telling Phil or Bill about the shot that night. It had been deliberate, I knew. But why? Frank as he had been about

Johnny Shannon I knew I had heard only part of the story: that Flaherty's murder was still in it, and Dawson; Judith, too, and perhaps even mother.

It was hours before I slept. I was back in the drawing room of the city house, with its Aubusson carpet and its petit point chairs. It must have been gloomy, that winter day, with Judith crouched in a chair, looking like an angel and lying her head off. And mother lying too.

She must have known the truth. She had paid Dawson an enormous sum to keep quiet. But with Flaherty there that day she was seeing all her hopes for Judith gone; Judith on the witness stand, admitting she had spent at least part of the night in Johnny Shannon's room, a soiled angel indeed. And Flaherty watching them all three, for Shannon claimed Dawson had let Judith out and waited for her to come home.

They must have been terrified, all three of them, have known Flaherty did not believe them. I could almost see him there, the law personified.

"I hope you realize what you are doing. You are sending this boy to the chair, or to life in prison. It's the end of everything for him."

And silence. No one speaking, and at last Flaherty grabbing his hat and going out to the young sergeant who was driving his car, swearing.

"She was in Shannon's room all right, O'Brien, but she's afraid to admit it. She sat there, knowing that boy may go to the chair, and as good as sent him there."

Had father known about it? I wondered. Had mother gone to him the day of the dinner party and asked for his help, for money to keep Dawson quiet or to get Judith out of town? He must have been in torture that night, honorable man that he was, faced with the dilemma of ruining his daughter's reputation or letting an innocent boy possibly die. Things were bad for him anyhow. He was bankrupt. He may have played with the idea of suicide before, but this was more than he could take.

So he left that strange note about his conscience for mother. Perhaps he hoped it would influence her, his last message before his death. But she never saw it, and she was beyond influence by that time.

For the first time that night I wondered about Helga. All along she had known something. Perhaps she had been awake and seen or heard Judith coming home. Perhaps Dawson's sudden affluence had set her to thinking. It was even possible she knew about the tobacco shop and told Flaherty where it was, only to have him shot before he could act on the knowledge.

She must have blamed herself for his death. Certainly it frightened her. I thought bleakly that she had probably been frightened for twenty years.

29

It seemed to me I had hardly got asleep when Jennie brought me the news that Helga's arthritis was bad and I would have to help with the breakfast. So it happened that I was resignedly fighting the huge old coal range when the boy came with the milk. He put down the bottles and stood goggle eyed in the doorway.

"Haven't heard the news, have you?" he inquired.

"What news, Tommy?"

"Man killed last night," he said importantly. "Nobody knows who he is. His car's down in the valley beside the road only a mile or so from your gate. I seen it."

"Killed!" I said. "How dreadful. What happened?"

But before he could answer Phil yelled for his breakfast, and when I came back from the dining room Tommy was gone. Phil raised his eyebrows when I placed his bacon and eggs in front of him.

"Oh, no! Not eggs again!" he said.

"You'd better thank God for O'Brien and his girls," I said indignantly. "And if it interests you, the milk boy says a man's been killed down the road."

"There should be a special place in hell for the man who invented wheels," he observed. "And another for the man who added an engine to them. Also for eggs," he added sourly. "Isn't there such a thing as sausage to be had?"

Which shows neither of us doubted it was the usual car accident. We had one every now and then during the summer. It was hours before we learned the dreadful truth.

Bill slept late that morning, so I fed Phil and took him to the train. O'Brien's car was gone, and at the scene of the accident there was a small crowd in the road. Down below it in the valley both the local police and the state men were busy, but Phil would not let me stay to look. Someone said the body had already been taken away, which was all we knew at the time.

It was still, of course, a matter of purely academic interest to us. Our roads are often tricky, winding around the hills as they do, and when I drove back from the station the police had cleared the place, and down in the valley only the Chief, a uniformed man or two and a half dozen State Troopers were there, as well as a photographer from town.

I stopped the car, and Fowler saw me and laboriously climbed the slope.

"Funny thing," he said. "That car down there has half a dozen bags in it. You wouldn't know anything about it, would you?"

I gasped.

"Bags?" I said. "What sort of bags?"

"Good looking. Expensive, I'd say. Your sister's initials are on them. Was she sending them anywhere?"

I looked down at the overturned car. It was on its side, but it was almost certainly the one that had called for Judith the night before. I must have turned pale, for Fowler hastened to reassure me.

"Nobody in it but the driver," he said. "Were you afraid there was someone else?"

"I thought it might be Mrs. Chandler," I told him bleakly. "She took a car like that one to go to New York last night. She was sailing on the *Queen Mary*."

"Maybe someone picked her up after it happened."

"She'd never have left her luggage," I said. "Only, where is she? I don't understand."

"Well, she'd had a pretty bad shock if she was in the car when it left the road. Turned over a couple of times. Might just have wandered off somewhere. Maybe you'd better come down and take a look. It's not bad," he added, seeing my face. "The fellow's gone. Not much blood either. Head wounds don't bleed much."

I followed him down the hill, my legs shaking and my head dizzy. The men stood aside to let me see the car, but it was not necessary. Judith's bags sat beside it on the grass, and her purse was with them, the big handsome one she always carried.

"It's the car," I said shakily. "It picked her up around half past eleven last night, and I put the bags in it myself."

"Didn't notice the driver, did you?"

"Only vaguely. I know he wore a chauffeur's cap, but we were in a hurry. I don't think he even got out. Only I don't see her jewel case. She had it when she left."

He stood rubbing his chin, which had missed its morning shave, and eying the luggage.

"Sure of that, are you?"

"Positive. She had it on her lap."

"Well, you never can tell," he said. "Those boys over there found the car. They were going fishing. One of them might have snitched it."

I had not noticed the boys before. There were four of them sitting on the hillside, and he called them over.

"Now listen, kids," he said sternly. "There's a small bag missing from this lot. Any of you take it?"

They disclaimed it immediately and loudly. They hadn't even touched anything. They had come across it at six o'clock or thereabouts, and they had hailed the first car that passed.

"Anybody else in the car or near it?" Fowler persisted. "A lady, for instance?"

They looked dazed. They hadn't

seen anyone but the chauffeur, and he was dead. Fowler let them go, and stood surveying the wreckage.

"This jewel case," he said. "It sort of changes things, doesn't it? Who knew she had it?"

"She always took it with her."

"Might be a case of assault and robbery," he said thoughtfully. "Maybe kidnaping too. Knock the driver out, grab the case, and take Mrs. Chandler along to gain some time. It wouldn't be hard to send the car over the edge. Road's narrow here."

It had been a stolen car, he said. The owner had missed it when he left the theater the night before, and reported it. As the thief had worn a chauffeur's uniform, no one noticed him.

I must have driven home, although I don't remember doing so. That blessed automatism which I believe comes from the spinal cord at least took me there and into the house. Jennie was taking up Judith's breakfast tray when I got back. I told her not to bother, that Mrs. Chandler had gone to the city, but I did not explain, for O'Brien was limping up the porch steps. He looked exhausted.

"Any extra coffee floating around?" he inquired. "I haven't had time for breakfast."

Still dazed I got Judith's tray and set it before him. He drank only a cup of black coffee, however.

"You saw the bags, I suppose?" he asked.

"Yes. They were hers."

"I'm afraid I have some bad news for you," he said quietly. "For you only," he added. "I've been to the mortuary. The dead man was Johnny Shannon, Lois. And he was murdered, poor guy. Shot."

"Shot!" I said weakly.

"Shot in the back of the head."

In the back of the head! I knew what he was thinking: Judith behind Johnny and learning who he was. Maybe his telling her, and she realizing how all she had built for twenty years was about to be destroyed.

"Hold it!" O'Brien said. "Put your head down."

I tried it, but it was no good. I simply fell forward on the porch floor and passed out.

When I came to I was in my own bed, with Helga beside me. She wouldn't let me talk at first. Finally, however, she broke down. Judith, she said, was still missing and they were beating the woods for her. Phil had come back from the city, and he and Bill had joined the searching parties. Also Anne was downstairs having hysterics, and—she said this was a certain unction—Jennie had put a bottle of household ammonia under her nose and nearly strangled her.

I had been out, it appeared, for several hours.

Anne was allowed to see me after lunch. She came in like a whirlwind. Judith had been kidnaped and probably killed, she said, and her jewel case was still missing. Also Ridge had called up, suggesting he send out a Homicide detective from New York, and the newspapers had the story. All sorts of reporters had been on the phone, and one of them had asked her if Judith shot the driver. And if so, why?

"A chauffeur?" she wailed. "Why would she kill a man like that? What's happened to this family? It isn't enough that you fall in love with a policeman. Now Judith kills a cab driver!"

I let that pass.

"How could she kill anybody?" I said. "She had no gun. I know. I helped her pack. I think they're all demented."

There was no question, however, that Judith had disappeared. Whatever had happened she had been able to leave the car. Anne was sure she had been kidnaped, and insisted on walking down to the mailbox to see if a ransom letter had arrived. But when Phil came in, late in the afternoon, dirty and utterly weary, he said they were sure she had gone on her own two feet. They found her high heel marks on the soft shoulder of the road, not far from where the car had gone over.

I was downstairs by that time, to Helga's disgust, and I brought him a drink and some food on the porch. He had had no lunch, and while he ate he said they had got out the Boy Scouts, and were sending for a helicopter.

"She may be dazed and wandering anywhere," he said. "That's pretty wild country. Of course she may be dead. Whoever shot the driver may have shot her too. Only he didn't kill her. She got

away. But where she got to is anybody's guess."

He had some real information, however. The telephone call had been a phony. The *Queen Mary* had sailed while Judith was still on the road. Moreover, there had been no last-minute cancellations, and none of the travel agencies had called her.

"Most of them close at six o'clock anyhow," he said.

But the police knew the identity of the dead man. I held my breath, but he went on calmly enough.

"New York driver's license in the name of Alec Morrison," he said. "How on earth did she get him? Was he a phony too?"

I told him that during the message about the *Queen Mary* whoever it was had offered to send a car for her. It was to stop for another passenger, a man, I thought. The car was to come first to The Birches and then pick him up.

"Very neat," he said. "A holdup, of course. The other passenger was the one who shot Morrison, and took the jewel case. Only where the hell is she? Did he take her with him?"

It seems incredible now that I had not told him about the shot the night before. At breakfast he had been in a hurry, and I had not seen him since. Now I told him, and Anne, having returned from the mailbox, heard me and gave a small shriek.

"Shot!" she said. "Who in the world would want to shoot you?"

"I don't know, Anne. O'Brien

thinks it was for him. It was dark, you know."

Phil turned a pair of cold eyes on me.

"Where was all this?" he demanded. "And when?"

"I suppose an hour or more after Judith left," I said guiltily. "I had some things to tell Lieutenant O'Brien, and I saw his light was on. I was at the door of the cottage when it happened."

He was still angry, furiously angry.

"For God's sake, why didn't you tell me you'd been shot at, when I brought you home from O'Brien's last night? What is he up to anyhow? It occurs to me that this was a quiet spot until he hit it. Since then we've had two murders and two shootings. And maybe a third death. Your own sister."

I never answered that. The helicopter appeared, flying low and some distance away, and we watched it with fascinated eyes. None of us, I think, noticed the car which had driven up until the man got out of it and climbed the steps.

It was Doctor Townsend.

"I'm sorry to intrude just now," he said, "but I gather from that machine in the air that you haven't located Mrs. Chandler."

"No," I said. "They're trying everything, of course. This is my sister Anne, Mrs. Harrison, doctor, and you may know my brother Phil. Won't you sit down?"

He did, but he declined Phil's offer of a drink.

"I have a radio in my car," he said. "I gather there is a rumor to the effect that Mrs. Chandler herself shot this driver and then escaped into the woods."

"That's idiotic," I told him. "I saw her off last night. I helped her pack too. She didn't have a gun. I don't think she ever had one. And she was happy when she left, happier than she had been for months."

"I see." It was a hot day, and he got out a handkerchief and mopped his face. "Of course I agree with you. She didn't do it. She was quite incapable of such a thing. The reason I came was this: If she could walk at all—and it seems she could—where would she be likely to go? As I drove past the place where the car went over I realized how wild it was. Knowing her, I don't think she would strike into those hills. She was a sensitive woman and a highly civilized one. It was a dark night too."

"All right," Phil said, annoyed. "Tell us where she would go. That's your business, isn't it? Knowing what people will or will not do?"

The doctor eyed him calmly.

"Quite definitely," he said. "Wearing the heels she always did she would stay on the road. Provided, of course, she could get there. She must have been in profound shock."

I suppose Phil was worried half sick, as we all were. Certainly he was exasperated.

"We may discover she took the *Queen Mary* after all!" he said. "Look, doctor, I'm sorry to be rude, but this is a hell of a situation. Judith hasn't been normal for months. We've put up with her locked doors, her shutting herself away. She tries to kill herself, and Lois here nurses her until she's exhausted. Now we've got this. If the sensational press thinks she killed this Morrison, we can't help it. But if you think we're hiding her here you're mistaken."

Doctor Townsend looked stubborn. He set his jaw.

"I didn't say that, Mr. Maynard. I do suggest a search of the grounds, even possibly of the pool down there. Where else could she go? In trouble most people strike for home. It means shelter, safety. Remember, even if she didn't kill this man she has been through a terrifying experience."

"The pool! Good God," Phil gasped. "Do you think she's there?"

The doctor shook his head.

"I have no idea where she is," he said. "I can only suggest that if she was able to move at all she would try to come here. Where else could she go?"

30

Bill returned as Phil went inside for his bathing trunks. He had no news. He was badly scratched and one leg of his gabardine slacks was torn from the knee down. Anne looked after him as he followed Phil into the house.

"You would think clothes grew on trees," she said acidly. "Did you ever learn who this Janey is? What's her last name?"

I hadn't an idea, and said so. Anne grunted.

"They never have any," she said fretfully. "They're Nell and Betty and God knows what. I often wonder what mother would think."

I didn't say anything. Down the drive by the pool I could see a girl in a pair of dirty white shorts who was trying to escape our attention. She had obviously been on the search with Bill and she was tying a handkerchief over what I imagined was a scratch on one of a pair of long and very bare legs. Anne was too shortsighted to see her, but so far as I could tell she was merely any seventeen-year-old, and probably Janey.

The men came out then and headed for the pool. Neither Anne nor I accompanied them. I was too shaken to move, and Anne was weeping into her drink, whether about Judith or Bill's slacks, I did not know. Janey did not move as the procession neared her, but when Bill stopped to explain to her she nodded, turned, and took a quick dive into the water, with a flash of slim legs and in what I imagined was a highly expensive sweater.

Then for fifteen minutes we waited. O'Brien's car drove in and stopped by the pool. When he came up to the house I saw by his face they had found nothing. Anne stopped crying to glare at him when he came up the steps.

"Sorry, old girl," he said. "It's pretty bad. But she's not dead. We'd have found her by now if she were. She's not in the pool either. I was in it myself around noon, looking for her." He glanced at Anne, or more specifically at her drink. "Hate to cadge your liquor," he said, "but I could do with one of those myself."

He sat down. If Bill had looked exhausted, O'Brien looked even worse. His shirt was torn and his slacks were stained and dirty. Anne gave him a frigid nod when I introduced him, but it didn't bother him. He sat back with his eyes closed until I gave him the whisky. He gulped it down and sat up, as if he had a new idea.

"Ever hear the story about the village idiot and the jackass?" He looked at Anne. "He just thought where he'd go if he was a jackass and . . ."

"I was raised on it," Anne said, her voice chilly. He ignored it, however.

"It's like this," he said. "I'm a woman, and I've been through something of an experience like—let's say—the driver of my car being shot and the car rolling down a hill. Perhaps I got out before that. Maybe I spilled out. I've got a bump or so or maybe the glass has cut me. But I can still walk. I know there's a killer around somewhere, and I wait awhile. Then it's all quiet. So what? Where do I head for? The woods? They're dark, and I don't know them anyhow. I do the only thing I can. I head for home."

"We've already heard that from Doctor Townsend," Anne said, still stiffly. "Only she isn't here, lieutenant."

"How do you know she isn't?" he demanded. "She gets back here, and only God knows what that mile or so cost her. She makes it, but just barely. And the house is dark, locked and dark. So she . . ." He got up abruptly. "Don't bother about another drink, Lois. It can wait. Has anybody looked in the stable?"

They had not, I thought, and followed him at a dogtrot as he raced down the steps and around the corner of the house. I caught up to him in the birch grove. He had gone rather pale, and he stopped and leaned against one of the trees.

"Excuse it, please," he said, trying to smile. "It's the old wound plus a couple of late ones. I keep forgetting the damned things."

He took a couple of deep breaths and started again. But at first the stable was a disappointment. There was nothing in what we called the carriage house but a rusty old sleigh. O'Brien did not stop there, however. He went through a door at the back and stopped dead in the doorway of the tack room.

Judith was there, on the floor.

She was unconscious, and even when he picked her up and she opened her eyes it was clear they saw nothing. She was a pitiable sight. There was a hideous bruise on her forehead, and one of her hands was badly cut. Her clothes were torn too, and one of her ankles was swollen, as though she had sprained it.

O'Brien handled her like a baby.

"Get somebody to turn down her bed," he said. "Fill some hot-water bottles too. And maybe she can swallow a little brandy. It won't hurt to try."

They were all on the porch when our small procession arrived, Phil and Bill still in bathing trunks, Doctor Townsend immaculate and calm. I shall never forget their shocked faces as we turned the corner of the old conservatory and reached the steps. There were cries of where had we found her, and both Phil and Bill rushed down to help O'Brien. He warded them off, however.

"She's not heavy," he said. "Get out of the way, all of you. She's unconscious."

"Is she hurt?" This was Phil. Anne seemed for once beyond speech.

"She's got a bad knock on the head," O'Brien said. "No fracture,

I think. Better notify the police, Mr. Maynard. They'll want to know this. And get a doctor."

"The police?" Phil looked mutinous. "She needs a hospital and medical care."

"She'll get them," O'Brien said grimly. "Only they have to know. At the moment she may be wanted for murder."

There was a shocked silence as we went into the house, and O'Brien did not elaborate. We got her into bed while Phil telephoned Fowler and Doctor Christy, and then followed us upstairs.

"Just what did you mean by that remark, O'Brien?" he demanded angrily. "She's been attacked herself. Look at her!"

"I'm not accusing her," O'Brien said mildly. "The driver of her car was shot in the back of her head. To the Chief of Police here that means only one thing at the moment. She wasn't attacked herself. She went down the hill in the car, and only God knows why she's alive."

"That in itself ought to prove her innocence to any man with sense."

O'Brien only smiled.

"Not necessarily," he said. "The driver's foot may have been on the gas and started it. It was an old model. Fowler's idea, not mine."

"Then where's the gun?"

"If you'll get out of the way I'll look for it."

"In the stable, I suppose," Phil jeered.

But O'Brien was too late. There

had been police in the grounds, and when he got downstairs one of them had already found it. She had dropped it in the grass near the stable door, and one of the local detectives was on the drive with it, wrapped in his handkerchief. Fowler came up on the porch and surveyed the crowd. I was not there, but I was told about it.

"Sorry about all this," he said. "I guess I'll have to talk to Mrs. Chandler."

"She's hurt," someone said. "She needs a hospital."

"Sure," he said. "We're taking her there as soon as the ambulance comes. But I hope you folks understand. That gun Jim has down there has been fired recently. Two or three times if it was fully loaded, and the cab driver was shot, if you don't happen to know it."

"But why?" Anne wailed. "Why would she shoot a man like that?"

The answer, so far as the others were concerned, came late that afternoon. They had taken the dead man's fingerprints, and as I already knew they proved to be those of Johnny Shannon, ex-convict and only a few months ago released from twenty years in prison for manslaughter. I was in the hospital with Judith, so I missed the army of reporters and cameramen that besieged the house.

I stayed in the hospital all night. Judith was still unconscious, and in the morning Phil came in with one of the New York papers and the news that her fingerprints

—and only hers—were on the gun. I went out into the hall to talk to him, and to see a policeman sitting there, outside Judith's room.

He handed me the paper.

"Maybe you can make some sense out of this," he said. "I can't. It's tabloid stuff, of course. The news is on another page."

I took it to a window and read it. It had been written by a well-known columnist.

"Did Judith Chandler, famous beauty and society woman, kill Johnny Shannon? And if so, why? It was well known, at the time of his trial, twenty years ago, that Inspector Flaherty before his own murder believed him innocent of the Mollie Preston slaying, and that he made at least one visit to the Maynard house, where the then Judith Maynard was queried.

"The case was further complicated by the disappearance before the trial of one Kate Henry, one of the chief witnesses for the prosecution. Other witnesses appeared, however, testifying to Shannon's presence in the building at or about the time of the murder, and the noisy quarrel which followed. It was believed that the defense hoped the then Judith Maynard could substantiate Shannon's alibi, but this failed to stand up, and Johnny Shannon was convicted. Not the least curious part of the present case is the participation in it of Flaherty's sergeant at the time, now Inspector Terrence O'Brien.

"It was largely due to O'Brien's efforts that Johnny Shannon was released some months ago. It is an odd coincidence that three people concerned in the long-ago murder of an unimportant East Side girl should again be involved in a crime: one of them the victim, another the woman possibly responsible for his life sentence, and the third a police officer who worked with Flaherty on the Mollie Preston case and who had never believed Shannon guilty.

"As for Judith Chandler—nee Maynard—herself, it is difficult to believe she would shoot and kill the driver of the car while it was still in motion. Such a course would be purely suicidal. Had Johnny Shannon stopped the car and revealed his identity? In that case she might have killed him in self-defense. But the car was apparently in motion, thus providing the authorities with a highly perplexing problem.

"So far there has been no arrest. The police move slowly when any member of a highly respected family is involved. And both the Chandlers and the Maynards have always stood for the best in the city. It is indicative of this that her ex-husband, Ridgely Chandler, is standing by Judith in this trying time."

Phil looked as though he had not slept. He took the tabloid from me and stuck it in his pocket.

"Fowler read it," he said. "That's why the cop's outside her door. She's under arrest whether she knows it or not. Maybe they call it protective custody, but they're holding her for first-degree murder."

That was when I took him into the drab reception room and told him O'Brien's story. He listened stoically.

"So she had to kill him," he said. "She wasn't going to admit she'd sent an innocent man to prison for twenty years. But how did she know the driver was Shannon?"

"I think he told her himself that night, Phil. Only how did he know she was going to need a cab?"

"He must have known she was waiting for a ship. Maybe he did the telephoning himself. O'Brien says all he wanted was vindication, poor devil. What he got was a cold-blooded murder."

It shows how we both felt that day. Neither of us really doubted Judith's guilt. Phil merely wondered how and when she had got the gun. He said she might have recognized Shannon's voice over the telephone and staged the whole thing as a holdup for her jewel case.

"Because the damned thing's still missing," he said. "Anne and I have searched the stable, as well as the whole house, attic and all. If she had it with her she must have hidden it somewhere along the road."

He was right, of course, but within limits. When the time came it was practically her sole defense.

It was a long time before that happened, however. It was a full week before she began to recover. She would lie in her high hospital bed, not awake and not asleep, in a partial coma which was pitiful to see. It seemed absurd to have a policeman sitting outside her door. Not only because she could not walk—one ankle was badly twisted —but because she made no effort whatever to move.

After a day or two they could rouse her to swallow liquid food and water. That is, she could get them down. Her eyes, however, remained blank, until one day she reached out a bandaged hand and touched me.

"Lois," she said.

It was the first sign of consciousness she had given.

Her skull was not fractured, but she had a bad concussion. Also she had walked on the sprained ankle, and even now I shiver at what that mile or so along the road at night must have meant.

I saw very little of O'Brien that week. He was seldom at the cottage, and I spent my days at the hospital. Once, however, he called me up there.

"Just to keep you from forgetting me, my darling," he said. "And also to let you know I'm still on the case."

"Always the policeman!" I said bitterly. "Are you going to send her to the chair?"

"Not necessarily," he said. "I may be able to surprise you before very long."

"I don't like your surprises. I've had all of them I can take."

He told me not to be like that and then hung up abruptly. Hours and days for his job, I thought dourly, and two minutes for dalliance, as he probably regarded it. I missed him sickeningly.

I am quite sure Judith had no idea she was under arrest at that time. She could not see the policeman from her bed, and under the doctor's orders Fowler and his minions left her strictly alone. I did feel, however, as time went on that her semicomatose condition was partly protective. Once in a while when the nurse was out I would find her watching me, and now and then she spoke. As the missing jewel case was in all our minds I asked her about it one day.

She seemed to come back from a far distance.

"Jewel case?" she said slowly.

"Yes. The one you had with you when you were hurt, Jude."

"The man took it," she said, and closed her eyes again.

I called Phil in great excitement when I got home. He was cool enough, however.

"Of course she'd say there was a man," he said. "What the hell did you expect?"

By the tenth day, with Fowler growing angrier and more impatient all the time at the delay, she was able to sit up in bed and even to eat a little. Her memory too was slowly coming back. That afternoon for the first time she inquired about the driver of the car.

"Was he dead?" she asked.

"I'm afraid he was, Judith."

"Who was he? Do you know?"

And then all Phil's theories and mine went into the discard.

"He called himself Morrison," I said, "but he was really Johnny Shannon."

"Johnny!" she said. "Oh, not Johnny! I can't bear it."

Then she was crying, loudly, hysterically. The police officer ran in, the nurse came flying, and soon after an intern. I was too shocked to move. They had to push me aside, and later on in the hall I had to answer questions. What had I done? What had I said to her? The intern was particularly insistent.

"Now see here, Miss Maynard," he said. "She didn't go off like that for nothing. She'd been quiet all day. It's on her record, the best day yet. Then all at once she goes off into a fit, and you were alone with her at the time."

I lied. What else could I do?

"I don't know what started her off," I said. "Perhaps she just remembered something."

"I wish to God she could," he said fervently. "You didn't by any chance tell her about the police?"

"Of course not. But she's seeing things now. If she caught sight of that officer . . ."

He says the door was closed when she began to yell."

But after that I was limited to two hours a day with her, with the nurse always in the room. Now and then as she improved I think she wanted to talk to me. There was no chance, however.

Ridge Chandler came out to The Birches about that time. He had telephoned frequently, and her hospital room was filled with the flowers he sent and which she did not notice. He looked haggard, as I daresay we all did, and he seemed as bewildered as the rest of us.

"Hasn't she talked at all?" he asked. "She must remember something."

"She's beginning to remember, Ridge. She's had a concussion, of course. We do know a few things. She says a man took her jewel case."

"It's hardly news," he said dryly. "We all know it was a hold-up."

It was September by that time. It was cool that day, and I had a fire in the living room. He got up and stood in front of mother's picture, looking up at it.

"Handsome old girl," he said. "Ever find out what she wanted the money for? The fifty thousand, I mean."

"Maybe to bribe Dawson. You may remember him. He was our butler at the time."

"Bribe him? Why?" He stared at me, but I went on recklessly.

"Because Judith was the alibi for a man accused of murder, Ridge. It won't hurt you to know it now. Apparently she lied, for he was convicted. His name was Shannon, Johnny Shannon."

"Good God!" he said. "The man who drove the car! Then she did kill him, after all!"

"That's fantastic, Ridge. She had no gun."

"No? Well, maybe not, although I wonder what became of the one your father used. The police returned it. And it might have been stored away somewhere.

"I never saw it," I said weakly.

But I was remembering the night I found Judith in the attic. She had been looking for something, definitely not her wedding pictures. I sat gazing at him, but he merely shrugged.

"Don't look at me like that," he said, his voice irritable. "God knows I don't want to drag my name in the mud. Shannon may have scared her. He had a right to, if she did what you say. I remember the case dimly, but how did you learn about it? You were only a child at the time. I suppose it was this policeman of yours. What's his name? O'Brien, isn't it?"

"Yes," I said dully. "It was O'Brien."

"It could be worse, of course," he said, "even if they prove the gun was your father's. She would probably get a light sentence. She's still a good-looking woman, and if necessary we can show she has not been normal for some time."

"I think she is normal," I said obstinately. "She's been afraid, that's all."

He left me in a wretched state of mind. Judith might have found father's gun in the attic. It might have been there. Also her handbag was large. She could have carried it with her. But why shoot Shannon and risk her own life when the car went over the edge of the road?

I didn't dare to risk talking to her again. But she was improving rapidly, and one day I realized the armistice was over.

She was better. Her ankle was in a cast, and they were talking of getting her up into a wheel chair. I went home more cheerful than I had been for a long time. When the haze completely lifted she would be able to tell us what had happened, and clear herself. Because by that time I felt sure she was innocent. She had not known the cab driver was Shannon, and why would she shoot an unknown man?

Then Fowler came to see me.

I was alone late that afternoon when he appeared. I had been getting mother's room ready for Judith when she was strong enough to be brought back to The Birches, so when I heard his voice I went down the stairs to find him in the lower hall with a heavy automatic in his hand.

"Know anything about this gun, Miss Maynard?" he said. "Recognize it, I mean."

"No. What about it?" I asked stupidly.

"It's the gun which killed Shannon," he said. "It also killed your father years ago. I wonder how your sister got hold of it?"

Father's gun! I sat down on one of the hall chairs, feeling faint. But I managed to speak.

"I don't know. I've never seen it before. It wasn't in the house. And she never killed anybody."

"Well, that's as may be," he said. "You have to do a little guessing in this case. I'll guess, for instance, that the telephone call about the ship was arranged for to impress you. I'll guess she knew this ex-convict Shannon a lot better than you realize. And I'll guess a bit more. She didn't expect to go off the road in that car. She had him stop it before she killed him, but the motor was running, so maybe his foot kicked the gas and she had no time to get out."

"You're making her a monster," I said wildly. "She isn't. She has her faults, but to think she would scheme like that, pack her bags, kiss me good-bye and go out to murder a man—it's crazy."

"Maybe that's the answer," he said laconically. "She'll cop a plea of temporary insanity, or her lawyers will. But it won't do her any good."

He left me in a state of collapse, and when Phil came home that night I gave one look at his tired, haggard face and decided not to tell him about father's gun. Maybe I was wrong, but he was sure to learn it sooner or later. He was entitled to one peaceful evening, if you could call it that.

When O'Brien called me later he said nothing to cheer me.

"I'm afraid things don't look too good," he said. "Who would think a damn-fool reporter in New York would bring Shannon in? Or that they would check back to your father's gun?"

But the thing was almost over, he said. Judith had not killed Johnny Shannon, and he hoped to prove it.

"I still don't see why anybody wanted to kill him," I said stubbornly. "Why kill *him*? If he'd killed her I could understand it."

"Leave the worrying to me. I can take it. And I'll say this much," he went on. "Several people are responsible for his death. Only one of them killed him, but more than one conscience must have kept its owner awake at night for a good many years."

He did not explain what he meant. He had really called, he said, to tell me that Fowler intended to interrogate Judith the next day, and I was to insist on being present.

"Just go there early and stay," he said. "I'll be there, if I have to break a window. After all, Shannon was in my jurisdiction. He was a New York resident."

Then for a few seconds he ceased being a police officer and became a man. "I'm missing you, darling, but this is my job. Someday soon it will be over, and you'll be my own sweet girl again."

Unfortunately I was not feeling sweet.

"Of course," I said. "In the intervals between cases, you mean. You'll come home to the little woman, put your gun away, and after food, a bath and a shave you'll look around to see if she's where you left her a week or so before."

"And what could be more wonderful, mavourneen?" he chuckled. "Just promise me you will be there."

"I'm just damn fool enough to promise I will be, with a steak ready for the broiler and your slippers ready for your feet."

The mention of the steak was unfortunate. Flaherty's wife had one ready the night he was killed, and he remembered it. The laughter went out of his voice.

"I'll come home to you, my darling," he said gravely. "That's as near a promise as I can make."

31

The nurse had done her best for Judith when I got there the next morning, had brushed her still lovely hair until it shone, and put a little color on her cheeks and lips. They only heightened her alarming pallor, but I did not say anything.

Fowler had said he would be there at eleven o'clock. He came promptly, but he was not alone. He had brought the detective who found the gun, and almost on his heels came the District Attorney for the county. Fowler looked displeased when he saw me, and even more so when O'Brien walked in. He did not care either for the presence of Doctor Christy, who sat by Judith's bed. But it was definitely Fowler's show.

He began urbanely enough.

"I don't want to distress you, Mrs. Chandler," he said. "But I think it's time we had a talk."

Judith did not move, but she looked at him.

"What do you want?" she asked,

slowly and painfully. "I don't remember very much."

"Well, you remember getting into the car at The Birches, don't you?"

"Yes."

"You were going abroad? On the *Queen Mary?*"

She made an effort.

"Yes," she said. "I got a message they had space for me."

He let that go.

"I see," he said. "So you called a cab. That's right, isn't it?"

She frowned in an attempt to remember.

"No. They said they were sending one for me. Whoever it was said a car was on the way. It was picking up another passenger later."

"Would it interest you to know," he said, still smoothly, "that no such message was ever sent?"

She looked puzzled.

"I don't understand. I got it. My sister Lois knows it. She was there."

The District Attorney stirred in his chair.

"I think we'd better get on with it, Chief," he said. "She's not very strong. We know the car picked her up. We know it was a stolen car. Let's take all this for granted."

Fowler scowled.

"I'd like to carry this on," he said. "The car was there, that's the important thing. Now, Mrs. Chandler, you got into the car, and it drove on a mile or two. What happened then?"

"It stopped. The driver said he was to pick up the other passenger there and take him to the ship. I said there wasn't much room, with all my bags, but anyhow we waited. Then a man came along the road. He stopped beside the rear door where I sat and jerked it open. I—"she looked about to faint—"I saw he was wearing something black over his face, and I guess I screamed. That was when he shot the driver. He tried to shoot me. Perhaps he thought he had, for I fainted just after that. The last thing I remember is his throwing the gun at me. It struck me on the head."

A wave of shock must have gone through everyone there. Even Fowler looked surprised. Then he smiled.

"I see. So that's how you got the gun?"

"The gun?" She was thinking hard, trying to remember. "But I didn't get it. It was in my hand when I came to."

Nobody believed her. There was sheer incredulity on every face in the room, including my own. Except O'Brien's. He was watching her intently. Fowler smiled.

"That's quite a statement," he said. "You fainted, the car crashed down the hill, after turning over at least a couple of times. And you wake up holding the gun! What happened then?"

"I must have been out a good while," she said. "I could see the car below me. Not the driver. Just the car. I think it was some time before I tried to climb the hill. My foot was very painful, but I couldn't stay there with that man around. That's really all I remember."

"Not quite," Fowler said. "You knew where you were, didn't you? You didn't go toward the town. You turned toward The Birches. No woman in a stupor did that, Mrs. Chandler. And you carried the gun with you."

"Are you saying I walked back home? With an ankle like this?"

"You did, unless someone took you there. Perhaps you'll claim this highwayman of yours did it! That's where you were found anyhow. In the old stable at The Birches. The gun was there too, the gun that killed Johnny Shannon."

I watched her, but the name did not startle her as it had before, although she went very pale.

"I never shot anybody," she said swiftly. "Not in all my life."

"But you knew Shannon?"

"A long time ago I knew a Johnny Shannon. He was a student at Columbia. He came a few times to the swimming pool at The Birches."

"Did you know he was driving the car that night?"

"No. Not until . . ." She stopped. She had made a misstep, and she knew it.

"Now we're getting places," Fowler said with considerable satisfaction. "Suppose you tell us why he stopped the car where he did. There were no houses near. Shannon wasn't picking up a passenger. This masked man wasn't a thief after your jewel case either. Matter of fact, isn't it possible there was no such man?"

I think she gave up then. She lay back on her pillows with her eyes closed, and the nurse held some aromatic ammonia under her nose. Doctor Christy spoke for the first time.

"I'm warning you, Fowler. This is no time or place for accusations. I said she could tell her story. That's all."

"If her story's a bundle of lies, I didn't promise to accept it."

Then O'Brien spoke.

"Suppose you let me tell it for her," he said. "I knew Johnny Shannon. I knew him off and on for twenty years. I knew he'd been trying ever since he left the pen to get a statement from Mrs. Chandler which would clear him of the murder which sent him up the river."

Fowler eyed him with acute dislike.

"I don't see where you come in on this," he said. "I'm supposed to be doing the questioning."

"Right, but I'm not asking questions. I'm telling you what Mrs. Chandler will have to tell, sooner or later. She knew Johnny Shannon never killed the Preston girl, and she knew it because she was in his room the night it happened. She was with him, in his room on Morningside Heights, from eleven o'clock to four in the morning. The Preston girl was killed at or about midnight."

There was a dead silence. No one in the room moved.

"She was pretty young at the time. Even then I think she might have come forward and cleared him, but her mother terrified her into keeping quiet. I'm only going to ask her one or two questions, Fowler. The rest is up to you." He glanced at Judith. "You heard me, Mrs. Chandler. That's the fact, isn't it? And when Johnny Shannon got you in the car it was in the hope you could be induced to clear him?"

She nodded weakly.

"I thought he would be acquitted at the trial," she said. "But mother took me to Arizona, and when I learned he had gone up for life I was in bed for weeks, sick."

"You didn't invent this masked man, did you?"

"No. He was there. We were to wait for him. He was to be a notary, or something like that. He was to take down what I said, and I was to sign it. Johnny told me after he stopped the car. I didn't know who he was until then."

"There was no real message about the ship. You know that now, don't you?"

"I think Johnny learned somehow that I hoped to sail. I realize now it must have been his voice over the telephone."

"And the rest is as you've told it?"

"About the man? Yes."

O'Brien grinned and looked at Fowler.

"Your witness, chief," he said.

Fowler was sulky. It was a moment or two before he leaned forward in his chair and spoke to Judith.

"Isn't it a fact, Mrs. Chandler," he said, "that as soon as you learned Shannon was released you went around in terror of your life? You lived behind locked doors for fear he would kill you?" Corny, I thought bitterly. But Fowler went on. "And isn't it a fact that when you learned his identity in the car that night you shot him before, as you thought, he would shoot you?"

O'Brien got up.

"This isn't a trial before a jury, Fowler," he said. "Mrs. Chandler will not answer that question while I'm here, or until she has a lawyer to defend her."

Fowler looked ugly.

"All right," he said. "She'll get a lawyer. She'll probably get a dozen of them. She married a Chandler, didn't she? But maybe you forget we've had two murders." He looked at Judith. "Did you know the woman who was knocked out and then drowned in your swimming pool not long ago?"

Judith closed her eyes, and the spots of rouge on her face stood out sickeningly. But her voice was clear.

"No. She was a complete stranger to me."

"Yet someone at The Birches took a golf club down there that night. You know that, don't you?"

"That doesn't necessarily follow," O'Brien said. "A good many people had access to those clubs. You did yourself, probably. So did I."

Fowler was seething with fury by that time. He got up and jammed on his hat.

"I had a vague idea that I was in charge of this case. If New York Homicide is taking over I'd like to know. Now I'm getting the hell out of here. Maybe O'Brien can produce this masked phantom, if there ever was one. This whole business looks to me like a conspiracy to protect Mrs. Chandler. But don't think I'm through. I'm only beginning."

He stalked out of the room, not without a certain dignity, and a moment later I heard his car starting. The detective he had brought heard it too. He shrugged.

"So he leaves me here," he said. "Looks like I'll have to bum a ride into town. But don't discount Fowler. He's got plenty on the ball."

That he had something was evident when he came to The Birches that night.

O'Brien had disappeared when the others did. He left an envelope for me with the clerk in the office at the hospital, but there was no letter inside. There was merely a prescription blank, on

which he had written just three
words. They were enough, however, to make me happy, and the
early part of the evening was very
pleasant.

After all, there was no real case
against Judith, as Phil agreed with
his lawyer's mind when I told him
about it.

"Unless they can prove she had
a gun," he said. "And that I doubt.
It's up to the gun and the jewel
case. Prove one and locate the
other. Then maybe you've got a
case. Or maybe you haven't."

We had another reason for feeling somewhat cheerful that evening. A real estate agent in New
York had called Phil up, and said
he had a faint nibble for The
Birches.

"Not too strong," he said, "but
they can pay plenty if they take
it. Scared of the atom bomb, I
gather, and have a raft of children.
Only," he added, "don't have any
more murders out there. You'd be
surprised how a whacking good
one affects the real estate market."

It shook me, rather. So much of
my life was tied up in the place.
In the spring the magnolias, pink
dogwoods, and cherry and other
fruit blossoms made it look almost
bridal. And the silver birches were
there the year round, lovely in
the snow, tall and dignified always. Father's garden, the pet
cemetery, the stall in the stable
where Fairy, my little pony, was
kept . . .

"Oh, no," I said when Phil told
me. "How can we?"

"How can't we?" he retorted. "I
have an idea you won't be here

long anyhow, and I'm not staying
on alone."

As it happened, Bill had
brought his Janey to dinner, and
Helga had extended herself—and
the grocery bill—to give her what
she called a bang-up dinner.
Janey was a nice slim little thing.
Bill must have known dozens exactly like her, with their girlish
voices and rather shy good manners. And she did have a last
name, after all. Not too surprisingly it was Jones. Just why Bill
found her unusual I couldn't see,
and Phil's only comment was that
she ate enough for a laboring
man, that when she stood up you
would have thought a hard-boiled
egg would show, and she didn't
even bulge.

He watched them as they wandered out to the porch.

"Funny kids these days," he
said. "Those two are as romantic
as a pair of china doorknobs. Ever
occur to you that we've knocked
romance for a loop by taking the
clothes off the youngsters and
bringing sex out into the open?"

But I was in no mood to argue,
so he let it drop. I was tired, and
I had not liked the way Judith
looked when Fowler spoke about
the woman in the pool. I did my
best, turned on the radio, so Bill
and Janey could dance in the hall,
and was about to go up to bed
when I heard a car stop in the drive.

It was Fowler, and he had
brought Ridge Chandler with him.
Both men looked sober, and Fowler asked to see us both alone. I
knew then there was trouble, bad
trouble. And there was.

32

We took them into the library, and against Bill's despairing glance firmly closed the door.

"What's all this about?" Phil asked gruffly. "Judith's told you all she knows, hasn't she?"

Ridge gave his usual glance at mother's portrait before he sat down. Fowler remained standing.

"I've been checking back a bit, Mr. Maynard," he said. "I don't like to bring up anything unpleasant, but after this length of time . . . You remember your father's death, of course."

"I do. Did you expect me to say I'd forgotten it?"

"You went to his office that night, I believe? After it happened?"

"I did. Is that any business of yours?"

"I think it is. You saw the gun he used."

"It was there, yes."

"Do you know what happened to it later? I mean, what became of it?"

"Good God, no," Phil said violently. "I never wanted to see the thing again." He pulled himself together. "Sorry, Fowler," he said, more quietly. "It was all an unholy mess. I had to help go over his papers. We were wiped out, of course, and my mother was in poor shape. We had to get rid of the town house too. There was a lot of confusion."

"That's why I brought Mr. Chandler," the Chief said smoothly. "He was attentive to your sister Judith at that time, so he was there a good bit. All right, Chandler, let's have it."

Ridge looked uncomfortable.

"I don't like being dragged into this, Phil," he said, "especially since Judith is involved. But the fact is the police returned the gun to your mother. I was there when it came."

"What's all this about?" Phil demanded. "What has father's gun to do with any of us? You're talking about twenty years ago, man."

"I'm talking about the past few days," Fowler said importantly. "As your sister here already knows, the gun which killed Shannon, Mr. Maynard, was your father's gun. I have the serial numbers. It was registered in the city in his name. He bought it when we had some burglaries out here in this district years ago."

Phil looked dumbfounded.

"Father's? You're sure of that?"

"I've seen his gun purchase permit, Mr. Maynard. Here's the description of the gun." He took a paper from his wallet. "Thirty-eight Police Positive Colt, blue finish, four-inch barrel, weight twenty-two ounces. It's the same gun your sister dropped at the stable. No doubt about it."

"Are you telling me," Phil said hoarsely, "that my sister had my father's gun, and killed Shannon with it? Why, for God's sweet sake?"

"I think you'll find she had a reason," Fowler said smoothly. "Anyhow it's the gun which killed him. That's one thing O'Brien couldn't stop. I sent it and the bullet to Ballistics in the city. They match all right. Got the report tonight."

Ridge had been quiet. It was obvious he disliked being there, disliked Fowler, disliked Phil and myself, probably disliked even the kids in the hall. Now he spoke.

"I suppose Lois has told you about today," he said, "but I don't think it will ever come to trial. She can be certified if necessary as of unsound mind."

"She's as sane as I am."

Ridge shrugged his elegantly padded shoulders.

"I am willing to testify to the contrary," he said stiffly. "Judith has not been herself for a long time. The attempt at suicide shows it clearly. She had everything to live for—health, adequate means, and a considerable remnant of her former beauty. When she wanted a divorce—for no reason whatever —I saw she got it."

He glanced again at mother's painting over the mantel and smiled faintly.

"I not only gave her everything she wanted after our marriage. I helped her out of trouble before it. Lois knows it. I told her some time ago. But after hearing Mr. Fowler's account of today at the hospital I feel I should make my own position clear."

He looked at Phil, but he was lighting a cigarette.

"What *is* your position, Ridge?" Phil asked. "You're not married to Judith now. You're not even a member of this family. Just why are you here?"

Ridge flushed.

"I might say I came to ask for the fifty thousand dollars I gave your mother twenty years ago after your father's death. It might just possibly interest you. I don't know."

Phil looked stupefied.

"Mother?" he said. "Why did she need it? It never showed on any of the bank statements."

"I paid it in cash. She wanted it that way, in small bills if possible. Even in those days of Prohibition it wasn't easy. I rather think my bank thought I was bootlegging."

If it was meant as a pleasantry it got nowhere.

"Just why did she want it?" Phil asked grimly. "She wasn't being blackmailed, was she?"

"I'm quite sure she was. At the time I thought I was paying to keep my future wife's name out of the newspapers. She had been out driving with some lad or other, and the car had hit a woman. It hadn't killed her, but she was badly hurt, and this was to remunerate her. That was the story I was told.

"It wasn't true, of course. I know it now. But I was very much in love, and so . . ."

He shrugged again.

"What I was actually doing was to bribe the butler you had at the time—a man named Dawson—to keep his mouth shut about the fact that Judith had been—let's say indiscreet—with a boy named Shannon. She had spent most of a night in his room, and she was his only alibi for a murder he was supposed to have committed while she was with him.

"I suppose Dawson had let her out of the house, and let her in again. He may have followed her too. I don't know. But as a result this boy, Johnny Shannon, was convicted and served twenty years to life in the pen. I don't need to tell you it was this same Shannon she shot and killed two weeks ago with your father's gun."

Nobody spoke for a moment. Phil looked profoundly shocked. Out in the hall Bill and Janey were shooting craps. We could hear the dice rattling on the bare floor. Then Phil moved.

"Why would she do such a thing?" he said. "If Shannon had shot her, I could understand it. But you say she killed him. Why?"

"You'll have to ask her," Ridge said. "I suppose she was afraid of him, for one thing. But if all this comes out, as it may, she can claim he threatened her. She shot in self-defense."

Fowler got up.

"I think I'd better say what I came to say," he said, "and then get out. As you know, I've been holding Mrs. Chandler as a material witness, but this matter of the gun changes things. As a matter of fact I have a warrant for her arrest in my pocket. She can't be moved yet, of course, and if she can prove self-defense it won't go hard with her. Or put it another way. Say she's been erratic at times. Had a psychiatrist, hasn't she? And the maid here, Jennie, says she's kept herself locked in ever since she came. There's a defense too—mental case."

He said something about not liking scandal when it touched the old and prominent families who had summer homes there. Secretly, however, I thought he was enormously pleased with himself as he went out. Bill and Janey were still noisily shooting craps. Both sprawled on the floor, as though there was no warrant in Fowler's pocket; as though Judith had not taken father's automatic from the trunk in the attic which held his fishing rods and old hunting gear; and as though Ridgely Chandler had not tonight paid her back for the years she had not loved him.

Phil and Fowler were already on the porch when Ridge tried to put an arm around me as he said good night. I freed myself quickly. "I hope you're happy," I said. "That story was unnecessary and uncalled for, Ridge. The gun was enough. The rest was pure spite, because she hated you. You couldn't forgive that, could you?"

He gave me a cold smile.

"No," he said. "You learn fast, don't you?"

Then he was gone, and Phil and I were left to our own unhappy thoughts. Some time later, after making cocoa for the kids, I found him in the library carefully inspecting the Laszlo portrait. He turned when he heard me.

"She must have had some dreadful times," he said slowly. "Times when she couldn't sleep for seeing an innocent boy shut away for the rest of his life. All of it so Judith could marry Chandler, the pipsqueak of a man who was here tonight." And then he said something I shall always remember.

"Maybe we are better now than we were then," he said. "There's not so much pride of the wrong sort, of money or place, or social position. Mother was of her world, but her world has gone kaput. I'm glad you're marrying O'Brien, Lois. He's a cop, but he's also a gent."

It was the next day that Judith told me about the woman in the pool.

She was looking better. The nurse had brushed her hair, and piled it high on her head. But I felt her real beauty was gone for good. There comes a time in every woman's life, I suppose, when she has to say farewell to the best things nature has done for her; the flawless skin goes, the lovely eyes fade, and she knows she is over the hill and, as the Indians say, going to the sun.

Evidently she had not yet been arrested. Fowler had not served his warrant. But now there were two men in the hall outside her door, one in uniform and one in plain clothes. They greeted me civilly enough but there was a subtle change in both of them, a watchfulness, an alertness I had not noticed before.

Judith was alone when I went in. She seemed glad to see me. She had never been a reader, and the long hours must have hung heavy on her hands. But the look she gave me was a wary one.

"What was all that about yesterday?" she asked. "Didn't they believe me?"

"I think they hoped you would remember more, Jude."

"I don't. I can't." She passed a hand wearily over her tired face. "But I must talk to somebody or I'll go mad. Lois, what do you remember about mother? Before she moved out to The Birches? You were pretty small, weren't you?"

"I was seven, almost eight, when father died."

She was watching me carefully.

"Was there anything queer about father's death?" she asked.

I was startled.

"Not so far as I know. There has never been any doubt he killed himself."

"I suppose he did," she said, and was thoughtful for a minute. Then: "I didn't shoot that man, Lois. Believe me, what I told was true. But I think I did something else equally dreadful. I think I killed the Benjamin woman." I must have looked horrified, for she went on gravely: "I tried to save her, as God is my witness, but I never was a good swimmer and she kept going down." She shuddered. "I had to tell you," she said. "I can't take any more. Is that policeman still out there?"

"He can't hear you. What do you mean, you tried to save her?"

"She was in the pool when I got there. Somebody meant to kill her. You see how it is. I'm under suspicion for what I did not do, and in a way I am guilty of something they don't even suspect! I suppose that's life for you, or maybe death."

It was a longish story she told me that day, her poor face raddled and her hands shaking. It began, she said, after she came back to The Birches from Reno. She didn't get much mail, but one day Jennie brought her a letter from the mailbox. It warned her she was in danger as Shannon was free. But that was all, and she knew about Shannon already. Nevertheless, the letter scared her, she said, but she did nothing about it until another one came. But by that time she was pretty desperate. The new one was rather ominous. It was signed Kate Henry, and it said Shannon was trying to get his case re-opened.

"I'm through with it," it went on. "Dawson's dead. He killed Mollie Preston, and if I go on the stand I'll tell them so. But Johnny's counting on you to alibi

him. I think we'd better talk this over."

She ended by saying she would be at the pool on a certain night, and Judith was to meet her there. Judith was terrified. She was afraid Johnny would be there too. She went, however. In the hall she picked up one of Phil's golf clubs, for defense if necessary. It was all she had. She never owned a gun. I knew that, didn't I?

"You were looking for something in the attic one night, Jude. They think you found the gun there."

She shook her head.

"No. I had hidden a letter from Johnny in your old doll house, Lois. It was under one of the floor mats. But it was gone. Perhaps mother found it, or Helga."

It was, she said, one he had sent her after his arrest, begging her to tell the truth and save him. It had almost killed her. She was in love with him, and perhaps someday she could produce it. But by that time it was too late. Dawson had been bought off, Flaherty was dead, and mother took her to Arizona.

"What do you mean by someday, Jude?"

"I thought he would be acquitted. If he wasn't . . ."

But mother had all those months in Arizona to work on her. Mother and Ridge. She was pretty young, she said, so when Ridge proposed to her—knowing the truth, as he did—she shifted the burden to him.

"Only he never did anything," she said bitterly. "He didn't even try to get Johnny out. At first I thought he was afraid of his mother. She was a terrible woman, Lois. But she died and still he refused to help Johnny. I gave up then."

She went back to the pool. She said the bench was empty when she got there, so she waited, the golf club beside her.

"It was dark, but there was some starlight," she said. "I sat down and waited but the woman didn't come." Then she heard someone in the shrubbery. Whoever it was didn't appear and suddenly she was terrified.

"I forgot all about the golf club," she said. "I simply beat it. I ran back to the house and sat on the porch, and before long I heard Ed Brown's taxi. It stopped to let someone out and went away, and after a while I screwed up my courage and went down to the pool again.

"She was there, Lois, but she wasn't on the bench. She was in the pool, floundering around in the deep end. I tried to reach her. I got down on my knees and tried to catch that awful hair of hers, but I couldn't hold her. I suppose I should have gone in after her, but I'm a rotten swimmer. Anyhow it was too late. She sank right before my eyes, and she never came up again."

She said she waited for a while. Quite literally she could not walk. The woman's hat came up and floated, then it sank too, and after a bit she picked up the golf club and went back to the house. It never occurred to her the golf

club had been the murder weapon. She simply put it back in the bag and forgot about it. But she had been almost frantic anyhow. For one thing, she had got pretty wet, and she had spent most of the night drying and pressing her clothes.

"I had my traveling iron, of course," she said, as though it mattered.

The curious thing was that until much later she did not even know the woman's identity. I realized she still did not know who she really was.

"Her name was Kate Henry, but she married Dawson. He'd changed his name to Benjamin, so she called herself Selina Benjamin. I imagine he told her the whole story, including the murder of a Homicide man named Flaherty. Inspector Flaherty."

That was when I realized I had lost her. The new frankness, even the friendliness, was gone. It was as though a hand had been drawn over her face, wiping out all expression.

"If he told her mother was mixed up in the death of Flaherty he was lying," she said sharply. "He probably had plenty of enemies. I guess I've talked too much, Lois, but I wanted you to know. I had nothing to do with the Benjamin woman's death. Do you mind ringing for the nurse?"

It was the first time Flaherty's name had entered the case, and I told O'Brien about it that night.

"She's right, of course, except it's odd the way she reacted.

Someday she'll come clean all the way, and she'll feel better when she does. It's the gun that bothers me now: Who had it all this time? Sure it wasn't in the attic?"

"I'm not sure about anything."

I went out to the porch with him, but he did not go back to the cottage. He kissed me lightly—he was definitely a man who did his own courting—and said he wanted a few words with Helga.

"She's probably in bed," I protested, but he only grinned.

"It won't be the first time I've disturbed her virgin slumbers," he said. "And 'tis a sorry spectacle she'll be, mavourneen."

I always suspected him when he lapsed into his Irish vernacular. It meant he was getting away with something I was not to know about. But he gave me no chance to question him.

He kissed me again and disappeared toward the service wing. I never doubted he had a key to it. And he had.

33

I never have known whether Fowler served his warrant or not. I did not see Judith the next day, for the offer for the property became definite that September morning, and the prospective owners arrived en masse to inspect it.

The children loved it. There was a little girl of seven or so with a front tooth out who reminded me of myself at the same age. But of course one of the boys promptly fell into the pool and I had to dive in after him while the mother screamed her head off. I think the husband liked the pool, nevertheless. He gave me rather a tired smile as I got my orders.

"I'm afraid it will have to go, my dear," he said as I stood dripping beside him. "At once, if you can manage it. I want the kids out of town as soon as possible."

I changed my clothes after they departed, and went out into the grounds again. A man had already arrived at the pool. He was struggling to open the sluice gate and I stood there watching him. Just so I must have stood years ago, with father holding my hand as it began to fill. Looking worried too.

"You'll have to learn to swim, baby," he said. "We can't have you falling into the thing unless you know how to get out."

I went over to his garden. It looked dreary at the end of the summer, but the birches still stood, tall and proud, over the little cemetery. They seemed to be whispering to each other, and I sat down under them and wept. My eyes were still red when Anne arrived later in the afternoon. She looked hot and tired, but exultant about her share of the money involved as she sat fanning herself on the porch.

"Of course the price includes the furniture, such as it is," I told her.

"But not mother's portrait!" she protested. "You wouldn't sell that, Lois."

"No. You can have it if you like. Phil doesn't want it. Nor do I."

My voice probably sounded bleak, for she stared at me.

"I rather thought you'd want it."

"I'll probably have no place for it, Anne."

"Then you *are* going to marry that policeman."

"I'm not sure. He hasn't really asked me yet."

She had a glass of iced tea in her hand, but she did not drink it. She was flushed with indignation.

"I think mother would turn in her grave if she thought you were serious about him," she said. "A policeman, and an Irish one at that! Good Lord, Lois, have you lost your mind?"

I wanted to say mother was probably whirling if she knew all about us. I did not, of course.

"I didn't know there was anything wrong with being Irish."

"Maybe not, but a policeman! A cop! What do they call them? A flatfoot!"

"He's hardly that, Anne. He's a lieutenant in the Homicide Department. Also he's a college man. He can even read and write. And before I forget it, Janey has another name. It's Jones."

I don't think she even heard me.

"Even Judith made a good marriage," she said scornfully. "You'll go far before you find a finer man than Ridge Chandler, even if she did divorce him. And my Martin may not be a millionaire, but he's a gentleman. That policeman, with his chickens! You're not really serious about this, Lois, are you?"

"I'm as serious as all hell," I said. "He's a man, and a real one. I'm terribly in love with him. And I'll tell you something else you don't know. Ridge Chandler may be a gentleman, but he bought Judith just the same. The exact price was fifty thousand dollars. Or so he says."

She dropped her fan and did not bother to pick it up.

"I don't believe it," she said flatly. "Why would he do a thing like that?"

"To save her reputation, and incidentally to send a man to prison for murder."

Sitting there, with Anne clutching a glass of iced tea she never drank, I told her the story of Judith's early days, as I had it from both Ridge and Judith herself. Her rather long face grew longer as I went on, her nice eyes bigger. I rather think her greatest shock was Ridge's part in it, for it was the only comment she made.

"He must have been crazy," she said. "After all, a Chandler . . ."

"He meant to marry her. He paid the fifty thousand dollars to save his family name. Not ours."

She did not even know of Judith's arrest! It surprises me now to think how little she really had known all along. But when I came to father's gun she was stunned. "What became of it, Anne?" I asked. "You know, after he died. Did the police send it back to us?"

"I don't know," she said. "I don't remember seeing it. Of course, with all the confusion at the time . . . Does it matter?"

"Matter? It may send Judith to the chair, or to life imprisonment. It was father's gun that killed the cab driver, Anne. He had a license for it, and the police have traced it. Ridge says it *was* returned. To mother. He was there when she got it."

She was too stunned even to put her glass down properly. She put it on the edge of the table, where it toppled to the floor and smashed. It belonged to a set mother had brought from Venice on her wedding trip, but she ignored it.

"Why?" she said. "Why would she kill such a person? She wouldn't even know him. How could she?"

"Because he was the man she sent to prison, the Johnny Shannon I told you about."

Thinking now of that talk I realize I had the whole case before me. The clues, as Sara Winters would say, were all there. But it was like not seeing the forest for the trees. I was too close, too tired, perhaps too stupid.

Sitting there on the porch, the house quiet behind us, I told her as much as I knew, beginning with father's suicide and the note he left, and ending with the warrant for Judith's arrest. I told her about Flaherty and Mollie Preston. I told her about Dawson and the bribe, and about Selina his wife, who had sworn away Johnny Shannon's liberty and then married Dawson under the name of Benjamin. I even told her of my excursion to their town, and the tobacco shop there. And finally I repeated Judith's story about Phil's golf club and how near we had come, Phil and I, to arrest because of it.

She tried to smile. After all, if Ridge was a Chandler she was a Maynard and the Maynards have their own standards of behavior.

"Bill says I'm a lame-brain," she said, "but I've got at least part of it. Only I thought Judith was claiming it was a holdup."

"She does, only they don't believe her. How would a thug like that get father's gun? It was his gun. The slugs matched."

None of us except Bill ate much dinner that night, although Helga was celebrating the sale of the house with fried chicken and an angel-food cake, undoubtedly the largess from O'Brien's girls. All Phil had to say was the warrant had been served and Judith was under arrest.

He pushed away his dessert, which was the ice cream he usually liked, and excusing himself went out into the grounds. Even Bill seemed subdued. He and Janey had had a fight, he said, but there were plenty of other fish in his particular ocean.

"The more I think of it the more I understand Joseph Smith," he said.

"Joseph Smith?" Anne said, looking puzzled. "Who on earth was he?"

She took Bill with her while she went over the house, so I was alone on the porch when Doctor Townsend drove up. He had been dining somewhere in the neighborhood, but as the others were about to play canasta, which he detested, he had made an excuse and left.

"I understand Mrs. Chandler is getting better," he said. "Terrific shock she'd had. It would have killed a lot of women."

"She's had a worse one today," I said. "She's been arrested for murder, doctor."

I think he already knew it, but he drew a long breath.

"I suppose it was inevitable, but still . . ."

"You don't think she did it, do you?"

"Almost anyone will kill, if sufficiently desperate," he said. "In fact"—he smiled faintly—"there is a school of thought which says we are all killers, only restrained by the laws we ourselves have made. The point is, why? Why would Mrs. Chandler kill this man? She doesn't even claim he attacked her. It's easier to believe in her highwayman."

The District Attorney, he said, had been at the dinner party that night and admitted the case was puzzling. For instance, if she had used the gun, why carry it back here with her? She was in shock, of course. He asked me if I knew Ballistics showed it was the murder weapon, and I nodded.

"Even semiconscious as she was," he said, "wouldn't she have thrown it away somewhere? Down a bank. Into a creek. Even into your own swimming pool? She was not completely in shock. That came later. She knew her way here. She even knew where the stable was."

He left soon after, leaving me somewhat cheered but still bewildered.

It was almost nine o'clock when O'Brien arrived. We must have looked like a normal family party, with Anne serving coffee from mother's big silver service on the table before her in the living room and Phil passing Benedictine in one of father's handsome decanters. There was a small fire going too, and I tried to forget how soon we were leaving it. Or, for that matter, what was to come.

Because I knew O'Brien had something to say. His voice over the telephone was his policeman's voice.

"That you, Lois?"

"Yes. Is anything wrong?"

"No more than usual," he said. "I'll be at The Birches as soon as I can make it. Don't let Helga go to bed. I'll want her."

He hung up, without so much as a good-bye, and I went upstairs in a fury and put on my blue silk dress, which had withstood the water in the pool after all, and remade my face.

When he did come he had evidently stopped at the cottage, for he was freshly shaved and he wore a fine pair of gabardine slacks and a tweed sports jacket. He had had a haircut too, and not since the case began had I seen him so resplendent or with such an air of tired dignity.

He took the highball Phil gave him, but he did not sit down. He stood by the mantel, glass in hand, and surveyed the three of us.

"I'll try to make this short," he said. "Some of it's damned unpleasant, and much of it Lois knows, but it has to be told. First of all, try to imagine Judith Chandler's state of mind last winter when she read in the papers that Johnny Shannon was free. She never doubted he would try to kill her. She has never doubted it since. But I didn't believe it. I met him when he came out, and eventually I gave him enough money to go west. What he really wanted was to be exonerated, and I told him I would try to do it. There was no revenge in him. He had had a long time to get over that, but it's hard for an ex-con to get anywhere, and he had studied law in prison. Once cleared, he could practice somewhere.

"He wrote me from Reno that he was driving a taxi and even saving some money. He hadn't changed a great deal. He had been a good-looking boy, and except that his hair was white he

was still much the same.

"I had a leave coming, and so I went out to Reno to see him. He was doing all right. He had a small room there. He even had a sweetheart. But he had an obsession, an *idée fixe*. He wouldn't marry her until his name was cleared.

"Then he saw Judith at the train in Reno. He was driving a taxi, and she was beautiful and smiling and—well, reeking of prosperity. She wore a mass of orchids, I remember. It made him pretty bitter, I imagine. All I know is what his girl wrote me. He'd left Reno after that and come east, and I began to worry. In Reno he'd changed his name to Alec Morrison. I knew that. But if he'd changed it again, or dyed his hair . . . There are twelve million people in and around New York. There are several thousand taxi drivers too. His Reno license would help him there.

"I spent days going over the list of cab drivers in the city. Also I put other men on it. I even advertised for him. But the plain fact is I had lost him. He knew where to find me, but he never showed up. And the first time I saw him after Reno was after he had been killed.

"All this is merely to tell you why I took the cottage here. I began to realize he might not be entirely normal, and I stayed up a good many nights when he began to haunt the grounds. As you all know, I never caught him."

He stopped then, and I thought he was listening for something. All he did, however, was to ask me if Helga was still up, and to bring her in if she was. She looked startled when I told her. She waited too to put on a clean apron, and I saw her old hands were shaking.

"What does he want?" she asked. "If it's about the eggs, why let them go rotten? I've fed his chickens enough to pay for them."

It was not about the eggs, of course. He stepped forward when she followed me into the room and gave her a chair. True to her training she sat only on the edge of it, but his voice was pleasant as he spoke to her.

"I want you to tell me something," he said. "It won't do any harm now. It may even help. I think you have known all along more than you have ever told."

"This is my family," she said bleakly. "It's all I have."

"That's understandable," he agreed. "But go back twenty years, Helga. You knew Miss Judith was out the night the Preston girl was murdered, didn't you?"

She swallowed hard.

"Yes, I knew it," she said defiantly. "Those children were like my own, lieutenant. And there was trouble enough, with the money all gone and Mr. Maynard shooting himself. Anyhow, who would believe me, with both Judith and her mother against me? I didn't even see Dawson let her in that night. I only heard it."

"What time was that?"

"It was after four in the morning. My legs were bad and I'd gone down to the kitchen for some aspirin. When I think of that

murdering devil blackmailing the madam, after what he'd done himself that night . . . !"

"What had he done, Helga?"

"What? He'd strangled the Preston girl. That's what. Crazy about her, he was, and at his age! Jealous too. I heard him often, over the pantry phone, begging to get her to see him. He was out that night too. I heard him go and come back. He had big ugly hands. They were strong too. That's what he did it with."

I think all of us were shocked. I know I was. But O'Brien was not interested in Dawson or his possible guilt.

"So you let this Shannon boy take the rap for something he didn't do," he said. "You knew Miss Judith was his alibi for that night. Why did you do it, Helga?"

"I didn't know him," she said defensively. "And I couldn't prove anything, could I? That's what Mrs. Maynard said too."

"Oh, so you told her?"

"Sure I told her."

Phil got up. He was very pale.

"Are you saying my mother knew all this and did nothing about it?"

"She knew, Mr. Phil, but I swore on the Bible I wouldn't talk. And I didn't. Until now, if it will help Judith any. That's why I took the things from the desk in the cottage, and you nearly caught me. I hid in the chicken house that night. The photograph was Dawson all right, no matter what he called himself."

She looked at O'Brien.

"You said you were only going

to ask me about the gun," she said.

But Phil had not finished. He went across the room and stood over her.

"How much of this did my father know?" he demanded, his face frozen.

"Don't you go blaming your father, Phil," she said. "He was the best man I ever knew. I think he knew Judith had been out that night, and why Dawson was blackmailing your mother. But he didn't know she'd been with the Shannon boy. If he had he'd have gone right before a jury and told them. That's what he was like."

Phil turned. He gave a despairing glance at the Laszlo over the fireplace. Then he sat down and put his head in his hands. Anne had not moved. She was staring straight ahead of her, but seeing nothing. As for me, I felt dizzy and sick. Mother, carrying that guilt all those years, dying with an innocent boy spending the best years of his life behind stone walls, and still not talking. Father's suicide too, that gentle kindly man driven to desperation and unable to raise the money to save Judith's reputation.

I think O'Brien had not meant to let things go so far, although he certainly knew them.

"Now about the gun," he said. "You know it was returned after his death, don't you?"

"I gave it to Mrs. Maynard with my own hands," she said.

"Have you ever seen it since?"

"No. It's never been around. I know every inch of this house. It's never been in it."

34

Nobody spoke for a minute or two. Then O'Brien drew a matchbox out of his pocket. He opened it and looked at it.

"For twenty years," he said quietly, "I have been on the trail of Inspector Flaherty's murderer. I've carried the slug which killed him in this box, and yesterday when the Chief of Police here in town sent to Ballistics in New York the gun Mrs. Chandler brought back with her, I was present when they tried it out.

"It was the same gun. Think about that for a minute. It had killed your father, but by his own hand. It had wounded me, although that's not important. It had murdered Johnny Shannon. I dug a slug from it out of the cottage wall. It comes close to convicting Judith Chandler of murder. And it killed Inspector Flaherty twenty years ago. That's quite a record.

"I want you all to think about Flaherty for a moment. He was a good cop. He had to take the risks of his job, as we all do. But he was no man's fool. He did not believe Johnny Shannon was guilty. He told me your sister Judith was lying, and—I'm sorry—your mother too. Then one day he told me he had located Dawson and meant to get the truth out of him.

"But he made one mistake. He told both Judith and your mother, and that night he was murdered."

He shoved the matchbox back into his pocket and going over to the hearth looked up at mother's portrait.

"A mother will do many things for a dearly loved daughter," he said slowly. "Or to save her own place in the world, her social position, or the good name of her family. But I do not believe murder is one of them. And quite definitely she did not shoot me, or Johnny Shannon. Nor did it seem likely Johnny had shot me, not with that gun.

"You see, the whole case turned on the gun. It still does. And I haven't been working alone. When Shannon came east I went to the Commissioner and told him the story, that he had come east and Mrs. Chandler might need protection. He knew who she was. Who didn't? And he didn't want her killed. So I got an extended leave and took the cottage by the main road. The papers said she

was here at The Birches, and from the start I felt sure Shannon was about the place at night. I even knew he was in the cottage the first day I saw it. He'd taken a drink of water and his prints were on the glass.

"I never caught him, however, and then a woman whose name was Selina Benjamin was drowned in your pool. I knew from the railroad ticket in her bag where she had come from, and when the Hunnewell woman who lived next door identified her I was positive she was the Kate Henry whose testimony had largely convicted Johnny. She had seen him in Mollie Preston's room and heard them quarreling, and she'd identified him in the line-up before she disappeared.

"It looked as though he had killed her. He had a motive, right enough. But the golf club was not his sort of weapon. I don't imagine he had ever used one in his life. I know now that Mrs. Chandler took it to the pool and left it there. At least so she told me today. There is no proof, of course. Nor was there any proof of her story about a holdup." He smiled. "I've heard even more imaginative stories many times, and the local men are positive she invented it. But today it had become a matter of fast work or she would go to jail. As I told Lois . . ."

We had never heard Ed Brown's taxi drive up, which shows the state we were in. But we heard his voice.

"Now mind you," he said,

"twenty minutes and no more. It's my bedtime."

"Oh, shut up, sourpuss," a woman said. "I'm not paying you until I get back to the station. Take it or lump it."

She came briskly up the porch steps, and O'Brien went out into the hall.

"Come in," he said. "I'm glad you got here."

"So am I! I thought the old bastard out there was going to dump me in the ditch."

It was Clarice, Judith's personal maid, and now shed of her fine manners. She gave a sharp look around the room as O'Brien brought her in.

"And maybe I ain't scared," she said. "You didn't say this place was spooky. What's the idea of a man stopping that rattletrap and shining a flashlight in my face? The driver nearly jumped out of his skin."

I thought O'Brien looked annoyed. He did not bother to introduce her. He put her in a chair near the door and stood by her.

"You telephoned, as I told you?" he asked.

She merely nodded. She was surveying all of us, especially Helga. She grinned at her.

"In kind of high-class company, aren't you?" she said. "What goes anyhow?"

Helga looked disgusted.

"It's none of your business," she said. "Keep your mouth shut until you're spoken to."

O'Brien ignored them both. He looked down at Clarice.

"Did you bring the list I asked for?" he inquired.

"All I could remember," she said.

She fished in her handbag, bringing out the usual lipstick and compact, a fine embroidered handkerchief which probably belonged to Judith, and finally a sheet of paper. O'Brien glanced at it and shoved it in his pocket.

"Did you see the gun?"

"I saw *a* gun. At the police station here in town. It looked the same. I can't be sure."

"When did it disappear?"

"It wasn't there when I went back with Miss Maynard to pack Mrs. Chandler's clothes. That's all I know."

Phil glared at her.

"Are you saying my sister took this gun, and had it with her when she left for Reno? I don't believe you."

O'Brien, however, did not let her answer. He motioned to Helga, who got up, and hauled some change out of his pocket.

"Pay off Ed Brown, will you?" he said. "And take Clarice here back to your sitting room. I'll see she gets back safely. Give her a cup of tea or something. She's had a trying evening."

If anyone ever looked less like giving Clarice a cup of tea than Helga at that moment, I can't imagine who. But Clarice took a hand.

"You might make it something stronger," she said. "I've still got the shakes."

As a result she left carrying a tall glass of whisky and soda, and looking definitely more cheerful.

Phil stirred.

"Why all the Mumbo Jumbo?" he demanded. "If you have a case against Judith, let's have it."

O'Brien was still standing. One of his pockets sagged and I knew he had a gun in it, but no one else apparently noticed. It frightened me, that gun. It seemed so unnecessary somehow. No one was going to attack him, although Phil looked rebellious enough for anything.

"I'm sorry," O'Brien said. "I didn't locate Clarice until tonight. I'd like to go back to the night Johnny Shannon was killed and Mrs. Chandler was hurt. You see, it was carefully arranged as a holdup. A masked man with a gun, the driver shot, and the jewel case taken. But even the best plans slip. This one did, for the simple fact that the engine of the car was still running, and some movement of the dying man pressed on the accelerator.

"I'll go a little further. Johnny Shannon expected to meet a man there, the one he told your sister was to take a deposition from her to clear his name. But he had not expected a mask. Something was wrong and he knew it. He may have put the car in gear then.

"However it happened, the masked man shot him and thought he had shot your sister. There is a bullet hole near where she sat. But she had only fainted, as it happened. He took the jewel case and was backing out of the car when it started.

"Mrs. Chandler says he threw the gun at her. I think she is wrong. It was jerked out of his hand. It may have struck her. I don't know. What we do know is that she did not go all the way with the car. She fell out as it turned over, and after she came to she had the gun in her hand. She's vague about all this. It's still possible she grabbed at it as he pointed it at her.

"She wasn't out very long. She was in shock and in pain, but she started back to The Birches. Remember, she thought the masked man was still around, so she carried the gun with her. For the same reason she did not use the drive. She took to the shrubbery. Her memory has improved now. I talked to her today, and she says she remembers that. She also remembers that near the pool she stumbled and fell, and the gun went off."

He glanced at me.

"That cleared up something which bothered me for some time, a shot both Lois and I heard that night. It was a couple of hours after the so-called holdup. The killer should have been gone a long time, establishing an alibi, or at least getting the hell out of there. At any time someone might see the car and investigate, and he needed . . . Keep down, Phil," he said quickly. "Don't move. Don't try anything."

He jerked the gun out of his pocket and I was suddenly faint. Phil, who had been out so late the night of the murder! Phil, who had little or no love for Judith. And Phil, who might have had father's gun for years.

O'Brien, however, was not looking at him. He was watching one of the open windows. It was near the old conservatory, and in the sudden silence we all heard what O'Brien's quick ears had caught before we did, the crushing of glass under a careful foot. It was followed almost immediately by a hand pushing back the curtains there, a gloved hand holding a gun.

The two shots were almost simultaneous. O'Brien's, however, was first. It knocked the gun into the room. The hand disappeared, and young Bill outside was yelling at the top of his lungs.

"Quick! I've got him."

Almost immediately men were shouting all over the place outside, and O'Brien, wearing his grim policeman's face, was dropping his own gun back into his pocket and swearing under his breath.

Anne was staring incredulously at the window, and Phil was grinning crookedly at O'Brien.

"By God," he said. "I thought you meant to shoot me!"

O'Brien did not answer. Fowler came in, looking flushed and apologetic.

"He took the back road," he said. "Came on foot down the hill by the stable. That's how we missed him. Narrow squeak, wasn't it? That nephew of theirs is some boy!"

"Too narrow," O'Brien said. "Did I kill him?"

"Got him in the arm. That's all. The boys are taking care of him all right. That his gun?" He went over and carefully picked it up. "Bought it yesterday in Bridgeport," he said. "We had the other one."

Anne was still looking dazed.

"Who was it?" she said, her lips white. "The man at the window. Who was it, Lois?"

"Ask Lieutenant O'Brien," I said shortly. "He hasn't bothered to tell me."

O'Brien smiled, for the first time that evening.

"It was—and is—a gentleman named Ridgely Chandler," he said, and put his arms around my shaking body.

35

I suppose I should have known. As I said earlier, I had all the clues. Except for Dawson, dead for months, who outside of mother or Judith had a motive for killing Inspector Flaherty? And who was desperately determined not to have Shannon's case reopened, as Selina Benjamin had agreed to do?

Ridge, I thought, had been a superb actor, or perhaps it is hard for women to think of small dapper men as killers. He would not be looking like a killer even now, sitting with dignity in the station house while a police surgeon dressed his wound.

"There is, of course, some absurd mistake, doctor. If you will look in my wallet you will see my name on a number of things."

His name! His proud family name, for which three people had died.

How far he meant to go that night I do not know but, as O'Brien said later while we sat around the fire and the men had drinks and Anne and I cigarettes, he had felt all along there was a smart scheming mind behind a good bit of what happened.

"He killed Flaherty years ago," he said. "As you've said more than once, Lois, he was a Chandler, and the Chandlers don't marry young women who have had to acknowledge being on more than friendly terms with a lad like Shannon. His old she-dragon of a mother was living at that time too. So when Flaherty got on the trail of Dawson he knew what it meant.

"Don't make any mistake about him. He knew Judith was lying, but he had lost his head entirely over her. In a way he was hardly responsible for what he did. I'd like to say this too. I don't think

your mother gave him your father's gun to shoot anyone. Most likely she simply didn't want it in the house.

"It's a queer thing that he kept it for twenty years. Clarice knew it was there. She did his mending, and she often saw it. Then the day she and Lois packed Judith's clothes she looked for it and it was gone. She didn't think much about it. He wasn't living in the apartment, although some of his clothes were still there. But she noticed it. When I located her she told me.

"He must have gone through hell when Johnny Shannon was released. I imagine Johnny called him up or saw him. He was determined to be cleared and he wanted his case reopened. Chandler had felt safe for a long time, but he knew I'd never given up the search for whoever killed Flaherty. And Johnny knew a lot. When he left the pen he located Selina Benjamin, who had testified against him before the grand jury, and scared her and Dawson so they left town.

"He even came out here and saw Helga, but he found her hard to deal with. She was willing to help him, but not if it hurt Judith. Also she had no real facts, as you all know now.

"So a lot of people were scared, if scared isn't too mild a word: the Benjamins, both the Chandlers, and even Helga. But the worse of the lot was our friend Ridgely. He wasn't in love with his wife by that time, but in an odd way he was proud of her, her looks, even her publicity. It was a long time since any Chandler had figured in anything but churches and hospitals.

"Then he had a respite of sorts. Johnny got discouraged and left town. Judith was getting a divorce and preparing to live abroad. It wasn't until she came back here and he learned I had taken the cottage that he began really to worry. I was bad news and he knew it.

"The story had to be stopped at all costs. I think Johnny told him where the Benjamins were. The husband was dead by that time, and Selina had come back to clear his estate. Don't forget, Selina was a real danger for him. She had lied and largely convicted Johnny, but only so Dawson could get your mother's bribe of fifty thousand dollars. You can't hide that amount of money, especially if you get it in cash, as Chandler did.

"I believe Chandler went to see Selina, and she realized she had a knee lock on him if Johnny's case was reopened. Her bank says she deposited five hundred dollars, again in cash, about that time, and it wasn't from Judith Chandler. She was in Reno.

"But Selina had changed. She took his money, but her conscience was bothering her. She had seen Johnny, with his hair snow-white at forty. It gave her some idea of what the years had done to him. And when he came back from Reno she began to worry.

"She notified Chandler of his re-turn, and it's evident he knew who was haunting the grounds here, the unknown who was trying so desperately to see Judith. Very probably he came here himself in the hope of killing Johnny. I knew he was in the grounds the night he shot me. That was later, of course. After Selina's body was found in the pool.

"But about Selina and her death. I know she called Chandler over long-distance at his office in New York—I have the record of the call—to say she was going to see Judith that night at the pool. You can hear how it would go.

"'Why?' he would say. 'What good will it do you?'

"'It might do Johnny Shannon a lot of good. He's back. He came to see me yesterday.'

"'Don't be a fool. If the case is reopened, you'll have to go to the pen for perjury.'

"'Let's say I have a conscience, or have got religion. They might go easy on me.'

"It was something like that. His secretary heard his part of it and remembered it.

"Judith's story fits it exactly. The woman was late and she herself was afraid. She forgot the golf club and left it there, so when Selina waited on the bench it was beside her. Probably Chandler meant to shoot her, but a shot is noisy and I was near by in the cottage. The club was better. He knocked her out with it and dragged her into the pool.

"He was, you see, getting rid of his troubles one by one. Selina was the first, after Flaherty. I came close to being the second, and Johnny himself was to be the third. Don't forget Judith either, if the case was reopened. She was frightened, but she wasn't the shivering obedient girl she had been before. She was a woman now. Perhaps she knew Chandler had bought and paid for her, and hated him for it. Or she might have developed the same conscience as Selina Benjamin.

"Then one day Johnny himself went to see him. The secretary knows it. She let him into Chandler's office and he was there a long time. When he came out he looked pleased.

"'Something nice happen to you?' she said.

"'About the best there is,' he told her. 'Wish me luck tonight, will you?'

"'Of course. Is it a girl?'

"'No girl is as important as this is.'

"That's when the scheme hatched," O'Brien said. "He was to get Judith and then pick up Chandler on the road. Chandler was to have a paper ready for her to sign, admitting her presence in Shannon's room the night of the Preston girl's murder, and confirming his alibi. Just what pressure they meant to use I don't know. Or what Shannon meant. Chandler had other plans.

"I know it sounds cracked, but Shannon wasn't entirely normal. It was obsession at its worst. And remember, from Chandler's point of view, how nearly it came off! Only the unexpected happened. Judith wasn't killed, and she car-ried off his gun. I have to guess a bit here. She says she came to with it in her hand. He may have followed her down the hill and thinking the fall or his shot at her had killed her, put it in her hand himself. Or she may have caught at it when he pointed it at her. I think this last is more likely. I doubt if he stayed around there very long. He had his car hidden near by, and he beat it back to the city.

"It still stood as a holdup, of course. Only he had grabbed her jewel case, and no matter how wealthy a man is, it takes a lot of guts"—he grinned at Anne—"to throw a quarter of a million dollars' worth of baubles into a river, or one of the reservoirs.

"Chandler didn't have that sort. The damn fool has been carrying them locked in the trunk of his car ever since. He had a special lock on it, but we opened it today. They were there.

"I don't think he knew we had them. The case is still in the car. But I knew he was after me. I knew too much. I believed Judith's story when no one else did. And I had his gun. Only he and I knew it had killed Flaherty. When I asked him to meet me here tonight I was confident he meant to kill me.

"So I laid a trap for him, and got him."

It was the end of the story. Months later, after all sorts of appeals, Ridgely Chandler was convicted of Johnny Shannon's murder. But I will always believe he actually went to the chair for the shooting of one Inspector Flaherty, dead for twenty years. As O'Brien says, the police have long memories when it comes to a cop-killer.

As always happens, many things were not brought out at his trial, although Homicide had them. A search of the Benjamin house, for example, disclosed a singular document fastened with Scotch tape to the back of the high-old fashioned tank of the toilet in the bathroom. It was signed by Benjamin himself, and notarized.

"I, Walter Benjamin — born Arthur Dawson—do hereby swear that I had nothing to do with the murder of Inspector John Flaherty. Flaherty was shot and killed by one Ridgely Chandler. I followed him that night and saw him do it.

"This is to state that the money I received, fifty thousand dollars, was for the purpose of confirming Judith Maynard's alibi in the death of Mollie Preston, and for no other purpose whatever."

Which was curious, to say the least, since Helga still believes he killed Mollie himself.

Of course you get used to things like that when you marry a police-man. During the long months since I began this story of my sister Judith I have done much of the work at night. The long endless nights when the telephone rings and O'Brien picks it up, says "yeah" a couple of times, and then throws on his clothes and looks around for his gun.

He is a captain now. I don't think he has to carry it, but it's a matter of habit. He feels undressed without it. Sometimes it's in his shoulder holster or stuck in his leather belt. Or again he merely drops it into a pocket. It is automatic. He doesn't always know he does it. His mind is out somewhere in this huge city where we live. I get a hasty absent-minded kiss and he is gone.

I go back to the kitchenette and get the coffee ready for his return. Not percolated. Just ready to turn the current on. But I never go to sleep again. I sit and wait or I sit and write. But even as I write I am waiting, for the sound of his key in the lock of the apartment, for his strong arms around me and the tenderness of his voice. For if he is both a police officer and a man, at least the man is mine.

BY DAPHNE du MAURIER

Five of the best stories by the author of REBECCA, *selected from* KISS ME AGAIN, STRANGER, *her newest anthology.*

KISS ME AGAIN, STRANGER

I looked around for a bit, after leaving the Army and before settling down, and then I found myself a job up Hampstead way, in a garage it was, at the bottom of Haverstock Hill near Chalk Farm, and it suited me fine. I'd always been one for tinkering with engines, and in R.E.M.E. that was my work and I was trained to it —it had always come easy to me, anything mechanical.

My idea of having a good time was to lie on my back in my greasy overalls under a car's belly, or a lorry's, with a spanner in my hand, working on some old bolt or screw, with the smell of oil about me, and someone starting up an engine, and the other chaps around clattering their tools and whistling. I never minded the smell or the dirt. As my old Mum used to say when I'd be that way as a kid, mucking about with a grease can, "It won't hurt him, it's clean dirt," and so it is, with engines.

COPYRIGHT, 1952, BY DAPHNE DU MAURIER, AND
PUBLISHED BY DOUBLEDAY & CO., INC., NEW YORK

The boss at the garage was a good fellow, easygoing, cheerful, and he saw I was keen on my work. He wasn't much of a mechanic himself, so he gave me the repair jobs, which was what I liked.

I didn't live with my old Mum —she was too far off, over Shepperton way, and I saw no point in spending half the day getting to and from my work. I like to be handy, have it on the spot, as it were. So I had a bedroom with a couple called Thompson, only about ten minutes' walk away from the garage. Nice people, they were. He was in the shoe business—cobbler, I suppose he'd be called—and Mrs. Thompson cooked the meals and kept the house for him over the shop. I used to eat with them, breakfast and supper—we always had a cooked supper—and being the only lodger, I was treated as family.

I'm one for routine. I like to get on with my job, and then when the day's work's over settle down to a paper and a smoke and a bit of music on the wireless, variety or something of the sort, and then turn in early. I never had much use for girls, not even when I was doing my time in the Army. I was out in the Middle East, too, Port Said and that.

No, I was happy enough living with the Thompsons, carrying on much the same day after day, until that one night, when it happened. Nothing's been the same since. Nor ever will be. I don't know . . .

The Thompsons had gone to see their married daughter up at Highgate. They asked me if I'd like to go along, but somehow I didn't fancy barging in, so instead of staying home alone after leaving the garage I went down to the picture palace and, taking a look at the poster, saw it was cowboy and Indian stuff—there was a picture of a cowboy sticking a knife into the Indian's guts. I like that— proper baby I am for westerns— so I paid my one and twopence and went inside. I handed my slip of paper to the usherette and said, "Back row, please," because I like sitting far back and leaning my head against the board.

Well, then I saw her. They dress the girls up no end in some of these places, velvet tams and all, making them proper guys. They hadn't made a guy out of this one, though. She had copper hair, page-boy style I think they call it, and blue eyes, the kind that look short-sighted but see further than you think, and go dark by night, nearly black, and her mouth was sulky-looking, as if she was fed up, and it would take someone giving her the world to make her smile. She hadn't freckles, nor a milky skin, but warmer than that, more like a peach, and natural too. She was small and slim, and her velvet coat—blue it was— fitted her close, and the cap on the back of her head showed up her copper hair.

I bought a programme—not that I wanted one, but to delay going in through the curtain—and I said to her, "What's the picture like?"

She didn't look at me. She just went on staring into nothing, at the opposite wall. "The knifing's amateur," she said, "but you can always sleep."

I couldn't help laughing. I could see she was serious though. She wasn't trying to have me on or anything.

"That's no advertisement," I said. "What if the manager heard you?"

Then she looked at me. She turned those blue eyes in my direction; still fed-up they were, not interested, but there was something in them I'd not seen before, and I've never seen it since, a kind of laziness, like someone waking from a long dream and glad to find you there. Cats' eyes have that gleam sometimes when you stroke them, and they purr and curl themselves into a ball and let you do anything you want. She looked at me this way a moment, and there was a smile lurking somewhere behind her mouth if you gave it a chance, and tearing my slip of paper in half, she said, "I'm not paid to advertise. I'm paid to look like this and lure you inside."

She drew aside the curtains and flashed her torch in the darkness. I couldn't see a thing. It was pitch black, like it always is at first until you get used to it and begin to make out the shapes of the other people sitting there, but there were two great heads on the screen and some chap saying to the other, "If you don't come clean I'll put a bullet through you," and somebody broke a pane of glass and a woman screamed.

"Looks all right to me," I said, and began groping for somewhere to sit.

She said, "This isn't the picture, it's the trailer for next week," and she flicked on her torch and showed me a seat in the back row, one away from the gangway.

I sat through the advertisements and the newsreel, and then some chap came and played the organ, and the colours of the curtains over the screen went purple and gold and green—funny, I suppose they think they have to give you your money's worth—and looking around, I saw the house was half empty—and I guessed the girl had been right, the big picture wasn't going to be much, and that's why nobody much was there.

Just before the hall went dark again she came sauntering down the aisle. She had a tray of ice creams, but she didn't even bother to call them out and try to sell them. She could have been walking in her sleep, so when she went up the other aisle I beckoned to her.

"Got a sixpenny one?" I said.

She looked across at me. I might have been something dead under her feet, and then she must have recognised me, because that half smile came back again, and the lazy look in the eye, and she walked round the back of the seats to me.

"Wafer or cornet?" she said.

I didn't want either, to tell the

truth. I just wanted to buy something from her and keep her talking.

"Which do you recommend?" I asked.

She shrugged her shoulders. "Cornets last longer," she said, and put one in my hand before I had time to give her my choice.

"How about one for you too?" I said.

"No, thanks," she said, "I saw them made."

And she walked off, and the place went dark, and there I was sitting with a great sixpenny cornet in my hand, looking a fool. The damn thing slopped all over the edge of the holder, spilling on to my shirt, and I had to ram the frozen stuff into my mouth as quick as I could for fear it would all go on my knees, and I turned sideways, because someone came and sat in the empty seat beside the gangway.

I finished it at last, and cleaned myself up with my pocket handkerchief, and then concentrated on the story flashing across the screen. It was a western all right, carts lumbering over prairies, and a train full of bullion being held to ransom, and the heroine in breeches one moment and full evening dress the next. That's the way pictures should be, not a bit like real life at all; but as I watched the story I began to notice the whiff of scent in the air, and I didn't know what it was or where it came from, but it was there just the same. There was a man to the right of me, and on my left were two empty seats, and it certainly

wasn't the people in front, and I couldn't keep turning round and sniffing.

I'm not a great one for liking scent. It's too often cheap and nasty, but this was different. There was nothing stale about it, or stuffy, or strong; it was like the flowers they sell up in the West End in the big flower shops before you get them on the barrows —three bob a bloom sort of touch, rich chaps buy them for actresses and such—and it was so darn good, the smell of it there in that murky old picture palace full of cigarette smoke, that it nearly drove me mad.

At last I turned right round in my seat, and I spotted where it came from. It came from the girl, the usherette; she was leaning on the back board behind me, her arms folded across it.

"Don't fidget," she said. "You're wasting one and twopence. Watch the screen."

But not out loud so that anyone could hear. In a whisper, for me alone. I couldn't help laughing to myself. The cheek of it! I knew where the scent came from now, and somehow it made me enjoy the picture more. It was as though she was beside me in one of the empty seats and we were looking at the story together.

When it was over and the lights went on, I saw I'd sat through the last showing and it was nearly ten. Everyone was clearing off for the night. So I waited a bit, and then she came down with her torch and started squinting under the seats to see if anybody had dropped a glove or a purse, the way they do and only remember about afterwards when they get home, and she took no more notice of me than if I'd been a rag which no one would bother to pick up.

I stood up in the back row, alone—the house was clear now—and when she came to me she said, "Move over, you're blocking the gangway," and flashed about with her torch, but there was nothing there, only an empty packet of Player's which the cleaners would throw away in the morning. Then she straightened herself and looked me up and down, and taking off the ridiculous cap from the back of her head that suited her so well, she fanned herself with it and said, "Sleeping here tonight?" and then went off, whistling under her breath, and disappeared through the curtains.

It was proper maddening. I'd never been taken so much with a girl in my life. I went into the vestibule after her, but she had gone through a door to the back, behind the box-office place and the commissionaire chap was already getting the doors to and fixing them for the night. I went out and stood in the street and waited. I felt a bit of a fool, because the odds were that she would come out with a bunch of others, the way girls do. There was the one who had sold me my ticket, and I dare say there were other usherettes up in the balcony, and perhaps a cloakroom attendant too, and they'd all be giggling together, and I wouldn't have the nerve to go up to her.

In a few minutes, though, she came swinging out of the place alone. She had a mac on, belted, and her hands in her pockets, and she had no hat. She walked straight up the street, and she didn't look to right or left of her. I followed, scared that she would turn round and see me off, but she went on walking, fast and direct, staring straight in front of her, and as she moved her copper page-boy hair swung with her shoulders.

Presently she hesitated, then crossed over and stood waiting for a bus. There was a queue of four or five people, so she didn't see me join the queue, and when the bus came she climbed on to it, ahead of the others, and I climbed too, without the slightest notion where it was going, and I couldn't have cared less. Up the stairs she went with me after her, and settled herself in the back seat, yawning, and closed her eyes.

I sat myself down beside her, nervous as a kitten, the point being that I never did that sort of thing as a rule and expected a rocket, and when the conductor stumped up and asked for fares I said, "Two sixpennies, please," because I reckoned she would never be going the whole distance and this would be bound to cover her fare and mine too.

He raised his eyebrows—they like to think themselves smart, some of these fellows—and he said, "Look out for the bumps when the driver changes gear. He's only just passed his test."

And he went down the stairs chuckling, telling himself he was no end of a wag, no doubt.

The sound of his voice woke the girl, and she looked at me out of her sleepy eyes, and looked, too, at the tickets in my hand—she must have seen by the colour they were sixpennies—and she smiled, the first real smile I had got out of her that evening, and said without any sort of surprise, "Hullo, stranger."

I took out a cigarette, to put myself at ease, and offered her one, but she wouldn't take it. She just closed her eyes again, to settle herself to sleep. Then, seeing there was no one else to notice up on the top deck, only an Air Force chap in the front slopped over a newspaper, I put out my hand and pulled her head down on my shoulder, and got my arm round her, snug and comfortable, thinking of course she'd throw it off and blast me to hell. She didn't, though. She gave a sort of laugh to herself, and settled down like as if she might have been in an armchair, and she said, "It's not every night I get a free ride and a free pillow. Wake me at the bottom of the hill, before we get to the cemetery."

I didn't know what hill she meant, or what cemetery, but I wasn't going to wake her, not me. I had paid for two sixpennies, and I was darn well going to get value for my money.

So we sat there together, jogging along in the bus, very close and very pleasant, and I thought to myself that it was a lot more fun than sitting at home in the bed-sit reading the football news, or spending an evening up Highgate at Mr. and Mrs. Thompson's daughter's place.

Presently I got more daring, and let my head lean against hers, and tightened up my arm a bit, not too obvious-like, but nicely. Anyone coming up the stairs to the top deck would have taken us for a courting couple.

Then, after we had had about fourpenny-worth, I got anxious. The old bus wouldn't be turning round and going back again when we reached the sixpenny limit; it would pack up for the night, we'd have come to the terminus. And there we'd be, the girl and I, stuck out somewhere at the back of beyond, with no return bus, and I'd got about six bob in my pocket and no more. Six bob would never pay for a taxi, not with a tip and all. Besides, there probably wouldn't be any taxis going.

What a fool I'd been not to come out with more money. It was silly, perhaps, to let it worry me, but I'd acted on impulse right from the start, and if only I'd known how the evening was going to turn out I'd have had my wallet filled. It wasn't often I went out with a girl, and I hate a fellow who can't do the thing in style. Proper slap-up do at a Corner House—they're good these days with that help-yourself service—and if she had a fancy for something stronger than coffee or orangeade, well, of course as late as this it wasn't much use, but nearer home I knew where to go.

There was a pub where my boss went, and you paid for your gin and kept it there, and could go in and have a drink from your bottle when you felt like it. They have the same sort of racket at the posh night clubs up West, I'm told, but they make you pay through the nose for it.

Anyway, here I was riding a bus to the Lord knows where, with my girl beside me—I called her "my girl" just as if she really was and we were courting—and bless me if I had the money to take her home. I began to fidget about, from sheer nerves, and I fumbled in one pocket after another, in case by a piece of luck I should come across a half-crown, or even a ten-bob note I had forgotten all about, and I suppose I disturbed her with all this, because she suddenly pulled my ear and said, "Stop rocking the boat."

Well, I mean to say . . . It just got me. I can't explain why. She held my ear a moment before she pulled it, like as though she were feeling the skin and liked it, and then she just gave it a lazy tug. It's the kind of thing anyone would do to a child, and the way she said it, as if she had known me for years and we were out picnicking together, "Stop rocking the boat." Chummy, matey, yet better than either.

"Look here," I said, "I'm awfully sorry, I've been and done a darn silly thing. I took tickets to the terminus because I wanted to sit beside you, and when we get there we'll be turned out of the bus, and it will be miles from anywhere, and I've only got six bob in my pocket."

"You've got legs, haven't you?" she said.

"What d'you mean, I've got legs?"

"They're meant to walk on. Mine were," she answered.

Then I knew it didn't matter, and she wasn't angry either, and the evening was going to be all right. I cheered up in a second, and gave her a squeeze, just to show I appreciated her being such a sport—most girls would have torn me to shreds—and I said, "We haven't passed a cemetery, as far as I know. Does it matter very much?"

"Oh, there'll be others," she said. "I'm not particular."

I didn't know what to make of that. I thought she wanted to get out at the cemetery stopping point because it was her nearest stop for home, like the way you say, "Put me down at Woolworth's," if you live handy. I puzzled over it for a bit, and then I said, "How do you mean, there'll be others? It's not a thing you see often along a bus route."

"I was speaking in general terms," she answered. "Don't bother to talk, I like you silent best."

It wasn't a slap on the face, the way she said it. Fact was, I knew what she meant. Talking's all very pleasant with people like Mr. and Mrs. Thompson, over supper, and you say how the day has gone, and one of you reads a bit out of the paper, and the other says, "Fancy, there now," and so it goes on, in bits and pieces, until one of you yawns, and somebody says, "Who's for bed?" Or it's nice enough with a chap like the boss, having a cuppa midmorning, or about three when there's nothing doing, "I tell you what I think, those blokes in the government are making a mess of things, no better than the last lot," and then we'll be interrupted with someone coming to fill up with petrol. And I like talking to my old Mum when I go and see her, which I don't do often enough, and she tells me how she spanked my bottom when I was a kid, and I sit on the kitchen table like I did then, and she bakes rock cakes and gives me peel, saying, "You always were one for peel." That's talk, that's conversation.

But I didn't want to talk to my girl. I just wanted to keep my arm round her the way I was doing, and rest my chin against her head, and that's what she meant when she said she liked me silent. I liked it too.

One last thing bothered me a bit, and that was whether I could kiss her before the bus stopped and we were turned out at the terminus. I mean, putting an arm round a girl is one thing, and kissing her is another. It takes a little time as a rule to warm up. You start off with a long evening ahead of you, and by the time you've been to a picture or a concert, and then had something to eat and to drink, well, you've got yourselves acquainted, and it's the usual thing to end up with a bit of kissing and a cuddle, the girls expect

it. Truth to tell, I was never much of a one for kissing. There was a girl I walked out with back home, before I went into the Army, and she was quite a good sort, I liked her. But her teeth were a bit prominent, and even if you shut your eyes and tried to forget who it was you were kissing, well, you knew it was her, and there was nothing to it. Good old Doris from next door. But the opposite kind are even worse, the ones that grab you and nearly eat you. You come across plenty of them when you're in uniform. They're much too eager, and they muss you about, and you get the feeling they can't wait for a chap to get busy about them. I don't mind saying it used to make me sick. Put me dead off, and that's a fact. I suppose I was born fussy. I don't know.

But now, this evening in the bus, it was all quite different. I don't know what it was about the girl—the sleepy eyes, and the copper hair, and somehow not seeming to care if I was there, yet liking me at the same time; I hadn't found anything like this before. So I said to myself, "Now, shall I risk it, or shall I wait?" and I knew, from the way the driver was going and the conductor was whistling below and saying good night to the people getting off, that the final stop couldn't be far away; and my heart began to thump under my coat, and my neck grow hot below the collar— darn silly, only a kiss, you know, she couldn't kill me—and then . . . It was like diving off a springboard. I thought, "Here goes," and I bent down, and turned her face to me, and lifted her chin with my hand, and kissed her good and proper.

Well, if I was poetical, I'd say what happened then was a revelation. But I'm not poetical, and I can only say that she kissed me back, and it lasted a long time, and it wasn't a bit like Doris.

Then the bus stopped with a jerk, and the conductor called out in a singsong voice, "All out, please." Frankly, I could have wrung his neck.

She gave me a kick on the ankle. "Come on, move," she said, and I stumbled from my seat and racketted down the stairs, she following behind, and there we were, standing in a street. It was beginning to rain too, not badly, but just enough to make you notice and want to turn up the collar of your coat, and we were right at the end of a great wide street, with deserted unlighted shops on either side, the end of the world it looked to me, and sure enough there was a hill over to the left, and at the bottom of the hill a cemetery. I could see the railings and the white tombstones behind, and it stretched a long way, nearly halfway up the hill. There were acres of it.

"God darn it," I said, "is this the place you meant?"

"Could be," she said, looking over her shoulder vaguely, and then she took my arm. "What about a cup of coffee first?" she said.

First . . . ? I wondered if she meant before the long trudge home, or was this home? It didn't really matter. It wasn't much after eleven. And I could do with a cup of coffee, and a sandwich too. There was a stall across the road, and they hadn't shut up shop.

We walked over to it, and the driver was there too, and the conductor, and the Air Force fellow who had been up in front on the top deck. They were ordering cups of tea and sandwiches, and we had the same, only coffee. They cut them tasty at the stalls, the sandwiches, I've noticed it before, nothing stingy about it, good slices of ham between thick white bread, and the coffee is piping hot, full cups too, good value, and I thought to myself, "Six bob will see this lot all right."

I noticed my girl looking at the Air Force chap, sort of thoughtful-like, as though she might have seen him before, and he looked at her too. I couldn't blame him for that. I didn't mind either; when you're out with a girl it gives you a kind of pride if other chaps notice her. And you couldn't miss this one. Not my girl.

Then she turned her back on him, deliberate, and leant with her elbows on the stall, sipping her hot coffee, and I stood beside her doing the same. We weren't stuck-up or anything; we were pleasant and polite enough, saying good evening all round, but anyone could tell that we were together, the girl and I, we were on our own. I liked that. Funny, it did something to me inside, gave me a protective feeling. For all they knew, we might have been a married couple on our way home.

They were chaffing a bit, the other three and the chap serving the sandwiches and tea, but we didn't join in.

"You want to watch out, in that uniform," said the conductor to the Air Force fellow, "or you'll end up like those others. It's late, too, to be out on your own."

They all started laughing. I didn't quite see the point, but I supposed it was a joke.

"I've been awake a long time," said the Air Force fellow. "I know a bad lot when I see one."

"That's what the others said, I shouldn't wonder," remarked the driver, "and we know what happened to them. Makes you shudder. But why pick on the Air Force, that's what I want to know?"

"It's the colour of our uniform," said the fellow. "You can spot it in the dark."

They went on laughing in that way. I lighted up a cigarette, but my girl wouldn't have one.

"I blame the war for all that's gone wrong with the women," said the coffee-stall bloke, wiping a cup and hanging it up behind. "Turned a lot of them balmy, in my opinion. They don't know the difference between right or wrong."

" 'Tisn't that, it's sport that's the trouble," said the conductor. "Develops their muscles and that, what weren't never meant to be developed. Take my two youngsters, f'r instance. The girl can

knock the boy down any time, she's a proper little bully. Makes you think."

"That's right," agreed the driver, "equality of the sexes, they call it, don't they? It's the vote that did it. We ought never to have given them the vote."

"Garn," said the Air Force chap, "giving them the vote didn't turn the women balmy. They've always been the same under the skin. The people out East know how to treat 'em. They keep 'em shut up out there. That's the answer. Then you don't get any trouble."

"I don't know what my old woman would say if I tried to shut her up," said the driver. And they all started laughing again.

My girl plucked at my sleeve and I saw she had finished her coffee. She motioned with her head towards the street.

"Want to go home?" I said.

Silly. I somehow wanted the others to believe we were going home. She didn't answer. She just went striding off, her hands in the pockets of her mac. I said good night and followed her, but not before I noticed the Air Force fellow staring after her over his cup of tea.

She walked off along the street, and it was still raining, dreary somehow, made you want to be sitting over a fire somewhere snug, and when she had crossed the street and had come to the railings outside the cemetery she stopped, and looked up at me, and smiled.

"What now?" I said.

"Tombstones are flat," she said, "sometimes."

"What if they are?" I asked, bewildered-like.

"You can lie down on them," she said.

She turned and strolled along, looking at the railings, and then she came to one that was bent wide, and the next beside it broken, and she glanced up at me and smiled again.

"It's always the same," she said. "You're bound to find a gap if you look long enough."

She was through that gap in the railings as quick as a knife through butter. You could have knocked me flat.

"Here, hold on," I said, "I'm not as small as you."

But she was off and away, wandering among the graves. I got through the gap, puffing and blowing a bit, and then I looked around, and bless me if she wasn't lying on a long flat gravestone, with her arms under her head and her eyes closed.

Well, I wasn't expecting anything. I mean, it had been in my mind to see her home and that. Date her up for the next evening. Of course, seeing as it was late, we could have stopped a bit when we came to the doorway of her place. She needn't have gone in right away. But lying there on the gravestone wasn't hardly natural.

I sat down and took her hand. "You'll get wet lying there," I said. Feeble, but I didn't know what else to say.

"I'm used to that," she said.

She opened her eyes and looked at me. There was a street light not far away, outside the railings, so it wasn't all that dark, and anyway, in spite of the rain, the night wasn't pitch black, more murky somehow. I wish I knew how to tell about her eyes, but I'm not one for fancy talk. You know how a luminous watch shines in the dark. I've got one myself. When you wake up in the night, there it is on your wrist, like a friend. Somehow my girl's eyes shone like that, but they were lovely too. And they weren't lazy cats' eyes any more. They were loving and gentle, and they were sad, too, all at the same time.

"Used to lying in the rain?" I said.

"Brought up to it," she answered. "They gave us a name in the shelters. The dead-end kids, they used to call us in the war days."

"Weren't you never evacuated?" I asked.

"Not me," she said. "I never could stop anyplace. I always came back."

"Parents living?"

"No. Both of them killed by the bomb that smashed my home." She didn't speak tragic-like. Just ordinary.

"Bad luck," I said.

She didn't answer that one. And I sat there, holding her hand, wanting to take her home.

"You been on your job some time at the picture house?" I asked.

"About three weeks," she said. "I don't stop anywhere long. I'll be moving on again soon."

"Why's that?"

"Restless," she said.

She put up her hands suddenly and took my face and held it. It was gentle the way she did it, not as you'd think.

"You've got a good kind face. I like it," she said to me.

It was queer. The way she said it made me feel daft and soft, not sort of excited like I had been in the bus, and I thought to myself, "Well, maybe this is it, I've found a girl at last I really want. But not for an evening, casual. For going steady."

"Got a bloke?" I asked.

"No," she said.

"I mean, regular."

"No, never."

It was a funny line of talk to be having in a cemetery, and she lying there like some figure carved on the old tombstone.

"I haven't got a girl either," I said. "Never think about it, the way other chaps do. Faddy, I guess. And then I'm keen on my job. Work in a garage—mechanic, you know—repairs, anything that's going. Good pay. I've saved a bit, besides what I send my old Mum. I live in digs. Nice people, Mr. and Mrs. Thompson, and my boss at the garage is a nice chap too. I've never been lonely, and I'm not lonely now. But since I've seen you, it's made me think. You know, it's not going to be the same any more."

She never interrupted once, and somehow it was like speaking my thoughts aloud.

"Going home to the Thompsons' is all very pleasant and nice," I said, "and you couldn't wish for kinder people. Good grub, too, and we chat a bit after supper, and listen to the wireless. But d'you know, what I want now is different. I want to come along and fetch you from the cinema, when the programme's over, and you'd be standing there by the curtains, seeing the people out, and you'd give me a bit of a wink to show me you'd be going through to change your clothes and I could wait for you. And then you'd come out into the street, like you did tonight, but you wouldn't go off on your own, you'd take my arm, and if you didn't want to wear your coat I'd carry it for you, or a parcel maybe, or whatever you had. Then we'd go off to the Corner House or some place for supper, handy. We'd have a table reserved—they'd know us, the waitresses and them; they'd keep back something special, just for us."

I could picture it too, clear as anything. The table with the ticket on, "Reserved." The waitress nodding at us, "Got curried eggs tonight." And we going through to get our trays, and my girl acting like she didn't know me, and me laughing to myself.

"D'you see what I mean?" I said to her. "It's not just being friends, it's more than that."

I don't know if she heard. She lay there looking up at me, touching my ear and my chin in that funny, gentle way. You'd say she was sorry for me.

"I'd like to buy you things," I said, "flowers sometimes. It's nice to see a girl with a flower tucked in her dress; it looks clean and fresh. And for special occasions, birthdays, Christmas, and that, something you'd seen in a shop-window, and wanted, but hadn't liked to go in and ask the price. A brooch perhaps, or a bracelet, something pretty. And I'd go in and get it when you weren't with me, and it'd cost much more than my week's pay, but I wouldn't mind."

I could see the expression on her face, opening the parcel. And she'd put it on, what I'd bought, and we'd go out together, and she'd be dressed up a bit for the purpose, nothing glaring I don't mean, but something that took the eye. You know, saucy.

"It's not fair to talk about getting married," I said, "not in these days, when everything's uncertain. A fellow doesn't mind the uncertainty, but it's hard on a girl. Cooped up in a couple of rooms maybe, and queueing and rations and all. They like their freedom, and being in a job, and not being tied down, the same as us. But it's nonsense the way they were talking back in the coffee stall just now. About girls not being the same as in old days, and the war to blame. As for the way they treat them out East—I've seen some of it. I suppose that fellow meant to be funny, they're all smart alecks in the Air Force, but it was a silly line of talk, I thought."

She dropped her hands to her side and closed her eyes. It was getting quite wet there on the tombstone. I was worried for her, though she had her mac of course,

but her legs and feet were damp in her thin stockings and shoes.

"You weren't ever in the Air Force, were you?" she said.

Queer. Her voice had gone quite hard. Sharp, and different. Like as if she was anxious about something, scared even.

"Not me," I said. "I served my time with R.E.M.E. Proper lot they were. No swank, no nonsense. You know where you are with them."

"I'm glad," she said. "You're good and kind. I'm glad."

I wondered if she'd known some fellow in the R.A.F. who had let her down. They're a wild crowd, the ones I've come across. And I remembered the way she'd looked at the boy drinking his tea at the stall. Reflective, somehow. As if she was thinking back. I couldn't expect her not to have been around a bit, with her looks, and then brought up to play about the shelters, without parents, like she said. But I didn't want to think of her being hurt by anyone.

"Why, what's wrong with them?" I said. "What's the R.A.F. done to you?"

"They smashed my home," she said.

"That was the Germans, not our fellows."

"It's all the same, they're killers, aren't they?" she said.

I looked down at her lying on the tombstone, and her voice wasn't hard any more, like when she'd asked me if I'd been in the Air Force, but it was tired, and sad, and oddly lonely, and it did something queer to my stomach, right in the pit of it, so that I wanted to do the darnedest silliest thing and take her home with me, back to where I lived with Mr. and Mrs. Thompson, and say to Mrs. Thompson—she was a kind old soul, she wouldn't mind—"Look, this is my girl. Look after her." Then I'd know she'd be safe, she'd be all right, nobody could do anything to hurt her. That was the thing I was afraid of suddenly, that someone would come along and hurt my girl.

I bent down and put my arms round her and lifted her up close.

"Listen," I said, "it's raining hard. I'm going to take you home. You'll catch your death lying here on the wet stone."

"No," she said, her hands on my shoulders, "nobody ever sees me home. You're going back where you belong, alone."

"I won't leave you here," I said.

"Yes, that's what I want you to do. If you refuse I shall be angry. You wouldn't want that, would you?"

I stared at her, puzzled. And her face was queer in the murky old light there, whiter than before, but it was beautiful, Jesus Christ, it was beautiful. That's blasphemy. But I can't say it no other way.

"What do you want me to do?" I asked.

"I want you to go and leave me here, and not look back," she said, "like someone dreaming, sleep-walking, they call it. Go back walking through the rain. It will take you hours. It doesn't matter; you're young and strong and you've got long legs. Go back to your room, wherever it is, and get into bed, and go to sleep, and wake and have your breakfast in the morning, and go off to work, the same as you always do."

"What about you?"

"Never mind about me. Just go."

"Can I call for you at the cinema tomorrow night? Can it be like what I was telling you, you know . . . going steady?"

She didn't answer. She only smiled. She sat quite still, looking into my face, and then she closed her eyes and threw back her head and said, "Kiss me again, stranger."

I left her, like she said. I didn't look back. I climbed through the railings of the cemetery, out on to the road. No one seemed to be about, and the coffee stall by the bus stop had closed down, the boards were up.

I started walking the way the bus had brought us. The road was straight, going on for ever. A High Street it must have been. There were shops on either side, and it was right away northeast of London, nowhere I'd ever been before. I was proper lost, but it didn't seem to matter. I felt like a sleepwalker, just as she said.

I kept thinking of her all the time. There was nothing else, only her face in front of me as I walked. They had a word for it in the Army, when a girl gets a fellow that way so he can't see straight or hear right or know what he's doing; and I thought it a lot of cock, or it only happened to drunks, and now I knew it was true and it had happened to me. I wasn't going to worry any more about how she'd get home; she'd told me not to, and she must have lived handy, she'd never have ridden out so far else, though it was funny living such a way from her work. But maybe in time she'd tell me more, bit by bit. I wouldn't drag it from her. I had one thing fixed in my mind, and that was to pick her up the next evening from the picture palace. It was firm and set, and nothing would budge me from that. The hours in between would just be a blank for me until 10 P.M. came round.

I went on walking in the rain, and presently a lorry came along and I thumbed a lift, and the driver took me a good part of the way before he had to turn left in the other direction, and so I got down and walked again, and it must have been close on three when I got home.

I would have felt bad, in an ordinary way, knocking up Mr. Thompson to let me in, and it had never happened before either, but I was all lit up inside from loving my girl, and I didn't seem to mind. He came down at last and opened the door. I had to ring several times before he heard, and there he was, grey with sleep, poor old chap, his pyjamas all crumpled from the bed.

"Whatever happened to you?" he said. "We've been worried, the wife and me. We thought you'd been knocked down, run over. We came back here and found the house empty and your supper not touched."

"I went to the pictures," I said.

"The pictures?" He stared up at me in the passageway. "The pictures stop at ten o'clock."

"I know," I said. "I went walking after that. Sorry. Good night."

And I climbed up the stairs to my room, leaving the old chap muttering to himself and bolting the door, and I heard Mrs. Thompson calling from her bedroom, "What is it? Is it him? Is he come home?"

I'd put them to trouble and to worry, and I ought to have gone in there and then and apologised, but I couldn't somehow, it wouldn't have come right; so I shut my door and threw off my clothes and got into bed, and it was like as if she was with me still, my girl, in the darkness.

They were a bit quiet at breakfast the next morning, Mr. and Mrs. Thompson. They didn't look at me. Mrs. Thompson gave me my kipper without a word, and he went on looking at his newspaper.

I ate my breakfast, and then I said, "I hope you had a nice evening up at Highgate?" and Mrs. Thompson, with her mouth a bit tight, she said, "Very pleasant, thank you, we were home by ten," and she gave a little sniff and poured Mr. Thompson out another cup of tea.

We went on being quiet, no one saying a word, and then Mrs. Thompson said, "Will you be in to supper this evening?" and I said, "No, I don't think so. I'm meeting a friend," and then I saw the old chap look at me over his spectacles.

"If you're going to be late," he said, "we'd best take the key for you."

Then he went on reading his paper. You could tell they were proper hurt that I didn't tell them anything, or say where I was going.

I went off to work, and we were busy at the garage that day, one job after the other came. along, and any other time I wouldn't have minded. I liked a full day and often worked overtime, but today I wanted to get away before the shops closed; I hadn't thought about anything else since the idea came into my head.

It was getting on for half-past four, and the boss came to me and said, "I promised the doctor he'd have his Austin this evening; I said you'd be through with it by seven-thirty. That's O.K., isn't it?"

My heart sank. I'd counted on getting off early, because of what I wanted to do. Then I thought quickly that if the boss let me off now, and I went out to the shop before it closed, and came back again to do the job on the Austin, it would be all right, so I said, "I don't mind working a bit of overtime, but I'd like to slip out now, for half an hour, if you're going to be here. There's something I want to buy before the shops shut."

He told me that suited him, so I took off my overalls and washed and got my coat and I went off to the line of shops down at the bottom of Haverstock Hill. I knew the one I wanted. It was a jeweller's, where Mr. Thompson used to take his clock to be repaired, and it wasn't a place where they sold trash at all, but good stuff, solid-silver frames and that, and cutlery.

There were rings, of course, and a few fancy bangles, but I didn't like the look of them. All the girls in the N.A.A.F.I. used to wear bangles with charms on them, quite common it was, and I went on staring in at the window and then I spotted it, right at the back.

It was a brooch. Quite small, not much bigger than your thumbnail, but with a nice blue stone on it and a pin at the back, and it was shaped like a heart. That was what got me, the shape. I stared at it a bit, and there wasn't a ticket to it, which meant it would cost a bit, but I went in and asked to have a look at it. The jeweller got it out of the window for me, and he gave it a bit of a polish and turned it this way and that, and I saw it pinned on my girl, showing up nice on her frock or her jumper, and I knew this was it.

"I'll take it," I said, and then asked him the price.

I swallowed a bit when he told me, but I took out my wallet and counted the notes, and he put the heart in a box wrapped up careful with cotton wool, and made a neat package of it, tied with fancy string. I knew I'd have to get an advance from the boss before I went off work that evening, but he was a good chap and I was certain he'd give it to me.

I stood outside the jeweller's, with the packet for my girl safe in my breast pocket, and I heard the church clock strike a quarter to five. There was time to slip down to the cinema and make sure she understood about the date for the evening, and then I'd beat it fast up the road and get back to the garage, and I'd have the Austin done by the time the doctor wanted it.

When I got to the cinema my heart was beating like a sledge hammer and I could hardly swallow. I kept picturing to myself how she'd look, standing there by the curtains going in, with that velvet jacket and the cap on the back of her head.

There was a bit of a queue outside, and I saw they'd changed the programme. The poster of the western had gone, with the cowboy throwing a knife in the Indian's guts, and they had instead a lot of girls dancing, and some chap prancing in front of them with a walking stick. It was a musical.

I went in, and didn't go near the box office but looked straight to the curtains, where she'd be. There was an usherette there all right, but it wasn't her. This was a great tall girl who looked silly in the clothes, and she was trying to do two things at once—tear off the slips of tickets as the people went past, and hang on to her torch at the same time.

I waited a moment. Perhaps they'd switched over positions and my girl had gone up to the circle. When the last lot had got in through the curtains and there was a pause and she was free, I went up to her and I said, "Excuse me, do you know where I could have a word with the other young lady?"

She looked at me. "What other young lady?"

"The one who was here last night, with copper hair," I said.

She looked at me closer then, suspicious-like.

"She hasn't shown up today," she said. "I'm taking her place."

"Not shown up?"

"No. And it's funny you should ask. You're not the only one. The police were here not long ago. They had a word with the manager, and the commissionaire too, and no one's said anything to me yet, but I think there's been trouble."

My heart beat different then. Not excited, bad. Like when someone's ill, took to hospital, sudden.

"The police?" I said. "What were they here for?"

"I told you, I don't know," she answered, "but it was something to do with her, and the manager went with them to the police station, and he hasn't come back yet. This way, please, circle on the left, stalls to the right."

I just stood there, not knowing what to do. It was like as if the floor had been knocked away from under me.

The tall girl tore another slip off a ticket and then she said to me, over her shoulder, "Was she a friend of yours?"

"Sort of," I said. I didn't know what to say.

"Well, if you ask me, she was queer in the head, and it wouldn't surprise me if she'd done away with herself and they'd found her dead. No, ice creams served in the interval, after the newsreel."

I went out and stood in the street. The queue was growing for the cheaper seats, and there were children too, talking, excited. I brushed past them and started walking up the street, and I felt sick inside, queer. Something had happened to my girl. I knew it now. That was why she had wanted to get rid of me last night, and for me not to see her home. She was going to do herself in, there in the cemetery. That's why she talked funny and looked so white, and now they'd found her, lying there on the gravestone by the railings.

If I hadn't gone away and left her she'd have been all right. If I'd stayed with her just five minutes longer, coaxing her, I'd have got her round to my way of thinking and seen her home, standing no nonsense, and she'd be at the picture palace now, showing the people to their seats.

It might be it wasn't as bad as what I feared. It might be she was found wandering, lost her memory and got picked up by the police and taken off, and then they found out where she worked and that, and now the police wanted to check up with the manager at the cinema to see if it was so. If I went down to the police station and asked them there, maybe they'd tell me what had happened, and I could say she was my girl, we were walking out, and it wouldn't matter if she didn't recognise me even, I'd stick to the story. I couldn't let down my boss, I had to get that job done on the Austin, but afterwards, when I'd finished, I could go down to the police station.

All the heart had gone out of me, and I went back to the garage hardly knowing what I was doing, and for the first time ever the smell of the place turned my stomach, the oil and the grease, and there was a chap roaring up his engine, before backing out his car, and a great cloud of smoke coming from his exhaust, filled the workshop with stink.

I went and got my overalls, and put them on, and fetched the tools, and started on the Austin, and all the time I was wondering what it was that had happened to my girl, if she was down at the police station, lost and lonely, or if she was lying somewhere . . . dead. I kept seeing her face all the time like it was last night.

It took me an hour and a half, not more, to get the Austin ready for the road, filled up with petrol and all, and I had her facing outwards to the street for the owner to drive out, but I was all in by then, dead tired, and the sweat pouring down my face. I had a bit of a wash and put on my coat, and I felt the package in the breast pocket. I took it out and looked at it, done so neat with the fancy ribbon, and I put it back again, and I hadn't noticed the boss come in—I was standing with my back to the door.

"Did you get what you want?" he said, cheerful-like and smiling.

He was a good chap, never out of temper, and we got along well.

"Yes," I said.

But I didn't want to talk about it. I told him the job was done and the Austin was ready to drive away. I went to the office with him so that he could note down the work done, and the overtime, and he offered me a fag from the packet lying on his desk beside the evening paper.

"I see Lady Luck won the three-thirty," he said. "I'm a couple of quid up this week."

He was entering my work in his ledger, to keep the payroll right.

"Good for you," I said.

"Only backed it for a place, like a clot," he said. "She was twenty-five to one. Still, it's all in the game."

I didn't answer. I'm not one for drinking, but I needed one bad just then. I mopped my forehead with my handkerchief. I wished he'd get on with the figures, and say good night, and let me go.

"Another poor devil's had it," he said. "That's the third now in three weeks, ripped right up the guts, same as the others. He died in hospital this morning. Looks like there's a hoodoo on the R.A.F."

"What was it, flying jets?" I asked.

"Jets?" he said. "No, damn it, murder. Sliced up the belly, poor

sod. Don't you ever read the papers? It's the third one in three weeks, done identical, all Air Force fellows, and each time they've found 'em near a grave-yard or a cemetery. I was saying just now, to that chap who came in for petrol, it's not only men who go off their rockers and turn sex maniacs, but women too. They'll get this one all right though, you see. It says in the paper they've a line on her and expect an arrest shortly. About time, too, before another poor blighter cops it."

He shut up his ledger and stuck his pencil behind his ear.

"Like a drink?" he said. "I've got a bottle of gin in the cupboard."

"No," I said, "no, thanks very much. I've . . . I've got a date."

"That's right," he said, smiling, "enjoy yourself."

I walked down the street and bought an evening paper. It was like what he said about the murder. They had it on the front page. They said it must have happened about 2 A.M. Young fellow in the Air Force, in northeast London. He had managed to stagger to a call box and get through to the police, and they found him there on the floor of the box when they arrived.

He made a statement in the ambulance before he died. He said a girl called to him, and he followed her, and he thought it was just a bit of love-making— he'd seen her with another fellow drinking coffee at a stall a little while before—and he thought she'd thrown this other fellow over and had taken a fancy to him, and then she got him, he said, right in the guts.

It said in the paper that he had given the police a full description of her, and it said also that the police would be glad if the man who had been seen with the girl earlier in the evening would come forward to help in identification.

I didn't want the paper any more. I threw it away. I walked about the streets till I was tired, and when I guessed Mr. and Mrs. Thompson had gone to bed I went home, and groped for the key they'd left on a piece of string hanging inside the letter box, and I let myself in and went upstairs to my room.

Mrs. Thompson had turned down the bed and put a Thermos of tea for me, thoughtful-like, and the evening paper, the late edition.

They'd got her. About three o'clock in the afternoon. I didn't read the writing, nor the name nor anything. I sat down on my bed and took up the paper, and there was my girl staring up at me from the front page.

Then I took the package from my coat and undid it, and threw away the wrapper and the fancy string, and sat there looking down at the little heart I held in my hand.

THE BIRDS

On December the third the wind changed overnight and it was winter. Until then the autumn had been mellow, soft. The leaves had lingered on the trees, golden-red, and the hedgerows were still green. The earth was rich where the plough had turned it.

Nat Hocken, because of a war-time disability, had a pension and did not work full-time at the farm. He worked three days a week, and they gave him the lighter jobs: hedging, thatching, repairs to the farm buildings.

Although he was married, with children, his was a solitary dis-position; he liked best to work alone. It pleased him when he was given a bank to build up, or a gate to mend at the far end of the peninsula, where the sea sur-rounded the farmland on either side. Then, at midday, he would pause and eat the pasty that his wife had baked for him, and, sit-ting on the cliff's edge, would watch the birds. Autumn was best for this, better than spring. In spring the birds flew inland, pur-poseful, intent; they knew where they were bound, the rhythm and ritual of their life brooked no delay. In autumn those that had

COPYRIGHT, 1952, BY DAPHNE DU MAURIER, AND
PUBLISHED BY DOUBLEDAY & CO., INC., NEW YORK

not migrated overseas but remained to pass the winter were caught up in the same driving urge, but because migration was denied them followed a pattern of their own. Great flocks of them came to the peninsula, restless, uneasy, spending themselves in motion; now wheeling, circling in the sky, now settling to feed on the rich new-turned soil, but even when they fed it was as though they did so without hunger, without desire. Restlessness drove them to the skies again.

Black and white, jackdaw and gull, mingled in strange partnership, seeking some sort of liberation, never satisfied, never still. Flocks of starlings, rustling like silk, flew to fresh pasture, driven by the same necessity of movement, and the smaller birds, the finches and the larks, scattered from tree to hedge as if compelled.

Nat watched them, and he watched the sea birds to. Down in the bay they waited for the tide. They had more patience. Oyster catchers, redshank, sanderling, and curlew watched by the water's edge; as the slow sea sucked at the shore and then withdrew, leaving the strip of seaweed bare and the shingle churned, the sea birds raced and ran upon the beaches. Then that same impulse to flight seized upon them too. Crying, whistling, calling, they skimmed the placid sea and left the shore. Make haste, make speed, hurry and begone; yet where, and to what purpose?

The restless urge of autumn, unsatisfying, sad, had put a spell upon them and they must flock, and wheel, and cry; they must spill themselves of motion before winter came.

"Perhaps," thought Nat, munching his pasty by the cliff's edge, "a message comes to the birds in autumn, like a warning. Winter is coming. Many of them perish. And like people who, apprehensive of death before their time, drive themselves to work or folly, the birds do likewise."

The birds had been more restless than ever this fall of the year, the agitation more marked because the days were still. As the tractor traced its path up and down the western hills, the figure of the farmer silhouetted on the driving seat, the whole machine and the man upon it would be lost momentarily in the great cloud of wheeling, crying birds. There were many more than usual, Nat was sure of this. Always, in autumn, they followed the plough, but not in great flocks like these, nor with such clamour.

Nat remarked upon it when hedging was finished for the day. "Yes," said the farmer, "there are more birds about than usual; I've noticed it too. And daring, some of them, taking no notice of the tractor. One or two gulls came so close to my head this afternoon I thought they'd knock my cap off! As it was, I could scarcely see what I was doing, when they were overhead and I had the sun in my eyes. I have a notion the weather will change. It will be a hard winter. That's why the birds are restless."

Nat, tramping home across the fields and down the lane to his cottage, saw the birds still flocking over the western hills, in the last glow of the sun. No wind, and the grey sea calm and full. Campion in bloom yet in the hedges, and the air mild. The farmer was right, though, and it was that night the weather turned. Nat's bedroom faced east. He woke just after two and heard the wind in the chimney. Not the storm and bluster of a sou' westerly gale, bringing the rain, but east wind, cold and dry. It sounded hollow in the chimney, and a loose slate rattled on the roof. Nat listened, and he could hear the sea roaring in the bay. Even the air in the small bedroom had turned chill: a draught came under the skirting of the door, blowing upon the bed. Nat drew the blanket round him, leant closer to the back of his sleeping wife, and stayed wakeful, watchful, aware of misgiving without cause.

Then he heard the tapping on the window. There was no creeper on the cottage walls to break loose and scratch upon the pane. He listened, and the tapping continued until, irritated by the sound, Nat got out of bed and went to the window. He opened it, and as he did so something brushed his hand, jabbing at his knuckles, grazing the skin. Then he saw the flutter of the wings and it was gone, over the roof, behind the cottage.

It was a bird; what kind of bird he could not tell. The wind must have driven it to shelter on the sill.

He shut the window and went back to bed, but, feeling his knuckles wet, put his mouth to the scratch. The bird had drawn blood. Frightened, he supposed, and bewildered, the bird, seeking shelter, had stabbed at him in the darkness. Once more he settled himself to sleep.

Presently the tapping came again, this time more forceful, more insistent, and now his wife woke at the sound and, turning in the bed, said to him, "See to the window, Nat, it's rattling."

"I've already seen to it," he told her; "there's some bird there trying to get in. Can't you hear the wind? It's blowing from the east, driving the birds to shelter."

"Send them away," she said, "I can't sleep with that noise."

He went to the window for the second time, and now when he opened it there was not one bird upon the sill but half a dozen; they flew straight into his face, attacking him.

He shouted, striking out at them with his arms, scattering them; like the first one, they flew over the roof and disappeared. Quickly he let the window fall and latched it.

"Did you hear that?" he said. "They went for me. Tried to peck my eyes." He stood by the window, peering into the darkness, and could see nothing. His wife,

THE BIRDS

heavy with sleep, murmured from the bed.

"I'm not making it up," he said, angry at her suggestion. "I tell you the birds were on the sill, trying to get into the room."

Suddenly a frightened cry came from the room across the passage where the children slept.

"It's Jill," said his wife, roused at the sound, sitting up in bed. "Go to her, see what's the matter."

Nat lit the candle, but when he opened the bedroom door to cross the passage the draught blew out the flame.

There came a second cry of terror, this time from both children, and stumbling into their room, he felt the beating of wings about him in the darkness. The window was wide open. Through it came the birds, hitting first the ceiling and the walls, then swerving in mid-flight, turning to the children in their beds.

"It's all right, I'm here," shouted Nat, and the children flung themselves, screaming, upon him, while in the darkness the birds rose and dived and came for him again.

"What is it, Nat, what's happened?" his wife called from the further bedroom, and swiftly he pushed the children through the door to the passage and shut it upon them, so that he was alone now in their bedroom with the birds.

He seized a blanket from the nearest bed and, using it as a weapon, flung it to right and left about him in the air. He felt the thud of bodies, heard the flutter-

ing of wings, but they were not yet defeated, for again and again they returned to the assault, jabbing his hands, his head, the little stabbing beaks sharp as pointed forks. The blanket became a weapon of defence; he wound it about his head, and then in greater darkness beat at the birds with his bare hands. He dared not stumble to the door and open it, lest in doing so the birds should follow him.

How long he fought with them in the darkness he could not tell, but at last the beating of the wings about him lessened and then withdrew, and through the density of the blanket he was aware of light. He waited, listened; there was no sound except the fretful crying of one of the children from the bedroom beyond. The fluttering, the whirring of the wings had ceased.

He took the blanket from his head and stared about him. The cold grey morning light exposed the room. Dawn and the open window had called the living birds; the dead lay on the floor. Nat gazed at the little corpses, shocked and horrified. They were all small birds, none of any size; there must have been fifty of them lying there upon the floor. There were robins, finches, sparrows, blue tits, larks, and bramblings, birds that by nature's law kept to their own flock and their own territory, and now, joining one with another in their urge for battle, had destroyed themselves against the bedroom walls, or in the strife had been destroyed by him. Some had lost feathers in the fight; others had blood, his blood, upon their beaks.

Sickened, Nat went to the window and stared out across his patch of garden to the fields.

It was bitter cold, and the ground had all the hard black look of frost. Not white frost, to shine in the morning sun, but the black frost that the east wind brings. The sea, fiercer now with the turning tide, white-capped and steep, broke harshly in the bay. Of the birds there was no sign. Not a sparrow chattered in the hedge beyond the garden gate, no early missel-thrush or blackbird pecked on the grass for worms. There was no sound at all but the east wind and the sea.

Nat shut the window and the door of the small bedroom, and went back across the passage to his own. His wife sat up in bed, one child asleep beside her, the smaller in her arms, his face bandaged. The curtains were tightly drawn across the window, the candles lit. Her face looked garish in the yellow light. She shook her head for silence.

"He's sleeping now," she whispered, "but only just. Something must have cut him, there was blood at the corner of his eyes. Jill said it was the birds. She said she woke up, and the birds were in the room."

His wife looked up at Nat, searching his face for confirmation. She looked terrified, bewildered, and he did not want her to know that he was also shaken, dazed almost, by the events of the past few hours.

"There are birds in there," he said, "dead birds, nearly fifty of them. Robins, wrens, all the little birds from hereabouts. It's as though a madness seized them, with the east wind." He sat down on the bed beside his wife, and held her hand. "It's the weather," he said, "it must be that, it's the hard weather. They aren't the birds, maybe, from here around. They've been driven down from upcountry."

"But, Nat," whispered his wife, "it's only this night that the weather turned. There's been no snow to drive them. And they can't be hungry yet. There's food for them out there in the fields."

"It's the weather," repeated Nat. "I tell you, it's the weather."

His face, too, was drawn and tired, like hers. They stared at one another for a while without speaking.

"I'll go downstairs and make a cup of tea," he said.

The sight of the kitchen reassured him. The cups and saucers, neatly stacked upon the dresser, the table and chairs, his wife's roll of knitting on her basket chair, the children's toys in a corner cupboard.

He knelt down, raked out the old embers, and relit the fire. The glowing sticks brought normality, the steaming kettle and the brown teapot comfort and security. He drank his tea, carried a cup up to his wife. Then he washed in the scullery, and, putting on his boots, opened the back door.

The sky was hard and leaden, and the brown hills that had gleamed in the sun the day before looked dark and bare. The east wind, like a razor, stripped the trees, and the leaves, crackling and dry, shivered and scattered with the wind's blast. Nat stubbed the earth with his boot. It was frozen hard. He had never known a change so swift and sudden. Black winter had descended in a single night.

The children were awake now. Jill was chattering upstairs and young Johnny crying once again. Nat heard his wife's voice, soothing, comforting. Presently they came down. He had breakfast ready for them, and the routine of the day began.

"Did you drive away the birds?" asked Jill, restored to calm because of the kitchen fire, because of day, because of breakfast.

"Yes, they've all gone now," said Nat. "It was the east wind brought them in. They were frightened and lost, they wanted shelter."

"They tried to peck us," said Jill. "They went for Johnny's eyes."

"Fright made them do that," said Nat. "They didn't know where they were in the dark bedroom."

"I hope they won't come again," said Jill. "Perhaps if we put bread for them outside the window they will eat that and fly away."

She finished her breakfast and then went for her coat and hood, her schoolbooks and her satchel. Nat said nothing, but his wife looked at him across the table. A silent message passed between them.

"I'll walk with her to the bus," he said. "I don't go to the farm today."

And while the child was washing in the scullery he said to his wife, "Keep all the windows closed, and the doors too. Just to be on the safe side. I'll go to the farm. Find out if they heard anything in the night." Then he walked with his small daughter up the lane. She seemed to have forgotten her experience of the night before. She danced ahead of him, chasing the leaves, her face whipped with the cold and rosy under the pixie hood.

"Is it going to snow, Dad?" she said. "It's cold enough."

He glanced up at the bleak sky, felt the wind tear at his shoulders.

"No," he said, "it's not going to snow. This is a black winter, not a white one."

All the while he searched the hedgerows for the birds, glanced over the top of them to the fields beyond, looked to the small wood above the farm where the rooks and jackdaws gathered. He saw none.

The other children waited by the bus stop, muffled, hooded like Jill, the faces white and pinched with cold.

Jill ran to them, waving. "My Dad says it won't snow," she called, "it's going to be a black winter."

She said nothing of the birds. She began to push and struggle with another little girl. The bus came ambling up the hill. Nat saw her on to it, then turned and walked back towards the farm. It was not his day for work, but he wanted to satisfy himself that all was well. Jim, the cowman, was clattering in the yard.

"Boss around?" asked Nat.

"Gone to market," said Jim. "It's Tuesday, isn't it?"

He clumped off round the corner of a shed. He had no time for Nat. Nat was said to be superior. Read books, and the like. Nat had forgotten it was Tuesday. This showed how the events of the preceding night had shaken him. He went to the back door of the farmhouse and heard Mrs. Trigg singing in the kitchen, the wireless making a background to her song.

"Are you there, missus?" called out Nat.

She came to the door, beaming, broad, a good-tempered woman.

"Hullo, Mr. Hocken," she said. "Can you tell me where this cold is coming from? Is it Russia? I've never seen such a change. And it's going on, the wireless says. Something to do with the Arctic Circle."

"We didn't turn on the wireless this morning," said Nat. "Fact is, we had trouble in the night."

"Kiddies poorly?"

"No . . ." He hardly knew how to explain it. Now, in daylight, the battle of the birds would sound absurd.

He tried to tell Mrs. Trigg what had happened, but he could see from her eyes that she thought his story was the result of a nightmare.

"Sure they were real birds," she said, smiling, "with proper feathers and all? Not the funny-shaped kind that the men see after closing hours on a Saturday night?"

"Mrs. Trigg," he said, "there are fifty dead birds, robins, wrens, and such, lying low on the floor of the children's bedroom. They went for me; they tried to go for young Johnny's eyes."

Mrs. Trigg stared at him doubtfully.

"Well there, now," she answered, "I suppose the weather brought them. Once in the bedroom, they wouldn't know where they were to. Foreign birds maybe, from that Arctic Circle."

"No," said Nat, "they were the birds you see about here every day."

"Funny thing," said Mrs. Trigg, "no explaining it, really. You ought to write up and ask the *Guardian*. They'd have some answer for it. Well, I must be getting on."

She nodded, smiled, and went back into the kitchen.

Nat, dissatisfied, turned to the farm gate. Had it not been for those corpses on the bedroom floor, which he must now collect and bury somewhere, he would have considered the tale exaggeration too.

Jim was standing by the gate.

"Had any trouble with the birds?" asked Nat.

"Birds? What birds?"

"We got them up our place last night. Scores of them, came in the children's bedroom. Quite savage they were."

"Oh?" It took time for anything to penetrate Jim's head. "Never heard of birds acting savage," he said at length. "They get tame, like, sometimes. I've seen them come to the windows for crumbs."

"These birds last night weren't tame."

"No? Cold, maybe. Hungry. You put out some crumbs."

Jim was no more interested than Mrs. Trigg had been. It was, Nat thought, like air raids in the war. No one down this end of the country knew what the Plymouth folk had seen and suffered. You had to endure something yourself before it touched you. He walked back along the lane and crossed the stile to his cottage. He found his wife in the kitchen with young Johnny.

"See anyone?" she asked.

"Mrs. Trigg and Jim," he answered. "I don't think they believed me. Anyway, nothing wrong up there."

"You might take the birds away," she said. "I daren't go into the room to make the beds until you do. I'm scared."

"Nothing to scare you now," said Nat. "They're dead, aren't they?"

He went up with a sack and dropped the stiff bodies into it, one by one. Yes, there were fifty of them, all told. Just the ordinary common birds of the hedgerow, nothing as large even as a thrush. It must have been fright that made them act the way they did. Blue tits, wrens—it was incredible to think of the power of their small beaks jabbing at his face and hands the night before. He took the sack out into the garden and was faced now with a fresh problem. The ground was too hard to dig. It was frozen solid, yet no snow had fallen, nothing had happened in the past hours but the coming of the east wind. It was unnatural, queer. The weather prophets must be right. The change was something connected with the Arctic Circle.

The wind seemed to cut him to the bone as he stood there uncertainly, holding the sack. He could see the white-capped seas breaking down under in the bay. He decided to take the birds to the shore and bury them.

When he reached the beach below the headland he could scarcely stand, the force of the east wind was so strong. It hurt to draw breath, and his bare hands were blue. Never had he known such cold, not in all the bad winters he could remember. It was low tide. He crunched his way over the shingle to the softer sand and then, his back to the wind, ground a pit in the sand with his heel. He meant to drop the birds into it, but as he opened up the sack the force of the wind carried them, lifted them, as though in flight again, and they were blown away from him along the beach, tossed like feathers, spread and scattered, the bodies of the fifty frozen birds. There was something ugly in the sight.

He did not like it. The dead birds were swept away from him by the wind.

"The tide will take them when it turns," he said to himself.

He looked out to sea and watched the crested breakers, combing green. They rose stiffly, curled, and broke again, and because it was ebb tide the roar was distant, more remote, lacking the sound and thunder of the flood.

Then he saw them. The gulls. Out there, riding the seas.

What he had thought at first to be the whitecaps of the waves were gulls. Hundreds, thousands, tens of thousands . . . They rose and fell in the trough of the seas, heads to the wind, like a mighty fleet at anchor, waiting on the tide. To eastward, and to the west, the gulls were there. They stretched as far as his eye could reach, in close formation, line upon line. Had the sea been still they would have covered the bay like a white cloud, head to head, body packed to body. Only the east wind, whipping the sea to breakers, hid them from the shore.

Nat turned and, leaving the beach, climbed the steep path home. Someone should know of this. Someone should be told. Something was happening, because of the east wind and the weather, that he did not understand. He wondered if he should go to the call box by the bus stop and ring up the police. Yet what could they do? What could anyone do? Tens and thousands of gulls riding the sea there in the

bay because of storm, because of hunger. The police would think him mad, or drunk, or take the statement from him with great calm. "Thank you. Yes, the matter has already been reported. The hard weather is driving the birds inland in great numbers." Nat looked about him. Still no sign of any other bird. Perhaps the cold had sent them all from upcountry? As he drew near to the cottage his wife came to meet him at the door. She called to him, excited. "Nat," she said, "it's on the wireless. They've just read out a special news bulletin. I've written it down."

"What's on the wireless?" he said.

"About the birds," she said. "It's not only here, it's everywhere. In London, all over the country. Something has happened to the birds."

Together they went into the kitchen. He read the piece of paper lying on the table.

"Statement from the Home Office at 11 A.M. today. Reports from all over the country are coming in hourly about the vast quantity of birds flocking above towns, villages, and outlying districts, causing obstruction and damage and even attacking individuals. It is thought that the Arctic air stream, at present covering the British Isles, is causing birds to migrate south in immense numbers, and that intense hunger may drive these birds to attack human beings. Householders are warned to see to their windows, doors, and chimneys, and to take reasonable precautions for the safety of their children. A further statement will be issued later."

A kind of excitement seized Nat; he looked at his wife in triumph.

"There you are," he said. "Let's hope they'll hear that at the farm. Mrs. Trigg will know it wasn't any story. It's true. All over the country. I've been telling myself all morning there's something wrong. And just now, down on the beach, I looked out to sea and there are gulls, thousands of them, tens of thousands—you couldn't put a pin between their heads— and they're all out there, riding on the sea, waiting."

"What are they waiting for, Nat?" she asked.

He stared at her, then looked down again at the piece of paper. "I don't know," he said slowly. "It says here the birds are hungry."

He went over to the drawer where he kept his hammer and tools.

"What are you going to do, Nat?"

"See to the windows and the chimneys too, like they tell you."

"You think they would break in, with the windows shut? Those sparrows and robins and such? Why, how could they?"

He did not answer. He was not thinking of the robins and the sparrows. He was thinking of the gulls. . . .

He went upstairs and worked there the rest of the morning, boarding the windows of the bedrooms, filling up the chimney bases. Good job it was his free day and he was not working at the farm. It reminded him of the old days, at the beginning of the war. He was not married then, and he had made all the black-out boards for his mother's house in Plymouth. Made the shelter too. Not that it had been of any use when the moment came. He wondered if they would take these precautions up at the farm. He doubted it. Too easygoing, Harry Trigg and his missus. Maybe they'd laugh at the whole thing. Go off to a dance or a whist drive.

"Dinner's ready." She called him, from the kitchen.

"All right. Coming down."

He was pleased with his handiwork. The frames fitted nicely over the little panes and at the bases of the chimneys.

When dinner was over and his wife was washing up, Nat switched on the one o'clock news. The same announcement was repeated, the one which she had taken down during the morning, but the news bulletin enlarged upon it. "The flocks of birds have caused dislocation in all areas," read the announcer, "and in London the sky was so dense at ten o'clock this morning that it seemed as if the city was covered by a vast black cloud.

"The birds settled on roof tops, on window ledges, and on chimneys. The species included blackbird, thrush, the common house sparrow, and, as might be expected in the metropolis, a vast quantity of pigeons and starlings, and that frequenter of the London river, the black-headed gull. The sight has been so unusual that traffic came to a standstill in many thoroughfares, work was abandoned in shops and offices, and the streets and pavements were crowded with people standing about to watch the birds."

Various incidents were recounted, the suspected reason of cold and hunger stated again, and warnings to householders repeated. The announcer's voice was smooth and suave. Nat had the impression that this man, in particular, treated the whole business as he would an elaborate joke. There would be others like him, hundreds of them, who did not know what it was to struggle in darkness with a flock of birds. There would be parties tonight in London, like the ones they gave on election nights. People standing about, shouting and laughing, getting drunk. "Come and watch the birds!"

Nat switched off the wireless. He got up and started work on the kitchen windows. His wife watched him, young Johnny at her heels.

"What, boards for down here too?" she said. "Why, I'll have to light up before three o'clock. I see no call for boards down here."

"Better be sure than sorry," answered Nat. "I'm not going to take any chances."

"What they ought to do," she said, "is to call the Army out and shoot the birds. That would soon scare them off."

"Let them try," said Nat. "How'd they set about it?"

"They have the Army to the docks," she answered, "when the dockers strike. The soldiers go down and unload the ships."

"Yes," said Nat, "and the population of London is eight million or more. Think of all the buildings, all the flats and houses. Do you think they've enough soldiers to go round shooting birds from every roof?"

"I don't know. But something should be done. They ought to do something."

Nat thought to himself that "they" were no doubt considering the problem at that very moment, but whatever "they" decided to do in London and the big cities would not help the people here, three hundred miles away. Each householder must look after his own.

"How are we off for food?" he said.

"Now, Nat, whatever next?"

"Never mind. What have you got in the larder?"

"It's shopping day tomorrow, you know that. I don't keep uncooked food hanging about, it goes off. Butcher doesn't call till the day after. But I can bring back something when I go in tomorrow."

Nat did not want to scare her. He thought it possible that she might not go to town tomorrow. He looked in the larder for himself, and in the cupboard where she kept her tins. They would do for a couple of days. Bread was low.

"What about the baker?"

"He comes tomorrow too."

He saw she had flour. If the

baker did not call she had enough to bake one loaf.

"We'd be better off in old days," he said, "when the women baked twice a week, and had pilchards salted, and there was food for a family to last a siege, if need be."

"I've tried the children with tinned fish, they don't like it," she said.

Nat went on hammering the boards across the kitchen windows. Candles. They were low in candles too. That must be another thing she meant to buy tomorrow. Well, it could not be helped. They must go early to bed tonight. That was, if . . .

He got up and went out of the back door and stood in the garden, looking down towards the sea. There had been no sun all day, and now, at barely three o'clock, a kind of darkness had already come, the sky sullen, heavy, colourless like salt. He could hear the vicious sea drumming on the rocks. He walked down the path, halfway to the beach. And then he stopped. He could see the tide had turned. The rock that had shown in midmorning was now covered, but it was not the sea that held his eyes. The gulls had risen. They were circling, hundreds of them, thousands of them, lifting their wings against the wind. It was the gulls that made the darkening of the sky. And they were silent. They made not a sound. They just went on soaring and circling, rising, falling, trying their strength against the wind.

Nat turned. He ran up the path, back to the cottage.

"I'm going for Jill," he said. "I'll wait for her at the bus stop."

"What's the matter?" asked his wife. "You've gone quite white."

"Keep Johnny inside," he said. "Keep the door shut. Light up now, and draw the curtains."

"It's only just gone three," she said.

"Never mind. Do what I tell you."

He looked inside the tool shed outside the back door. Nothing there of much use. A spade was too heavy, and a fork no good. He took the hoe. It was the only possible tool, and light enough to carry.

He started walking up the lane to the bus stop, and now and again glanced back over his shoulder.

The gulls had risen higher now, their circles were broader, wider, they were spreading out in huge formation across the sky.

He hurried on; although he knew the bus would not come to the top of the hill before four o'clock he had to hurry. He passed no one on the way. He was glad of this. No time to stop and chatter.

At the top of the hill he waited. He was much too soon. There was half an hour still to go. The east wind came whipping across the fields from the higher ground. He stamped his feet and blew upon his hands. In the distance he could see the clay hills, white and clean, against the heavy pallor of the sky. Something black rose from behind them, like a smudge at first, then widening, becoming deeper, and the smudge became a cloud, and the cloud divided again into five other clouds, spreading north, east, south, and west, and they were not clouds at all; they were birds. He watched them travel across the sky, and as one section passed overhead, within two or three hundred feet of him, he knew, from their speed, they were bound inland, up-country; they had no business with the people here on the peninsula. They were rooks, crows, jackdaws, magpies, jays, all birds that usually preyed upon the smaller species; but this afternoon they were bound on some other mission.

"They've been given the towns," thought Nat; "they know what they have to do. We don't matter so much here. The gulls will serve for us. The others go to the towns."

He went to the call box, stepped inside, and lifted the receiver. The exchange would do. They would pass the message on.

"I'm speaking from Highway," he said, "by the bus stop. I want to report large formations of birds travelling upcountry. The gulls are also forming in the bay."

"All right," answered the voice, laconic, weary.

"You'll be sure and pass this message on to the proper quarter?"

"Yes . . . yes . . ." Impatient now, fed-up. The buzzing note resumed.

"She's another," thought Nat,

"she doesn't care. Maybe she's had to answer calls all day. She hopes to go to the pictures tonight. She'll squeeze some fellow's hand, and point up at the sky, and 'Look at all them birds!' She doesn't care."

The bus came lumbering up the hill. Jill climbed out, and three or four other children. The bus went on towards the town.

"What's the hoe for, Dad?"

They crowded around him, laughing, pointing.

"I just brought it along," he said. "Come on now, let's get home. It's cold, no hanging about. Here, you. I'll watch you across the fields, see how fast you can run."

He was speaking to Jill's companions, who came from different families, living in the council houses. A short cut would take them to the cottages.

"We want to play a bit in the lane," said one of them.

"No, you don't. You go off home or I'll tell your Mammy."

They whispered to one another, round-eyed, then scuttled off across the fields. Jill stared at her father, her mouth sullen.

"We always play in the lane," she said.

"Not tonight, you don't," he said. "Come on now, no dawdling."

He could see the gulls now, circling the fields, coming in towards the land. Still silent. Still no sound.

"Look, Dad, look over there, look at all the gulls."

"Yes. Hurry, now."

"Where are they flying to? Where are they going?"

"Upcountry, I dare say. Where it's warmer."

He seized her hand and dragged her after him along the lane.

"Don't go so fast. I can't keep up."

The gulls were copying the rooks and crows. They were spreading out in formation across the sky. They headed, in bands of thousands, to the four compass points.

"Dad, what is it? What are the gulls doing?"

They were not intent upon their flight, as the crows, as the jackdaws had been. They still circled overhead. Nor did they fly so high. It was as though they waited upon some signal. As though some decision had yet to be given. The order was not clear.

"Do you want me to carry you, Jill? Here, come pick-a-back."

This way he might put on speed; but he was wrong. Jill was heavy. She kept slipping. And she was crying too. His sense of urgency, of fear, had communicated itself to the child.

"I wish the gulls would go away. I don't like them. They're coming closer to the lane."

He put her down again. He started running, swinging Jill after him. As they went past the farm turning he saw the farmer backing his car out of the garage. Nat called to him.

"Can you give us a lift?" he said.

"What's that?"

Mr. Trigg turned in the driving seat and stared at them. Then a smile came to his cheerful, rubicund face.

"It looks as though we're in for some fun," he said. "Have you seen the gulls? Jim and I are going to take a crack at them. Everyone's gone bird-crazy, talking of nothing else. I hear you were troubled in the night. Want a gun?"

Nat shook his head.

The small car was packed. There was just room for Jill, if she crouched on top of petrol tins on the back seat.

"I don't want a gun," said Nat, "but I'd be obliged if you'd run Jill home. She's scared of the birds."

He spoke briefly. He did not want to talk in front of Jill.

"O.K.," said the farmer, "I'll take her home. Why don't you stop behind and join the shooting match? We'll make the feathers fly."

Jill climbed in, and, turning the car, the driver sped up the lane. Nat followed after. Trigg must be crazy. What use was a gun against a sky of birds?

Now Nat was not responsible for Jill, he had time to look about him. The birds were circling still above the fields. Mostly herring gull, but the black-backed gull amongst them. Usually they kept apart. Now they were united. Some bond had brought them together. It was the black-backed gull that attacked the smaller birds, and even newborn lambs, so he'd heard. He'd never seen it done. He remembered this now, though, looking above him in the sky. They were coming in towards the farm. They were circling lower in the sky, and the black-backed gulls were to the front, the black-backed gulls were leading. The farm, then, was their target. They were making for the farm.

Nat increased his pace towards his own cottage. He saw the farmer's car turn and come back along the lane. It drew up beside him with a jerk.

"The kid has run inside," said the farmer. "Your wife was watching for her. Well, what do you make of it? They're saying in town the Russians have done it. The Russians have poisoned the birds."

"How could they do that?" asked Nat.

"Don't ask me. You know how stories get around. Will you join my shooting match?"

"No, I'll get along home. The wife will be worried else."

"My missus says if you could eat gull there'd be some sense in it," said Trigg, "we'd have roast gull, baked gull, and pickle 'em into the bargain. You wait until I let off a few barrels into the brutes. That'll scare 'em."

"Have you boarded your windows?" asked Nat.

"No. Lot of nonsense. They like to scare you on the wireless. I've had more to do today than to go round boarding up my windows."

"I'd board them now, if I were you."

"Garn. You're windy. Like to come to our place to sleep?"

"No, thanks all the same."

"All right. See you in the morning. Give you a gull breakfast."

The farmer grinned and turned his car to the farm entrance.

Nat hurried on. Past the little wood, past the old barn, and then across the stile to the remaining field.

As he jumped the stile he heard the whir of wings. A black-backed gull dived down at him from the sky, missed, swerved in flight, and rose to dive again. In a moment it was joined by others, six, seven, a dozen, black-backed and herring mixed. Nat dropped his hoe. The hoe was useless. Covering his head with his arms, he ran towards the cottage. They kept coming at him from the air, silent save for the beating wings. The terrible, fluttering wings. He would feel the blood on his hands, his wrists, his neck. Each stab of a swooping beak tore his flesh. If only he could keep them from his eyes. Nothing else mattered. He must keep them from his eyes. They had not learnt yet how to cling to a shoulder, how to rip clothing, how to dive in mass upon the head, upon the body. But with each dive, with each attack, they became bolder. And they had no thought for themselves. When they dived low and missed, they crashed, bruised and broken, on the ground. As Nat ran he stumbled, kicking their spent bodies in front of him.

He found the door; he hammered upon it with his bleeding hands. Because of the boarded windows no light shone. Everything was dark.

"Let me in," he shouted, "it's Nat. Let me in."

He shouted loud to make himself heard above the whir of the gulls' wings.

Then he saw the gannet, poised for the dive, above him in the sky. The gulls circled, retired, soared, one after another, against the wind. Only the gannet remained. One single gannet above him in the sky. The wings folded suddenly to its body. It dropped like a stone. Nat screamed, and the door opened. He stumbled across the threshold, and his wife threw her weight against the door.

They heard the thud of the gannet as it fell.

His wife dressed his wounds. They were not deep. The backs of his hands had suffered most, and his wrists. Had he not worn a cap they would have reached his head. As to the gannet . . . the gannet could have split his skull.

The children were crying, of course. They had seen the blood on their father's hands.

"It's all right now," he told them. "I'm not hurt. Just a few scratches. You play with Johnny, Jill. Mammy will wash these cuts."

He half shut the door to the scullery so that they could not see. His wife was ashen. She began running water from the sink.

"I saw them overhead," she whispered. "They began collecting just as Jill ran in with Mr. Trigg. I shut the door fast, and it jammed. That's why I couldn't open it at once when you came."

"Thank God they waited for me," he said. "Jill would have fallen at once. One bird alone would have done it."

Furtively, so as not to alarm the children, they whispered together as she bandaged his hands and the back of his neck.

"They're flying inland," he said, "thousands of them. Rooks, crows, all the bigger birds. I saw them from the bus stop. They're making for the towns."

"But what can they do, Nat?"

"They'll attack. Go for everyone out in the streets. Then they'll try the windows, the chimneys."

"Why don't the authorities do something? Why don't they get the Army, get machine guns, anything?"

"There's been no time. Nobody's prepared. We'll hear what they have to say on the six o'clock news."

Nat went back into the kitchen, followed by his wife. Johnny was playing quietly on the floor. Only Jill looked anxious.

"I can hear the birds," she said. "Listen, Dad."

Nat listened. Muffled sounds came from the windows, from the door. Wings brushing the surface, sliding, scraping, seeking a way of entry. The sound of many bodies, pressed together, shuffling on the sills. Now and again came a thud, a crash, as some bird dived and fell. "Some of them will kill themselves that way," he thought, "but not enough. Never enough."

"All right," he said aloud, "I've got boards over the windows, Jill. The birds can't get in."

He went and examined all the

windows. His work had been thorough. Every gap was closed. He would make extra certain, however. He found wedges, pieces of old tin, strips of wood and metal, and fastened them at the sides to reinforce the boards. His hammering helped to deafen the sound of the birds, the shuffling, the tapping, and more ominous—he did not want his wife or the children to hear it—the splinter of cracked glass.

"Turn on the wireless," he said, "let's have the wireless."

This would drown the sound also. He went upstairs to the bedrooms and reinforced the windows there. Now he could hear the birds on the roof, the scraping of claws, a sliding, jostling sound.

He decided they must sleep in the kitchen, keep up the fire, bring down the mattresses, and lay them out on the floor. He was afraid of the bedroom chimneys. The boards he had placed at the chimney bases might give way. In the kitchen they would be safe because of the fire. He would have to make a joke of it. Pretend to the children they were playing at camp. If the worst happened, and the birds forced an entry down the bedroom chimneys, it would be hours, days perhaps, before they could break down the doors. The birds would be imprisoned in the bedrooms. They could do no harm there. Crowded together, they would stifle and die.

He began to bring the mattresses downstairs. At sight of them his wife's eyes widened in apprehension. She thought the birds had already broken in upstairs.

"All right," he said cheerfully, "we'll all sleep together in the kitchen tonight. More cosy here by the fire. Then we shan't be worried by those silly old birds tapping at the windows."

He made the children help him rearrange the furniture, and he took the precaution of moving the dresser, with his wife's help, across the window. It fitted well. It was an added safeguard. The mattresses could now be lain, one beside the other, against the wall where the dresser had stood.

"We're safe enough now," he thought. "We're snug and tight, like an air-raid shelter. We can hold out. It's just the food that worries me. Food, and coal for the fire. We've enough for two or three days, not more. By that time . . ."

No use thinking ahead as far as that. And they'd be giving directions on the wireless. People would be told what to do. And now, in the midst of many problems, he realised that it was dance music only coming over the air. Not Children's Hour, as it should have been. He glanced at the dial. Yes, they were on the Home Service all right. Dance records. He switched to the Light programme. He knew the reason. The usual programmes had been abandoned. This only happened at exceptional times. Elections and such. He tried to remember if it had happened in the war, during the heavy raids on London. But of course. The B.B.C. was not stationed in London during the war. The programmes were broadcast from other, temporary quarters. "We're better off here," he thought; "we're better off here in the kitchen, with the windows and the doors boarded, than they are up in the towns. Thank God we're not in the towns."

At six o'clock the records ceased. The time signal was given. No matter if it scared the children, he must hear the news. There was a pause after the pips. Then the announcer spoke. His voice was solemn, grave. Quite different from midday.

"This is London," he said. "A National Emergency was proclaimed at four o'clock this afternoon. Measures are being taken to safeguard the lives and property of the population, but it must be understood that these are not easy to effect immediately, owing to the unforeseen and unparalleled nature of the present crisis. Every householder must take precautions to his own building, and where several people live together, as in flats and apartments, they must unite to do the utmost they can to prevent entry. It is absolutely imperative that every individual stay indoors tonight and that no one at all remain on the streets, or roads, or anywhere withoutdoors. The birds, in vast numbers, are attacking anyone on sight, and have already begun an assault upon buildings; but these, with due care, should be impenetrable. The population is asked to remain calm and not to panic. Owing to the exceptional nature

of the emergency, there will be no further transmission from any broadcasting station until 7 A.M. tomorrow."

They played the National Anthem. Nothing more happened. Nat switched off the set. He looked at his wife. She stared back at him.

"What's it mean?" said Jill. "What did the news say?"

"There won't be any more programmes tonight," said Nat. "There's been a breakdown at the B.B.C."

"Is it the birds?" asked Jill. "Have the birds done it?"

"No," said Nat, "it's just that everyone's very busy, and then of course they have to get rid of the birds, messing everything up, in the towns. Well, we can manage without the wireless for one evening."

"I wish we had a gramophone," said Jill, "that would be better than nothing."

She had her face turned to the dresser backed against the windows. Try as they did to ignore it, they were all aware of the shuffling, the stabbing, the persistent beating and sweeping of wings.

"We'll have supper early," suggested Nat, "something for a treat. Ask Mammy. Toasted cheese, eh? Something we all like?"

He winked and nodded at his wife. He wanted the look of dread, of apprehension, to go from Jill's face.

He helped with the supper, whistling, singing, making as much clatter as he could, and it seemed to him that the shuffling and the tapping were not so intense as they had been at first. Presently he went up to the bedrooms and listened, and he no longer heard the jostling for place upon the roof.

"They've got reasoning powers," he thought; "they know it's hard to break in here. They'll try elsewhere. They won't waste their time with us."

Supper passed without incident, and then, when they were clearing away, they heard a new sound, droning, familiar, a sound they all knew and understood.

His wife looked up at him, her face alight. "It's planes," she said; "they're sending out planes after the birds. That's what I said they ought to do all along. That will get them. Isn't that gunfire? Can't you hear guns?"

It might be gunfire out at sea. Nat could not tell. Big naval guns might have an effect upon the gulls out at sea, but the gulls were inland now. The guns couldn't shell the shore because of the population.

"It's good, isn't it," said his wife, "to hear the planes?" And Jill, catching her enthusiasm, jumped up and down with Johnny. "The planes will get the birds. The planes will shoot them."

Just then they heard a crash about two miles distant, followed by a second, then a third. The droning became more distant, passed away out to sea.

"What was that?" asked his wife. "Were they dropping bombs on the birds?"

"I don't know," answered Nat.

"I don't think so."

He did not want to tell her that the sound they had heard was the crashing of aircraft. It was, he had no doubt, a venture on the part of the authorities to send out reconnaissance forces, but they might have known the venture was suicidal. What could aircraft do against birds that flung themselves to death against propeller and fuselage, but hurtle to the ground themselves? This was being tried now, he supposed, over the whole country. And at a cost. Someone high up had lost his head.

"Where have the planes gone, Dad?" asked Jill.

"Back to base," he said. "Come on, now, time to tuck down for bed."

It kept his wife occupied, undressing the children before the fire, seeing to the bedding, one thing and another, while he went round the cottage again, making sure that nothing had worked loose. There was no further drone of aircraft, and the naval guns had ceased. "Waste of life and effort," Nat said to himself. "We can't destroy enough of them that way. Cost too heavy. There's always gas. Maybe they'll try spraying with gas, mustard gas. We'll be warned first, of course, if they do. There's one thing, the best brains of the country will be on to it tonight."

Somehow the thought reassured him. He had a picture of scientists, naturalists, technicians, and all those chaps they called the back-room boys, summoned to a council; they'd be working on the problem now. This was not a job for the government, for the chiefs of staff—they would merely carry out the orders of the scientists.

"They'll have to be ruthless," he thought. "Where the trouble's worst they'll have to risk more lives, if they use gas. All the live-stock, too, and the soil—all con-taminated. As long as everyone doesn't panic. That's the trouble. People panicking, losing their heads. The B.B.C. was right to warn us of that."

Upstairs in the bedrooms all was quiet. No further scraping and stabbing at the windows. A lull in battle. Forces regrouping. Wasn't that what they called it in the old wartime bulletins? The wind hadn't dropped, though. He could still hear it roaring in the chimneys. And the sea breaking down on the shore. Then he re-membered the tide. The tide would be on the turn. Maybe the lull in battle was because of the tide. There was some law the birds obeyed, and it was all to do with the east wind and the tide.

He glanced at his watch. Nearly eight o'clock. It must have gone high water an hour ago. That ex-plained the lull: the birds at-tacked with the flood tide. It might not work that way inland, upcountry, but it seemed as if it was so this way on the coast. He reckoned the time limit in his head. They had six hours to go without attack. When the tide turned again, around one-twenty in the morning, the birds would come back. . . .

There were two things he could

do. The first to rest, with his wife and the children, and all of them snatch what sleep they could, until the small hours. The second to go out, see how they were far-ing at the farm, see if the tele-phone was still working there, so that they might get news from the exchange.

He called softly to his wife, who had just settled the children. She came halfway up the stairs and he whispered to her.

"You're not to go," she said at once, "you're not to go and leave me alone with the children. I can't stand it."

Her voice rose hysterically. He hushed her, calmed her.

"All right," he said, "all right. I'll wait till morning. And we'll get the wireless bulletin then too, at seven. But in the morning, when the tide ebbs again, I'll try for the farm, and they may let us have bread and potatoes, and milk too."

His mind was busy again, plan-ning against emergency. They would not have milked, of course, this evening. The cows would be standing by the gate, waiting in the yard, with the household in-side, battened behind boards, as they were here at the cottage. That is, if they had time to take precautions. He thought of the farmer, Trigg, smiling at him from the car. There would have been no shooting party, not tonight.

The children were asleep. His wife, still clothed, was sitting on her mattress. She watched him, her eyes nervous.

"What are you going to do?"

she whispered.

He shook his head for silence. Softly, stealthily, he opened the back door and looked outside.

It was pitch dark. The wind was blowing harder than ever, coming in steady gusts, icy, from the sea. He kicked at the step outside the door. It was heaped with birds. There were dead birds everywhere. Under the windows, against the walls. These were the suicides, the divers, the ones with broken necks. Wherever he looked he saw dead birds. No trace of the living. The living had flown seaward with the turn of the tide. The gulls would be riding the seas now, as they had done in the forenoon.

In the far distance, on the hill where the tractor had been two days before, something was burning. One of the aircraft that had crashed; the fire, fanned by the wind, had set light to a stack.

He looked at the bodies of the birds, and he had a notion that if he heaped them, one upon the other, on the window sills they would make added protection for the next attack. Not much, perhaps, but something. The bodies would have to be clawed at, pecked, and dragged aside before the living birds could gain purchase on the sills and attack the panes. He set to work in the darkness. It was queer; he hated touching them. The bodies were still warm and bloody. The blood matted their feathers. He felt his stomach turn, but he went on with his work. He noticed grimly that every windowpane was shattered.

Only the boards had kept the birds from breaking in. He stuffed the cracked panes with the bleeding bodies of the birds.

When he had finished he went back into the cottage. He barricaded the kitchen door, made it doubly secure. He took off his bandages, sticky with the birds' blood, not with his own cuts, and put on fresh plaster.

His wife had made him cocoa and he drank it thirstily. He was very tired.

"All right," he said, smiling, "don't worry. We'll get through."

He lay down on his mattress and closed his eyes. He slept at once. He dreamt uneasily, because through his dreams there ran a thread of something forgotten. Some piece of work, neglected, that he should have done. Some precaution that he had known well but had not taken, and he could not put a name to it in his dreams. It was connected in some way with the burning aircraft and the stack upon the hill. He went on sleeping, though; he did not awake. It was his wife shaking his shoulder that awoke him finally.

"They've begun," she sobbed, "they've started this last hour. I can't listen to it any longer alone. There's something smelling bad too, something burning."

Then he remembered. He had forgotten to make up the fire. It was smouldering, nearly out. He got up swiftly and lit the lamp. The hammering had started at the windows and the doors, but it was not that he minded now. It was the smell of singed feathers. The smell filled the kitchen. He knew at once what it was. The birds were coming down the chimney, squeezing their way down to the kitchen range.

He got sticks and paper and put them on the embers, then reached for the can of paraffin.

"Stand back," he shouted to his wife. "We've got to risk this."

He threw the paraffin on to the fire. The flame roared up the pipe, and down upon the fire fell the scorched, blackened bodies of the birds.

The children woke, crying. "What is it?" said Jill. "What's happened?"

Nat had no time to answer. He was raking the bodies from the chimney, clawing them out on to the floor. The flames still roared, and the danger of the chimney catching fire was one he had to take. The flames would send away the living birds from the chimney top. The lower joint was the difficulty, though. This was choked with the smouldering, helpless bodies of the birds caught by fire. He scarcely heeded the attack on the windows and the door: let them beat their wings, break their beaks, lose their lives, in the attempt to force an entry into his home. They would not break in. He thanked God he had one of the old cottages, with small windows, stout walls. Not like the new council houses. Heaven help them up the lane in the new council houses.

"Stop crying," he called to the children. "There's nothing to be afraid of, stop crying."

He went on raking at the burning, smouldering bodies as they fell into the fire.

"This'll fetch them," he said to himself, "the draught and the flames together. We're all right, as long as the chimney doesn't catch. I ought to be shot for this. It's all my fault. Last thing, I should have made up the fire. I knew there was something."

Amid the scratching and tearing at the window boards came the sudden homely striking of the kitchen clock. Three A.M. A little more than four hours yet to go. He could not be sure of the exact time of high water. He reckoned it would not turn much before half-past seven, twenty to eight.

"Light up the Primus," he said to his wife. "Make us some tea, and the kids some cocoa. No use sitting around doing nothing."

That was the line. Keep her busy, and the children too. Move about, eat, drink; always best to be on the go.

He waited by the range. The flames were dying. But no more blackened bodies fell from the chimney. He thrust his poker up as far as it could go and found nothing. It was clear. The chimney was clear. He wiped the sweat from his forehead.

"Come on now, Jill," he said, "bring me some more sticks. We'll have a good fire going directly." She wouldn't come near him, though. She was staring at the heaped singed bodies of the birds.

"Never mind them," he said, "we'll put those in the passage

when I've got the fire steady."

The danger of the chimney was over. It could not happen again, not if the fire was kept burning day and night.

"I'll have to get more fuel from the farm tomorrow," he thought. "This will never last. I'll manage, though. I can do all that with the ebb tide. It can be worked, fetching what we need, when the tide's turned. We've just got to adapt ourselves, that's all."

They drank tea and cocoa and ate slices of bread and Bovril. Only half a loaf left, Nat noticed. Never mind though, they'd get by.

"Stop it," said young Johnny, pointing to the windows with his spoon, "stop it, you old birds."

"That's right," said Nat, smiling, "we don't want the old beggars, do we? Had enough of 'em."

They began to cheer when they heard the thud of the suicide birds.

"There's another, Dad," cried Jill, "he's done for."

"He's had it," said Nat. "There he goes, the blighter."

This was the way to face up to it. This was the spirit. If they could keep this up, hang on like this until seven, when the first news bulletin came through, they would not have done too badly.

"Give us a fag," he said to his wife. "A bit of a smoke will clear away the smell of the scorched feathers."

"There's only two left in the packet," she said. "I was going to buy you some from the Co-op."

"I'll have one," he said, "t'other will keep for a rainy day."

No sense trying to make the children rest. There was no rest to be got while the tapping and the scratching went on at the windows. He sat with one arm round his wife and the other round Jill, with Johnny on his mother's lap and the blankets heaped about them on the mattress.

"You can't help admiring the beggars," he said; "they've got persistence. You'd think they'd tire of the game, but not a bit of it."

Admiration was hard to sustain. The tapping went on and on and a new rasping note struck Nat's ear, as though a sharper beak than any hitherto had come to take over from its fellows. He tried to remember the names of birds; he tried to think which species would go for this particular job. It was not the tap of the woodpecker. That would be light and frequent. This was more serious, because if it continued long the wood would splinter as the glass had done. Then he remembered the hawks. Could the hawks have taken over from the gulls? Were there buzzards now upon the sills, using talons as well as beaks? Hawks, buzzards, kestrels, falcons—he had forgotten the birds of prey. He had forgotten the gripping power of the birds of prey. Three hours to go, and while they waited, the sound of the splintering wood, the talons tearing at the wood.

Nat looked about him, seeing what furniture he could destroy to fortify the door. The windows were safe because of the dresser. He was not certain of the door.

He went upstairs, but when he reached the landing he paused and listened. There was a soft patter on the floor of the children's bedroom. The birds had broken through. . . . He put his ear to the door. No mistake. He could hear the rustle of wings and the light patter as they searched the floor. The other bedroom was still clear. He went into it and began bringing out the furniture, to pile at the head of the stairs should the door of the children's bedroom go. It was preparation. It might never be needed. He could not stack the furniture against the door, because it opened inward. The only possible thing was to have it at the top of the stairs.

"Come down, Nat, what are you doing?" called his wife.

"I won't be long," he shouted. "Just making everything ship-shape up here."

He did not want her to come; he did not want her to hear the pattering of the feet in the children's bedroom, the brushing of those wings against the door.

At five-thirty he suggested breakfast, bacon and fried bread; if only to stop the growing look of panic in his wife's eyes and to calm the fretful children. She did not know about the birds upstairs. The bedroom, luckily, was not over the kitchen. Had it been so, she could not have failed to hear the sound of them up there, tapping the boards. And the silly, senseless thud of the suicide birds, the death and glory boys, who flew into the bedroom, smashing their heads against the walls. He knew them of old, the herring gulls. They had no brains. The black-backs were different; they knew what they were doing. So did the buzzards, the hawks . . .

He found himself watching the clock, gazing at the hands that went so slowly round the dial. If his theory was not correct, if the attack did not cease with the turn of the tide, he knew they were beaten. They could not continue through the long day without air, without rest, without more fuel, without . . . His mind raced. He knew there were so many things they needed to withstand siege. They were not fully prepared. They were not ready. It might be that it would be safer in the towns after all. If he could get a message through on the farm telephone to his cousin, only a short journey by train upcountry, they might be able to hire a car. That would be quicker—hire a car between tides . . .

His wife's voice, calling his name, drove away the sudden, desperate desire for sleep.

"What is it? What now?" he said sharply.

"The wireless," said his wife. "I've been watching the clock. It's nearly seven."

"Don't twist the knob," he said, impatient for the first time. "It's on the Home where it is. They'll speak from the Home."

They waited. The kitchen clock struck seven. There was no sound. No chimes, no music. They waited until a quarter past, switching to the Light. The result was the same. No news bulletin came through.

"We've heard wrong," he said. "They won't be broadcasting until eight o'clock."

They left it switched on, and Nat thought of the battery, wondered how much power was left in it. It was generally recharged when his wife went shopping in the town. If the battery failed they would not hear the instructions.

"It's getting light," whispered his wife. "I can't see it, but I can feel it. And the birds aren't hammering so loud."

She was right. The rasping, tearing sound grew fainter every moment. So did the shuffling, the jostling for place upon the step, upon the sills. The tide was on the turn. By eight there was no sound at all. Only the wind. The children, lulled at last by the stillness, fell asleep. At half-past eight Nat switched the wireless off.

"What are you doing? We'll miss the news," said his wife.

"There isn't going to be any news," said Nat. "We've got to depend upon ourselves."

He went to the door and slowly pulled away the barricades. He drew the bolts and, kicking the bodies from the step outside the door, breathed the cold air. He had six working hours before him, and he knew he must reserve his strength for the right things, not waste it in any way. Food, and light, and fuel; these were the necessary things. If he could get them in sufficiency, they could endure another night.

He stepped into the garden, and as he did so he saw the living birds. The gulls had gone to ride the sea, as they had done before; they sought sea food, and the buoyancy of the tide, before they returned to the attack. Not so the land birds. They waited and watched. Nat saw them, on the hedgerows, on the soil, crowded in the trees, outside in the field, line upon line of birds, all still, doing nothing.

He went to the end of his small garden. The birds did not move. They went on watching him.

"I've got to get food," said Nat to himself. "I've got to go to the farm to find food."

He went back to the cottage. He saw to the windows and the doors. He went upstairs and opened the children's bedroom. It was empty, except for the dead birds on the floor. The living were out there, in the garden, in the fields. He went downstairs.

"I'm going to the farm," he said.

His wife clung to him. She had seen the living birds from the open door.

"Take us with you," she begged. "We can't stay here alone. I'd rather die than stay here alone."

He considered the matter. He nodded.

"Come on, then," he said. "Bring baskets, and Johnny's pram. We can load up the pram."

They dressed against the biting wind, wore gloves and scarves. His wife put Johnny in the pram. Nat took Jill's hand.

"The birds," she whimpered, "they're all out there in the fields."

"They won't hurt us," he said, "not in the light."

They started walking across the field towards the stile, and the birds did not move. They waited, their heads turned to the wind.

When they reached the turning to the farm, Nat stopped and told his wife to wait in the shelter of the hedge with the two children.

"But I want to see Mrs. Trigg," she protested. "There are lots of things we can borrow if they went to market yesterday; not only bread, and . . ."

"Wait here," Nat interrupted. "I'll be back in a moment."

The cows were lowing, moving restlessly in the yard, and he could see a gap in the fence where the sheep had knocked their way through, to roam unchecked in the front garden before the farmhouse. No smoke came from the chimneys. He was filled with misgiving. He did not want his wife or the children to go down to the farm.

"Don't gib now," said Nat, harshly, "do what I say."

She withdrew with the pram into the hedge, screening herself and the children from the wind.

He went down alone to the farm. He pushed his way through the herd of bellowing cows, which turned this way and that, distressed, their udders full. He saw the car standing by the gate, not put away in the garage. The windows of the farmhouse were smashed. There were many dead gulls lying in the yard and around the house. The living birds perched on the group of trees behind the farm and on the roof of the house. They were quite still. They watched him.

Jim's body lay in the yard . . . what was left of it. When the birds had finished, the cows had trampled him. His gun was beside him. The door of the house was shut and bolted, but as the windows were smashed it was easy to lift them and climb through. Trigg's body was close to the telephone. He must have been trying to get through to the exchange when the birds came for him. The receiver was hanging loose, the instrument torn from the wall. No sign of Mrs. Trigg. She would be upstairs. Was it any use going up? Sickened, Nat knew what he would find.

"Thank God," he said to himself, "there were no children."

He forced himself to climb the stairs, but halfway he turned and descended again. He could see her legs protruding from the open bedroom door. Beside her were the bodies of the black-backed gulls, and an umbrella, broken.

"It's no use," thought Nat, "doing anything. I've only got five hours, less than that. The Triggs would understand. I must load up with what I can find."

He tramped back to his wife and children.

"I'm going to fill up the car with stuff," he said. "I'll put coal in it, and paraffin for the Primus. We'll take it home and return for a fresh load."

"What about the Triggs?" asked his wife.

"They must have gone to friends," he said.

"Shall I come and help you, then?"

"No; there's a mess down there. Cows and sheep all over the place. Wait, I'll get the car. You can sit in it."

Clumsily he backed the car out of the yard and into the lane. His wife and the children could not see Jim's body from there.

"Stay here," he said, "never mind the pram. The pram can be fetched later. I'm going to load the car."

Her eyes watched his all the time. He believed she understood, otherwise she would have suggested helping him to find the bread and groceries.

They made three journeys altogether, backwards and forwards between their cottage and the farm, before he was satisfied they had everything they needed. It was surprising, once he started thinking, how many things were necessary. Almost the most important of all was planking for the windows. He had to go round searching for timber. He wanted to renew the boards on all the windows at the cottage. Candles, paraffin, nails, tinned stuff; the list was endless. Besides all that, he milked three of the cows. The rest, poor brutes, would have to go on bellowing.

On the final journey he drove the car to the bus stop, got out, and went to the telephone box. He waited a few minutes, jangling the receiver. No good, though. The line was dead. He climbed on to a bank and looked over the countryside, but there was no sign of life at all, nothing in the fields but the waiting, watching birds. Some of them slept—he could see the beaks tucked into the feathers.

"You'd think they'd be feeding," he said to himself, "not just standing in that way."

Then he remembered. They were gorged with food. They had eaten their fill during the night. That was why they did not move this morning. . . .

No smoke came from the chimneys of the council houses. He thought of the children who had run across the fields the night before.

"I should have known," he thought; "I ought to have taken them home with me."

He lifted his face to the sky. It was colourless and grey. The bare trees on the landscape looked bent and blackened by the east wind. The cold did not affect the living birds waiting out there in the fields.

"This is the time they ought to get them," said Nat; "they're a sitting target now. They must be doing this· all over the country. Why don't our aircraft take off now and spray them with mustard gas? What are all our chaps doing? They must know, they must see for themselves."

He went back to the car and got into the driver's seat.

"Go quickly past that second gate," whispered his wife. "The postman's lying there. I don't want Jill to see."

He accelerated. The little Morris bumped and rattled along the lane. The children shrieked with laughter.

"Up - a - down, up - a - down," shouted young Johnny.

It was a quarter to one by the time they reached the cottage. Only an hour to go.

"Better have cold dinner," said Nat. "Hot up something for yourself and the children, some of that soup. I've no time to eat now. I've got to unload all this stuff."

He got everything inside the cottage. It could be sorted later. Give them all something to do during the long hours ahead. First he must see to the windows and the doors.

He went round the cottage methodically, testing every window, every door. He climbed on to the roof also, and fixed boards across every chimney, except the kitchen. The cold was so intense he could hardly bear it, but the job had to be done. Now and again he would look up, searching the sky for aircraft. None came. As he worked he cursed the inefficiency of the authorities.

"It's always the same," he muttered, "they always let us down. Muddle, muddle, from the start. No plan, no real organisation. And we don't matter down here. That's what it is. The people upcountry have priority. They're using gas up there, no doubt, and all the aircraft. We've got to wait and take what comes."

He paused, his work on the bedroom chimney finished, and looked out to sea. Something was moving out there. Something grey and white amongst the breakers.

"Good old Navy," he said, "they never let us down. They're coming down-channel, they're turning in the bay."

He waited, straining his eyes, watering in the wind, towards the sea. He was wrong, though. It was not ships. The Navy was not there. The gulls were rising from the sea. The massed flocks in the fields, with ruffled feathers, rose in formation from the ground and, wing to wing, soared upwards to the sky.

The tide had turned again.

Nat climbed down the ladder and went inside the kitchen. The family were at dinner. It was a little after two. He bolted the door, put up the barricade, and lit the lamp.

"It's nighttime," said young Johnny.

His wife had switched on the wireless once again, but no sound came from it.

"I've been all round the dial," she said, "foreign stations, and that lot. I can't get anything."

"Maybe they have the same trouble," he said, "maybe it's the same right through Europe."

She poured out a plateful of the Triggs' soup, cut him a large slice of the Triggs' bread, and spread their dripping upon it.

They ate in silence. A piece of the dripping ran down young Johnny's chin and fell on to the table.

"Manners, Johnny," said Jill, "you should learn to wipe your mouth."

The tapping began at the windows, at the door. The rustling, the jostling, the pushing for position on the sills. The first thud of the suicide gulls upon the step.

"Won't America do something?" said his wife. "They've always been our allies, haven't they? Surely America will do something?"

Nat did not answer. The boards were strong against the windows, and on the chimneys too. The cottage was filled with stores, with fuel, with all they needed for the next few days. When he had finished dinner he would put the stuff away, stack it neatly, get everything shipshape, handy-like. His wife could help him, and the children too. They'd tire themselves out, between now and a quarter to nine, when the tide would ebb; then he'd tuck them down on their mattresses, see that they slept good and sound until three in the morning.

He had a new scheme for the windows, which was to fix barbed wire in front of the boards. He had brought a great roll of it from the farm. The nuisance was, he'd have to work at this in the dark, when the lull came between nine and three. Pity he had not thought of it before. Still, as long as the wife slept, and the kids, that was the main thing.

The smaller birds were at the window now. He recognised the light tap-tapping of their beaks and the soft brush of their wings. The hawks ignored the windows. They concentrated their attack upon the door. Nat listened to the tearing sound of splintering wood, and wondered how many million years of memory were stored in those little brains, behind the stabbing beaks, the piercing eyes, now giving them this instinct to destroy mankind with all the deft precision of machines.

"I'll smoke that last fag," he said to his wife. "Stupid of me, it was the one thing I forgot to bring back from the farm."

He reached for it, switched on the silent wireless. He threw the empty packet on the fire, and watched it burn.

THE LITTLE PHOTOGRAPHER

The marquise lay on her chaise longue on the balcony of the hotel. She wore only a wrapper, and her sleek gold hair, newly set in pins, was bound close to her head in a turquoise bandeau that matched her eyes. Beside her chair stood a little table, and on it were three bottles of nail varnish all of a different shade.

She had dabbed a touch of colour on to three separate finger-nails, and now she held her hand in front of her to see the effect. No, the varnish on the thumb was too red, too vivid, giving a heated look to her slim olive hand, almost as if a spot of blood had fallen there from a fresh-cut wound.

In contrast, her forefinger was a striking pink, and this too seemed to her false, not true to her present mood. It was the elegant rich pink of drawing-rooms, of ball gowns, of herself standing at some reception, slowly moving to and fro her ostrich feather fan, and in the distance the sound of violins.

The middle finger was touched with a sheen of silk neither crimson nor vermilion, but somehow softer, subtler; the sheen of a peony in bud, not yet opened to the heat of the day but with the

COPYRIGHT, 1952, BY DAPHNE DU MAURIER, AND
PUBLISHED BY DOUBLEDAY & CO., INC., NEW YORK

dew of the morning upon it still. A peony, cool and close, looking down upon lush grass from some terraced border, and later, at high noon, the petals unfolding to the sun.

Yes, that was the colour. She reached for cotton wool and wiped away the offending varnish from her other fingernails, and then slowly, carefully, she dipped the little brush into the chosen varnish and, like an artist, worked with swift, deft strokes.

When she had finished she leant back in her chaise longue, exhausted, waving her hands before her in the air to let the varnish harden—a strange gesture, like that of a priestess. She looked down at her toes, appearing from her sandals, and decided that presently, in a few moments, she would paint them too; olive hands, olive feet, subdued and quiet, surprised into sudden life.

Not yet, though. She must rest, relax. It was too hot to move from the supporting back of the chaise longue and lean forward, crouching, Eastern fashion, for the adorning of her feet. There was plenty of time. Time, in fact, stretched before her in an unwinding pattern through the whole long, languorous day.

She closed her eyes.

The distant sound of hotel life came to her as in a dream, and the sounds were hazy, pleasant, because she was part of that life yet free as well, bound no longer to the tyranny of home. Someone on a balcony above scraped back a chair. Below, on the terrace, the waiters set up the gay striped umbrellas over the little luncheon tables; she could hear the maître d'hôtel call directions from the dining-room. The *femme de chambre* was doing the rooms in the adjoining suite. Furniture was moved, a bed creaked, the *valet de chambre* came out on to the next balcony and swept the boards with a straw brush. Their voices murmured, grumbled. Then they went away. Silence again. Nothing but the lazy splash of the sea as effortlessly it licked the burning sand; and somewhere, far away, too distant to make an irritation, the laughter of children playing, her own amongst them.

A guest ordered coffee on the terrace below. The smoke of his cigar came floating upwards to the balcony. The Marquise sighed, and her lovely hands drooped down like lilies on either side of the chaise longue. This was peace, this was contentment. If she could hold the moment thus for one more hour . . . But something warned her, when the hour was past, the old demon of dissatisfaction, of tedium, would return, even here where she was free at last, on holiday.

A bumblebee flew on to the balcony, hovered over the bottle of nail varnish, and entered the open flower, picked by one of the children, lying beside it. His humming ceased when he was inside the flower. The Marquise opened her eyes and saw the bee crawl forth, intoxicated. Then dizzily once more he took the air and hummed his way. The spell was broken. The Marquise picked up the letter from Edouard, her husband, that had fallen on to the floor of the balcony. ". . . And so, my dearest, I find it impossible to get to you and the children after all. There is so much business to attend to here at home, and you know I can rely on no one but myself. I shall, of course, make every effort to come and fetch you at the end of the month. Meanwhile, enjoy yourself, bathing and resting. I know the sea air will do you good. I went to see Maman yesterday, and Madeleine, and it seems the old curé . . ."

The Marquise let the letter fall back again on to the balcony floor. The little droop at the corner of her mouth, the one telltale sign that spoilt the smooth lovely face, intensified. It had happened again. Always his work. The estate, the farms, the forests, the businessmen that he must see, the sudden journeys that he must take, so that in spite of his devotion for her he had no time to spare, Edouard, her husband.

They had told her, before her marriage, how it would be. "C'est un homme très sérieux, Monsieur le Marquis, vous comprenez." How little she had minded, how gladly she had agreed, for what could be better in life than a marquis who was also un homme sérieux? What more lovely than that château and those vast estates? What more imposing than the house in Paris, the retinue of servants, humble, bowing, calling her Madame la Marquise? A fairy-tale world to someone like herself, brought up in Lyons, the daughter of a hard-working surgeon, an ailing mother. But for the sudden arrival of Monsieur le Marquis she might have found herself married to her father's young assistant, and that same day-by-day in Lyons continuing forever.

A romantic match, surely. Frowned on at first by his relatives, most certainly. But Monsieur le Marquis, homme sérieux, was past forty. He knew his own mind. And she was beautiful. There was no further argument. They married. They had two little girls. They were happy. Yet sometimes . . . The Marquise rose from the chaise longue and, going into the bedroom, sat down before the dressing table and removed the pins from her hair. Even this effort exhausted her. She threw off her wrapper and sat naked before her mirror. Sometimes she found herself regretting that day-by-day in Lyons. She remembered the laughter, the joking with other girls, the stifled giggles when a passing man looked at them in the street, the confidences, the exchange of letters, the whispering in bedrooms when her friends came to tea.

Now, as Madame la Marquise, she had no one with whom to share confidences, laughter. Everyone about her was middle-aged, dull, rooted to a life long-lived that never changed. Those interminable visits of Edouard's relatives to the château. His mother, his sisters, his brothers, his sisters-in-law. In the winter, in

Paris, it was just the same. Never a new face, never the arrival of a stranger. The only excitement was the appearance, perhaps, at luncheon of one of Edouard's business friends, who, surprised at her beauty when she entered the salon, flickered a daring glance of admiration, then bowed and kissed her hand.

Watching such a one during luncheon, she would make a fantasy to herself of how they would meet in secret, how a taxi would take her to his apartment, and, entering a small, dark *ascenseur,* she would ring a bell and vanish into a strange unknown room. But, the long luncheon over, the business friend would bow and go his way. And afterwards she would think to herself he was not even passably good-looking; even his teeth were false. But the glance of admiration, swiftly suppressed—she wanted that.

Now she combed her hair before the mirror and, parting it on one side, tried a new effect; a ribbon, the colour of her fingernails, threaded through the gold. Yes, yes . . . And the white frock, later, and that chiffon scarf, thrown carelessly over the shoulders, so that when she went out on to the terrace, followed by the children and the English governess, and the maître d'hôtel, bowing, led the way to the little table at the corner under the striped umbrella, people would stare, would whisper, and the eyes would follow her as deliberately she would stoop to one of the children, pat its curls in a fond

maternal gesture, a thing of grace, of beauty.

But now, before the mirror, only the naked body and the sad, sulky mouth. Other women would have lovers. Whispers of scandal came to her ears, even during those long heavy dinners, with Edouard at the far end of the table. Not only in the smart riffraff society to which she never penetrated, but even amongst the old noblesse to which she now belonged. "*On dit, vous savez . . .*" and the suggestion, the murmur, passed from one to the other, with a lifted eyebrow, a shrug of the shoulder.

Sometimes, after a tea party, a guest would leave early, before six o'clock, giving as an excuse that she was expected elsewhere, and the Marquise, echoing regrets, bidding the guest au revoir, would wonder, "Is she going to a rendezvous?" Could it be that in twenty minutes—less, perhaps— that dark, rather ordinary little comtesse would be shivering, smiling secretly, as she let her clothes slip to the floor?

Even Elise, her friend of lycée days in Lyons, married now six years, had a lover. She never wrote of him by name. She always called him "*mon ami.*" Yet they managed to meet twice a week, on Mondays and Thursdays. He had a car and drove her into the country, even in winter. And Elise would write to the Marquise and say, "But how plebeian my little affair must seem to you, in high society. How many admirers you must have, and what adventures! Tell me of Paris, and the parties, and who is the man of your choice this winter." The Marquise would reply, hinting, suggesting, laughing off the question, and launch into a description of her frock, worn at some reception. But she did not say that the reception ended at midnight, that it was formal, dull, and that all she, the Marquise, knew of Paris was the drives she took in the car with the children, and the drives to the couturier to be fitted for yet another frock, and the drives to the coiffeur to have her hair rearranged and set to perhaps a different style. As to life at the château, she would describe the rooms, yes, the many guests, the solemn long avenue of trees, the acres of woodland; but not the rain in spring, day after day, nor the parching heat of early summer, when silence fell upon the place like a great white pall.

"*Ah! Pardon, je croyais que Madame était sortie . . .*" He had come in without knocking, the *valet de chambre*, his straw brush in his hand, and now he backed out of the room again, discreetly, but not before he had seen her there, naked before the mirror. And surely he must have known she had not gone out, when only a few moments before she had been lying on the balcony? Was it compassion she saw in his eyes as well as admiration before he left the room? As though to say, "So beautiful, and all alone? We are not used to that in this hotel, where people come for pleasure. . . ."

Heavens, it was hot. No breeze even from the sea. Trickles of perspiration ran down from her arms to her body.

She dressed languidly, putting on the cool white dress, and then, strolling out on to the balcony once more, pulled up the sun blind, let the full heat of the day fall upon her. Dark glasses hid her eyes. The only touch of colour lay on her mouth, her feet, her hands, and in the scarf thrown about her shoulders. The dark lenses gave a deep tone to the day. The sea, by natural eye a periwinkle blue, had turned to purple, and the white sands to olive brown. The gaudy flowers in their tubs upon the terrace had a tropical texture. As the Marquise leant upon the balcony the heat of the wooden rail burnt her hands. Once again the smell of a cigar floated upwards from some source unknown. There was a tinkle of glasses as a waiter brought apéritifs to a table on the terrace. Somewhere a woman spoke, and a man's voice joined with the woman's, laughing.

An Alsatian dog, his tongue dripping moisture, padded along the terrace towards the wall, searching for a cold stone slab on which to lie. A group of young people, bare and bronzed, the salt from the warm sea scarce dried upon their bodies, came running up from the sands, calling for martinis. Americans, of course. They flung their towels upon the chairs. One of them whistled to the Alsatian, who did not move. The Marquise looked down upon them with disdain, yet merged with her disdain was a kind of envy. They were free to come and go, to climb into a car, to move onward to some other place. They lived in a state of blank, ferocious gaiety. Always in groups. Six or eight of them. They paired off, of course; they pawed each other, forming into couples. But—and here she gave full play to her contempt—their gaiety held no mystery. In their open lives there could be no moment of suspense. No one waited, in secret, behind a half-closed door.

The savour of a love affair should be quite otherwise, thought the Marquise, and breaking off a rose that climbed the trellis of the balcony, she placed it in the opening of her dress, below her neck. A love affair should be a thing of silence, soft, unspoken. No raucous voice, no burst of sudden laughter, but the kind of stealthy curiosity that comes with fear, and when the fear has gone, a brazen confidence. Never the give-and-take between good friends, but passion between strangers . . .

One by one they came back from the sands, the visitors to the hotel. The tables began to fill up. The terrace, hot and deserted all the morning, became alive once more. And guests, arriving by car for luncheon only, mingled with the more familiar figures belonging to the hotel. A party of six in the right-hand corner. A party of three below. And now more bustle, more chatter, more tinkling of glasses and clatter of plates, so that the splash of the sea, which had been the foremost sound since early morning, now seemed secondary, remote. The tide was going out, the water rippling away across the sands.

Here came the children with their governess, Miss Clay. They prinked their way like little dolls across the terrace, followed by Miss Clay in her striped cotton dress, her crimped hair straggling from her bathe, and suddenly they looked up to the balcony, they waved their hands. "Maman . . . Maman . . ." She leant down, smiling at them; and then, as usual, the little clamour brought distraction. Somebody glanced up with the children, smiling, some man at a left-hand table laughed and pointed to his companion, and it began, the first wave of admiration that would come again in full measure when she descended, the Marquise, the beautiful Marquise and her cherubic children, whispers wafting towards her in the air like the smoke from the cigarettes, like the conversation the guests at the other tables shared with one another. This, then, was all that déjeuner on the terrace would bring to her, day after day, the ripple of admiration, respect, and then oblivion. Each and all went his way, to swim, to golf, to tennis, to drive, and she was left, beautiful, unruffled, with the children and Miss Clay.

"Look, Maman, I found a little starfish on the beach. I am going to take him home with me when we go."

"No, no, that isn't fair, it's mine. I saw it first."

The little girls, with flushed

faces, fell out with one another.

"Hush, Céleste and Hélène: you make my head ache."

"Madame is tired? You must rest after lunch. It will do you good, in such heat." Miss Clay, tactful, bent down to scold the children. "Everyone is tired. It will do us all good to rest," she said.

Rest . . . "But," thought the Marquise, "I never do anything else. My life is one long rest." *Il faut reposer. Repose-toi, ma chérie, tu as mauvaise mine.* Winter and summer, those were the words she heard. From her husband, from the governess, from sisters-in-law, from all those aged, tedious friends. Life was one long sequence of resting, of getting up, and of resting again. Because with her pallor, with her reserve, they thought her delicate. Heavens above, the hours of her married life she had spent resting, the bed turned down, the shutters closed. In the house in Paris, in the château in the country. Two to four, resting, always resting.

"I'm not in the least tired," she said to Miss Clay, and for once her voice, usually melodious and soft, was sharp, high-pitched. "I shall go walking after lunch. I shall go into the town."

The children stared at her, round-eyed, and Miss Clay, her goat-face startled to surprise, opened her mouth in protest.

"You'll kill yourself, in the heat. Besides, the few shops always close between one and three. Why not wait until after tea? Surely it would be wiser to wait until after tea? The children could go with you and I could do some ironing."

The Marquise did not answer. She rose from the table, and now, because the children had lingered over déjeuner—Céleste was always slow with her food—the terrace was almost deserted. No one of any importance would watch the progress back to the hotel.

The Marquise went upstairs and once again touched her face with powder, circled her mouth, dipped her forefinger in scent. Next door she could hear the droning of the children as Miss Clay settled them to rest and closed the shutters. The Marquise took her handbag, made of plaited straw, put in it her purse, a roll of film, a few odds and ends, and, tiptoeing past the children's room, went downstairs again and out of the hotel grounds to the dusty road.

The gravel forced its way at once into her open sandals and the glare of the sun beat down upon her head, and at once what had seemed to her, on the spur of the moment, an unusual thing to do struck her now, in the doing of it, as foolish, pointless. The road was deserted, the sands were deserted, the visitors who had played and walked all morning, while she had lain idle on her balcony, were now taking their ease in their rooms, like Miss Clay and the children. Only the Marquise trod the sun-baked road into the little town.

And here it was even as Miss Clay had warned her. The shops were closed, the sun blinds were all down, the hour of siesta, inviolate, unbroken, held sway over the shops and their inhabitants.

The Marquise strolled along the street, her straw handbag swinging from her hand, the one walker in a sleeping, yawning world. Even the café at the corner was deserted, and a sand-coloured dog, his face between his paws, snapped with closed eyes at the flies that bothered him. Flies were everywhere. They buzzed at the window of the *pharmacie*, where dark bottles, filled with mysterious medicine, rubbed glass shoulders with skin tonic, sponges, and cosmetics. Flies danced behind the panes of the shop filled with sunshades, spades, pink dolls, and rope-soled shoes. They crawled upon the empty bloodstained slab of the butcher's shop, behind the iron shutter. From above the shop came the jarring sound of the radio, suddenly switched off, and the heavy sigh of someone who would sleep and would not be disturbed. Even the *bureau de poste* was shut. The Marquise, who had thought to buy stamps, rattled the door to no purpose.

Now she could feel the sweat trickling under her dress, and her feet, in the thin sandals, ached from the short distance she had walked. The sun was too strong, too fierce, and as she looked up and down the empty street, and at the houses, with the shops between, every one of them closed from her, withdrawn into the blessed peace of their siesta, she felt a sudden longing for any place that might be cool, that might be dark—a cellar, perhaps, where there was dripping water from a tap. The sound of water falling to a stone floor would soothe her nerves, now jagged from the sun.

Frustrated, almost crying, she turned into an alleyway between two shops. She came to steps leading down to a little court where there was no sun, and paused there a moment, her hand against the wall, so cold and firm. Beside her there was a window, shuttered, against which she leant her head, and suddenly, to her confusion, the shutter was withdrawn and a face looked out upon her from some dark room within.

"*Je regrette . . .*" she began, swept to absurdity that she should be discovered here, intruding, like one peering into the privacy and squalor of life below a shop. And then her voice dwindled and died away, foolishly, for the face that looked out upon her from the open window was so unusual, so gentle, that it might have come straight from a stained-glass saint in a cathedral. His face was framed in a cloud of dark curled hair, his nose was small and straight, his mouth a sculptured mouth, and his eyes, so solemn, brown, and tender, were like the eyes of a gazelle.

"*Vous désirez, Madame la Marquise?*" he said in answer to her unfinished words.

He knows me, she thought in wonder, he has seen me before, but even this was not so unexpected as the quality of his voice, not rough, not harsh, not the voice of someone in a cellar under a shop, but cultivated, liquid, a voice that matched the eyes of the gazelle.

"It was so hot up in the street," she said. "The shops were closed and I felt faint. I came down the steps. I am very sorry, it is private, of course."

The face disappeared from the window. He opened a door somewhere that she had not seen, and suddenly she found a chair beneath her and she was sitting down, inside the doorway, and it was dark and cool inside the room, even like the cellar she had imagined, and he was giving her water from an earthenware cup.

"Thank you," she said, "thank you very much." Looking up, she saw that he was watching her, with humility, with reverence, the pitcher of water in his hand; and he said to her in his soft, gentle voice, "Is there anything else I can get for you, Madame la Marquise?"

She shook her head, but within her stirred the feeling she knew so well, the sense of secret pleasure that came with admiration, and, conscious of herself for the first time since he had opened the window, she drew her scarf closer about her shoulders, the gesture deliberate, and she saw the gazelle eyes fall to the rose tucked in the bodice of her dress.

She said, "How do you know who I am?"

He answered, "You came into my shop three days ago. You had your children with you. You bought a film for your camera."

She stared at him, puzzled. She remembered buying the film from the little shop that advertised Kodaks in the window, and she remembered too the ugly, shuffling, crippled woman who had served her behind the counter. The woman had walked with a limp, and afraid that the children would notice and laugh, and that she herself, from nervousness, would be betrayed to equally heartless laughter, she had ordered some things to be sent to the hotel, and then departed.

"My sister served you," he said in explanation. "I saw you from the inner room. I do not often go behind the counter. I take photographs of people, of the countryside, and then they are sold to the visitors who come here in the summer."

"Yes," she said, "I see, I understand."

And she drank again from the earthenware cup, and drank, too, the adoration in his eyes.

"I have brought a film to be developed," she said. "I have it here in my bag. Would you do that for me?"

"Of course, Madame la Marquise," he said. "I will do anything for you, whatever you ask. Since that day you came into my shop I . . ." Then he stopped, a flush came over his face, and he looked away from her, deeply embarrassed.

The Marquise repressed a desire to laugh. It was quite absurd, his admiration. Yet, funny . . . it gave her a sense of power.

"Since I came into your shop, what?" she asked.

He looked at her again. "I have thought of nothing else, but nothing," he said to her, and with such intensity that it almost frightened her.

She smiled; she handed back the cup of water. "I am quite an ordinary woman," she said. "If you knew me better, I should disappoint you." How odd it is, she thought to herself, that I am so much mistress of this situation, I am not at all outraged or shocked. Here I am, in the cellar of a shop, talking to a photographer who has just expressed his admiration for me. It is really most amusing, and yet he, poor man, is in earnest, he really means what he says.

"Well," she said, "are you going to take my film?"

It was as though he could not drag his eyes away from her, and boldly she stared him out of face, so that his eyes fell and he flushed again.

"If you will go back the way you came," he said, "I will open up the shop for you." And now it was she who let her eyes linger upon him; the open vest, no shirt, the bare arms, the throat, the head of curling hair, and she said, "Why cannot I give you the film here?"

"It would not be correct, Madame la Marquise," he said to her.

She turned, laughing, and went back up the steps to the hot street. She stood on the pavement, she heard the rattle of the key in the door behind, she heard the door open. And then presently, in her own time, having deliberately stood outside to keep him waiting, she went into the shop, which was stuffy now, and close, unlike the cool quiet cellar.

He was behind the counter and she saw, with disappointment, that he had put on his coat, a grey cheap coat worn by any man serving in a shop, and his shirt was much too stiff, and much too blue. He was ordinary, a shopkeeper, reaching across the counter for the film.

"When will you have them ready?" she said.

"Tomorrow," he answered, and once again he looked at her with his dumb brown eyes. And she forgot the common coat and the blue stiff shirt, and saw the vest under the coat, and the bare arms.

"If you are a photographer," she said, "why don't you come to the hotel and take some photographs of me and my children?"

"You would like me to do that?" he asked.

"Why not?" she answered.

A secret look came into his eyes and went again, and he bent below the counter, pretending to search for string. But she thought, smiling to herself, "This is exciting to him, his hands are trembling"; and for the same reason her heart beat faster than before.

"Very well, Madame la Marquise," he said, "I will come to the hotel at whatever time is convenient to you."

"The morning, perhaps, is best," she said, "at eleven o'clock."

Casually she strolled away. She did not even say good-bye.

She walked across the street and, looking for nothing in the window of a shop opposite, she saw, through the glass, that he had come to the door of his own shop and was watching her. He had taken off his jacket and his shirt. The shop would be closed again, the siesta was not yet over. Then she noticed, for the first time, that he too was crippled, like his sister. His right foot was encased in a high fitted boot. Yet, curiously, the sight of this did not repel her, nor bring her to nervous laughter, as it had done before when she had seen the sister. His high boot had a fascination, strange, unknown.

The Marquise walked back to the hotel along the dusty road.

At eleven o'clock the next morning the concierge of the hotel sent up word that Monsieur Paul, the photographer, was below in the hall, and awaited the instructions of Madame la Marquise. The instructions were sent back that Madame la Marquise would be pleased if Monsieur Paul would go upstairs to the suite. Presently she heard the knock on the door, hesitant, timid.

"*Entrez,*" she called, and standing, as she did, on the balcony, her arms around the two children, she made a tableau, ready set, for him to gaze upon.

Today she was dressed in silk shantung the colour of chartreuse, and her hair was not the little-girl hair of yesterday, with the ribbon, but parted in the centre and drawn back to show her ears, with the gold clips upon them.

He stood in the entrance of the doorway, he did not move. The children, shy, gazed with wonder at the high boot, but they said nothing. Their mother had warned them not to mention it.

"These are my babies," said the Marquise. "And now you must tell us how to pose, and where you want us placed."

The children did not make their usual curtsey, as they did to guests. Their mother had told them it would not be necessary. Monsieur Paul was a photographer, from the shop in the little town.

"If it would be possible, Madame la Marquise," he said, "to have one pose just as you are standing now. It is quite beautiful. So very natural, so full of grace."

"Why, yes, if you like. Stand still, Hélène."

"Pardon. It will take a few moments to fix the camera."

His nervousness had gone. He was busy with the mechanical tricks of his trade. And as she watched him set up the tripod, fix the velvet cloth, make the adjustments to his camera, she noticed his hands, deft and efficient, and they were not the hands of an artisan, of a shopkeeper, but the hands of an artist.

Her eyes fell to the boot. His limp was not so pronounced as the sister's, he did not walk with that lurching, jerky step that produced stifled hysteria in the watcher. His step was slow, more dragging, and the Marquise felt a kind of compassion for his deformity, for surely the misshapen foot beneath the boot must pain him constantly, and the high boot, especially in hot weather, crush and sear his flesh.

"Now, Madame la Marquise," he said, and guiltily she raised her eyes from the boot and struck her pose, smiling gracefully, her arms embracing the children.

"Yes," he said, "just so. It is very lovely."

The dumb brown eyes held hers. His voice was low, gentle. The sense of pleasure came upon her just as it had done in the shop the day before. He pressed the bulb. There was a little clicking sound.

"Once more," he said.

She went on posing, the smile on her lips; and she knew that the reason he paused this time before pressing the bulb was not from professional necessity, because she or the children had moved, but because it delighted him to gaze upon her.

"There," she said, and breaking the pose, and the spell, she moved towards the balcony, humming a little song.

After half an hour the children became tired, restless.

The Marquise apologised. "It's so very hot," she said, "you must excuse them. Céleste, Hélène, get your toys and play on the other corner of the balcony."

They ran chattering to their own room. The Marquise turned her back upon the photographer. He was putting fresh plates into his camera.

"You know what it is with children," she said. "For a few min-utes it is a novelty, then they are sick of it, they want something else. You have been very patient, Monsieur Paul."

She broke off a rose from the balcony and, cupping it in her hands, bent her lips to it.

"Please," he said with urgency, "if you would permit me, I scarcely like to ask you . . ."

"What?" she said.

"Would it be possible for me to take one or two photographs of you alone, without the children?"

She laughed. She tossed the rose over the balcony to the ter-race below.

"But of course," she said, "I am at your disposal. I have nothing else to do."

She sat down on the edge of the chaise longue and, leaning back against the cushion, rested her head against her arm.

"Like this?" she said.

He disappeared behind the vel-vet cloth, and then, after an ad-justment to the camera, came limping forward.

"If you will permit me," he said, "the hand should be raised a little, so . . . And the head, just slightly on one side."

He took her hand and placed it to his liking; and then gently, with hesitation, put his hand under her chin, lifting it. She closed her eyes. He did not take his hand away. Almost imperceptibly his thumb moved, lingering, over the long line of her neck, and his fingers followed the movement of the thumb. The sensation was feather-weight, like the brushing of a bird's wing against her skin.

"Just so," he said, "that is per-fection."

She opened her eyes. He limped back to his camera.

The Marquise did not tire as the children had done. She per-mitted Monsieur Paul to take one photograph, then another, then another. The children returned, as she had bidden them, and played together at the far end of the balcony, and their chatter made a background to the busi-ness of the photography, so that, both smiling at the prattle of the children, a kind of adult intimacy developed between the Marquise and the photographer, and the at-mosphere was not so tense as it had been.

He became bolder, more confi-dent of himself. He suggested poses and she acquiesced, and once or twice she placed herself badly and he told her of it.

"No, Madame la Marquise. Not like that. Like this."

Then he would come over to the chair, kneel beside her, move her foot perhaps, or turn her shoulder, and each time he did so his touch became more certain, became stronger. Yet when she forced him to meet her eyes he looked away, humble and diffi-dent, as though he was ashamed of what he did, and his gentle eyes, mirroring his nature, would deny the impulse of his hands. She sensed a struggle within him, and it gave her pleasure.

At last, after he had rearranged her dress the second time, she noticed that he had gone quite white and there was perspiration on his forehead.

"It is very hot," she said, "per-haps we have done enough for to-day."

"If you please, Madame la Mar-quise," he answered, "it is indeed very warm. I think it is best that we should stop now."

She rose from the chair, cool and at her ease. She was not tired, nor was she troubled. Rather was she invigorated, full of a new en-ergy. When he had gone she would walk down to the sea and swim. It was very different for the pho-tographer. She saw him wipe his face with his handkerchief, and as he packed up his camera and his tripod, and put them in the case, he looked exhausted and dragged his high boot more heavily than before.

She made a pretence of glanc-ing through the snapshots he had developed for her from her own film.

"These are very poor," she said lightly. "I don't think I handle my camera correctly. I should take lessons from you."

"It is just a little practice that you need, Madame la Marquise," he said. "When I first started I had a camera much the same as yours. Even now, when I take ex-teriors, I wander out on the cliffs above the sea, with a small cam-era, and the effects are just as good as with the larger one."

She put the snapshots down on the table. He was ready to go. He carried the case in his hand.

"You must be very busy in the season," she said. "How do you get time to take exteriors?"

"I make time, Madame la Marquise," he said. "I prefer it, actually, to taking studio portraits. It is only occasionally that I find true satisfaction in photographing people. Like, for instance, today."

She looked at him and she saw again the devotion, the humility, in his eyes. She stared at him until he dropped his eyes, abashed.

"The scenery is very beautiful along the coast," he said. "You must have noticed it, when walking. Most afternoons I take my small camera and go on to the cliffs, above the big rock that stands there so prominent, to the right of the bathing beach."

He pointed from the balcony, and she followed the direction of his hand. The green headland shimmered hazily in the intense heat.

"It was only by chance that you found me at home yesterday," he said. "I was in the cellar, developing prints that had been promised for visitors who were to leave today. But usually I go walking on the cliffs at that time."

"It must be very hot," she said.

"Perhaps," he answered. "But above the sea there is a little breeze. And best of all, between one and four there are so few people. They are all taking their siesta in the afternoon. I have all that beautiful scenery to myself."

"Yes," said the Marquise, "I understand."

For a moment they both stood silent. It was as though something unspoken passed between them. The Marquise played with her chiffon handkerchief, then tied it loosely round her wrist, a casual, lazy gesture.

"Sometime I must try it for myself," she said at last, "walking in the heat of the day."

Miss Clay came on to the balcony, calling the children to come and be washed before déjeuner. The photographer stepped to one side, deferential, apologising. And the Marquise, glancing at her watch, saw that it was already *midi*, and that the tables below on the terrace were filled with people and the usual bustle and chatter were going on, the tinkle of glasses, the rattle of plates, and she had noticed none of it.

She turned her shoulder to the photographer, dismissing him, deliberately cool and indifferent now that the session was over and Miss Clay had come to fetch the children.

"Thank you," she said. "I shall call in at the shop to see the proofs in a few days' time. Good morning."

He bowed, he went away, an employee who had fulfilled his orders.

"I hope he has taken some good photographs," said Miss Clay. "The Marquis will be very pleased to see the results."

The Marquise did not answer. She was taking off her gold clips from her ears that now, for some reason, no longer matched her mood. She would go down to déjeuner without jewellery, without rings; she felt, for today, her own beauty would suffice.

Three days passed, and the

Marquise did not once descend into the little town. The first day she swam, she watched the tennis in the afternoon. The second day she spent with the children, giving Miss Clay leave of absence to take a tour by charabanc to visit the old walled cities, further inland, along the coast. The third day she sent Miss Clay and the children into the town to enquire for the proofs, and they returned with them wrapped in a neat package. The Marquise examined them. They were very good indeed, and the studies of herself the best she had ever had taken.

Miss Clay was in raptures. She begged for copies to send home to England. "Who would believe it," she exclaimed, "that a little photographer by the sea like this could take such splendid pictures? And then you go and pay heaven knows what to real professionals in Paris."

"They are not bad," said the Marquise, yawning. "He certainly took a lot of trouble. They are better of me than they are of the children." She folded the package and put it away in a drawer. "Did Monsieur Paul seem pleased with them himself?" she asked the governess.

"He did not say," replied Miss Clay. "He seemed disappointed that you had not gone down for them yourself; he said they had been ready since yesterday. He asked if you were well, and the children told him Maman had been swimming. They were quite friendly with him."

"It's much too hot and dusty down in the town," said the Marquise.

The next afternoon, when Miss Clay and the children were resting and the hotel itself seemed asleep under the glare of the sun, the Marquise changed into a short sleeveless frock, very simple and plain, and softly, so as not to disturb the children, went downstairs, her small box camera slung over her arm, and, walking through the hotel grounds on to the sands, she followed a narrow path that led upwards, to the greensward above. The sun was merciless. Yet she did not mind. Here on the springy grass there was no dust, and presently, by the cliff's edge, the bracken, growing thicker, brushed her bare legs.

The little path wound in and out amongst the bracken, at times coming so close to the cliff's edge that a false step, bringing a stumble, would spell danger. But the Marquise, walking slowly, with the lazy swing of the hips peculiar to her, felt neither frightened nor exhausted. She was merely intent on reaching a spot that overlooked the great rock standing out from the coast in the middle of the bay. She was quite alone on the headland. No one was in sight. Away behind her, far below, the white walls of the hotel and the rows of bathing cabins on the beach looked like bricks played with by children. The sea was very smooth and still. Even where it washed upon the rock in the bay it left no ripple.

Suddenly the Marquise saw something flash in the bracken

ahead of her. It was the lens of a camera. She took no notice. Turning her back, she pretended to examine her own camera, and took up a position as though to photograph the view. She took one, took another, and then she heard the swish of someone walking towards her through the bracken.

She turned, surprised. "Why, good afternoon, Monsieur Paul," she said.

He had discarded the cheap stiff jacket and the bright blue shirt. He was not on business. It was the hour of the siesta, when he walked, as it were, incognito. He wore only the vest and a pair of dark blue trousers, and the grey squash hat, which she had noticed with dismay the morning he had come to the hotel, was also absent. His thick dark hair made a frame to his gentle face. His eyes had such a rapturous expression at the sight of her that she was forced to turn away to hide her smile.

"You see," she said lightly, "I have taken your advice, and strolled up here to look at the view. But I am sure I don't hold my camera correctly. Show me how."

He stood beside her and, taking her camera, steadied her hands, moving them to the correct position.

"Yes, of course," she said, and then moved away from him, laughing a little, for it had seemed to her that when he stood beside her and guided her hands she had heard his heart beating, and the sound brought excitement, which

she wished to conceal from him.

"Have you your own camera?" she said.

"Yes, Madame la Marquise," he answered. "I left it over in the bracken there, with my coat. It is a favourite spot of mine, close to the edge of the cliff. In spring I come here to watch the birds and take photographs of them."

"Show me," she said.

He led the way, murmuring "Pardon," and the path he had made for himself took them to a little clearing, like a nest, hidden on all sides by bracken that was now waist-high. Only the front of the clearing was open, and this was wide to the cliff face and the sea.

"But how lovely," she said, and, passing through the bracken into the hiding place, she looked about her, smiling, and sitting down, gracefully, naturally, like a child at a picnic, she picked up the book that was lying on top of his coat beside his camera.

"You read much?" she said.

"Yes, Madame la Marquise," he answered. "I am very fond of reading." She glanced at the cover, and read the title. It was a cheap romance, the sort of book she and her friends had smuggled into their satchels at the lycée in old days. She had not read that sort of stuff for years. Once again she had to hide her smile. She put the book back on the coat.

"Is it a good story?" she asked him.

He looked down at her solemnly, with his great eyes like a gazelle's.

"It is very tender, Madame la Marquise," he said.

Tender . . . What an odd expression. She began to talk about the proofs of the photographs, and how she preferred one to another, and all the while she was conscious of an inner triumph that she was in such command of the situation. She knew exactly what to do, what to say, when to smile, when to look serious. It reminded her strangely of childhood days, when she and her young friends would dress up in their mothers' hats and say, "Let's pretend to be ladies." She was pretending now; not to be a lady, as then, but to be—what? She was not sure. But something other than the self who now, for so long, was in truth a real lady, sipping tea in the salon at the château, surrounded by so many ancient things and people that each one of them had the mustiness of death.

The photographer did not talk much. He listened to the Marquise. He agreed, nodded his head, or simply remained silent, and she heard her own voice trilling on in a sort of wonder. He was merely a witness she could ignore, a nonentity, while she listened to the brilliant, charming woman that had suddenly become herself.

At last there came a pause in the one-sided conversation, and he said to her shyly, "May I dare to ask you something?"

"Of course," she said.

"Could I photograph you here, alone, with this background?"

Was that all? How timid he was, and how reluctant. She laughed.

"Take as many as you want," she said. "It is very pleasant sitting here. I may even go to sleep."

"La belle au bois dormant," he said quickly, and then, as if ashamed of his familiarity, he murmured "Pardon" once more and reached for the camera behind her.

This time he did not ask her to pose, to change position. He photographed her as she sat, lazily nibbling at a stem of grass, and it was he who moved, now here, now there, so that he had shots of her from every angle, full-face, profile, three-quarter.

She began to feel sleepy. The sun beat down upon her uncovered head, and the dragonflies, gaudy and green and gold, swung and hovered before her eyes. She yawned and leant back against the bracken.

"Would you care for my coat as a pillow for your head, Madame la Marquise?" he asked her.

Before she could reply he had taken his coat, folded it neatly, and placed it in a little roll against the bracken. She leant back against it, and the despised grey coat made a softness to her head, easy and comfortable.

He knelt beside her, intent upon his camera, doing something to the film, and she watched him, yawning, between half-closed eyes, and noticed that as he knelt he kept his weight upon one knee only, thrusting the deformed foot in the high boot to one side. Idly, she wondered if it hurt to lean upon it. The boot was highly polished, much brighter than the leather shoe upon the left foot, and she had a sudden vision of him taking great pains with the boot every morning when he dressed, polishing it, rubbing it, perhaps, with a wash-leather cloth.

A dragonfly settled on her hand. It crouched, waiting, a sheen upon its wings. What was it waiting for? She blew upon it and it flew away. Then it came back again, hovering, insistent.

Monsieur Paul had put aside his camera, but he was still kneeling in the bracken beside her. She was aware of him, watching her, and she thought to herself, "If I move he will get up, and it will all be over."

She went on staring at the glittering, shivering dragonfly, but she knew that in a moment or two she must look somewhere else, or the dragonfly would go, or the present silence would become so tense and so strained that she would break it with a laugh and so spoil everything. Reluctantly, against her will, she turned to the photographer, and his large eyes, humble and devoted, were fixed upon her with all the deep abasement of a slave.

"Why don't you kiss me?" she said, and her own words startled her, shocked her into sudden apprehension.

He said nothing. He did not move. He went on gazing at her. She closed her eyes, and the dragonfly went from her hand. Presently, when the photographer bent to touch her, it was not what she expected. There was no sudden crude embrace. It was just as though the dragonfly had returned, and now with silken wings brushed and stroked the smooth surface of her skin.

When he went away it was with tact and delicacy. He left her to herself so that there should be no aftermath of awkwardness, of embarrassment, no sudden strain of conversation.

The Marquise lay back in the bracken, her hands over her eyes, thinking about what had happened to her, and she had no sense of shame. She was clear-headed and quite calm. She began to plan how she would walk back to the hotel in a little while, giving him good time to gain the sands before her, so that if by chance people from the hotel should see him they would not connect him with her, who would follow after, say in half an hour.

She got up, rearranged her dress, took out her powder compact from her pocket, with her lipstick, and, having no mirror, judged carefully how much powder to put upon her face. The sun had lost its power, and a cool breeze blew inland from the sea.

"If the weather holds," thought the Marquise as she combed her hair, "I can come out here every day, at the same time. No one will ever know. Miss Clay and the children always rest in the afternoon. If we walk separately and go back separately, as we have done today, and come to this same place, hidden by the bracken, we cannot possibly be discovered. There are over three weeks still to the holiday. The great thing is to pray for this hot weather to continue. If it should rain . . ."

As she walked back to the hotel she wondered how they would manage, should the weather break. She could not very well set out to walk the cliffs in a mackintosh, and then lie down while the rain and the wind beat the bracken. There was of course the cellar, beneath the shop. But she might be seen in the village. That would be dangerous. No, unless it rained in torrents, the cliff was safest.

That evening she sat down and wrote a letter to her friend Elise. ". . . This is a wonderful place," she wrote, "and I am amusing myself as usual, and without my husband, *bien entendu!*" But she gave no details of her conquest, though she mentioned the bracken and the hot afternoon. She felt that if she left it vague Elise would picture to herself some rich American, travelling for pleasure, alone, without his wife.

The next morning, dressing herself with great care—she stood for a long while before her wardrobe, finally choosing a frock rather more elaborate than was usual for the seaside, but this was deliberate on her part—she went down into the little town, accompanied by Miss Clay and the children. It was market day, and the cobbled streets and the square were full of people. Many came from the countryside around, but there were quantities of visitors, English and American, who strolled to see the sights, to buy souvenirs and picture-postcards, or to sit down at the café at the corner and look about them.

The Marquise made a striking figure, walking in her indolent way in her lovely dress, hatless, carrying a sunshade, with the two little girls prancing beside her. Many people turned to look at her, or even stepped aside to let her pass, in unconscious homage to her beauty. She dawdled in the market place and made a few purchases, which Miss Clay put into the shopping bag she carried, and then, still casual, still answering with gay, lazy humour the questions of the children, she turned into the shop which displayed Kodaks and photographs in the window.

It was full of visitors waiting their turn to be served, and the Marquise, who was in no hurry, pretended to examine a book of local views, while at the same time she could see what was happening in the shop. They were both there, Monsieur Paul and his sister, he in his stiff shirt, an ugly pink this time, worse even than the blue, and the cheap grey coat, while the sister, like all women who served behind a counter, was in drab black, a shawl over her shoulders.

He must have seen her come into the shop, because almost at once he came forward from the counter, leaving the queue of visitors to the care of his sister, and was by her side, humble, polite, anxious to know in what manner he could serve her. There was no trace of familiarity, no look of knowledge in his eyes, and she took care to assure herself of this by staring directly at him. Then deliberately, bringing the children and Miss Clay into the conversation, asking Miss Clay to make her choice of the proofs which were to be sent to England, she kept him there by her side, treating him with condescension, with a sort of hauteur, even finding fault with certain of the proofs, which, so she told him, did not do the children justice, and which she could not possibly send to her husband, the Marquis. The photographer apologised. Most certainly the proofs mentioned did not do the children justice. He would be willing to come again to the hotel and try again, at no extra charge, of course. Perhaps on the terrace or in the gardens the effect would be better.

One or two people turned to look at the Marquise as she stood there. She could feel their eyes upon her, absorbing her beauty, and still in a tone of condescension, coldly, almost curtly, she told the photographer to show her various articles in his shop, which he hastened to do in his anxiety to please.

The other visitors were becoming restive, they shuffled their feet waiting for the sister to serve them, and she, hemmed about with customers, limped wretchedly from one end of the counter to the other, now and again raising her head, peering to see if her brother, who had so suddenly deserted her, would come to the rescue.

At last the Marquise relented. She had had her fill. The delicious furtive sense of excitement that had risen in her since her entrance to the shop died down and was appeased.

"One of these mornings I will let you know," she said to Monsieur Paul, "and then you can come out and photograph the children again. Meanwhile, let me pay what I owe. Miss Clay, attend to it, will you?"

And she strolled from the shop, not bidding him good morning, putting out her hands to the two children.

She did not change for déjeuner. She wore the same enchanting frock, and the hotel terrace, more crowded than ever because of the many visitors who had come on an excursion, seemed to her to buzz and hum with a murmur of conversation, directed at her and her beauty, and at the effect she made, sitting there at the table in the corner. The maître d'hôtel, the waiters, even the manager himself, were drawn towards her, obsequious, smiling, and she could hear her name pass from one to the other.

All things combined to her triumph: the proximity of people, the smell of food and wine and cigarettes, the scent of the gaudy flowers in their tubs, the feel of the hot sun beating down, the close sound of the splashing sea.

When she rose at last with the children and went upstairs, she had a sense of happiness that she felt must only come to a prima donna after the clamour of long applause.

The children, with Miss Clay, went to their rooms to rest; and swiftly, hurriedly, the Marquise changed her frock and her shoes and tiptoed down the stairs and out of the hotel, across the burning sands to the path and the bracken headland.

He was waiting for her, as she expected, and neither of them made any reference to her visit in the morning, or to what brought her there on the cliff this afternoon. They made at once for the little clearing by the cliff's edge and sat down of one accord, and the Marquise, in a tone of banter, described the crowd at lunch, and the fearful bustle and fatique of the terrace with so many people, and how delicious it was to get away from them all to the fresh clean air of the headland, above the sea.

He agreed with her humbly, watching her as she spoke of such mundane matters as though the wit of the world flowed in her speech, and then, exactly as on the previous day, he begged to take a few photographs of her, and she consented, and presently she lay back in the bracken and closed her eyes.

There was no sense of time to the long, languorous afternoon. Just as before, the dragonflies winged about her in the bracken, and the sun beat down upon her body, and with her sense of deep enjoyment at all that happened went the curiously satisfying knowledge that what she did was without emotion of any sort. Her mind and her affections were quite untouched. She might almost have been relaxing in a beauty parlour, back in Paris, having the first telltale lines smoothed from her face and her hair shampooed, although these things brought only a lazy contentment and no pleasure.

Once again he departed, leaving her without a word, tactful and discreet, so that she could arrange herself in privacy. And once again, when she judged him out of sight, she rose to her feet and began the long walk back to the hotel.

Her good luck held and the weather did not break. Every afternoon, as soon as déjeuner was over and the children had gone to rest, the Marquise went for her promenade, returning about half-past four, in time for tea. Miss Clay, at first exclaiming at her energy, came to accept the walk as a matter of routine. If the Marquise chose to walk in the heat of the day, it was her own affair; certainly it seemed to do her good. She was more human towards her, Miss Clay, and less nagging to the children. The constant headaches and attacks of migraine were forgotten, and it seemed that the Marquise was really enjoying this simple seaside holiday alone with Miss Clay and the two little girls.

When a fortnight had passed, the Marquise discovered that the first delight and bliss of her experience were slowly fading. It was not that Monsieur Paul failed her in any way, but that she herself was becoming used to the daily ritual. Like an inoculation that "took" at the first with very great success, on constant repetition the effect lessened, dulled, and the Marquise found that to recapture her enjoyment she was obliged to treat the photographer no longer as a nonentity, or as she would a coiffeur who had set her hair, but as a person whose feelings she could wound. She would find fault with his appearance, complain that he wore his hair too long, that his clothes were cheap, ill-cut, or even that he ran his little shop in the town with inefficiency, that the material and paper he used for his prints were shoddy.

She would watch his face when she told him this, and she would see anxiety and pain come into his large eyes, pallor to his skin, a look of dejection fall upon his whole person as he realised how unworthy he was of her, how inferior in every way, and only when she saw him thus did the original excitement kindle in her again.

Deliberately she began to cut down the hours of the afternoon. She would arrive late at the rendezvous in the bracken and find him waiting for her with that same look of anxiety on his face, and if her mood was not sufficiently ripe for what should happen she would get through the business quickly, with an ill grace,

and then dispatch him hastily on his return journey, picturing him limping back, tired and unhappy, to the shop in the little town.

She permitted him to take photographs of her still. This was all part of the experience, and she knew that it troubled him to do this, to see her to perfection, so she delighted in taking advantage of it, and would sometimes tell him to come to the hotel during the morning, and then she would pose in the grounds, exquisitely dressed, the children beside her, Miss Clay an admiring witness, the visitors watching from their rooms or from the terrace.

The contrast of these mornings, when as an employee he limped back and forth at her bidding, moving the tripod first here, first there, while she gave him orders, with the sudden intimacy of the afternoons in the bracken under the hot sun, proved, during the third week, to be her only stimulation.

Finally, a day breaking when quite a cold breeze blew in from the sea, and she did not go to the rendezvous as usual but rested on her balcony reading a novel, the change in the routine came as a real relief.

The following day was fine and she decided to go to the headland, and for the first time since they had encountered one another in the cool dark cellar below the shop he upbraided her, his voice sharp with anxiety.

"I waited for you all yesterday afternoon," he said. "What happened?"

She stared at him in astonishment.

"It was an unpleasant day," she replied. "I preferred to read on my balcony in the hotel."

"I was afraid you might have been taken ill," he went on. "I very nearly called at the hotel to enquire for you. I hardly slept last night, I was so upset."

He followed her to the hiding place in the bracken, his eyes still anxious, lines of worry on his brow, and though in a sense it was a stimulation to the Marquise to witness his distress, at the same time it irritated her that he should so forget himself to find fault in her conduct. It was as though her coiffeur in Paris, or her masseur, expressed anger when she broke an appointment fixed for a certain day.

"If you think I feel myself bound to come here every afternoon, you are very much mistaken," she said. "I have plenty of other things to do."

At once he apologised, he was abject. He begged her to forgive him.

"You cannot understand what this means to me," he said. "Since I have known you, everything in my life is changed. I live only for these afternoons."

His subjection pleased her, whipping her to a renewal of interest, and pity came to her too, as he lay by her side, pity that this creature should be so utterly devoted, depending on her like a child. She touched his hair, feeling for a moment quite compassionate, almost maternal. Poor fellow, limping all this way because of her, and then sitting in the biting wind of yesterday, alone and wretched. She imagined the letter she would write to her friend Elise.

"I am very much afraid I have broken Paul's heart. He has taken this little *affaire des vacances au sérieux*. But what am I to do? After all, these things must have an end. I cannot possibly alter my life because of him. *Enfin,* he is a man, he will get over it." Elise would picture the beautiful blond American playboy climbing wearily into his Packard, setting off in despair to the unknown.

The photographer did not leave her today, when the afternoon session had ended. He sat up in the bracken and stared out towards the great rock jutting out into the sea.

"I have made up my mind about the future," he said quietly.

The Marquise sensed the drama in the air. Did he mean he was going to kill himself? How very terrible. He would wait, of course, until she had left the hotel and had returned home. She need never know.

"Tell me," she said gently.

"My sister will look after the shop," he said. "I will make it all over to her. She is very capable. For myself, I shall follow you, wherever you go, whether it is to Paris, or to the country. I shall be close at hand; whenever you want me, I shall be there."

The Marquise swallowed. Her heart went still.

"You can't possibly do that,"

she said. "How would you live?"
"I am not proud," he said. "I
know, in the goodness of your
heart, you would allow me something. My needs would be very
small. But I know that it is impossible to live without you,
therefore the only thing to do is
to follow you, always. I will find
a room close to your house in
Paris, and in the country too. We
will find ways and means of being
together. When love is as strong
as this there are no difficulties."
He spoke with his usual humility, but there was a force behind his words that was unexpected, and she knew that for him
this was no false drama, ill-timed
to the day, but true sincerity. He
meant every word. He would in
truth give up the shop, follow her
to Paris, follow her also to the
château in the country.
"You are mad," she said violently, sitting up, careless of her
appearance and her dishevelled
hair. "Once I have left here I am
no longer free. I cannot possibly
meet you anywhere, the danger
of discovery would be too great.
You realise my position? What it
would mean to me?"
He nodded his head. His face
was sad, but quite determined. "I
have thought of everything," he
answered, "but as you know, I am
very discreet. You need never be
apprehensive on that score. It has
occurred to me that it might be
possible to obtain a place in your
service as footman. It would not
matter to me, the loss of personal
dignity. I am not proud. But in
such a capacity our life together

could continue much as it does
now. Your husband, the Marquis,
must be a very busy man, often
out during the day, and your
children and the English miss no
doubt go walking in the country
in the afternoon. You see, everything would be very simple if we
had the courage."
The Marquise was so shocked
that she could not answer. She
could not imagine anything more
terrible, more disastrous, than
that the photographer should take
a place in the house as footman.
Quite apart from his disability—
she shuddered to think of him
limping round the table in the
great *salle à manger*—what misery
she would suffer knowing that he
was there, in the house, that he
was waiting for her to go up to
her room in the afternoon, and
then, timidly, the knock upon the
door, the hushed whisper. The
degradation of this—this creature
—there was really no other word
for him—in the house, always
waiting, always hoping.
"I am afraid," she said firmly,
"that what you are suggesting is
utterly impossible. Not only the
idea of coming to my house as a
servant, but of our ever being
able to meet again once I return
home. Your own common sense
must tell you so. These afternoons
have been—have been pleasant,
but my holiday is very nearly
over. In a few days' time my husband will be coming to fetch me
and the children, and that finishes
everything."
To show finality she got up,
brushed her crumpled frock,

combed her hair, powdered her nose, and, reaching for her bag, fumbled inside it for her note case.

She drew out several ten-thousand-franc notes.

"This is for the shop," she said, "any little fittings it may require. And buy something for your sister. And remember, I shall always think of you with great tenderness."

To her consternation his face went dead white, then his mouth began to work violently and he rose to his feet.

"No, no," he said, "I will never take them. You are cruel, wicked, to suggest it." And suddenly he began to sob, burying his face in his hands, his shoulders heaving with emotion.

The Marquise watched him helplessly, uncertain whether to go or to stay. His sobs were so violent that she was afraid of hysteria, and she did not know what might happen. She was sorry for him, deeply sorry, but even more sorry for herself, because now, on parting, he cut such a ridiculous figure in her eyes. A man who gave way to emotion was pitiable. And it seemed to her that the clearing in the bracken took on a sordid, shameful appearance, which once had seemed so secret and so warm. His shirt, lying on a stem of bracken, looked like old linen spread by washerwomen in the sun to dry. Beside it lay his tie and the cheap trilby hat. It needed only orange peel and silver paper

from a chocolate carton to complete the picture.

"Stop that noise," she said in sudden fury. "For God's sake pull yourself together."

The crying ceased. He took his hands away from his ravaged face. He stared at her, trembling, his brown eyes blind with pain. "I have been mistaken in you," he said. "I know you now for what you are. You are a wicked woman and you go about ruining the lives of innocent men like myself. I shall tell your husband everything."

The Marquise said nothing. He was unbalanced, mad. . . .

"Yes," said the photographer, still catching at his breath, "that is what I shall do. As soon as your husband comes to fetch you I will tell him everything. I will show him the photographs I have taken here on the headland. I will prove to him without a doubt that you are false to him, that you are bad. And he will believe me. He cannot help but believe me. What he does to me does not matter. I cannot suffer more than I suffer now. But your life, that will be finished, I promise you. He will know, the English miss will know, the manager of the hotel will know; I will tell everybody how you have been spending your afternoons."

He reached for his coat, he reached for his hat, he slung his camera around his shoulder, and panic seized the Marquise, rose from her heart to her throat. He would do all that he threatened to do; he would wait there in the hall of the hotel by the reception desk, he would wait for Edouard to come.

"Listen to me," she began, "we will think of something, we can perhaps come to some arrangement . . ."

But he ignored her. His face was set and pale. He stooped, by the opening at the cliff's edge, to pick up his stick, and as he did so the terrible impulse was born in her, and flooded her whole being, and would not be denied. Leaning forward, her hands outstretched, she pushed his stooping body. He did not utter a single cry. He fell, and was gone.

The Marquise sank back on her knees. She did not move. She waited. She felt the sweat trickle down her face, to her throat, to her body. Her hands were also wet. She waited there in the clearing, upon her knees, and presently, when she was cooler, she took her handkerchief and wiped away the sweat from her forehead, and her face, and her hands.

It seemed suddenly cold. She shivered. She stood up and her legs were firm; they did not give way, as she feared. She looked about her, over the bracken, and no one was in sight. As always, she was alone upon the headland. Five minutes passed, and then she forced herself to the brink of the cliff and looked down. The tide was in. The sea was washing the base of the cliff below. It surged, and swept the rocks, and sank, and surged again. There was no sign of his body on the cliff face, nor could there be, because the cliff was sheer. No sign of his body in the water, and had he fallen and floated it would have shown there, on the surface of the still blue sea. When he fell he must have sunk immediately.

The Marquise turned back from the opening. She gathered her things together. She tried to pull the flattened bracken to its original height, and so smooth out the signs of habitation, but the hiding place had been made so long that this was impossible. Perhaps it did not matter. Perhaps it would be taken for granted that people came out upon the cliff and took their ease.

Suddenly her knees began to tremble and she sat down. She waited a few moments, then glanced at her watch. She knew that it might be important to remember the time. A few minutes after half-past three. If she was asked, she could say, "Yes, I was out on the headland at about half-past three, but I heard nothing." That would be the truth. She would not be lying. It would be the truth.

She remembered with relief that today she had brought her mirror in her bag. She glanced at it fearfully. Her face was chalk-white, blotched and strange. She powdered carefully, gently; it seemed to make no difference. Miss Clay would notice something was wrong. She dabbed dry rouge on to her cheeks, but this stood out like the painted spots on a clown's face.

"There is only one thing to do," she thought, "and that is to go straight to the bathing cabin on the beach, and undress, and put on my swimming suit, and bathe. Then if I return to the hotel with my hair wet, and my face wet too, it will seem natural, and I shall have been swimming, and that also will be true."

She began to walk back along the cliff, but her legs were weak, as though she had been lying ill in bed for many days, and when she came to the beach at last she was trembling so much she thought she would fall. More than anything she longed to lie down on her bed, in the hotel bedroom, and close the shutters, even the windows, and hide there by herself in the darkness. Yet she must force herself to play the part she had decided.

She went to the bathing cabin and undressed. Already there were several people lying on the sands, reading or sleeping, the hour of siesta drawing to its close. She walked down to the water's edge, kicked off her rope-soled shoes, drew on her cap, and as she swam to and fro in the still, tepid water, and dipped her face, she wondered how many of the people on the beach noticed her, watched her, and afterwards might say, "But don't you remember, we saw a woman come down from the headland in the middle of the afternoon?"

She began to feel very cold, but she continued swimming, backwards and forwards, with stiff, mechanical strokes, until suddenly, seeing a little boy who was playing with a dog point out to sea, and the dog run in barking towards some dark object that might have been a piece of timber, nausea and terror combined to turn her faint, and she stumbled from the sea back to the bathing cabin and lay on the wooden floor, her face in her hands. It might be, she thought, that had she gone on swimming she would have touched him with her feet, as his body came floating in towards her on the water.

In four days' time the Marquis was due to arrive by car and pick up his wife, the governess, and the children, and drive them home. The Marquise put a call through to him at the château and asked if it would be possible for him to come sooner. Yes, the weather was still good, she said, but somehow she had become tired of the place. It was now getting too full of people, it was noisy, and the food had gone off. In fact she had turned against it. She longed to be back at home, she told her husband, amongst her own things, and the gardens would be looking lovely.

The Marquis regretted very much that she was bored, but surely she could stick it out for just the four days, he said. He had made all his arrangements, and he could not come sooner. He had to pass through Paris anyway for an important business meeting. He would promise to reach her by the morning of the Thursday, and then they could leave immediately after lunch.

"I had hoped," he said, "that you would want to stay on for the week end, so that I too could get some bathing. The rooms are held surely until the Monday?"

But no, she had told the manager, she said, that they would not require the rooms after Thursday, and he had already let them to someone else. The place was crowded. The charm of it had gone, she assured him. Edouard would not care for it at all, and at the week end it became quite insupportable. So would he make every effort to arrive in good time on the Thursday, and then they could leave after an early lunch?

The Marquise put down the receiver and went out to the balcony to the chaise longue. She took up a book and pretended to read, but in reality she was listening, waiting for the sound of footsteps, voices, at the entrance to the hotel, and presently for her telephone to ring, and it would be the manager asking her, with many apologies, if she would mind descending to his office. The fact was, the matter was delicate . . . but the police were with him. They had some idea that she could help them. The telephone did not ring. There were no voices. No footsteps. Life continued as before. The long hours dragged through the interminable day. Lunch on the terrace, the waiters bustling, obsequious, the tables filled with the usual faces or with new visitors to take the place of old, the children chattering, Miss

Clay reminding them of their manners. And all the while the Marquise listened, waited. . . .

She forced herself to eat, but the food she put in her mouth tasted of sawdust. Lunch over, she mounted to her room, and while the children rested she lay on the chaise longue on the balcony. They descended to the terrace again for tea, but when the children went to the beach for their second bathe of the day she did not go with them. She had a little chill, she told Miss Clay; she did not fancy the water. So she went on sitting there, on her balcony.

When she closed her eyes at night and tried to sleep, she felt his stooping shoulders against her hands once more, and the sensation that it had given her when she pushed them hard. The ease with which he fell and vanished, one moment there, and the next, nothing. No stumble, no cry.

In the daytime she used to strain her eyes towards the headland, in search of figures walking there amongst the bracken—would they be called "a cordon of police"? But the headland shimmered under the pitiless sun, and no one walked there in the bracken.

Twice Miss Clay suggested going down into the town in the mornings to make purchases, and each time the Marquise made an excuse.

"It's always so crowded," she said, "and so hot. I don't think it's good for the children. The gardens are more pleasant, the lawn at the back of the hotel is shady and quiet."

She herself did not leave the hotel. The thought of the beach brought back the pain in her belly, and the nausea. Nor did she walk.

"I shall be quite all right," she told Miss Clay, "when I have thrown off this tiresome chill."

She lay there on the balcony, turning over the pages of the magazines she had read a dozen times.

On the morning of the third day, just before déjeuner, the children came running on to the balcony, waving little windmill flags.

"Look, Maman," said Hélène, "mine is red, and Céleste's is blue. We are going to put them on our sand castles after tea."

"Where did you get them?" asked the Marquise.

"In the market place," said the child. "Miss Clay took us to the town this morning instead of playing in the garden. She wanted to pick up her snapshots that were to be ready today."

A feeling of shock went through the Marquise. She sat very still.

"Run along," she said, "and get ready for déjeuner."

She could hear the children chattering to Miss Clay in the bathroom. In a moment or two Miss Clay came in. She closed the door behind her. The Marquise forced herself to look up at the governess. Miss Clay's long, rather stupid face was grave and concerned.

"Such a dreadful thing has happened," she said, her voice low.

"I don't want to speak of it in front of the children. I am sure you will be very distressed. It's poor Monsieur Paul."

"Monsieur Paul?" said the Marquise. Her voice was perfectly calm. But her tone had the right quality of interest.

"I went down to the shop to fetch my snapshots," said Miss Clay, "and I found it shut. The door was locked and the shutters were up. I thought it rather odd, and I went into the *pharmacie* next door and asked if they knew whether the shop was likely to be open after tea. They said no, Mademoiselle Paul was too upset, she was being looked after by relatives. I asked what had happened, and they told me there had been an accident, that poor Monsieur Paul's body had been found by some fishermen three miles up the coast, drowned."

Miss Clay had quite lost colour as she told her tale. She was obviously deeply shocked. The Marquise, at sight of her, gained courage.

"How perfectly terrible," she said. "Does anybody know when it happened?"

"I couldn't go into details at the *pharmacie* because of the children," said Miss Clay, "but I think they found the body yesterday. Terribly injured, they said. He must have hit some rocks before falling into the sea. It's so dreadful I can't bear to think of it. And his poor sister, whatever will she do without him?"

The Marquise put up her hand for silence and made a warning

face. The children were coming into the room.

They went down to the terrace for déjeuner, and the Marquise ate better than she had done for two days. For some reason her appetite had returned. Why this should be so she could not tell. She wondered if it could possibly be that part of the burden of her secret was now lifted. He was dead. He had been found. These things were known. After déjeuner she told Miss Clay to ask the manager if he knew anything of the sad accident. Miss Clay was to say that the Marquise was most concerned and grieved. While Miss Clay went about this business the Marquise took the children upstairs.

Presently the telephone rang. The sound that she had dreaded. Her heart missed a beat. She took off the receiver and listened.

It was the manager. He said Miss Clay had just been to him. He said it was most gracious of Madame la Marquise to show concern at the unfortunate accident that had befallen Monsieur Paul. He would have spoken of it when the accident was discovered yesterday, but he did not wish to distress the clientele. A drowning disaster was never very pleasant at a seaside resort, it made people feel uncomfortable. Yes, of course, the police had been called in directly the body was found. It was assumed that he had fallen from the cliffs somewhere along the coast. It seemed he was very fond of photographing the sea views. And of course, with his dis-

ability, he could easily slip. His sister had often warned him to be careful. It was very sad. He was such a good fellow. Everyone liked him. He had no enemies. And such an artist, too, in his way. Madame la Marquise had been pleased with the studies Monsieur Paul had done of herself and the children? The manager was so glad. He would make a point of letting Mademoiselle Paul know this, and also of the concern shown by Madame la Marquise. Yes, indeed, she would be deeply grateful for flowers, and for a note of sympathy. The poor woman was quite brokenhearted. No, the day of the funeral had not yet been decided . . .

When he had finished speaking, the Marquise called to Miss Clay and told her she must order a taxi and drive to the town seven miles inland, where the shops were larger, and where she seemed to remember there was an excellent florist. Miss Clay was to order flowers, lilies for choice, and to spare no expense, and the Marquise would write a note to go with them; and then if Miss Clay gave them to the manager when she returned he would see that they reached Mademoiselle Paul.

The Marquise wrote the note for Miss Clay to take with her to pin on the flowers. "In deepest sympathy at your great loss." She gave Miss Clay some money, and the governess went off to find a taxi.

Later the Marquise took the children to the beach.

"Is your chill better, Maman?"

asked Céleste.

"Yes, chérie, now Maman can bathe again."

And she entered the warm yielding water with the children, and splashed with them.

Tomorrow Edouard would arrive, tomorrow Edouard would come in his car and drive them away, and the white dusty roads would lengthen the distance between her and the hotel. She would not see it any more, nor the headland, nor the town, and the holiday would be blotted out like something that had never been.

"When I die," thought the Marquise as she stared out across the sea, "I shall be punished. I don't fool myself. I am guilty of taking life. When I die, God will accuse me. Until then, I will be a good wife to Edouard, and a good mother to Céleste and Hélène. I will try to be a good woman from now. I will try and atone for what I have done by being kinder to everyone, to relations, friends, servants."

She slept well for the first time in three days.

Her husband arrived the next morning while she was still having her breakfast. She was so glad to see him that she sprang from her bed and flung her arms round his neck. The Marquis was touched at this reception.

"I believe my girl has missed me after all," he said.

"Missed you? But of course I've missed you. That's why I rang up. I wanted you to come so much."

"And you are quite determined to leave today after lunch?"

"Oh yes, yes . . . I couldn't bear to stay. Our packing is done, there are only the last things to put in the suitcases."

He sat on the balcony drinking coffee, laughing with the children, while she dressed and stripped the room of her personal possessions. The room that had been hers for a whole month became bare once more, and quite impersonal. In a fever of hurry she cleared the dressing table, mantelpiece, the table by her bed. It was finished with. The *femme de chambre* would come in presently with clean sheets and make all fresh for the next visitor. And she, the Marquise, would have gone.

"Listen, Edouard," she said, "why must we stay for déjeuner? Wouldn't it be more fun to lunch somewhere on the way? There is always something a little dreary in lunching at a hotel when one has already paid the bill. Tipping, everything, has been done. I cannot bear a sense of anticlimax."

"Just as you like," he said. She had given him such a welcome that he was prepared to gratify every whim. Poor little girl. She had been really lonely without him. He must make up to her for it.

The Marquise was making up her mouth in front of the mirror in the bathroom when the telephone rang.

"Answer it, will you?" she called to her husband. "It is probably the concierge about the luggage."

The Marquis did so, and in a few moments he shouted through to his wife.

"It's for you, dear. It's a Mademoiselle Paul who has called to see you, and asks if she may thank you for her flowers before you go."

The Marquise did not answer at once, and when his wife came into the bedroom it seemed to him that the lipstick had not enhanced her appearance. It made her look almost haggard, older. How very strange. She must have changed the colour. It was not becoming.

"Well," he asked, "what shall I say? You probably don't want to be bothered with her now, whoever she is. Would you like me to go down and get rid of her?"

The Marquise seemed uncertain, troubled. "No," she said, "no, I think I had better see her. The fact is, it's a very tragic thing. She and her brother kept a little shop in the town—I had some photographs done of myself and the children—and then a dreadful thing happened, the brother was drowned. I thought it only right to send flowers."

"How thoughtful of you," said her husband, "a very kind gesture. But do you need to bother now? Why, we are ready to go."

"Tell her that," said his wife, "tell her that we are leaving almost immediately."

The Marquis turned to the telephone again, and after a word or two put his hand over the receiver and whispered to his wife.

"She is very insistent," he said. "She says she has some prints belonging to you that she wants to give to you personally."

A feeling of panic came over the Marquise. Prints? What prints?

"But everything is paid for," she whispered back. "I don't know what she can mean."

The Marquis shrugged his shoulders.

"Well, what am I to say? She sounds as if she is crying."

The Marquise went back into the bathroom, dabbed more powder on her nose.

"Tell her to come up," she said, "but repeat that we are leaving in five minutes. Meanwhile, you go down, take the children to the car. Take Miss Clay with you. I will see the woman alone."

When he had gone she looked about the room. Nothing remained but her gloves, her handbag. One last effort, and then the closing door, the *ascenseur*, the farewell bow to the manager, and freedom.

There was a knock at the door. The Marquise waited by the entrance to the balcony, her hands clasped in front of her.

"*Entrez*," she said.

Mademoiselle Paul opened the door. Her face was blotched and ravaged from weeping; her old-fashioned mourning dress was long, nearly touching the ground. She hesitated, then lurched forward, her limp grotesque, as though each movement must be agony.

"Madame la Marquise . . ." she began, then her mouth worked, she began to cry.

"Please don't," said the Marquise gently. "I am so dreadfully sorry for what has happened."

Mademoiselle Paul took her

handkerchief and blew her nose.

"He was all I had in the world," she said. "He was so good to me. What am I to do now? How am I to live?"

"You have relatives?"

"They are poor folk, Madame la Marquise. I cannot expect them to support me. Nor can I keep the shop alone, without my brother. I haven't the strength. My health has always been my trouble."

The Marquise was fumbling in her bag. She took out a twenty-thousand-franc note.

"I know this is not much," she said, "but perhaps it will help just a little. I am afraid my husband has not many contacts in this part of the country, but I will ask him, perhaps he will be able to make some suggestions."

Mademoiselle Paul took the notes. It was strange. She did not thank the Marquise. "This will keep me until the end of the month," she said. "It will help to pay the funeral expenses."

She opened her bag. She took out three prints.

"I have more, similar to these, back in the shop," she said. "It seemed to me that perhaps, going away suddenly as you are doing, you had forgotten all about them. I found them amongst my poor brother's other prints and negatives in the cellar, where he used to develop them."

She handed the prints to the Marquise. The Marquise went cold when she saw them. Yes, she had forgotten. Or rather, she had not been aware of their existence. They were three views of her

taken in the bracken. Careless, abandoned, half sleeping, with her head against his coat for a pillow, she had heard the click-click of the camera, and it had added a sort of zest to the afternoon. Some he had shown her. But not these.

She took the photographs and put them in her bag.

"You say you have others?" she asked, her voice without expression.

"Yes, Madame la Marquise."

She forced herself to meet the woman's eyes. They were swollen still with weeping, but the glint was unmistakable.

"What do you want me to do?" asked the Marquise.

Mademoiselle Paul looked about her in the hotel bedroom. Tissue paper strewn on the floor, odds and ends thrown into the waste-paper basket, the tumbled, un-made bed.

"I have lost my brother," she said, "my supporter, my reason for being alive. Madame la Marquise has had an enjoyable holiday and now returns home. I take it that Madame la Marquise would not desire her husband or her family to see these prints?"

"You are right," said the Marquise, "I do not even wish to see them myself."

"In which case," said Mademoiselle Paul, "twenty thousand francs is really very little return for a holiday that Madame la Marquise so much enjoyed."

The Marquise looked in her bag again. She had two *mille* notes and a few hundred francs.

"This is all I have," she said;

"you are welcome to these as well."

Mademoiselle Paul blew her nose once more.

"I think it would be more satisfactory for both of us if we came to a more permanent arrangement," she said. "Now my poor brother has gone the future is very uncertain. I might not even wish to live in a neighbourhood that holds such sad memories. I cannot but ask myself how my brother met his death. The afternoon before he disappeared he went out to the headland and came back very distressed. I knew something had upset him, but I did not ask him what. Perhaps he had hoped to meet a friend, and the friend had not appeared. The next day he went again, and that night he did not return. The police were informed, and then three days later his body was found. I have said nothing of possible suicide to the police, but have accepted it, as they have done, as accidental. But my brother was a very sensitive soul, Madame la Marquise. Unhappy, he would have been capable of anything. If I make myself wretched thinking over these things, I might go to the police, I might suggest he did away with himself after an unhappy love affair. I might even give them leave to search through his effects for photographs."

In agony the Marquise heard her husband's footsteps outside the door.

"Are you coming, dearest?" he called, bursting it open and entering the room. "The luggage is all in, the children are clamouring to be off."

He said good morning to Mademoiselle Paul. She curtseyed.

"I will give you my address," said the Marquise, "both in Paris and in the country." She sought in her bag feverishly for cards. "I shall expect to hear from you in a few weeks' time."

"Possibly before that, Madame la Marquise," said Mademoiselle Paul. "If I leave here, and find myself in your neighbourhood, I would come and pay my humble respects to you and Miss, and the little children. I have friends not so very far away. I have friends in Paris too. I have always wanted to see Paris."

The Marquise turned with a terrible bright smile to her husband.

"I have told Mademoiselle Paul," she said, "that if there is anything I can do for her at any time she has only to let me know."

"Of course," said her husband. "I am so sorry to hear of your tragedy. The manager here has been telling me all about it."

Mademoiselle Paul curtseyed again, looking from him back to the Marquise.

"He was all I had in the world, Monsieur le Marquis," she said. "Madame la Marquise knows what he meant to me. It is good to know that I may write to her, and that she will write to me, and when that happens I shall not feel alone and isolated. Life can be very hard for someone who is alone in the world. May I wish you a pleasant journey, Madame la Marquise, and happy memories of your holidays, and above all no regrets?"

Once more Mademoiselle Paul curtseyed, then turned and limped from the room.

"Poor woman," said the Marquis, "and what an appearance. I understand from the manager that the brother was crippled too?"

"Yes . . ." She fastened her handbag. Took her gloves. Reached for her dark glasses.

"Curious thing, but it often runs in families," said the Marquis as they walked along the corridor. He paused and rang the bell for the *ascenseur*. "You have never met Richard du Boulay, have you, an old friend of mine? He was crippled, much as this unfortunate little photographer seems to have been, but for all that, a charming, perfectly normal girl fell in love with him, and they got married. A son was born, and he turned out to be a hopeless clubfoot like his father. You can't fight that sort of thing. It's a taint in the blood that passes on."

They stepped into the *ascenseur* and the doors closed upon them.

"Sure you won't change your mind and stay for lunch? You look pale. We've got a long drive before us, you know."

"I'd rather go."

They were waiting in the hall to see her off. The manager, the receptionist, the concierge, the maître d'hôtel.

"Come again, Madame la Marquise. There will always be a welcome for you here. It has been such a pleasure looking after you. The hotel will not be the same once you have gone."

"Good-bye . . . Good-bye . . ."

The Marquise climbed into the car beside her husband. They turned out of the hotel grounds on to the road. Behind her lay the headland, the hot sands, and the sea. Before her lay the long straight road to home and safety. Safety . . . ?

THE APPLE TREE

It was three months after she died that he first noticed the apple tree. He had known of its existence, of course, with the others, standing upon the lawn in front of the house, sloping upwards to the field beyond. Never before, though, had he been aware of this particular tree looking in any way different from its fellows, except that it was the third one on the left, a little apart from the rest and leaning more closely to the terrace.

It was a fine clear morning in early spring, and he was shaving by the open window. As he leant out to sniff the air, the lather on his face, the razor in his hand, his eye fell upon the apple tree. It was a trick of light, perhaps, something to do with the sun coming up over the woods, that happened to catch the tree at this particular moment; but the likeness was unmistakable.

He put his razor down on the window ledge and stared. The

COPYRIGHT, 1952, BY DAPHNE DU MAURIER, AND
PUBLISHED BY DOUBLEDAY & CO., INC., NEW YORK

tree was scraggy and of a depressing thinness, possessing none of the gnarled solidity of its companions. Its few branches, growing high up on the trunk like narrow shoulders on a tall body, spread themselves in martyred resignation, as though chilled by the fresh morning air. The roll of wire circling the tree, and reaching to about halfway up the trunk from the base, looked like a grey tweed skirt covering lean limbs; while the topmost branch, sticking up into the air above the ones below, yet sagging slightly, could have been a drooping head poked forward in an attitude of weariness.

How often he had seen Midge stand like this, dejected. No matter where it was, whether in the garden, or in the house, or even shopping in the town, she would take upon herself this same stooping posture, suggesting that life treated her hardly, that she had been singled out from her fellows to carry some impossible burden, but in spite of it would endure to the end without complaint. "Midge, you look worn out, for heaven's sake sit down and take a rest!" But the words would be received with the inevitable shrug of the shoulder, the inevitable sigh, "Someone has got to keep things going," and, straightening herself, she would embark upon the dreary routine of unnecessary tasks she forced herself to do, day in, day out, through the interminable changeless years.

He went on staring at the apple tree. That martyred bent position,

the stooping top, the weary branches, the few withered leaves that had not blown away with the wind and rain of the past winter and now shivered in the spring breeze like wispy hair; all of it protested soundlessly to the owner of the garden looking upon it, "I am like this because of you, because of your neglect."

He turned away from the window and went on shaving. It would not do to let his imagination run away with him and start building fancies in his mind just when he was settling at long last to freedom. He bathed and dressed and went down to breakfast. Eggs and bacon were waiting for him on the hot plate, and he carried the dish to the single place laid for him at the dining table. *The Times,* folded smooth and new, was ready for him to read. When Midge was alive he had handed it to her first, from long custom, and when she gave it back to him after breakfast, to take with him to the study, the pages were always in the wrong order and folded crookedly, so that part of the pleasure of reading it was spoilt. The news, too, would be stale to him after she had read the worst of it aloud, which was a morning habit she used to take upon herself, always adding some derogatory remark of her own about what she read. The birth of a daughter to mutual friends would bring a click of the tongue, a little jerk of the head. "Poor things, another girl," or if a son, "A boy can't be much fun to educate these days." He used to think it psychological, because they themselves were childless, that she should so grudge the entry of new life into the world; but as time passed it became thus with all bright or joyous things, as though there was some fundamental blight upon good cheer.

"It says here that more people went on holiday this year than ever before. Let's hope they enjoyed themselves, that's all." But no hope lay in her words, only disparagement. Then, having finished breakfast, she would push back her chair and sigh and say, "Oh well . . ." leaving the sentence unfinished; but the sigh, the shrug of the shoulders, the slope of her long, thin back as she stooped to clear the dishes from the serving table—thus sparing work for the daily maid—were all part of her long-term reproach, directed at him, that had marred their existence over a span of years.

Silent, punctilious, he would open the door for her to pass through to the kitchen quarters, and she would labour past him, stooping under the weight of the laden tray that there was no need for her to carry, and presently, through the half-open door, he would hear the swish of the running water from the pantry tap. He would return to his chair and sit down again, the crumpled *Times*, a smear of marmalade upon it, lying against the toast rack; and once again, with monotonous insistence, the question hammered at his mind, "What have I done?"

It was not as though she nagged. Nagging wives, like mothers-in-law, were chestnut jokes for music halls. He could not remember Midge ever losing her temper or quarrelling. It was just that the undercurrent of reproach, mingled with suffering nobly borne, spoilt the atmosphere of his home and drove him to a sense of furtiveness and guilt.

Perhaps it would be raining and he, seeking sanctuary within his study, electric fire aglow, his after-breakfast pipe filling the small room with smoke, would settle down before his desk in a pretence of writing letters, but in reality to hide, to feel the snug security of four safe walls that were his alone. Then the door would open and Midge, struggling into a raincoat, her wide-brimmed felt hat pulled low over her brow, would pause and wrinkle her nose in distaste.

"Phew! What a fug."

He said nothing, but moved slightly in his chair, covering with his arm the novel he had chosen from a shelf in idleness.

"Aren't you going into the town?" she asked him.

"I had not thought of doing so."

"Oh! Oh well, it doesn't matter." She turned away again towards the door.

"Why, is there anything you want done?"

"It's only the fish for lunch. They don't deliver on Wednesdays. Still, I can go myself if you are busy. I only thought . . ."

She was out of the room without finishing her sentence.

"It's all right, Midge," he called, "I'll get the car and go and fetch it presently. No sense in getting wet."

Thinking she had not heard, he went out into the hall. She was standing by the open front door, the mizzling rain driving in upon her. She had a long flat basket over her arm and was drawing on a pair of gardening gloves.

"I'm bound to get wet in any case," she said, "so it doesn't make much odds. Look at those flowers, they all need staking. I'll go for the fish when I've finished seeing to them."

Argument was useless. She had made up her mind. He shut the front door after her and sat down again in the study. Somehow the room no longer felt so snug, and a little later, raising his head to the window, he saw her hurry past, her raincoat not buttoned properly and flapping, little drips of water forming on the brim of her hat and the garden basket filled with limp Michaelmas daisies already dead. His conscience pricking him, he bent down and turned out one bar of the electric fire.

Or yet again it would be spring, it would be summer. Strolling out hatless into the garden, his hands in his pockets, with no other purpose in his mind but to feel the sun upon his back and stare out upon the woods and fields and the slow winding river, he would hear, from the bedrooms above, the high-pitched whine of the Hoover slow down suddenly, gasp, and die. Midge called down to him as he stood there on the terrace.

"Were you going to do anything?" she said.

He was not. It was the smell of spring, of early summer, that had driven him out into the garden. It was the delicious knowledge that, being retired now, no longer working in the City, time was a thing of no account, he could waste it as he pleased.

"No," he said, "not on such a lovely day. Why?"

"Oh, never mind," she answered, "it's only that the wretched drain under the kitchen window has gone wrong again. Completely plugged up and choked. No one ever sees to it, that's why. I'll have a go at it myself this afternoon."

Her face vanished from the window. Once more there was a gasp, a rising groan of sound, and the Hoover warmed to its task again. What foolishness that such an interruption could damp the brightness of the day. Not the demand, nor the task itself—clearing a drain was in its own way a schoolboy piece of folly, playing with mud—but that wan face of hers looking out upon the sunlit terrace, the hand that went up wearily to push back a strand of falling hair, and the inevitable sigh before she turned from the window, the unspoken "I wish I had the time to stand and do nothing in the sun. Oh well . . ."

He had ventured to ask once why so much cleaning of the house was necessary. Why there must be the incessant turning out of rooms. Why chairs must be lifted to stand upon other chairs, rugs rolled up and ornaments huddled together on a sheet of newspaper. And why, in particular, the sides of the upstairs corridor, on which no one ever trod, must be polished laboriously by hand, Midge and the daily woman taking it in turns to crawl upon their knees the whole endless length of it, like slaves of bygone days.

Midge had stared at him, not understanding.

"You'd be the first to complain," she said, "if the house was like a pigsty. You like your comforts."

So they lived in different worlds, their minds not meeting. Had it been always so? He did not remember. They had been married nearly twenty-five years and were two people who, from force of habit, lived under the same roof.

When he had been in business, it seemed different. He had not noticed it so much. He came home to eat, to sleep, and to go up by train again in the morning. But when he retired he became aware of her forcibly, and day by day his sense of her resentment, of her disapproval, grew stronger.

Finally, in that last year before she died, he felt himself engulfed in it, so that he was led into every sort of petty deception to get away from her, making a pretence of going up to London to have his hair cut, to see the dentist, to lunch with an old business friend; and in reality he would be sitting by his club window, anonymous, at peace.

It was mercifully swift, the illness that took her from him. Influenza, followed by pneumonia, and she was dead within a week. He hardly knew how it happened, except that as usual she was overtired and caught a cold, and would not stay in bed. One evening, coming home by the late train from London, having sneaked into a cinema during the afternoon, finding release amongst the crowd of warm friendly people enjoying themselves—for it was a bitter December day—he found her bent over the furnace in the cellar, poking and thrusting at the lumps of coke.

She looked up at him, white with fatigue, her face drawn.

"Why, Midge, what on earth are you doing?" he said.

"It's the furnace," she said, "we've had trouble with it all day, it won't stay alight. We shall have to get the men to see it tomorrow. I really cannot manage this sort of thing myself."

There was a streak of coal dust on her cheek. She let the stubby poker fall on the cellar floor. She began to cough, and as she did so winced with pain.

"You ought to be in bed," he said, "I never heard of such nonsense. What the dickens does it matter about the furnace?"

"I thought you would be home early," she said, "and then you might have known how to deal with it. It's been bitter all day, I can't think what you found to do with yourself in London."

She climbed the cellar stairs slowly, her back bent, and when she reached the top she stood shivering and half closed her eyes.

"If you don't mind terribly," she said, "I'll get your supper right away, to have it done with. I don't want anything myself."

"To hell with my supper," he said, "I can forage for myself. You go up to bed. I'll bring you a hot drink."

"I tell you, I don't want anything," she said. "I can fill my hot-water bottle myself. I only ask one thing of you. And that is to remember to turn out the lights everywhere, before you come up." She turned into the hall, her shoulders sagging.

"Surely a glass of hot milk?" he began uncertainly, starting to take off his overcoat; and as he did so the torn half of the ten-and-six-penny seat at the cinema fell from his pocket on to the floor. She saw it. She said nothing. She coughed again and began to drag herself upstairs.

The next morning her temperature was a hundred and three. The doctor came and said she had pneumonia. She asked if she might go to a private ward in the cottage hospital, because having a nurse in the house would make too much work. This was on the Tuesday morning. She went there right away, and they told him on the Friday evening that she was not likely to live through the night. He stood inside the room, after they told him, looking down at her in the high impersonal hospital bed, and his heart was wrung with pity, because surely they had given her too many pil-

lows, she was propped too high, there could be no rest for her that way. He had brought some flowers, but there seemed no purpose now in giving them to the nurse to arrange, because Midge was too ill to look at them. In a sort of delicacy he put them on a table beside the screen, when the nurse was bending down to her.

"Is there anything she needs?" he said. "I mean, I can easily . . ." He did not finish the sentence, he left it in the air, hoping the nurse would understand his intention, that he was ready to go off in the car, drive somewhere, fetch what was required.

The nurse shook her head. "We will telephone you," she said, "if there is any change."

What possible change could there be? he wondered as he found himself outside the hospital. The white pinched face upon the pillows would not alter now, it belonged to no one.

Midge died in the early hours of Saturday morning.

He was not a religious man, he had no profound belief in immortality, but when the funeral was over, and Midge was buried, it distressed him to think of her poor lonely body lying in that brand-new coffin with the brass handles: it seemed such a churlish thing to permit. Death should be different. It should be like bidding farewell to someone at a station before a long journey, but without the strain. There was something of indecency in this haste to bury underground the thing that but for ill-chance would be a living, breathing person. In his distress he fancied he could hear Midge saying with a sigh, "Oh well . . ." as they lowered the coffin into the open grave.

He hoped with fervour that after all there might be a future in some unseen Paradise and that poor Midge, unaware of what they were doing to her mortal remains, walked somewhere in green fields. But who with? he wondered. Her parents had died in India many years ago; she would not have much in common with them now if they met her at the gates of Heaven. He had a sudden picture of her waiting her turn in a queue, rather far back, as was always her fate in queues, with that large shopping bag of woven straw which she took everywhere, and on her face that patient martyred look. As she passed through the turnstile into Paradise she looked at him reproachfully.

These pictures, of the coffin and the queue, remained with him for about a week, fading a little day by day. Then he forgot her. Freedom was his, and the sunny empty house, the bright crisp winter. The routine he followed belonged to him alone. He never thought of Midge until the morning he looked out upon the apple tree.

Later that day he was taking a stroll round the garden, and he found himself drawn to the tree through curiosity. It had been stupid fancy after all. There was nothing singular about it. An apple tree like any other apple tree. He remembered then that it had always been a poorer tree than its fellows, was in fact more than half dead, and at one time there had been talk of chopping it down, but the talk came to nothing. Well, it would be something for him to do over the week end. Axing a tree was healthy exercise, and apple wood smelt good. It would be a treat to have it burning on the fire.

Unfortunately wet weather set in for nearly a week after that day, and he was unable to accomplish the task he had set himself. No sense in pottering out of doors this weather, and getting a chill into the bargain. He still noticed the tree from his bedroom window. It began to irritate him, humped there, straggling and thin, under the rain. The weather was not cold, and the rain that fell upon the garden was soft and gentle. None of the other trees wore this aspect of dejection. There was one young tree—only planted a few years back, he recalled quite well—growing to the right of the old one and standing straight and firm, the lithe young branches lifted to the sky, positively looking as if it enjoyed the rain. He peered through the window at it, and smiled. Now why the devil should he suddenly remember that incident, years back, during the war, with the girl who came to work on the land for a few months at the neighbouring farm? He did not suppose he had thought of her in months. Besides, there was nothing to it. At week ends he had helped them at the farm himself—war work of a sort

—and she was always there, cheerful and pretty and smiling; she had dark curling hair, crisp and boyish, and a skin like a very young apple.

He looked forward to seeing her, Saturdays and Sundays; it was an antidote to the inevitable news bulletins put on throughout the day by Midge, and to ceaseless war talk. He liked looking at the child—she was scarcely more than that, nineteen or so—in her slim breeches and gay shirts; and when she smiled it was as though she embraced the world.

He never knew how it happened, and it was such a little thing; but one afternoon he was in the shed doing something to the tractor, bending over the engine, and she was beside him, close to his shoulder, and they were laughing together; and he turned round, to take a bit of waste to clean a plug, and suddenly she was in his arms and he was kissing her. It was a happy thing, spontaneous and free, and the girl so warm and jolly, with her fresh young mouth. Then they went on with the work of the tractor, but united now, in a kind of intimacy that brought gaiety to them both, and peace as well. When it was time for the girl to go and feed the pigs he followed her from the shed, his hand on her shoulder, a careless gesture that meant nothing really, a half caress; and as they came out into the yard he saw Midge standing there, staring at them.

"I've got to go in to a Red Cross meeting," she said. "I can't get the car to start. I called you. You didn't seem to hear."

Her face was frozen. She was looking at the girl. At once guilt covered him. The girl said good evening cheerfully to Midge, and crossed the yard to the pigs.

He went with Midge to the car and managed to start it with the handle. Midge thanked him, her voice without expression. He found himself unable to meet her eyes. This, then, was adultery. This was sin. This was the second page in a Sunday newspaper— "Husband Intimate with Land Girl in Shed. Wife Witnesses Act." His hands were shaking when he got back to the house and he had to pour himself a drink. Nothing was ever said. Midge never mentioned the matter. Some craven instinct kept him from the farm the next week end, and then he heard that the girl's mother had been taken ill and she had been called back home.

He never saw her again. Why, he wondered, should he remember her suddenly, on such a day, watching the rain falling on the apple trees? He must certainly make a point of cutting down the old dead tree, if only for the sake of bringing more sunshine to the little sturdy one; it hadn't a fair chance, growing there so close to the other.

On Friday afternoon he went round to the vegetable garden to find Willis, the jobbing gardener, who came three days a week, to pay him his wages. He wanted, too, to look in the tool shed and see if the axe and saw were in

good condition. Willis kept everything neat and tidy there—this
was Midge's training—and the axe
and saw were hanging in their
accustomed place upon the wall.

He paid Willis his money, and
was turning away when the man
suddenly said to him, "Funny
thing, sir, isn't it, about the old
apple tree?"

The remark was so unexpected
that it came as a shock. He felt
himself change colour.

"Apple tree? What apple tree?"
he said.

"Why, the one at the far end,
near the terrace," answered Willis. "Been barren as long as I've
worked here, and that's some
years now. Never an apple from
her, nor as much as a sprig of
blossom. We were going to chop
her up that cold winter, if you remember, and we never did. Well,
she's taken on a new lease now.
Haven't you noticed?" The gardener watched him, smiling, a
knowing look in his eye.

What did the fellow mean? It
was not possible that he had been
struck also by that fantastic freak
resemblance—no, it was out of the
question, indecent, blasphemous;
besides, he had put it out of his
own mind now, he had not
thought of it again.

"I've noticed nothing," he said,
on the defensive.

Willis laughed. "Come round to
the terrace, sir," he said, "I'll show
you."

They went together to the sloping lawn, and when they came to
the apple tree Willis put his hand
up and pulled down a branch

within reach. It creaked a little as
he did so, as though stiff and unyielding, and Willis brushed away
some of the dry lichen and revealed the spiky twigs. "Look
there, sir," he said, "she's growing
buds. Look at them, feel them for
yourself. There's life here yet, and
plenty of it. Never known such a
thing before. See this branch too."
He released the first, and leant up
to reach another.

Willis was right. There were
buds in plenty, but so small and
brown that it seemed to him they
scarcely deserved the name; they
were more like blemishes upon
the twig, dusty, and dry. He put
his hands in his pockets. He felt a
queer distaste to touch them.

"I don't think they'll amount to
much," he said.

"I don't know, sir," said Willis,
"I've got hopes. She's stood the
winter, and if we get no more bad
frosts there's no knowing what
we'll see. It would be some joke to
watch the old tree blossom. She'll
bear fruit yet." He patted the
trunk with his open hand, in a
gesture at once familiar and affec-
tionate.

The owner of the apple tree
turned away. For some reason he
felt irritated with Willis. Anyone
would think the damned tree
lived. And now his plan to axe the
tree over the week end would
come to nothing.

"It's taking the light from the
young tree," he said. "Surely it
would be more to the point if we
did away with this one, and gave
the little one more room?"

He moved across to the young

tree and touched a limb. No lichen here. The branches smooth. Buds upon every twig, curling tight. He let go the branch and it sprang away from him, resilient.

"Do away with her, sir," said Willis, "while there's still life in her? Oh no, sir, I wouldn't do that. She's doing no harm to the young tree. I'd give the old tree one more chance. If she doesn't bear fruit, we'll have her down next winter."

"All right, Willis," he said, and walked swiftly away. Somehow he did not want to discuss the matter any more.

That night, when he went to bed, he opened the window wide as usual and drew back the curtains; he could not bear to wake up in the morning and find the room close. It was full moon, and the light shone down upon the terrace and the lawn above it, ghostly pale and still. No wind blew. A hush upon the place. He leant out, loving the silence. The moon shone full upon the little apple tree, the young one. There was a radiance about it in this light that gave it a fairy-tale quality. Small and lithe and slim, the young tree might have been a dancer, her arms upheld, poised ready on her toes for flight. Such a careless, happy grace about it. Brave young tree. Away to the left stood the other one, half of it in shadow still. Even the moon-light could not give it beauty. What in heaven's name was the matter with the thing that it had to stand there, humped and stoop-ing, instead of looking upwards to

the light? It marred the still quiet night, it spoilt the setting. He had been a fool to give way to Willis and agree to spare the tree. Those ridiculous buds would never blos-som, and even if they did . . .

His thoughts wandered, and for the second time that week he found himself remembering the land girl and her joyous smile. He wondered what had happened to her. Married, probably, with a young family. Made some chap happy, no doubt. Oh well . . . He smiled. Was he going to make use of that expression now? Poor Midge! Then he caught his breath and stood quite still, his hand upon the curtain. The apple tree, the one on the left, was no longer in shadow. The moon shone upon the withered branches, and they looked like skeleton's arms raised in supplication. Frozen arms, stiff and numb with pain. There was no wind, and the other trees were motionless; but there, in those topmost branches, something shivered and stirred, a breeze that came from nowhere and died away again. Suddenly a branch fell from the apple tree to the ground below. It was the near branch, with the small dark buds upon it, which he would not touch. No rustle, no breath of movement came from the other trees. He went on staring at the branch as it lay there on the grass, under the moon. It stretched across the shadow of the young tree close to it, pointing as though in accusation.

For the first time in his life that he could remember he drew the curtains over the window to shut out the light of the moon.

Willis was supposed to keep to the vegetable garden. He had never shown his face much round the front when Midge was alive. That was because Midge attended to the flowers. She even used to mow the grass, pushing the wretched machine up and down the slope, her back bent low over the handles.

It had been one of the tasks she set herself, like keeping the bedrooms swept and polished. Now Midge was no longer there to attend to the front garden and to tell him where he should work, Willis was always coming through to the front. The gardener liked the change. It made him feel responsible.

"I can't understand how that branch came to fall, sir," he said on the Monday.

"What branch?"

"Why, the branch on the apple tree. The one we were looking at before I left."

"It was rotten, I suppose. I told you the tree was dead."

"Nothing rotten about it, sir. Why, look at it. Broke clean off."

Once again the owner was obliged to follow his man up the slope above the terrace. Willis picked up the branch. The lichen upon it was wet, bedraggled-looking, like matted hair.

"You didn't come again to test the branch, over the week end, and loosen it in some fashion, did you, sir?" asked the gardener.

"I most certainly did not," replied the owner, irritated. "As a matter of fact, I heard the branch fall during the night. I was opening the bedroom window at the time."

"Funny. It was a still night too."

"These things often happen to old trees. Why you bother about this one I can't imagine. Anyone would think . . ."

He broke off; he did not know how to finish the sentence.

"Anyone would think that the tree was valuable," he said.

The gardener shook his head. "It's not the value," he said. "I don't reckon for a moment that this tree is worth any money at all. It's just that after all this time, when we thought her dead, she's alive and kicking, as you might say. Freak of nature, I call it. We'll hope no other branches fall before she blossoms."

Later, when the owner set off for his afternoon walk, he saw the man cutting away the grass below the tree and placing new wire around the base of the trunk. It was quite ridiculous. He did not pay the fellow a fat wage to tinker about with a half-dead tree. He ought to be in the kitchen garden, growing vegetables. It was too much effort, though, to argue with him.

He returned home about half-past five. Tea was a discarded meal since Midge had died, and he was looking forward to his armchair by the fire, his pipe, his whisky-and-soda, and silence.

The fire had not long been lit and the chimney was smoking. There was a queer, rather sickly smell about the living-room. He threw open the windows and went upstairs to change his heavy shoes. When he came down again the smoke still clung about the room and the smell was as strong as ever. Impossible to name it. Sweetish, strange. He called to the woman out in the kitchen.

"There's a funny smell in the house," he said. "What is it?"

The woman came out into the hall from the back.

"What sort of a smell, sir?" she said, on the defensive.

"It's in the living-room," he said. "The room was full of smoke just now. Have you been burning something?"

Her face cleared. "It must be the logs," she said. "Willis cut them up specially, sir, he said you would like them."

"What logs are those?"

"He said it was apple wood, sir, from a branch he had sawed up. Apple wood burns well, I've always heard. Some people fancy it very much. I don't notice any smell myself, but I've got a slight cold."

Together they looked at the fire. Willis had cut the logs small. The woman, thinking to please him, had piled several on top of one another, to make a good fire to last. There was no great blaze. The smoke that came from them was thin and poor. Greenish in colour. Was it possible she did not notice that sickly rancid smell?

"The logs are wet," he said abruptly. "Willis should have known better. Look at them. Quite useless on my fire."

The woman's face took on a set, rather sulky expression. "I'm very sorry," she said. "I didn't notice anything wrong with them when I came to light the fire. They seemed to start well. I've always understood apple wood was very good for burning, and Willis said the same. He told me to be sure and see that you had these on the fire this evening, he had made a special job of cutting them for you. I thought you knew about it and had given orders."

"Oh, all right," he answered abruptly. "I dare say they'll burn in time. It's not your fault."

He turned his back on her and poked at the fire, trying to separate the logs. While she remained in the house there was nothing he could do. To remove the damp smouldering logs and throw them somewhere round the back and then light the fire afresh with dry sticks would arouse comment. He would have to go through the kitchen to the back passage where the kindling wood was kept, and she would stare at him, and come forward and say, "Let me do it, sir. Has the fire gone out then?" No, he must wait until after supper, when she had cleared away and washed up and gone off for the night. Meanwhile, he would endure the smell of the apple wood as best he could.

He poured out his drink, lit his pipe, and stared at the fire. It gave out no heat at all, and with the central heating off in the house the living-room struck chill. Now and again a thin wisp of the greenish smoke puffed from the logs, and with it seemed to come that sweet, sickly smell, unlike any sort of wood smoke that he knew. That interfering fool of a gardener . . . Why saw up the logs? He must have known they were damp. Riddled with damp. He leant forward, staring more closely. Was it damp, though, that oozed there in a thin trickle from the pale logs? No, it was sap, unpleasant, slimy.

He seized the poker, and in a fit of irritation thrust it between the logs, trying to stir them to flame, to change that green smoke into a normal blaze. The effort was useless. The logs would not burn. And all the while the trickle of sap ran on to the grate and the sweet smell filled the room, turning his stomach. He took his glass and his book and went and turned on the electric fire in the study and sat in there instead.

It was idiotic. It reminded him of the old days, how he would make a pretence of writing letters, and go and sit in the study because of Midge in the living-room. She had a habit of yawning in the evenings, when her day's work was done; a habit of which she was quite unconscious. She would settle herself on the sofa with her knitting, the click-click of the needles going fast and furious; and suddenly they would start, those shattering yawns, rising from the depths of her, a prolonged "Ah . . . Ah . . . Hi-oh!" followed by the inevitable sigh. Then there would be silence except for the knitting needles, but as he sat behind his book, waiting, he knew that within a few minutes another yawn would come, another sigh.

A hopeless sort of anger used to stir within him, a longing to throw down his book and say, "Look, if you are so tired, wouldn't it be better if you went to bed?"

Instead, he controlled himself, and after a little while, when he could bear it no longer, he would get up and leave the living-room, and take refuge in the study. Now he was doing the same thing all over again because of the apple logs. Because of the damned sickly smell of the smouldering wood.

He went on sitting in his chair by the desk, waiting for supper. It was nearly nine o'clock before the daily woman had cleared up, turned down his bed, and gone for the night.

He returned to the living-room, which he had not entered since leaving it earlier in the evening. The fire was out. It had made some effort to burn, because the logs were thinner than they had been before, and had sunk low into the basket grate. The ash was meagre, yet the sickly smell clung to the dying embers. He went out into the kitchen and found an empty scuttle and brought it back into the living-room. Then he lifted the logs into it, and the ashes too. There must have been some damp residue in the scuttle, or the logs were still not dry, because as they settled there they seemed to turn darker than before, with a kind of scum upon them. He carried the scuttle down to the cellar, opened the door of the central heating furnace, and threw the lot inside.

He remembered then, too late, that the central heating had been given up now for two or three weeks, owing to the spring weather, and that unless he relit it now the logs would remain there, untouched, until the following winter. He found paper, matches, and a can of paraffin, and, setting the whole alight, closed the door of the furnace and listened to the roar of flames. That would settle it. He waited a moment and then went up the steps, back to the kitchen passage, to lay and relight the fire in the living-room. The business took time, he had to find kindling and coal, but with patience he got the new fire started, and finally settled himself down in his armchair before it.

He had been reading perhaps for twenty minutes before he became aware of the banging door. He put down his book and listened. Nothing at first. Then, yes, there it was again. A rattle, a slam of an unfastened door in the kitchen quarters. He got up and went along to shut it. It was the door at the top of the cellar stairs. He could have sworn he had fastened it. The catch must have worked loose in some way. He switched on the light at the head of the stairs, and bent to examine the catch. There seemed nothing wrong with it. He was about to close the door firmly when he noticed the smell again. The sweet, sickly smell of smouldering apple wood. It was creeping up from the cellar, finding its way to the passage above.

Suddenly, for no reason, he was seized with a kind of fear, a feeling of panic almost. What if the smell filled the whole house through the night, came up from the kitchen quarters to the floor above, and while he slept found its way into his bedroom, choking him, stifling him, so that he could not breathe? The thought was ridiculous, insane—and yet . . .

Once more he forced himself to descend the steps into the cellar. No sound came from the furnace, no roar of flames. Wisps of smoke, thin and green, oozed their way from the fastened furnace door; it was this that he had noticed from the passage above.

He went to the furnace and threw open the door. The paper had all burnt away, and the few shavings with them. But the logs, the apple logs, had not burnt at all. They lay there as they had done when he threw them in, one charred limb above another, black and huddled, like the bones of someone darkened and dead by fire. Nausea rose in him. He thrust his handkerchief into his mouth, choking. Then scarcely knowing what he did, he ran up the steps to find the empty scuttle, and with a shovel and tongs tried to pitch the logs back into it, scraping for them through the narrow door of the furnace. He was retching in his belly all the while. At last the scuttle was filled, and he carried it up the steps and through the kitchen to the back door.

He opened the door. Tonight there was no moon and it was

raining. Turning up the collar of his coat, he peered about him in the darkness, wondering where he should throw the logs. Too wet and dark to stagger all the way to the kitchen garden and chuck them on the rubbish heap, but in the field behind the garage the grass was thick and long and they might lie there hidden. He crunched his way over the gravel drive and, coming to the fence beside the field, threw his burden on to the concealing grass. There they could rot and perish, grow sodden with rain, and in the end become part of the mouldy earth; he did not care. The responsibility was his no longer. They were out of his house, and it did not matter what became of them.

He returned to the house, and this time made sure the cellar door was fast. The air was clear again, the smell had gone.

He went back to the living-room to warm himself before the fire, but his hands and feet, wet with the rain, and his stomach, still queasy from the pungent apple smoke, combined together to chill his whole person, and he sat there, shuddering.

He slept badly when he went to bed that night, and awoke in the morning feeling out of sorts. He had a headache, and an ill-tasting tongue. He stayed indoors. His liver was thoroughly upset. To relieve his feelings he spoke sharply to the daily woman.

"I've caught a bad chill," he said to her, "trying to get warm last night. So much for apple wood. The smell of it has affected my in-sides as well. You can tell Willis, when he comes tomorrow."

She looked at him in disbelief. "I'm sure I'm very sorry," she said. "I told my sister about the wood last night, when I got home, and that you had not fancied it. She said it was most unusual. Apple wood is considered quite a luxury to burn, and burns well, what's more."

"This lot didn't, that's all I know," he said to her, "and I never want to see any more of it. As for the smell . . . I can taste it still, it's completely turned me up."

Her mouth tightened. "I'm sorry," she said. And then, as she left the dining-room, her eye fell on the empty whisky bottle on the sideboard. She hesitated a moment, then put it on her tray.

"You've finished with this, sir?" she said.

Of course he had finished with it. It was obvious. The bottle was empty. He realised the implication, though. She wanted to suggest that the idea of apple-wood smoke upsetting him was all my eye, he had done himself too well. Damned impertinence.

"Yes," he said, "you can bring another in its place."

That would teach her to mind her own business.

He was quite sick for several days, queasy and giddy, and finally rang up the doctor to come and have a look at him. The story of the apple wood sounded nonsense, when he told it, and the doctor, after examining him, appeared unimpressed.

"Just a chill on the liver," he

said, "damp feet, and possibly something you've eaten combined. I hardly think wood smoke has much to do with it. You ought to take more exercise, if you're inclined to have a liver. Play golf. I don't know how I should keep fit without my week-end golf." He laughed, packing up his bag. "I'll make you up some medicine," he said, "and once this rain has cleared off, I should get out and into the air. It's mild enough, and all we want now is a bit of sunshine to bring everything on. Your garden is farther ahead than mine. Your fruit trees are ready to blossom." And then, before leaving the room, he added, "You mustn't forget, you had a bad shock a few months ago. It takes time to get over these things. You're still missing your wife, you know. Best thing is to get out and about and see people. Well, take care of yourself."

His patient dressed and went downstairs. The fellow meant well, of course, but his visit had been a waste of time. "You're still missing your wife, you know." How little the doctor understood. Poor Midge . . . At least he himself had the honesty to admit that he did not miss her at all, that now she was gone he could breathe, he was free, and that apart from the upset liver he had not felt so well for years.

During the few days he had spent in bed the daily woman had taken the opportunity to spring-clean the living-room. An unnecessary piece of work, but he supposed it was part of the legacy Midge had left behind her. The room looked scrubbed and straight and much too tidy. His own personal litter cleared, books and papers neatly stacked. It was an infernal nuisance, really, having anyone to do for him at all. It would not take much for him to sack her and fend for himself as best he could. Only the bother, the tie of cooking and washing up, prevented him. The ideal life, of course, was that led by a man out East, or in the South Seas, who took a native wife. No problem there. Silence, good service, perfect waiting, excellent cooking, no need for conversation; and then, if you wanted something more than that, there she was, young, warm, a companion for the dark hours. No criticism ever, the obedience of an animal to its master, and the lighthearted laughter of a child. Yes, they had wisdom all right, those fellows who broke away from convention. Good luck to them.

He strolled over to the window and looked out up the sloping lawn. The rain was stopping and tomorrow it would be fine; he would be able to get out, as the doctor had suggested. The man was right, too, about the fruit trees. The little one near the steps was in flower already, and a blackbird had perched himself on one of the branches, which swayed slightly under his weight.

The raindrops glistened and the opening buds were very curled and pink, but when the sun broke through tomorrow they would turn white and soft against the blue of the sky. He must find his old camera, and put a film in it, and photograph the little tree. The others would be in flower, too, during the week. As for the old one, there on the left, it looked as dead as ever; or else the so-called buds were so brown they did not show up from this distance. Perhaps the shedding of the branch had been its finish. And a good job too.

He turned away from the window and set about rearranging the room to his taste, spreading his things about. He liked pottering, opening drawers, taking things out and putting them back again. There was a red pencil in one of the side tables that must have slipped down behind a pile of books and been found during the turn-out. He sharpened it, gave it a sleek fine point. He found a new film in another drawer, and kept it out to put in his camera in the morning. There were a number of papers and old photographs in the drawer, heaped in a jumble, and snapshots too, dozens of them. Midge used to look after these things at one time and put them in albums; then during the war she must have lost interest, or had too many other things to do.

All this junk could really be cleared away. It would have made a fine fire the other night, and might have got even the apple logs to burn. There was little sense in keeping any of it. This appalling photo of Midge, for instance, taken heaven knows how many years ago, not long after their marriage, judging from the style of it.

Did she really wear her hair that way? That fluffy mop, much too thick and bushy for her face, which was long and narrow even then. The low neck, pointing to a V, and the dangling earrings, and the smile, too eager, making her mouth seem larger than it was. In the left-hand corner she had written, "To my own darling Buzz, from his loving Midge." He had completely forgotten his old nickname. It had been dropped years back, and he seemed to remember he had never cared for it: he had found it ridiculous and embarrassing and had chided her for using it in front of people.

He tore the photograph in half and threw it on the fire. He watched it curl up upon itself and burn, and the last to go was that vivid smile. My own darling Buzz . . . Suddenly he remembered the evening dress in the photograph. It was green, not her colour ever, turning her sallow; and she had bought it for some special occasion, some big dinner party with friends who were celebrating their wedding anniversary. The idea of the dinner had been to invite all those friends and neighbours who had been married roughly around the same time, which was the reason Midge and he had gone.

There was a lot of champagne, and one or two speeches, and much conviviality, laughter, and joking—some of the joking rather broad—and he remembered that when the evening was over, and they were climbing into the car to drive away, his host, with a gust of laughter, said, "Try paying your addresses in a top hat, old boy, they say it never fails!" He had been aware of Midge beside him, in that green evening frock, sitting very straight and still, and on her face that same smile which she had worn in the photograph just destroyed, eager yet uncertain, doubtful of the meaning of the words that her host, slightly intoxicated, had let fall upon the evening air, yet wishing to seem advanced, anxious to please, and more than either of these things desperately anxious to attract.

When he had put the car away in the garage and gone into the house he had found her waiting there in the living-room for no reason at all. Her coat was thrown off to show the evening dress, and the smile, rather uncertain, was on her face.

He yawned and, settling himself down in a chair, picked up a book. She waited a little while, then slowly took up her coat and went upstairs. It must have been shortly afterwards that she had that photograph taken. "My own darling Buzz, from his loving Midge." He threw a great handful of dry sticks on to the fire. They crackled and split and turned the photograph to ashes. No damp green logs tonight . . .

It was fine and warm the following day. The sun shone, and the birds sang. He had a sudden impulse to go to London. It was a day for sauntering along Bond Street, watching the passing crowds. A day for calling in at his tailor's, for having a haircut, for eating a dozen oysters at his favourite bar. The chill had left him. The pleasant hours stretched before him. He might even look in at a matinee.

The day passed without incident, peaceful, untiring, just as he had planned, making a change from day-to-day country routine. He drove home about seven o'clock, looking forward to his drink and to his dinner. It was so warm he did not need his overcoat, not even now, with the sun gone down. He waved a hand to the farmer, who happened to be passing the gate as he turned into the drive.

"Lovely day," he shouted.

The man nodded, smiled. "Can do with plenty of these from now on," he shouted back. Decent fellow. They had always been very matey since those war days, when he had driven the tractor.

He put away the car and had a drink, and while waiting for supper took a stroll around the garden. What a difference those hours of sunshine had made to everything. Several daffodils were out, narcissi too, and the green hedgerows fresh and sprouting. As for the apple trees, the buds had burst, and they were all of them in flower. He went to his little favourite and touched the blossom. It felt soft to his hand and he gently shook a bough. It was firm, well set, and would not fall. The scent was scarcely perceptible as yet, but in a day or two, with a little more sun, perhaps a shower or two, it would come from the open flower and softly fill the air,

never pungent, never strong, a
modest scent. A scent which you
would have to find for yourself, as
the bees did. Once found, it
stayed with you, it lingered always, alluring, comforting, and
sweet. He patted the little tree
and went down the steps into the
house.

Next morning, at breakfast,
there came a knock on the dining-
room door, and the daily woman
said that Willis was outside and
wanted to have a word with him.
He asked Willis to step in.

The gardener looked aggrieved.
Was it trouble, then?

"I'm sorry to bother you, sir," he
said, "but I had a few words with
Mr. Jackson this morning. He's
been complaining."

Jackson was the farmer who
owned the neighbouring fields.

"What's he complaining about?"

"Says I've been throwing wood
over the fence into his field, and
the young foal out there, with the
mare, tripped over it and went
lame. I've never thrown wood over
the fence in my life, sir. Quite
nasty he was, sir. Spoke of the
value of the foal, and it might
spoil his chances to sell it."

"I hope you told him, then, it
wasn't true."

"I did, sir. But the point is,
someone has been throwing wood
over the fence. He showed me the
very spot. Just behind the garage.
I went with Mr. Jackson, and
there they were. Logs had been
tipped there, sir. I thought it best
to come to you about it before I
spoke in the kitchen, otherwise
you know how it is, there would

be unpleasantness."

He felt the gardener's eye upon
him. No way out, of course. And
it was Willis' fault in the first
place.

"No need to say anything in the
kitchen, Willis," he said. "I threw
the logs there myself. You brought
them into the house, without my
asking you to do so, with the result that they put out my fire, filled
the room with smoke, and ruined
an evening. I chucked them over
the fence in a devil of a temper,
and if they have damaged Jackson's foal you can apologise for
me, and tell him I'll pay him compensation. All I ask is that you
don't bring any more logs like
those into the house again."

"No, sir. I understood they had
not been a success. I didn't think,
though, that you would go so far
as to throw them out."

"Well, I did. And there's an end
to it."

"Yes, sir." He made as if to go,
but before he left the dining-room
he paused and said, "I can't understand about the logs not burning, all the same. I took a small
piece back to the wife, and it
burnt lovely in our kitchen, bright
as anything."

"It did not burn here."

"Anyway, the old tree is making
up for one spoilt branch, sir. Have
you seen her this morning?"

"No."

"It's yesterday's sun that has
done it, sir, and the warm night.
Quite a treat she is, with all the
blossom. You should go out and
take a look at her directly."

Willis left the room, and he continued his breakfast

Presently he went out on to the terrace. At first he did not go up on to the lawn; he made a pretence of seeing to other things, of getting the heavy garden seat out, now that the weather was set fair. And then, fetching a pair of clippers, he did a bit of pruning to the few roses under the windows. Yet, finally, something drew him to the tree.

It was just as Willis said. Whether it was the sun, the warmth, the mild still night, he could not tell; but the small brown buds had unfolded themselves, had ripened into flower, and now spread themselves above his head into a fantastic cloud of white, moist blossom. It grew thickest at the top of the tree, the flowers so clustered together that they looked like wad upon wad of soggy cotton wool, and all of it, from the topmost branches to those nearer to the ground, had this same pallid colour of sickly white.

It did not resemble a tree at all; it might have been a flapping tent left out in the rain by campers who had gone away, or else a mop, a giant mop, whose streaky surface had been caught somehow by the sun, and so turned bleached. The blossom was too thick, too great a burden for the long thin trunk, and the moisture clinging to it made it heavier still. Already, as if the effort had been too much, the lower flowers, those nearest the ground, were turning brown; yet there had been no rain.

Well, there it was. Willis had been proved right. The tree had blossomed. But instead of blossoming to life, to beauty, it had somehow, deep in nature, gone awry and turned a freak. A freak which did not know its texture or its shape, but thought to please. Almost as though it said, self-conscious, with a smirk, "Look. All this is for you."

Suddenly he heard a step behind him. It was Willis.

"Fine sight, sir, isn't it?"

"Sorry, I don't admire it. The blossom is far too thick."

The gardener stared at him and said nothing. It struck him that Willis must think him very difficult, very hard, and possibly eccentric. He would go and discuss him in the kitchen with the daily woman.

He forced himself to smile at Willis.

"Look here," he said, "I don't mean to damp you. But all this blossom doesn't interest me. I prefer it small and light and colourful, like the little tree. But you take some of it back home to your wife. Cut as much of it as you like, I don't mind at all. I'd like you to have it."

He waved his arm generously. He wanted Willis to go now, and fetch a ladder, and carry the stuff away.

The man shook his head. He looked quite shocked.

"No, thank you, sir, I wouldn't dream of it. It would spoil the tree. I want to wait for the fruit. That's what I'm banking on, the fruit."

There was no more to be said. "All right, Willis. Don't bother, then."

He went back to the terrace. But when he sat down there in the sun, looking up the sloping lawn, he could not see the little tree at all, standing modest and demure above the steps, her soft flowers lifting to the sky. She was dwarfed and hidden by the freak, with its great cloud of sagging petals, already wilting, dingy white, on to the grass beneath. And whichever way he turned his chair, this way or that upon the terrace, it seemed to him that he could not escape the tree, that it stood there above him, reproachful, anxious, desirous of the admiration that he could not give.

That summer he took a longer holiday than he had done for many years—a bare ten days with his old mother in Norfolk, instead of the customary month that he used to spend with Midge, and the rest of August and the whole of September in Switzerland and Italy.

He took his car, and so was free to motor from place to place as the mood inclined. He cared little for sight-seeing or excursions, and was not much of a climber. What he liked most was to come upon a little town in the cool of the evening, pick out a small but comfortable hotel, and then stay there, if it pleased him, for two or three days at a time, doing nothing, mooching.

He liked sitting about in the sun all morning, at some café or restaurant, with a glass of wine in front of him, watching the people; so many gay young creatures seemed to travel nowadays. He enjoyed the chatter of conversation around him, as long as he did not have to join in; and now and again a smile would come his way, a word or two of greeting from some guest in the same hotel, but nothing to commit him, merely a sense of being in the swim, of being a man of leisure on his own, abroad.

The difficulty in the old days, on holiday anywhere with Midge, would be her habit of striking up acquaintance with people, some other couple who struck her as looking "nice" or, as she put it, "our sort." It would start with conversation over coffee, and then pass on to mutual planning of shared days, car drives in four-somes—he could not bear it, the holiday would be ruined.

Now, thank heaven, there was no need for this. He did what he liked, in his own time. There was no Midge to say, "Well, shall we be moving?" when he was still sitting contentedly over his wine, no Midge to plan a visit to some old church that did not interest him.

He put on weight during his holiday, and he did not mind. There was no one to suggest a good long walk to keep fit after the rich food, thus spoiling the pleasant somnolence that comes with coffee and dessert; no one to glance, surprised, at the sudden wearing of a jaunty shirt, a flamboyant tie.

Strolling through the little towns and villages, hatless, smoking a cigar, receiving smiles from the jolly young folk around him, he felt himself a dog. This was the life, no worries, no cares. No "We have to be back on the fifteenth because of that committee meeting at the hospital"; no "We can't possibly leave the house shut up for longer than a fortnight, something might happen." Instead, the bright lights of a little country fair, in a village whose name he did not even bother to find out; the tinkle of music, boys and girls laughing, and he himself, after a bottle of the local wine, bowing to a young thing with a gay handkerchief round her head and sweeping her off to dance under the hot tent. No matter if her steps did not harmonize with his—it was years since he had danced—this was the thing, this was it. He released her when the music stopped, and off she ran, giggling, back to her young friends, laughing at him no doubt. What of it? He had had his fun.

He left Italy when the weather turned, at the end of September, and was back home the first week in October. No problem to it. A telegram to the daily woman, with the probable date of arrival, and that was all. Even a brief holiday with Midge and the return meant complications. Written instructions about groceries, milk, and bread; airing of beds, lighting of fires, reminders about the delivery of the morning papers. The whole business turned into a chore.

He turned into the drive on a mellow October evening and there was smoke coming from the chimneys, the front door open, and his pleasant home awaiting him. No rushing through to the back regions to learn of possible plumbing disasters, breakages, water shortages, food difficulties; the daily woman knew better than to bother him with these. Merely, "Good evening, sir. I hope you had a good holiday. Supper at the usual time?" And then silence. He could have his drink, light his pipe, and relax; the small pile of letters did not matter. No feverish tearing of them open, and then the start of the telephoning, the hearing of those endless one-sided conversations between women friends. "Well? How are things? Really? My dear . . . And what did you say to that? . . . She did? . . . I can't possibly on Wednesday . . ."

He stretched himself contentedly, stiff after his drive, and gazed comfortably around the cheerful, empty living-room. He was hungry after his journey up from Dover, and the chop seemed rather meagre after foreign fare. But there it was, it wouldn't hurt him to return to plainer food. A sardine on toast followed the chop, and then he looked about him for dessert.

There was a plate of apples on the sideboard. He fetched them and put them down in front of him on the dining-room table.

Poor-looking things. Small and wizened, dullish brown in colour. He bit into one, but as soon as the taste of it was on his tongue he spat it out. The thing was rotten. He tried another. It was just the same. He looked more closely at the pile of apples. The skins were leathery and rough and hard; you would expect the insides to be sour. On the contrary, they were pulpy-soft, and the cores were yellow. Filthy-tasting things. A stray piece stuck to his tooth and he pulled it out. Stringy, beastly . . .

He rang the bell, and the woman came through from the kitchen.

"Have we any other dessert?" he said.

"I am afraid not, sir. I remembered how fond you were of apples, and Willis brought in these from the garden. He said they were especially good, and just ripe for eating."

"Well, he's quite wrong. They're uneatable."

"I'm very sorry, sir. I wouldn't have put them through had I known. There's a lot more outside too. Willis brought in a great basketful."

"All the same sort?"

"Yes, sir. The small brown ones. No other kind at all."

"Never mind, it can't be helped. I'll look for myself in the morning."

He got up from the table and went through to the living-room. He had a glass of port to take away the taste of the apples, but it seemed to make no difference, not even a biscuit with it. The pulpy rotten tang clung to his tongue and the roof of his mouth, and in the end he was obliged to go up to the bathroom and clean his teeth. The maddening thing was that he could have done with a good clean apple, after that rather indifferent supper: something with a smooth clear skin, the inside not too sweet, a little sharp in flavour. He knew the kind. Good biting texture. You had to pick them, of course, at just the right moment.

He dreamt that night he was back again in Italy, dancing under the tent in the little cobbled square. He woke with the tinkling music in his ear, but he could not recall the face of the peasant girl or remember the feel of her tripping against his feet. He tried to recapture the memory, lying awake, over his morning tea, but it eluded him.

He got up out of bed and went over to the window, to glance at the weather. Fine enough, with a slight nip in the air.

Then he saw the tree. The sight of it came as a shock, it was so unexpected. Now he realised at once where the apples had come from the night before. The tree was laden, bowed down, under her burden of fruit. They clustered, small and brown, on every branch, diminishing in size as they reached the top, so that those on the high boughs, not grown yet to full size, looked like nuts. They weighed heavy on the tree, and because of this it seemed bent and twisted out of shape, the lower branches nearly sweeping the ground; and on the grass, at the foot of the tree, were more and yet more apples, windfalls, the first-grown, pushed off by their clamouring brothers and sisters. The ground was covered with them, many split open and rotting where the wasps had been. Never in his life had he seen a tree so laden with fruit. It was a miracle that it had not fallen under the weight.

He went out before breakfast —curiosity was too great—and stood beside the tree, staring at it. There was no mistake about it, these were the same apples that had been put in the dining-room last night. Hardly bigger than tangerines, and many of them smaller than that, they grew so close together on the branches that to pick one you would be forced to pick a dozen.

There was something monstrous in the sight, something distasteful; yet it was pitiful, too, that the months had brought this agony upon the tree, for agony it was, there could be no other word for it. The tree was tortured by fruit, groaning under the weight of it, and the frightful part about it was that not one of the fruit was eatable. Every apple was rotten through and through. He trod them underfoot, the windfalls on the grass, there was no escaping them; and in a moment they were mush and slime, clinging about his heels—he had to clean the mess off with wisps of grass.

It would have been far better if the tree had died, stark and bare, before this ever happened. What use was it to him or anyone, this load of rotting fruit, littering up the place, fouling the ground? And the tree itself, humped, as it were, in pain and yet, he could almost swear, triumphant, gloating.

Just as in spring, when the mass of fluffy blossom, colourless and sodden, dragged the reluctant eye away from the other trees, so it did now. Impossible to avoid seeing the tree, with its burden of fruit. Every window in the front part of the house looked out upon it. And he knew how it would be. The fruit would cling there until it was picked, staying upon the branches through October and November, and it never would be picked, because nobody could eat it. He could see himself being bothered with the tree throughout the autumn. Whenever he came out on to the terrace there it would be, sagging and loathsome.

It was extraordinary, the dislike he had taken to the tree. It was a perpetual reminder of the fact that he . . . well, he was blessed if he knew what . . . a perpetual reminder of all the things he most detested, and always had, he could not put a name to them. He decided then and there that Willis should pick the fruit and take it away, sell it, get rid of it, anything, as long as he did not have to eat it, and as long as he was not forced to watch the tree drooping there, day after day, throughout the autumn.

He turned his back upon it and was relieved to see that none of the other trees had so degraded themselves to excess. They carried a fair crop, nothing out of the way, and as he might have known, the young tree, to the right of the old one, made a brave little show on its own, with a light load of medium-sized, rosy-looking apples, not too dark in colour, but freshly reddened where the sun had ripened them. He would pick one now, and take it in, to eat with breakfast. He made his choice, and the apple fell at the first touch into his hand. It looked so good that he bit into it with appetite. That was it, juicy, sweet-smelling, sharp, the dew upon it still. He did not look back at the old tree. He went indoors, hungry, to breakfast.

It took the gardener nearly a week to strip the tree, and it was plain he did it under protest.

"I don't care what you do with them," said his employer. "You can sell them and keep the money, or you can take them home and feed them to your pigs. I can't stand the sight of them, and that's all there is to it. Find a long ladder, and start on the job right away."

It seemed to him that Willis, from sheer obstinacy, spun out the time. He would watch the man from the windows act as though in slow motion. First the placing of the ladder. Then the laborious climb, and the descent to steady it again. After that the performance of plucking off the fruit, dropping them, one by one, into the basket. Day after day it was the same. Willis was always there

on the sloping lawn with his ladder under the tree, the branches creaking and groaning, and beneath him on the grass baskets, pails, basins, any receptacle that would hold the apples.

At last the job was finished. The ladder was removed, the baskets and pails also, and the tree was stripped bare. He looked out at it, the evening of that day, in satisfaction. No more rotting fruit to offend his eye. Every single apple gone.

Yet the tree, instead of seeming lighter from the loss of its burden, looked, if it were possible, more dejected than ever. The branches still sagged, and the leaves, withering now to the cold autumnal evening, folded upon themselves and shivered. "Is this my reward?" it seemed to say. "After all I've done for you?"

As the light faded, the shadow of the tree cast a blight upon the dank night. Winter would soon come. And the short, dull days.

He had never cared much for the fall of the year. In the old days, when he went up to London every day to the office, it had meant that early start by train on a nippy morning. And then, before three o'clock in the afternoon, the clerks were turning on the lights, and as often as not there would be fog in the air, murky and dismal, and a slow chugging journey home, daily breaders like himself sitting five abreast in a carriage, some of them with colds in their heads. Then the long evening followed, with Midge opposite him before the living-room fire, and he listening, or feigning to listen, to the account of her days and the things that had gone wrong.

If she had not shouldered any actual household disaster, she would pick upon some current event to cast a gloom. "I see fares are going up again. What about your season ticket?" or "This business in South Africa looks nasty, quite a long bit about it on the six o'clock news," or yet again, "Three more cases of polio over at the isolation hospital. I don't know, I'm sure, what the medical world thinks it's doing. . . ."

Now, at least, he was spared the role of listener, but the memory of those long evenings was with him still, and when the lights were lit and the curtains were drawn he would be reminded of the click-click of the needles, the aimless chatter, and the "Hi-oh" of the yawns. He began to drop in, sometimes before supper, sometimes afterwards, at the Green Man, the old public house a quarter of a mile away on the main road. Nobody bothered him there. He would sit in a corner, having said good evening to genial Mrs. Hill, the proprietress, and then, with a cigarette and a whisky-and-soda, watch the local inhabitants stroll in to have a pint, to throw a dart, to gossip.

In a sense it made a continuation of his summer holiday. It bore resemblance, admittedly slight, to the carefree atmosphere of the cafés and the restaurants; and there was a kind of warmth about the bright smoke-filled bar, crowded with workingmen who did not bother him, which he found pleasant, comforting. These visits cut into the length of the dark winter evenings, making them more tolerable.

A cold in the head, caught in mid-December, put a stop to this for more than a week. He was obliged to keep to the house. And it was odd, he thought to himself, how much he missed the Green Man, and how sick to death he became of sitting about in the living-room or in the study, with nothing to do but read or listen to the wireless. The cold and the boredom made him morose and irritable, and the enforced inactivity turned his liver sluggish. He needed exercise. Whatever the weather, he decided towards the end of yet another cold grim day, he would go out tomorrow. The sky had been heavy from mid-afternoon and threatened snow, but no matter, he could not stand the house for a further twenty-four hours without a break.

The final edge to his irritation came with the fruit tart at supper. He was in that final stage of a bad cold when the taste is not yet fully returned, appetite is poor, but there is a certain emptiness within that needs ministration of a particular kind. A bird might have done it. Half a partridge, roasted to perfection, followed by a cheese soufflé. As well ask for the moon. The daily woman, not gifted with imagination, produced plaice, of all fish the most tasteless, the most dry. When she had borne the remains of this away—he had left most of it upon his plate—she returned with a tart, and because hunger was far from being satisfied, he helped himself to it liberally.

One taste was enough. Choking, spluttering, he spat out the contents of his spoon upon the plate. He got up and rang the bell.

The woman appeared, a query on her face, at the unexpected summons.

"What the devil is this stuff?"

"Jam tart, sir."

"What sort of jam?"

"Apple jam, sir. Made from my own bottling."

He threw down his napkin on the table.

"I guessed as much. You've been using some of those apples that I complained to you about months ago. I told you and Willis quite distinctly that I would not have any of those apples in the house."

The woman's face became tight and drawn.

"You said, sir, not to cook the apples, or to bring them in for dessert. You said nothing about not making jam. I thought they would taste all right as jam. And I made some myself, to try. It was perfectly all right. So I made several bottles of jam from the apples Willis gave me. We always made jam here, Madam and myself."

"Well, I'm sorry for your trouble, but I can't eat it. Those apples disagreed with me in the autumn, and whether they are made into jam or whatever you like, they will do so again. Take the tart away, and don't let me see it, or the jam,

again. I'll have some coffee in the living-room."

He went out of the room, trembling. It was fantastic that such a small incident should make him feel so angry. God! What fools people were. She knew, Willis knew, that he disliked the apples, loathed the taste and the smell of them, but in their cheese-paring way they decided that it would save money if he was given home-made jam, jam made from the apples he particularly detested.

He swallowed down a stiff whisky and lit a cigarette.

In a moment or two she appeared with the coffee. She did not retire immediately on putting down the tray.

"Could I have a word with you, sir?"

"What is it?"

"I think it would be for the best if I gave in my notice."

Now this, on top of the other. What a day, what an evening.

"What reason? Because I can't eat apple tart?"

"It's not just that, sir. Somehow I feel things are very different from what they were. I have meant to speak several times."

"I don't give much trouble, do I?"

"No, sir. Only in the old days, when Madam was alive, I felt my work was appreciated. Now it's as though it didn't matter one way or the other. Nothing's ever said, and although I try to do my best I can't be sure. I think I'd be happier if I went where there was a lady again who took notice of what I did."

"You are the best judge of that, of course. I'm sorry if you haven't liked it here lately."

"You were away so much too, sir, this summer. When Madam was alive it was never for more than a fortnight. Everything seems so changed. I don't know where I am, or Willis either."

"So Willis is fed-up too?"

"That's not for me to say, of course. I know he was upset about the apples, but that's some time ago. Perhaps he'll be speaking to you himself."

"Perhaps he will. I had no idea I was causing so much concern to you both. All right, that's quite enough. Good night."

She went out of the room. He stared moodily about him. Good riddance to them both, if that was how they felt. Things weren't the same. Everything so changed. Damned nonsense. As for Willis being upset about the apples, what infernal impudence. Hadn't he a right to do what he liked with his own tree? To hell with his cold and with the weather. He couldn't stand sitting about in front of the fire thinking about Willis and the cook. He would go down to the Green Man and forget the whole thing.

He put on his overcoat and muffler and his old cap and walked briskly down the road, and in twenty minutes he was sitting in his usual corner in the Green Man, with Mrs. Hill pouring out his whisky and expressing her delight to see him back. One or two of the habitués smiled at him, asked after his health.

"Had a cold, sir? Same everywhere. Everyone's got one."

"That's right."

"Well, it's the time of year, isn't it?"

"Got to expect it. It's when it's on the chest it's nasty."

"No worse than being stuffed up, like, in the head."

"That's right. One's as bad as the other. Nothing to it."

Likeable fellows. Friendly. Not harping at one, not bothering.

"Another whisky, please."

"There you are, sir. Do you good. Keep out the cold."

Mrs. Hill beamed behind the bar. Large, comfortable old soul. Through a haze of smoke he heard the chatter, the deep laughter, the click of the darts, the jocular roar at a bull's eye.

". . . and if it comes on to snow, I don't know how we shall manage," Mrs. Hill was saying, "them being so late delivering the coal. If we had a load of logs it would help us out, but what do you think they're asking? Two pounds a load. I mean to say . . ."

He leant forward and his voice sounded far away, even to himself.

"I'll let you have some logs," he said.

Mrs. Hill turned round. She had not been talking to him.

"Excuse me?" she said.

"I'll let you have some logs," he repeated. "Got an old tree, up at home, needed sawing down for months. Do it for you tomorrow."

He nodded, smiling.

"Oh no, sir. I couldn't think of putting you to the trouble. The coal will turn up, never fear."

"No trouble at all. A pleasure. Like to do it for you; the exercise, you know, do me good. Putting on weight. You count on me."

He got down from his seat and reached rather carefully for his coat.

"It's apple wood," he said. "Do you mind apple wood?"

"Why, no," she answered, "any wood will do. But can you spare it, sir?"

He nodded mysteriously. It was a bargain, it was a secret.

"I'll bring it down to you in my trailer tomorrow night," he said.

"Careful, sir," she said, "mind the step . . ."

He walked home through the cold crisp night, smiling to himself. He did not remember undressing or getting into bed, but when he woke the next morning the first thought that came to his mind was the promise he had made about the tree.

It was not one of Willis' days, he realised with satisfaction. There would be no interfering with his plan. The sky was heavy and snow had fallen in the night. More to come. But as yet nothing to worry about, nothing to hamper him.

He went through to the kitchen garden, after breakfast, to the tool shed. He took down the saw, the wedges, and the axe. He might need all of them. He ran his thumb along the edges. They would do. As he shouldered his tools and walked back to the front garden he laughed to himself, thinking that he must resemble an execu-

tioner of old days setting forth to behead some wretched victim in the Tower.

He laid his tools down beneath the apple tree. It would be an act of mercy, really. Never had he seen anything so wretched, so utterly woebegone, as the apple tree. There couldn't be any life left in it. Not a leaf remained. Twisted, ugly, bent, it ruined the appearance of the lawn. Once it was out of the way, the whole setting of the garden would change.

A snowflake fell on to his hand, then another. He glanced down past the terrace to the dining-room window. He could see the woman laying his lunch. He went down the steps and into the house. "Look," he said, "if you like to leave my lunch ready in the oven, I think I'll fend for myself today. I may be busy, and I don't want to be pinned down for time. Also, it's going to snow. You had better go off early today and get home, in case it becomes really bad. I can manage perfectly well. And I prefer it."

Perhaps she thought his decision came through offence at her giving notice the night before. Whatever she thought, he did not mind. He wanted to be alone. He wanted no face peering from the window.

She went off at about twelve-thirty, and as soon as she had gone he went to the oven and got his lunch. He meant to get it over, so that he could give up the whole short afternoon to the felling of the tree.

No more snow had fallen, apart from a few flakes that did not lie.

He took off his coat, rolled up his sleeves, and seized the saw. With his left hand he ripped away the wire at the base of the tree. Then he placed the saw about a foot from the bottom and began to work it, backwards, forwards.

For the first dozen strokes all went smoothly. The saw bit into the wood, the teeth took hold. Then after a few moments the saw began to bind. He had been afraid of that.

He tried to work it free, but the opening that he had made was not yet large enough, and the tree gripped upon the saw and held it fast. He drove in the first wedge, with no result. He drove in the second, and the opening gaped a little wider, but still not wide enough to release the saw.

He pulled and tugged at the saw, to no avail. He began to lose his temper. He took up his axe and started hacking at the tree, pieces of the trunk flying outwards, scattering on the grass.

That was more like it. That was the answer.

Up and down went the heavy axe, splitting and tearing at the tree. Off came the peeling bark, the great white strips of underwood, raw and stringy. Hack at it, blast at it, gouge at the tough tissue, throw the axe away, claw at the rubbery flesh with the bare hands. Not far enough yet, go on, go on.

There goes the saw, and the wedge, released. Now up with the axe again. Down there, heavy, where the stringy threads cling so steadfast. Now she's groaning, now she's splitting, now she's rocking and swaying, hanging there upon one bleeding strip. Boot her, then. That's it, kick her, kick her again, one final blow, she's over, she's falling . . . she's down . . . damn her, blast her . . . she's down, splitting the air with sound, and all her branches spread about her on the ground.

He stood back, wiping the sweat from his forehead, from his chin. The wreckage surrounded him on either side, and below him, at his feet, gaped the torn, white, jagged stump of the axed tree.

It began snowing.

His first task, after felling the apple tree, was to hack off the branches and the smaller boughs, and so to grade the wood in stacks, which made it easier to drag away.

The small stuff, bundled and roped, would do for kindling; Mrs. Hill would no doubt be glad of that as well. He brought the car, with the trailer attached, to the garden gate, hard by the terrace. This chopping up of the branches was simple work; much of it could be done with a hook. The fatigue came with bending and tying the bundles, and then heaving them down past the terrace and through the gate up on to the trailer. The thicker branches he disposed of with the axe, then split them into three or four lengths, which he could also rope and drag, one by one, to the trailer.

He was fighting all the while

against time. The light, what there was of it, would be gone by half-past four, and the snow went on falling. The ground was already covered, and when he paused for a moment in his work, and wiped the sweat away from his face, the thin frozen flakes fell upon his lips and made their way, insidious and soft, down his collar to his neck and body. If he lifted his eyes to the sky he was blinded at once. The flakes came thicker, faster, swirling about his head, and it was as though the heaven had turned itself into a canopy of snow, ever descending, coming nearer, closer, stifling the earth. The snow fell upon the torn boughs and the hacked branches, hampering his work. If he rested but an instant to draw breath and renew his strength, it seemed to throw a protective cover, soft and white, over the pile of wood.

He could not wear gloves. If he did so he had no grip upon his hook or his axe, nor could he tie the rope and drag the branches. His fingers were numb with cold, soon they would be too stiff to bend. He had a pain now, under the heart, from the strain of dragging the stuff on to the trailer; and the work never seemed to lessen. Whenever he returned to the fallen tree the pile of wood would appear as high as ever, long boughs, short boughs, a heap of kindling there, nearly covered with the snow, which he had forgotten: all must be roped and fastened and carried or pulled away.

It was after half-past four, and almost dark, when he had disposed of all the branches, and nothing now remained but to drag the trunk, already hacked into three lengths, over the terrace to the waiting trailer.

He was very nearly at the point of exhaustion. Only his will to be rid of the tree kept him to the task. His breath came slowly, painfully, and all the while the snow fell into his mouth and into his eyes and he could barely see.

He took his rope and slid it under the cold slippery trunk, knotting it fiercely. How hard and unyielding was the naked wood, and the bark was rough, hurting his numb hands.

"That's the end of you," he muttered, "that's your finish."

Staggering to his feet, he bore the weight of the heavy trunk over his shoulder, and began to drag it slowly down over the slope to the terrace and to the garden gate. It followed him, bump . . . bump . . . down the steps of the terrace. Heavy and lifeless, the last bare limbs of the apple tree dragged in his wake through the wet snow.

It was over. His task was done. He stood panting, one hand upon the trailer. Now nothing more remained but to take the stuff down to the Green Man before the snow made the drive impossible. He had chains for the car, he had thought of that already.

He went into the house to change the clothes that were clinging to him and to have a drink. Never mind about his fire, never mind about drawing curtains, seeing what there might be for supper, all the chores the daily woman usually did—that would come later. He must have his drink and get the wood away.

His mind was numb and weary, like his hands and his whole body. For a moment he thought of leaving the job until the following day, flopping down into the arm-chair, and closing his eyes. No, it would not do. Tomorrow there would be more snow, tomorrow the drive would be two or three feet deep. He knew the signs. And there would be the trailer, stuck outside the garden gate, with the pile of wood inside it, frozen white. He must make the effort and do the job tonight.

He finished his drink, changed, and went out to start the car. It was still snowing, but now that darkness had fallen a colder, cleaner feeling had come into the air, and it was freezing. The dizzy, swirling flakes came more slowly now, with precision.

The engine started and he be-gan to drive downhill, the trailer in tow. He drove slowly, and very carefully, because of the heavy load. And it was an added strain, after the hard work of the after-noon, peering through the falling snow, wiping the windscreen. Never had the lights of the Green Man shone more cheerfully as he pulled up into the little yard.

He blinked as he stood within the doorway, smiling to himself. "Well, I've brought your wood," he said.

Mrs. Hill stared at him from behind the bar, one or two fel-lows turned and looked at him, and a hush fell upon the dart players.

"You never . . ." began Mrs. Hill, but he jerked his head at the door and laughed at her.

"Go and see," he said, "but don't ask me to unload it tonight."

He moved to his favourite cor-ner, chuckling to himself, and there they all were, exclaiming and talking and laughing by the door, and he was quite a hero, the fellows crowding round with questions, and Mrs. Hill pouring out his whisky and thanking him and laughing and shaking her head. "You'll drink on the house tonight," she said.

"Not a bit of it," he said, "this is my party. Rounds one and two to me. Come on, you chaps."

It was festive, warm, jolly, and good luck to them all, he kept say-ing, good luck to Mrs. Hill, and to himself, and to the whole world. When was Christmas? Next week, the week after? Well, here's to it, and a merry Christmas. Never mind the snow, never mind the weather. For the first time he was one of them, not isolated in his corner. For the first time he drank with them, he laughed with them, he even threw a dart with them, and there they all were in that warm, stuffy, smoke-filled bar, and he felt they liked him, he belonged, he was no longer "the gentleman" from the house up the road.

The hours passed, and some of them went home, and others took their place, and he was still sit-ting there, hazy, comfortable, the warmth and the smoke blending together. Nothing of what he heard or saw made very much sense, but somehow it did not seem to matter, for there was jolly, fat, easygoing Mrs. Hill to minister to his needs, her face glowing at him over the bar.

Another face swung into his view, that of one of the labourers from the farm, with whom, in the old war days, he had shared the driving of the tractor. He leant forward, touching the fellow on the shoulder.

"What happened to the little girl?" he said.

The man lowered his tankard. "Beg pardon, sir?" he said.

"You remember. The little land girl. She used to milk the cows, feed the pigs, up at the farm. Pretty girl, dark curly hair, always smiling."

Mrs. Hill turned round from serving another customer.

"Does the gentleman mean May, I wonder?" she asked.

"Yes, that's it, that was the name, young May," he said.

"Why, didn't you ever hear about it, sir?" said Mrs. Hill, filling up his glass. "We were all very much shocked at the time, everyone was talking of it, weren't they, Fred?"

"That's right, Mrs. Hill."

The man wiped his mouth with the back of his hand.

"Killed," he said, "thrown from the back of some chap's motor bike. Going to be married very shortly. About four years ago, now. Dreadful thing, eh? Nice kid too."

"We all sent a wreath, from just around," said Mrs. Hill. "Her mother wrote back, very touched, and sent a cutting from the local paper, didn't she, Fred? Quite a big funeral they had, ever so many floral tributes. Poor May. We were all fond of May."

"That's right," said Fred.

"And fancy you never hearing about it, sir!" said Mrs. Hill.

"No," he said, "no, nobody ever told me. I'm sorry about it. Very sorry."

He stared in front of him at his half-filled glass.

The conversation went on around him, but he was no longer part of the company. He was on his own again, silent, in his corner. Dead. That poor, pretty girl was dead. Thrown off a motor bike. Been dead for three or four years. Some careless, bloody fellow, taking a corner too fast, the girl behind him, clinging on to his belt, laughing probably in his ear, and then crash . . . finish. No more curling hair blowing about her face, no more laughter.

May, that was the name; he remembered clearly now. He could see her smiling over her shoulder when they called to her. "Coming," she sang out, and put a clattering pail down in the yard and went off, whistling, with big clumping boots. He had put his arm about her and kissed her for one brief, fleeting moment. May, the land girl, with the laughing eyes.

"Going, sir?" said Mrs. Hill.

"Yes. Yes, I think I'll be going now."

He stumbled to the entrance and opened the door. It had frozen hard during the past hour and it was no longer snowing. The heavy pall had gone from the sky and the stars shone.

"Want a hand with the car, sir?" said someone.

"No, thank you," he said, "I can manage."

He unhitched the trailer and let it fall. Some of the wood lurched forward heavily. That would do tomorrow. Tomorrow, if he felt like it, he would come down again and help to unload the wood. Not tonight. He had done enough. Now he was really tired; now he was spent.

It took him some time to start the car, and before he was halfway up the side road leading to his house he realised that he had made a mistake to bring it at all. The snow was heavy all about him, and the track he had made earlier in the evening was now covered. The car lurched and slithered, and suddenly the right wheel dipped and the whole body plunged sideways. He had got into a drift.

He climbed out and looked about him. The car was deep in the drift, impossible to move without two or three men to help him, and even then, if he went for assistance, what hope was there of trying to continue further, with the snow just as thick ahead? Better leave it. Try again in the morning, when he was fresh. No sense in hanging about now, spending half the night pushing and shoving at the car, all to no purpose. No harm would come to it here on the side road; nobody else would be coming this way tonight.

He started walking up the road towards his own drive. It was bad luck that he had got the car into the drift. In the centre of the road the going was not bad and the snow did not come above his ankles. He thrust his hands deep in the pockets of his overcoat and ploughed on up the hill, the countryside a great white waste on either side of him.

He remembered that he had sent the daily woman home at midday and that the house would strike cheerless and cold on his return. The fire would have gone out, and in all probability the furnace too. The windows, uncurtained, would stare bleakly down at him, letting in the night. Supper to get into the bargain. Well, it was his own fault. No one to blame but himself. This was the moment when there should be someone waiting, someone to come running through from the living-room to the hall, opening the front door, flooding the hall with light. "Are you all right, darling? I was getting anxious."

He paused for breath at the top of the hill and saw his home, shrouded by trees, at the end of the short drive. It looked dark and forbidding without a light in any window. There was more friendliness in the open, under the bright stars, standing on the crisp white snow, than in the sombre house.

He had left the side gate open,

and he went through that way to the terrace, shutting the gate behind him. What a hush had fallen upon the garden—there was no sound at all. It was as though some spirit had come and put a spell upon the place, leaving it white and still.

He walked softly over the snow towards the apple trees.

Now the young one stood alone, above the steps, dwarfed no longer; and with her branches spread, glistening white, she belonged to the spirit world, a world of fantasy and ghosts. He wanted to stand beside the little tree and touch the branches, to make certain she was still alive, that the snow had not harmed her, so that in the spring she would blossom once again.

She was almost within his reach when he stumbled and fell, his foot twisted underneath him, caught in some obstacle hidden by the snow. He tried to move his foot, but it was jammed, and he knew suddenly, by the sharpness of the pain biting his ankle, that what had trapped him was the jagged split stump of the old apple tree he had felled that afternoon.

He leant forward on his elbows, in an attempt to drag himself along the ground, but such was his position, in falling, that his leg was bent backwards, away from his foot, and every effort that he made only succeeded in imprisoning the foot still more firmly in the grip of the trunk. He felt for the ground under the snow, but wherever he felt his hands touched the small broken twigs from the apple tree that had scattered there when the tree fell and then were covered by the falling snow. He shouted for help, knowing in his heart no one could hear.

"Let me go," he shouted, "let me go," as though the thing that held him there in its mercy had the power to release him, and as he shouted tears of frustration and of fear ran down his face. He would have to lie there all night, held fast in the clutch of the old apple tree. There was no hope, no escape, until they came to find him in the morning, and supposing it was then too late, that when they came he was dead, lying stiffly in the frozen snow?

Once more he struggled to release his foot, swearing and sobbing as he did so. It was no use. He could not move. Exhausted, he laid his head upon his arms and wept. He sank deeper, ever deeper into the snow, and when a stray piece of brushwood, cold and wet, touched his lips, it was like a hand, hesitant and timid, feeling its way towards him in the darkness.

NO MOTIVE

Mary Farren went into the gun room one morning about half-past eleven and took her husband's revolver and loaded it, then shot herself. The butler heard the sound of the gun from the pantry. He knew Sir John was out and would not be back until lunch time, and no one had any business to be in the gun room at that hour of the day.

He went to investigate, and there he saw Lady Farren lying on the floor, in her own pool of blood. She was dead.

Aghast, he called the housekeeper, and after consultation they agreed he must first telephone the doctor, then the police, and lastly Sir John himself, who was at a board meeting.

The butler told the doctor and the police, who arrived within a few minutes of each other, what had happened; his message on the telephone had been the same to each.

"Her ladyship has had an accident. She is lying in the gun room with a gunshot wound in her head. I fear she is dead."

The message summoning Sir John home was worded differently. It just said, would Sir John please return home at once, as her ladyship had met with an accident.

The doctor, therefore, had to

COPYRIGHT, 1952, BY DAPHNE DU MAURIER, AND
PUBLISHED BY DOUBLEDAY & CO., INC., NEW YORK

break the news to the husband when he came.

It was a painful, wretched business. He had known John Farren for years; both he and Mary Farren were patients of his; a happier married couple did not exist, and they were both looking forward to the baby that was to be born to them in the spring. No difficulties were expected; Mary Farren was normal, healthy, and delighted at the prospect of being a mother.

The suicide, therefore, did not make sense. Because it was suicide. There was no doubt about it. Mary Farren had scribbled three words on a writing pad, which she had put on the desk in the gun room. The words were, "Forgive me, darling."

The gun had been put away unloaded, as always. Mary Farren had quite definitely taken out the gun, loaded it, then shot herself. The police corroborated with the doctor that the wound had been self-inflicted. Mercifully, she must have died at once.

Sir John Farren was a broken man. In that half hour, talking to the doctors and the police, he aged about twenty years. "But why did she do it?" he kept asking in agony. "We were so happy. We loved each other; the baby was on its way. There was no motive, I tell you, absolutely no motive."

Neither the police nor the doctor had an answer for him.

The usual formalities were gone through, the official business of an inquest, with the expected verdict, "Suicide, with no evidence to show the state of mind of the deceased."

Sir John Farren talked to the doctor again and again, but neither of them could come to any conclusion.

"Yes, it is possible," said the doctor, "women can become temporarily deranged at such a time, but you would have noticed signs of it, and so would I. You tell me she was perfectly normal the night before, perfectly normal at breakfast. As far as you know, there was nothing on her mind at all?"

"Absolutely nothing," said Sir John. "We breakfasted together, as we always did; we made plans for the afternoon; after I returned from the board meeting I was going to take her for a drive. She was cheerful and completely happy."

Lady Farren's cheerfulness was also corroborated by the servants.

The housemaid, who had gone to the bedroom at half-past ten, found her ladyship examining shawls that had come by the parcel post. Lady Farren, delighted with the work, had shown the shawls to her and had said she would keep both pink and blue, for boy or girl.

At eleven a travelling salesman had called from a firm that made garden furniture. Her ladyship had seen the man, chosen two large garden seats from his catalogue. The butler knew this, because Lady Farren had shown him the catalogue after the man had gone, when he had come to enquire if there were any orders for the chauffeur, and her ladyship had said, "No, I shan't be going out until after lunch, when Sir John will be taking me for a drive."

The butler had gone from the room, leaving her ladyship drinking a glass of milk. He was the last person to see Lady Farren alive.

"It comes to this," said Sir John, "between that time, which was approximately twenty minutes past eleven, and eleven-thirty, when she shot herself, Mary went off her head. It doesn't make sense. There *must* have been something wrong. I've got to find out what it was. I shall never rest until I do."

The doctor did his best to dissuade him, but it was no use. He himself was convinced that Mary Farren had succumbed to a sudden brain storm, owing to her condition, and, not knowing what she was doing, had made an end of herself.

Let it stay there. Let it rest. And Time only would help John Farren to forget.

John Farren did not try to forget. He went to a private-detective agency and interviewed a man called Black, recommended by the firm as trustworthy and discreet. Sir John told him the story. Black was a canny Scot. He didn't talk much, but he listened. It was his private opinion that the doctor's theory was right, and a sudden brain storm, owing to pregnancy, was the motive for the suicide. However, he was thorough at his job, and he went down to the country and interviewed the household. He asked many questions that the police had not asked, chatted with the doctor, checked up on the mail that had come for Lady Farren during the past few weeks, enquired about telephone calls and encounters with personal friends; and still there was no answer he could give to his client.

The one obvious solution that had come to his practised mind— that Lady Farren was expecting a child by a lover—did not work. Check and double check revealed no possibility of this. Husband and wife were devoted and had not been apart since their marriage three years previously. The servants all spoke of their great attachment for one another. There were no financial worries. Nor could the shrewd Black trace any infidelity on the part of Sir John. Servants, friends, neighbours, all spoke of his high integrity. Therefore, his wife had not shot herself through any fault of his that had come to light.

Temporarily Black was baffled. But not beaten. Once he took on a case, he liked to see it through to the end, and hardened though he was, he felt sorry to see Sir John's agony of mind.

"You know, sir," he said, "in cases of this sort we often have to go back in a person's life, rather further than the immediate past. I've been through every inch of your wife's desk, with your permission, and searched her papers and all correspondence, and I have found nothing to give the faintest clue to the trouble on her mind—if there was trouble.

"You have told me that you met Lady Farren—Miss Marsh, as she was then—while on a visit to Switzerland. She was living with an invalid aunt, Miss Vera Marsh, who had brought her up, her parents being dead."

"That is correct," said Sir John.

"They lived in Sierre and also in Lausanne, and you met both the Misses Marsh at the house of a mutual friend in Sierre. You struck up a friendship with the younger Miss Marsh, and by the end of your holiday you had fallen in love with her, and she with you, and you asked her to marry you."

"Yes."

"The elder Miss Marsh made no objection; in fact, she was delighted. It was arranged between you that you should make her an allowance to cover the expenses of a companion to take her niece's place, and within a couple of months or so you were married at Lausanne."

"Correct again."

"There was no question of the aunt coming to live with you in England?"

"No," said Sir John. "Mary wanted her to—she was much attached to her aunt—but the old lady refused. She had lived in Switzerland so long, she couldn't face the English climate or the English food. Incidentally, we have been out twice to see her since we married."

Black asked if Sir John had heard from his wife's aunt since the tragedy. Yes. He had written, of course, at once, and she had seen the news in the papers too. She was horrified. She could give no reason why Mary should have taken her life. A happy letter, written a week before, full of her happiness at the prospect of the future baby, had arrived in Sierre only a few days prior to the calamity. Miss Marsh had enclosed the letter for Sir John to read. And Sir John gave it to Black.

"I take it," said Black, "that the two ladies, when you met them first three years ago, were living very quietly?"

"They had this small villa, as I told you before," said Sir John, "and about twice a year they used to go down to Lausanne and take rooms in a pension. The old lady had some sort of trouble with her lungs, but not serious enough for a sanatorium or anything like that. Mary was a most devoted niece. It was one of the first things that drew me to her. Her gentleness and sweet temper to the old lady, who, like many elderly people, semi-invalid, was apt to be fractious at times."

"So your wife, the younger Miss Marsh, did not get about much? Not many friends her own age, and that sort of thing?"

"I suppose not. It did not seem to worry her. Hers was such a contented nature."

"And this had been her life since she was quite small?"

"Yes. Miss Marsh was Mary's only relative. She had adopted

her when Mary's parents died. Mary was a child at the time."

"And how old was your wife when you married her?"

"Thirty-one."

"No history of a previous engagement or a love affair?"

"Absolutely none. I used to tease Mary about it. She said she had never seen anyone to give her the slightest flutter. And her aunt agreed. I remember Miss Marsh saying to me when we became engaged, 'It's rare to find anyone so unspoilt as Mary. She's got the prettiest face and is quite unaware of it, and the sweetest nature and doesn't realise that either. You're a very lucky man.' And I was."

Sir John sat staring at Black with such abject misery in his eyes that the tough Scot hardly liked to cross-question him further.

"So it really was a love match on both sides?" he said. "You are quite certain there was no pull in your title and position? I mean, the aunt might have told her niece that here was a chance she mustn't miss, another man like you might not come along. After all, ladies do think of these things."

Sir John shook his head.

"Miss Marsh might have had an eye to the main chance, I don't know," he said, "but certainly Mary had not.

"Right from the beginning it was I who sought out her, not the other way round. If Mary had been looking about for a husband, she would have shown signs of it when we first met. And you know

what cats women can be. The friend at whose chalet I originally met the Marshes would have warned me that here was a girl, past thirty, in search of a husband. She said no such thing. She said, 'I want you to meet a perfect darling of a girl whom we all adore and feel rather sorry for because she leads such a lonely life.'"

"Yet she didn't appear lonely to you?"

"Not at all. She seemed perfectly content."

Black handed back Miss Marsh's letter to Sir John.

"You still want me to go on with this enquiry?" he said. "You don't think it would be simpler to decide, once and for all, that your doctor was right about Lady Farren, and she had some sort of a blackout which affected her mind and made her take her life?"

"No," said Sir John, "I tell you, somewhere there is a clue to this tragedy, and I shan't give up until I've found it. Or rather you find it for me. That's why I'm employing you."

Black rose from his chair.

"Very well," he said, "if that's the way you feel about it, I'll go right ahead with the case."

"What are you going to do?" asked Sir John.

"I shall fly to Switzerland to-morrow."

Black handed in his card at the Chalet Bon Repos at Sierre and was shown into a small salon that gave on to a balcony with a fine view across the Rhone Valley.

A woman, Miss Marsh's companion he supposed, led him through the salon on to the balcony. Black had time to notice that the room was furnished neatly, with good taste, but nothing out of the way, very much the room of an elderly English spinster living abroad who did not fling her money around.

There was a large picture of Lady Farren on the mantelpiece, taken recently, a duplicate of the one he had seen in Sir John's study. And another on a writing bureau of Lady Farren aged about twenty, he judged. A pretty, shy-looking girl, her hair worn rather longer than in the more recent portrait.

Black went on to the balcony and introduced himself to the elderly lady seated there in a wheeled chair as a friend of Sir John Farren's.

Miss Marsh had white hair, blue eyes, and a firm mouth. From the way she spoke to her companion, who immediately left them together, Black decided she was hard on those who served her. She seemed, however, genuinely pleased to see Black, and at once asked after Sir John with much concern and wanted to know if any light at all had been thrown on the tragedy.

"I'm sorry to say, none," answered Black. "In fact, I am here to ask you what you know about it. You knew Lady Farren better than any of us, even her husband. Sir John thinks you may have some ideas on the subject."

Miss Marsh looked surprised.

"But I wrote and told Sir John I was horrified and completely baffled," she said. "I enclosed Mary's last letter. Did he tell you?"

"Yes," said Black, "I saw the letter. And you have others?"

"I kept all her letters," said Miss Marsh. "She wrote me regularly, every week, after she married. If Sir John wants me to send him the letters I shall be pleased to do so. There is not one letter that isn't full of her affection for him, and her pride and delight in her new home. It was her one regret that I wouldn't stir myself to go and visit her. But you see, I am such an invalid."

"You look hearty enough," thought Black, "but perhaps you just didn't want to go."

"I gather you and your niece were much attached?" he said.

"I was deeply fond of Mary, and I like to think she was equally fond of me," was the swift reply. "Heaven knows I can be cantankerous at times, but Mary never seemed to mind. She was the sweetest-natured girl."

"You were sorry to lose her?"

"Of course I was sorry. I missed her terribly, and still do. But naturally her happiness came first."

"Sir John told me he made you an allowance to cover the cost of your present companion."

"Yes. It was generous of him. Will it continue, do you know?"

The inflection in her voice was sharp. Black decided that his original idea of Miss Marsh as someone who did not wholly disregard money was probably sound.

"Sir John didn't say. But I feel sure, if it was otherwise, you would have heard from him or from his lawyers," said Black.

Black looked at Miss Marsh's hands. They tapped the sides of the wheeled chair in a little nervous gesture.

"There was nothing in your niece's past that would account for her suicide?" he said.

She looked startled. "What on earth do you mean?"

"No previous engagement, or love affair gone wrong?"

"Good heavens, no."

Curious. She seemed relieved at the wording of his question.

"Sir John was Mary's only love. She led rather a solitary life with me, you know. Not many young people in the district. Even in Lausanne she never seemed to seek out people nearer her own age. It was not that she was particularly shy or reserved. Just self-contained."

"What about school friends?"

"I taught her lessons myself when she was small. She had a few terms in Lausanne when she was older, but as a day girl; we lived in a pension close by. I seem to remember one or two girls coming in for tea. But no especial friend."

"Have you any photographs of her at that age?"

"Yes. Several. I've got them all in an album somewhere. Would you care to see them?"

"I think I should. Sir John showed me several photographs, but I don't think he had any dating before their marriage."

Miss Marsh pointed to the bureau in the salon behind and told him to open the second drawer and bring back an album. He did so, and putting on spectacles, she opened the album, and he drew his seat beside her.

They went through the album at random. There were many snapshots, none of any particular interest. Lady Farren alone. Miss Marsh alone. Lady Farren and Miss Marsh in groups with other people. Snaps of the chalet. Snaps of Lausanne. Black turned the pages. No clue here.

"Is that the lot?" he said.

"I'm afraid it is," said Miss Marsh. "She was such a pretty girl, wasn't she? Those warm brown eyes. It is the most dreadful thing . . . Poor Sir John."

"You haven't any snaps of her when she was a child, I notice. These seem to start when she was around fifteen."

There was a pause, and then Miss Marsh replied, "No . . . no, I don't think I had a camera in those days."

Black had a well-trained ear. It was an easy matter for him to detect a falsehood. Miss Marsh was lying about something. About what?

"What a pity," he said. "I always think it's interesting to trace the child in the adult face. I'm a married man myself. My wife and I wouldn't be without the first albums of our youngster for the world."

"Yes, it was stupid of me, wasn't

it?" said Miss Marsh.

She put the album down in front of her on the table.

"I expect you have the ordinary studio portraits?" said Black.

"No," said Miss Marsh, "or if I once had, I must have lost them. In the move, you know. We didn't come here until Mary was fifteen. We were in Lausanne before that."

"And you adopted Mary when she was five, I think Sir John said?"

"Yes. She would have been about five."

Again the momentary hesitation, the inflection in her voice.

"Have you any photographs of Lady Farren's parents?"

"No."

"Yet her father was your only brother, I understand?"

"My only brother, yes."

"What decided you to adopt Lady Farren as a child?"

"The mother was dead, and my brother did not know how to take care of her. She was a delicate child. We both of us felt it was the best solution."

"Of course your brother made you an allowance for the child's upkeep and education?"

"Naturally. I couldn't have managed otherwise." Then Miss Marsh made a mistake. But for this one mistake, Black might have let the whole thing go.

"You ask the most extraordinarily remote questions, Mr. Black," she said with a hard little laugh. "I don't see that the allowance paid to me by Mary's father can be of the slightest interest to

you. What you want to know is why poor Mary killed herself, and so does her husband, and so do I."

"Anything even remotely connected with Lady Farren's past life is of interest to me," said Black. "You see, Sir John has employed me for that very purpose. Perhaps it is time that I explained to you I am not a personal friend of his. I am a private detective."

Miss Marsh turned grey. Her composure went. She became suddenly a very frightened old woman.

"What have you come to find out?" she said.

"Everything," said Black.

Now it was a favourite theory of the Scot's, which he often expounded to the director of the agency for whom he worked, that there are very few people in this world who haven't got something to hide. Time and time again he had seen men and women in the witness box, under cross-examination, and one and all were afraid; not of the questions put to them, which they must answer, and which might shed light on the particular case then under trial; but that in answering the questions, they would, by some mishap, by some slip of the tongue, reveal some personal secret pertaining to themselves which would discredit them.

Black was certain that Miss Marsh found herself in this position now. She might know nothing of Mary Farren's suicide or of its cause. But Miss Marsh herself was guilty of something that she had long sought to hide.

"If Sir John has found out about the allowance and thinks I have been defrauding Mary all these years, he might have had the decency to tell me himself, and not employ a detective," she said.

"Oh, ho, here we go," thought Black. "Give the old lady enough rope and she'll hang herself."

"Sir John did not mention the word fraud," he replied to Miss Marsh; "he merely thought the circumstances were rather strange."

Black was taking a chance, but he felt the result might be worth it.

"Of course they were strange," said Miss Marsh. "I tried to act for the best, and I believed I did. I can swear to you, Mr. Black, that I used very little money on myself, and that the most part of it went for Mary's upkeep, according to the agreement with the child's father. When Mary married, and as it happened married well, I did not think there was any harm in keeping the capital for myself. Sir John was rich, and Mary would not miss it."

"I take it," said Black, "that Lady Farren knew nothing of what was going on financially?"

"Nothing," said Miss Marsh. "She was never interested in money matters, and she believed herself entirely dependent on me. You don't think Sir John is going to prosecute me, Mr. Black? If he won a case against me, which he undoubtedly would, I should be destitute."

Black stroked his chin and pretended to consider.

"I don't think Sir John intends anything of the sort, Miss Marsh," he said. "But he would like to know the truth of what happened."

Miss Marsh sank back in her wheeled chair. No longer stiff and upright, she looked a tired old lady.

"Now that Mary is dead, it can't hurt her, the truth coming out," she said. "The fact is, Mr. Black, she wasn't my niece at all. I was paid a large sum of money to look after her. The money should have gone to her on her majority, but I kept it myself. Mary's father, with whom I signed the agreement, had died in the meantime. Living here in Switzerland, no one knew anything about the matter. It was so simple to keep it secret. I intended no harm."

It was always the way, thought Black. Temptation came to a man or a woman, and they gave way to it. They never "intended" harm.

"I see," he said. "Well, Miss Marsh, I don't want to go into the details of what you did or how you spent the money intended for Lady Farren. What does interest me is this. If she wasn't your niece, who was she?"

"She was the only daughter of a Mr. Henry Warner. That is all I ever knew. He never told me his address, or where he lived. All I knew was the address of his bankers, and the branch in London; four cheques were paid to me from that address. After I took Mary in my care, Mr. Warner went to Canada and died there five years later.

"The bank informed me of this, and as I never heard from them again, I believed myself safe to do—what I did—with her money."

Black noted the name Henry Warner, and Miss Marsh gave him the address of the bank.

"Mr. Warner was not a personal friend of yours?" he asked.

"Oh no. I only met him twice. The first time was when I answered his advertisement to a box number for someone to take charge, indefinitely, of a delicate girl. I was very poor at the time and had just lost a post as governess to an English family returning to England.

"I did not want to take a position in a school, and this advertisement came as a godsend, especially as the sum to be paid for the child's upkeep, which the father intended to accumulate, was so generous. I knew I should be able to live as I had, frankly, never lived before. You can hardly blame me."

Something of her former confidence was returning. She looked sharply at Black.

"I am not blaming you," he said. "Tell me more about Henry Warner."

"There is little to tell," she said. "He asked very few questions about myself or my background. The only point he made clear was that he wanted Mary to remain with me for good; he had no intention of having her back with him again, or corresponding with her. He planned to go to Canada, he told me, and cut himself off

from all former connections. I was entirely free to bring up his daughter as I thought fit. In other words, he washed his hands of her."

"A callous sort of customer?" suggested Black.

"Not exactly callous," replied Miss Marsh. "He looked anxious and careworn, as though the responsibility of looking after the child had been too much for him. His wife apparently was dead. Then I enquired in what way his daughter was delicate, because I knew little of nursing and did not particularly relish an ailing child.

"He explained to me that she was not physically delicate, but that she had witnessed a terrible train accident a few months previously, and the shock of this had caused her to lose her memory.

"She was perfectly normal otherwise, perfectly sane. But she remembered nothing previous to the shock. She did not even know he was her father. This was the reason, he told me, why he wanted her to begin a new life in another country."

Black jotted down some notes. The case at last was beginning to show possibilities.

"So you were willing to take the risk of having this child—suffering from mental shock—on your hands for life?" he asked.

He had not intended his question to be cynical, but Miss Marsh saw a sting in it. She flushed.

"I am used to teaching and used to children," she said; "also, independence was dear to me. I accepted Mr. Warner's offer, on condition I took to the child and the child took to me. At our second meeting he brought Mary with him. It was impossible not to feel an affection for her at once. That pretty little face, those large eyes, and the soft, gentle manner. She seemed quite normal, but young for her age. I chatted with her and asked her if she would like to come and stay with me, and she said she would; she put her hand in mine in the most confiding way. I told Mr. Warner 'Yes,' and the bargain was struck. He left Mary with me that evening, and we neither of us ever saw him again. It was easy enough to tell the child she was my niece, as she remembered nothing of her past; she accepted anything I cared to tell her about herself as gospel truth. It was all too easy."

"And from that day she did not once recover her memory, Miss Marsh?"

"Never. Life began for her when her father handed her over to me at that hotel in Lausanne, and it really began for me too. I could not have loved her better had she been in truth my niece."

Black glanced through his notes and put them in his pocket.

"So beyond the fact that you knew she was the daughter of a Mr. Henry Warner, you were completely ignorant as to her background?" he asked.

"Completely," said Miss Marsh. "She was merely a little girl of five years old who had lost her memory?"

"Fifteen," corrected Miss Marsh.

"How do you mean, fifteen?" said Black.

Miss Marsh flushed again.

"I forgot," she said. "I misled you earlier in the afternoon. I always told Mary, and everybody else, that I had adopted my niece when she was five. It made it so much easier for me, and easier for Mary too, because she remembered nothing of her life previous to the time she came to live with me. She was, in point of fact, fifteen. You will realise now why I have no snapshots or photographs of Mary as a child."

"Indeed, yes," said Black. "And I must thank you, Miss Marsh, for being so helpful. I don't think Sir John is likely to raise any questions about the money, and for the present, at any rate, I shall keep the whole story of what you have told me as entirely confidential. What I now have to find out is where Lady Farren—Mary Warner—was living for the first fifteen years of her life, and what that life was. It may have some bearing on the suicide."

Miss Marsh rang for her companion to show Black out. She had not quite recovered her equanimity.

"There is only one thing that has always puzzled me," she said. "I feel her father, Henry Warner, did not speak the truth. Mary showed no fear of trains at any time, and though I made several enquiries of many people, I could learn of no severe train accident that had happened in England, or anywhere else for that matter, during the months before Mary came to me."

Black returned to London, but he did not get in touch with Sir John Farren, because he thought it best to wait until he had more definite news to communicate.

It seemed to him unnecessary to reveal the truth about Miss Marsh and the adoption. It would only unsettle Sir John further, and it was hardly likely that this fact had suddenly come to light and driven his wife to suicide.

The more intriguing possibility was that Lady Farren had received a shock which, in the timing of a moment, had pierced the veil which had shrouded her memory for nineteen years.

It was Black's business to discover the nature of that shock. The first thing he did in London was to go to the branch of the bank where Henry Warner had kept an account. He saw the manager and explained his mission.

It appeared that Henry Warner had indeed gone to Canada, had married again when he was out there, and had subsequently died. The widow had written, closing the account in England. The manager did not know whether Henry Warner had left a second family in Canada, nor did he know the address of the widow. Henry Warner's first wife had died many years previously. Yes, the manager knew about the daughter of the first marriage. She had been adopted by a Miss Marsh in Switzerland. Cheques had been paid to Miss Marsh, and they ceased when Henry Warner married a second time. The only positive information that the bank manager could give Black which might be helpful was Henry Warner's old address. And the piece of news, which Henry Warner had certainly not told Miss Marsh, that his profession was the Church, and that at the time Miss Marsh had adopted his daughter he was vicar of All Saints, in the parish of Long Common, Hampshire.

Black travelled down to Hampshire with a pleasurable feeling of anticipation. He always began to enjoy himself when the clues began to unravel. It reminded him of boyhood days of hide-and-seek. It was his interest in the unexpected that had called him to be a private detective in the first place, and he had never regretted his call.

He believed in keeping an open mind about his case, but it was difficult not to see the Reverend Henry Warner as the villain of this piece. The sudden handing over of a mentally sick daughter to a perfect stranger abroad, and then cutting himself loose from her and going to Canada seemed an extraordinarily heartless thing for a clergyman to do.

Black smelt scandal, and if the taint still lingered in Long Common after nineteen years, it would not be difficult to ferret out what the scandal had been.

Black put up at the local inn,

describing himself as a writer on old churches in Hampshire, and with this same excuse he wrote a polite note to the present incumbent, asking if he might call.

His wish was granted, and the vicar, a young man, an enthusiast on architecture, showed him every corner of the church from nave to belfry, with a wealth of detail about fifteenth-century carving.

Black listened politely, disguising his own ignorance, and finally led the vicar round to talking of his predecessors.

Unfortunately the present vicar had been at Long Common for only six years, and he knew little about Warner, who had been succeeded by someone who had moved to Hull, but Warner had definitely held the living for twelve years, and his wife was buried in the churchyard.

Black saw the grave and noted the headstone. "Emily Mary, dearly beloved wife of Henry Warner who passed to rest safe in the arms of Jesus."

He also noted the date. The daughter Mary would have been ten years old at the time.

Yes, said the present vicar, he had heard that Warner had given up the living in a great hurry and gone to the Dominions, Canada, he believed. Some of the people in the village would remember him, especially the older ones. Possibly his own gardener would remember most. He had been gardener at the rectory for thirty years.

But as far as he, the vicar, knew, Warner had not been a historian or a collector; he had done no research work on the church.

If Mr. Black would care to come to the rectory, he, the present vicar, had many interesting books on Long Common history.

Mr. Black excused himself. He had got all he wanted out of the present incumbent. He felt that an evening at the bar of the inn where he was staying would prove more profitable, and it did.

He learnt no more about fifteenth-century carving, but a good deal about the Reverend Henry Warner.

The vicar had been respected in the parish, but never deeply liked because of his rigid views and his intolerance. He was not the sort of man to whom his parishioners went when they were in trouble; he was always more likely to condemn than to console. He never entered the bar of the inn, never mixed in friendly fashion with the humble.

He was known to have private means, and he was not dependent on his benefice. He liked to be invited to the few large houses in the neighbourhood, because he placed social values high; but he had not been particularly popular there either.

In short, the Reverend Henry Warner had been an intolerant, narrow-minded snob, which were three poor qualities for a vicar to hold. His wife, on the contrary, had been much loved by all, and it had been universally regretted when she died after an operation for cancer. She had been a most sweet-tempered lady, very thoughtful for others, most kind-hearted, and her little girl took after her.

Had the child been much affected by her mother's death?

No one remembered. It was thought not. She went away to school and was only home during the holidays. One or two recollected her riding about on her bicycle, a pretty, friendly little thing. The gardener and his wife had acted as married couple for the Reverend Henry Warner, the same gardener that was up at the rectory now. Old Harris. No, he did not come down to the pub of an evening. He was a teetotaller. He lived up in one of the cottages near the church. No, his wife was dead. He lived with a married daughter. He was a great rose fancier and won prizes for his roses every year at the local show.

Black finished his pint and departed. The evening was yet young. He dropped out of his disguise as a writer on old Hampshire churches and slipped into the role of a collector of Hampshire roses. He found old Harris smoking a pipe outside his cottage. There were roses growing up his fence. Black stopped to admire them. The conversation was launched.

It took him the better part of an hour to lead Harris from roses to past vicars, from past vicars to Warner, from Warner to Mrs. Warner, from Mrs. Warner to Mary Warner, but the picture unfolded, and there was nothing very remarkable to see in it. The

same tale was repeated that he had heard in the village.

The Reverend Warner was a hard man, not given to being friendly-like; very sparing, he was, with his praises. Took no interest in the garden. Stuck-up sort of chap. But down on you like a ton of bricks if anything was wrong. The lady was very different. Proper shame when she died. Miss Mary was a nice child too. His wife had been very fond of Miss Mary. Nothing stuck-up or proud about her.

"I suppose the Reverend Warner gave up the living because he was lonely after Mrs. Warner died?" said Black, offering Harris some of his own tobacco.

"No, it wasn't nothing to do with that. It was along of Miss Mary's health, and her having to live abroad after being so ill with the rheumatic fever. They went off to Canada, and we never heard from them no more."

"Rheumatic fever?" said Black. "That's a nasty thing to get."

"It wasn't anything to do with the beds here," said old Harris; "my wife kept the place aired and looked after everything, just as she used to when Mrs. Warner was living. It was at school Miss Mary caught it, and I remember saying to my wife that the vicar ought to sue the teachers up there for neglect. The child nearly died of it."

Black fingered the rose Harris had picked for him and placed it neatly in his buttonhole.

"Why didn't the vicar sue the school?" he asked.

"He never told us if he did or

not," said the gardener; "all we was told was to pack up Miss Mary's things and send them off to the address in Cornwall he gave us, and then to get his own things packed, and dust covers put over the furniture, and before we knew what was happening a great van came to pack the furniture and take it to store, or to be sold—we heard afterwards it was sold, and then that the vicar had given up the living and they was going off to Canada. My wife was most upset about Miss Mary; she never had a word from her or from the vicar, and we had served them all those years."

Black agreed that it was a poor return for what they had done. "So the school was in Cornwall?" he observed. "I'm not surprised at anyone catching rheumatic fever in Cornwall. A very damp county."

"Oh no, sir," said old Harris. "Miss Mary went down to Cornwall for her convalescence. Place called Carnleath, I believe it was. She was at school at Hythe, in Kent."

"I have a daughter at school near Hythe," lied Black with ease. "I hope it's not the same place. What was the name of Miss Mary's school?"

"Couldn't tell you, sir," said old Harris, shaking his head, "it's too long ago. But I remember Miss Mary saying it was a lovely place, right on the sea, and she was very happy there, fond of the games and that."

"Ah," said Black, "can't be the same then. My daughter's school

is inland. It's funny how people get hold of the wrong end of the stick. I heard Mr. Warner's name spoken down in the village this evening—queer, if you hear a name once in a day you hear it again—and someone was saying the reason they went to Canada was because the daughter had been badly injured in a train accident."

Old Harris laughed scornfully.

"Them fellows at the pub will say anything when they've a drop of beer inside them," he said. "Train accident indeed. Why, the whole village knew at the time it was rheumatic fever and that the vicar was almost out of his mind with the worry of it, being sent for so sudden up to the school and all. I've never seen a man so demented. To tell you the truth, neither the wife nor myself had ever thought him so fond of Miss Mary until that happened. He used to neglect her, we thought. She was so much her mother's girl. But his face was terrible when he came back from being sent for to the school, and he said to my wife that it was for God to punish the head teacher there for criminal negligence. Those were his words. Criminal negligence."

"Perhaps," said Black, "he had an uneasy conscience and blamed the school for neglect, when at heart he blamed himself."

"Could be," said old Harris, "could be. He'd always look for the fault in the other fellow."

Black considered the time had come to pass from the Warners to the roses once again. He lingered five more minutes, made a note of the blooms recommended for planting by an amateur like himself who wanted quick results, said good evening, and went back to the inn. He slept soundly and caught the first train back to London in the morning. He did not think he would secure any more information at Long Common. In the afternoon he took a train to Hythe. On this expedition he did not bother the local vicar, but addressed himself to the manageress of his hotel.

"I am looking around the coast for a suitable school for my daughter," he said, "and I understand that there are one or two in this part of the world that are very good indeed. I wonder if you happen to know the names of any you could recommend."

"Oh yes," said the manageress, "there are two very good schools in Hythe. There is Miss Braddock's, up at the top of the hill, and of course there is St. Bees, the big co-educational school right on the front. Here at the hotel we mostly get parents with children at St. Bees."

"Co-educational?" said Black. "Has it always been so?"

"Since it was first founded, thirty years ago," said the manageress. "Mr. and Mrs. Johnson are still the principals, though of course they are both elderly now. It's very well run and has an excellent tone. I know there is sometimes prejudice against a co-educational school, because people say it makes the girls masculine and the boys effeminate, but I've never seen a sign of that myself. The children always look very happy and just like other children, and they only take them up to fifteen anyway. Would you care for me to make an appointment for you to see either Mr. or Mrs. Johnson? I know them well."

Mr. Black wondered if she got a commission on pupils to whom she had recommended the school.

"Thank you very much," he said, "I would be pleased if you would." The appointment was made for eleven-thirty the next morning.

Black was surprised at St. Bees' being co-educational. He had not thought that the Reverend Henry Warner would have been open-minded on mixed tuition. St. Bees it must be, however, from the description given by old Harris, the gardener. St. Bees was certainly facing the sea, with a fine surround. The other school, Miss Braddock's, was tucked away behind the hill at the top of the town, with hardly any view at all, and no playing fields. Black had made sure of this by going to look at the outside before keeping his appointment at St. Bees.

A smell of shining linoleum, scrubbed floors, and varnish greeted him as he stood at the entrance, having mounted the school steps. A parlourmaid answered his bell and showed him into a large study on the right of the hall.

An elderly man with a bald head, horn spectacles, and an effusive smile rose to his feet and greeted him.

"Glad to meet you, Mr. Black,"

he said. "So you are looking for a school for your daughter? I hope you are going to leave St. Bees believing that you have found it."

Mr. Black summed him up in a word. "Salesman," he said to himself. Aloud he proceeded to spin a neat yarn about his daughter Phyllis, who was just reaching the awkward age.

"Awkward?" said Mr. Johnson. "Then St. Bees is the place for Phyllis. We have no awkward children here. All the odd spots get rubbed off. We pride ourselves on our happy, healthy boys and girls. Come and have a look at them."

He clapped Black upon the back and proceeded to lead him round the school. Black was not interested in schools, co-educational or otherwise; he was only interested in Mary Warner's rheumatic fever of nineteen years ago. But he was a patient man and allowed himself to be shown every classroom, every dormitory—the two wings were separated for the two sexes—the gymnasium, the swimming bath, the lecture hall, the playing fields, and finally the kitchen.

He then returned with a triumphant Mr. Johnson to the study. "Well, Mr. Black?" said the principal, smiling behind his horn rims. "And are we to be allowed to have Phyllis?"

Black sat back and folded his hands, the picture of a fond father. "Yours is a delightful school," he said, "but I must tell you that we have to be very careful of Phyllis' health. She is not a strong child and gets colds very easily. I am only wondering whether the air might not be too strong for her."

Mr. Johnson laughed and, opening a drawer in his desk, took out a book.

"My dear Mr. Black," he said, "St. Bees has one of the best health records of any school in England. A child develops a cold. He or she is isolated at once. That cold does not spread. In the winter months noses and throats are sprayed as a matter of routine. In the summer months the children do exercises for the lungs in front of open windows. We have not had an influenza epidemic for five years. One case of measles two years ago. One case of whooping cough three years ago. I have here a list of illnesses contracted by the boys and girls over the years, and it is a list I am proud to show to every parent."

He handed the book to Mr. Black, who took it with evidence of pleasure. It was just the evidence he wanted.

"This is remarkable," he said, turning the pages, "and of course modern methods of hygiene have helped you to have such a good health record. It can't have been the same some years ago."

"It has always been the same," said Mr. Johnson, getting up and reaching for another volume on his shelf. "Choose any year you fancy. You won't catch me out."

Without hesitation Black chose the year that Mary Warner had been removed from the school by her father.

Mr. Johnson ran his hand along the volumes and produced the year in question. Black turned the pages in search of rheumatic fever. There were cold cases, one broken leg, one German measles, one sprained ankle, one mastoid—but not the case he sought.

"Have you ever had a case of rheumatic fever?" he enquired. "My wife is particularly afraid of that for Phyllis."

"Never," said Mr. Johnson firmly. "We are far too careful. The boys and girls always have a rub-down after games, and the linen and clothing are most scrupulously aired."

Black shut up the book. He decided upon direct tactics.

"I like what I have seen of St. Bees," he said, "but I feel I must be frank with you. My wife was given a list of schools, with yours amongst it, and she at once struck it off the list because she remembered being very put off it by a friend many years ago. This friend had a friend—you know how it is —but the long and short of it was that the friend was obliged to remove his daughter from St. Bees and even talked of suing the school for negligence."

Mr. Johnson's smile had gone. His eyes looked small behind the horn-rimmed glasses.

"I should be very much obliged if you would give me the name of the friend," he said coldly.

"Certainly," said Black. "The friend afterwards left this country and went to Canada. He was a clergyman. And his name was the Reverend Henry Warner."

The horn-rimmed glasses did not disguise the odd, wary flicker in Mr. Johnson's eyes. He ran his tongue over his lips.

"The Reverend Henry Warner," he said, "now let me see." He leant back in his chair and seemed to be pondering. Black, trained to evasion, knew that the principal of St. Bees was thinking hard and playing for time.

"Criminal negligence was the word used, Mr. Johnson," he said, "and oddly enough I ran across a relative of Warner's only the other day, who happened to bring the matter up. I was told that Mary Warner nearly died."

Mr. Johnson took off his horn glasses and slowly polished them. His expression had quite changed. The over-genial schoolmaster had turned into the hardheaded businessman.

"You obviously know the story from the relative's point of view only," he said. "Any criminal negligence was on the part of the father, Henry Warner, and not on ours."

Black shrugged his shoulders.

"How can a parent be sure?" he murmured.

His words were calculated to draw the principal further.

"How can you be sure?" shouted Mr. Johnson, all pretence at geniality gone, and slapping his hand on his desk. "Because I would have you know that Mary Warner's case was one isolated incident that had never happened before and has never happened since.

"We were careful then. And we

are careful now. I told the father that what had occurred must have occurred during the holidays, and most definitely and finally not at school. He would not believe me, and insisted that our boys here were to blame, through lack of supervision. I had every boy over a certain age up here before me, in this very room, and questioned them privately. My boys spoke the truth. They were not to blame. It was useless to try to get any sense out of the girl herself; she did not know what we were talking about or what we were asking her. I need hardly tell you, Mr. Black, that the whole thing was the most frightful shock to myself and my wife, and to the whole staff, and the story is one which, thank God, we have lived down and which we had hoped was forgotten."

His face showed fatigue and strain. The story may have been lived down, but it had definitely not been forgotten by the principal.

"What happened?" asked Black. "Did Warner tell you he was going to remove his daughter?"

"Did he tell us?" said Mr. Johnson. "No, indeed, we told him. How could we possibly keep Mary Warner here when we found she was five months pregnant?"

The jigsaw puzzle was fitting together rather nicely, thought Black. It was remarkable how the pieces came to hand if you set your mind to the job. Finding out the truth through other people's lies was always stimulating. First Miss Marsh; he had to break through her iron curtain. The Reverend Henry Warner, too, had certainly gone out of his way to build a fictitious barricade. A train accident to one, rheumatic fever to another. Poor devil, what a shock it must have been to him. No wonder he packed his daughter off to Cornwall to hide her secret, and shut up the house and left the neighbourhood.

Callous, though, to wash his hands of her when the business was through. The loss of memory must have been genuine enough. But Black wondered what had caused this. Had the world of childhood suddenly become nightmare to a schoolgirl of fourteen or fifteen, and nature taken charge and mercifully blotted out what had happened?

It looked this way to Black. But he was a thorough man; he was being paid well for his time of research, and he was not going to his client with a tale half told. It must be the whole story. He remembered Carnleath was the place where Mary Warner had gone for her convalescence after the supposed rheumatic fever. Black decided to go there.

The firm for which he worked supplied him with a car, and Black set out. It occurred to him that another word or two with old Harris, the gardener, might prove fruitful, and as it was on his way to the West Country, he stopped off at Long Common, bringing as excuse a small rose tree which he had purchased off a market gardener en route. He would tell the gardener this came from his own garden, as a small return for the advice given him the previous visit.

Black drew up outside the gardener's cottage at midday, at which hour he judged the old fellow would be home for his dinner. Unfortunately Harris was not at home. He had gone to a flower show at Alton. The married daughter came to the door, a baby in her arms, and said she had no idea when he would be back. She seemed a pleasant, friendly sort of woman. Black lit a cigarette, handed over the rose tree, and admired the baby.

"I have a youngster like that at home," he said with his usual facility for playing fictitious roles.

"Really, sir?" said the woman. "I have two others, but Roy is the baby of the family."

They exchanged baby gossip while Black smoked his cigarette. "Tell your father I was in Hythe a day or two ago," he said, "seeing my girl, who is at school there. And curiously enough I met the headmaster of St. Bees, the school where Miss Mary Warner was educated—your father was telling me about it—and how angry the vicar was that his daughter caught rheumatic fever—and the headmaster remembered Miss Warner well. He insisted, after all these years, that it was not rheumatic fever, but some virus the child had picked up at home."

"Oh, really," said the woman.

"Well, I suppose he had to say something for the sake of the school. Yes, that was the name. St. Bees. I remember Miss Mary talking about St. Bees often enough. We were much of an age, and when she was home she used to let me ride her bicycle. It seemed a great treat to me then."

"More friendly than the vicar then," said Black. "I gather your father had no great liking for him."

The woman laughed.

"No," she said, "I'm afraid nobody had much opinion of him, though I dare say he was a very good man. Miss Mary was a dear. Everyone liked Miss Mary."

"You must have been sorry," said Black, "that she went down to Cornwall and never came home to say good-bye."

"Oh, I was. I never could understand it. And I wrote to her down there, but never had no answer. It hurt me quite a bit, and Mother too. So unlike Miss Mary."

Black played with the tassle of the baby's shoe. The face was puckered to cry, and Black thought this might distract him. He did not want Harris' daughter to go back inside the cottage.

"It must have been lonely at the rectory all on her own," said Black. "I expect she was glad of your company during the holidays."

"I don't think Miss Mary was ever lonely," said the woman; "she was such a friendly soul, with a word for everyone, not stuck-up like the vicar. We used to have

fine games together, pretending
we were Indians and such. You
know what kiddies are."

"No boy friends and cinemas
then?"

"Oh no. Miss Mary wasn't that
sort. The girls are terrible today,
aren't they? Like young women.
They chase the men."

"I bet you had admirers, both of
you, for all that."

"No, really, sir, we didn't. Miss
Mary was so used to boys at St.
Bees, she never thought them out
of the ordinary. Besides, the vicar
would never have allowed anything like 'admirers.' "

"I suppose not. Was Miss Mary
afraid of him?"

"I don't know about afraid. But
she was careful not to displease
him."

"Always had to be home before
dark, I suppose."

"Oh yes. Miss Mary was never
out after dark."

"I wish I could keep my daughter from coming back late," said
Black. "In summer evenings it's
sometimes nearly eleven o'clock
before she is in. It's not right. Especially when you read the things
that happen in the newspapers."

"Shocking, isn't it?" agreed the
gardener's daughter.

"But this is a quiet neighbourhood. I don't suppose you get any
bad characters around here, and
didn't in those days either."

"No," said the woman, "though
of course when the hoppers come
it's a bit lively."

Black threw away his cigarette.
It was burning his fingers.

"The hoppers?" he said.

"Yes, sir. It's a great district for
growing hops. And in the summer
the hoppers come down and camp
in the neighbourhood, and they're
quite a rough crowd, from some of
the worst parts in London."

"How interesting. I had no idea
they grew hops in Hampshire."

"Oh yes, sir. It's been an industry for a long time."

Black dangled a flower before
the baby's eyes.

"I suppose you weren't allowed
anywhere near them when you
were young, or Miss Mary either,"
he said.

The woman smiled.

"We weren't supposed to, but
we did," she said, "and we'd have
got into a proper old row if we'd
been found out. I remember one
time—— What is it, Roy? Is it time
for your nap? He's getting sleepy."

"You remember one time," said
Black.

"Oh, the hoppers, yes. I remember one time we did go off to see
them after supper—we'd got
friendly with one of the families,
you know—and they were having
a celebration, what for I don't remember—someone's birthday, I
suppose—and they gave me and
Miss Mary beer to drink; we'd
never tasted it before, and we got
real tipsy.

"Miss Mary was worse than I
was; she told me afterwards she
didn't remember a thing that happened all evening—we were sitting round the tents, you know,
where the people lived, and when
we got home our heads were
going round and round, we were
quite scared. I've often thought

since, whatever would the vicar have said if he'd known, and my old Dad too, for that matter. I would have got a thrashing, and Miss Mary a sermon."

"Deserved it too," said Black. "What age were you both then?"

"Oh, I was around thirteen, and Miss Mary had turned fourteen. It was the last summer holidays she ever had at the rectory. Poor Miss Mary. I often wonder what became of her. Married, no doubt, over in Canada. They say it's a lovely country."

"Yes, Canada's a fine place, by all accounts. Well, I mustn't stay here gossiping. Don't forget to give the rose tree to your father. And put that youngster to bed before he drops off in your arms."

"I will, sir, good day to you, and thank you."

"Thank you, on the contrary," thought Black. The visit had been worth while. Old Harris' daughter had been better value than old Harris. Hoppers and beer. Fair enough. Mr. Johnson of St. Bees would say conclusive. The time factor fitted too. The boys of St. Bees were absolved. What a damnable thing, though. Black let in the clutch and drove off through the village of Long Common towards the west. He felt it was important to discover at what point Mary Warner had lost her memory. That she remembered nothing of what must have happened at the hop-picking celebration was plain. A reeling head, a black-out, and two scared kids making for home at top speed before they were discovered.

Johnson of St. Bees, still warm in the defence of his school, had told Black that there was no doubt Mary Warner had been completely ignorant of her condition.

When the matron, aghast, had discovered the fact and taxed the child, Mary Warner was bewildered. She thought the matron had gone mad. "What do you mean?" she had said. "I'm not grown up, and I'm not married. Do you mean I'm like Mary in the Bible?"

She had not the remotest idea of the facts of life.

The school doctor had advised against questioning the child further. The father had been sent for. And Mary Warner was removed. That, so far as Mr. Johnson and the staff of St. Bees were concerned, was the end of the matter.

Black wondered what the vicar had said to his daughter. He suspected that the vicar had questioned the unfortunate child until he had given her brain fever. The shock must be enough to turn any child mental for life. Perhaps he would get the solution down at Carnleath. The only trouble was that Black did not know quite what he was looking for. The Reverend Warner must surely have changed their names.

Carnleath turned out to be a small fishing port on the south coast. It had probably enlarged itself during the past nineteen years, because there were three or four fair-sized hotels, a sprinkling of villas, and it was evident that the populace now devoted them-

selves to the business of catching
tourists before catching fish.

Black's family, Phyllis and the
boy, returned to the mythical land
whence they sprang. Black was
now a newly married man, and
his wife, a girl of eighteen, was
expecting her first baby. Black felt
doubtful as he enquired for nursing homes. But he was not disappointed. There was a nursing
home in Carnleath, and it did
specialise in maternity cases only.
Sea View, it was called. Right out
on the cliff's edge, above the har-
bour.

He backed his car against a
wall, got out, and went to the
front door and rang the bell. He
asked to see the matron. Yes, it
was about booking a room for a
future case.

He was shown into the matron's
private sitting-room. She was
small and plump and jolly, and he
felt certain that he would be well
advised to leave his mythical wife
—Pearl, he decided to call her in a
sudden flight of the imagination—
in the matron's capable care.

"And when do you expect the
happy event?"

No Cornish woman this, but a
hearty, ringing Cockney. Black
felt at home with her at once.

"In May," said Black. "My wife
is with my in-laws at the moment,
and so I've come on this little trip
alone. She is determined to be
beside the sea for the great occasion, and as we spent our honeymoon here, she feels a sentimental
liking for the spot, and so do I."
Black gave what he intended to be
a sheepish, prospective father's

smile. The matron was undaunted.

"Very nice too, Mr. Black," she
said, "back to the scene of the
crime, eh?" She laughed heartily.
"Not all my patients are so fond of
the backward glance. You'd be
surprised."

Black handed the matron a
cigarette. She took it and puffed
at it with relish.

"I hope you aren't going to shat-
ter my illusions," he said.

"Illusions?" said the matron.
"We have few illusions here. They
all go west in the labour ward.
What was sauce for the gander
turns out to be a pain under the
pinny for the goose."

Black began to be sorry for the
fictitious Pearl.

"Oh well," said Black, "my
wife's a plucky girl. She's not
frightened. I may say, she's considerably younger than myself.
Only just turned eighteen. That's
the one thing that worries me
about this business. Is that too
young to be having a baby, Matron?"

"They can't be too young," said
the matron, puffing a cloud of
smoke into the air; "the younger
the better. Their bones aren't so
set, and they're not muscle-bound.
It's the old ones that give me my
headaches. Come to me at thirty-
five and think they're in for a picnic. We soon show 'em. Your wife
play a lot of tennis?"

"Doesn't play at all."

"Good for her. Had a girl here
last week, she was local champion
over in Newquay, and she was so
muscle-bound she was in labour
for thirty-six hours. Sister and I

were worn to a frazzle at the end
of it."

"What about the girl?"

"Oh, she was all right once we
stitched her up."

"You have had patients as
young as eighteen before?" he
asked.

"Younger than that," she said;
"we cater for all ages here, fourteen to forty-five. And they
haven't all had pleasant honey-
moons. Would you like to see
some of my babies? I've a little
fellow born an hour ago, and Sister is just making him pretty for
Mother."

Black steeled himself for the
ordeal. If Matron was as forth-
right as this over one cigarette,
how would she be after two double gins? He knew he must ask
her to dinner. He went round the
nursing home, saw one or two
prospective mothers, saw several
more whose illusions had apparently been shattered, and when he
had inspected the babies, the labour ward, and the laundry, he
made a silent vow to remain
childless.

He booked a room with a view
over the sea for Pearl, he gave the
date in May—he even paid a deposit—and then he asked Matron
to dine.

"That's very nice of you," she
said, "I'd enjoy it. The Smuggler's
Rest is only a small place, nothing
to look at from outside, but the
bar's the best in Carnleath."

"Then the Smuggler's Rest it
shall be," said Black, and they
arranged to meet at seven.

By nine-thirty, after two double

gins, lobster, and a bottle of
Chablis, with brandy to follow,
the difficulty was not to make
Matron talk, but to get her to stop.

She launched into the finer
sides of midwifery with a wealth
of detail that nearly turned Black
dizzy. He told her she should
write her reminiscences. She said
she would when she retired.

"No names, of course," he said,
"and don't tell me all your patients
have been married women, because I shan't believe you."

Matron tossed down her first
brandy.

"I told you before we had all
sorts at Sea View," she said, "but
don't let that shock you. We're
very discreet."

"I'm unshockable," said Black,
"and so is Pearl."

Matron smiled.

"You know your onions," she
said; "it's a pity all husbands don't.
We'd have fewer tears at Sea
View." She leant forward inti-
mately. "You'd be staggered to
know what some people pay," she
said; "I don't mean the honest-to-
God married people like yourself.
But those who have slipped up.
They come down here to get the
business over, and they pretend to
be aboveboard, and everything
nice and pretty, but they can't de-
ceive me. I've been in the game
too long. We've had titled patients
at Sea View, pretending to be
Mrs., and their husbands think
they are having a holiday in the
South of France. Not a bit of it.
They're having what they didn't
reckon to have—at Sea View."

Black ordered another brandy.

"What happens to the unwanted baby?" he asked.

"Oh, I have contacts," said Matron; "there're plenty of foster mothers in this part of the world who won't say no to twenty-five shillings a week until a child reaches school age. No questions asked. Sometimes I've seen the face of the real mother in the papers afterwards. I show it to Sister and we have a quiet laugh. 'She didn't wear that pretty smile in the labour ward,' I say to Sister. Yes, I'll write my memoirs one of these days. I dare say they'd be worth something, and they'd sell like hot cakes."

Matron took another of Black's cigarettes.

"I'm still worried about my wife's age," he said. "What's the youngest you've ever had?"

Matron paused for reflection, breathing smoke into the air.

"Sixteen, fifteen," she said. "Yes, we had a fifteen-year-old once, barely fifteen, if I remember rightly. That was a sad case. Long time ago now, though."

"Tell me about it," said Black.

Matron sipped her brandy.

"She came of well-to-do people too," she said; "the father would have paid anything I asked, but I'm not a grasper. I told him a sum I thought fair, and he was so pleased to dump his daughter on me, he gave me a bit extra. I had her here for five months, which is a thing I don't do as a rule, but he said it was either that or a remand home, and I felt so sorry for the poor kid I took her."

"How did it happen?" asked Black.

"Co-ed school, the father said. But I never believed that yarn. The amazing thing was that the little girl couldn't tell any of us what had happened. I generally get at the truth from my patients, but I never got it from her. She told us at Sea View that her father said it was the greatest disgrace could ever come upon any girl, and she couldn't make it out, she said, because her father was a clergyman, and he was forever preaching what had happened to the Virgin Mary as being the most wonderful thing in the world."

The waiter came with the bill, but Black waved him away.

"You mean to say the girl thought the whole business was supernatural?" he asked.

"That's exactly what she did think," said the matron, "and nothing would shake her. We told her the facts of life, and she wouldn't believe us. She said to Sister that something horrid like that might happen to other people, but it certainly hadn't happened to her. She said she had sometimes dreamt about angels, and probably one had come in the night, when she was asleep, and that her father would be the first to say he was sorry when the baby was born, because of course it would be a new messiah.

"Do you know, it was really pathetic to hear her talk, she was so sure of herself. She told us she loved children and wasn't a bit afraid, and she only hoped she was really good enough to be its mother; she knew this time he really would save the world."

"What a frightful story," said Black. He ordered coffee.

Matron became more human, more understanding. She forgot to smack her lips.

"We became ever so fond of the child, Sister and I," she said, "you couldn't help it. She had such a sweet nature. And we almost came to believe in her theory ourselves. She reminded us that Mary had only been a year or so younger than she was when Jesus was born, and that Joseph had tried to hide her away because he was shocked at her having a baby too. 'You see,' she told us, 'there'll be a great star in the sky the night my baby is born,' and sure enough, there was. It was only Venus, of course, but both Sister and I were glad for the child's sake it was there. It made it easier for her, took her mind off what was happening."

Matron drank her coffee and glanced at her watch.

"I ought to be going," she said; "we're doing a Caesarean at eight tomorrow morning, and I must have a good night's sleep."

"Finish your story first," said Black. "What was the end of it all?"

"She had her baby, and it was a boy, and I've never seen anything so sweet as that child sitting up in bed with her baby in her arms; it might have been a doll given her for a birthday present; she was so pleased she couldn't say a word.

She just said, 'Oh, Matron, oh, Matron,' over and over again, and Lord knows I'm no softie, but I nearly cried, and so did Sister.

"But I can tell you one thing, whoever was responsible for that bit of work was a redhead. I remember saying to the child, 'Well, he's a proper little Carrots and no mistake,' and Carrots he became to all of us, and to the poor little girl as well. I don't ever want to go through again what happened when we parted them."

"Parted them?" asked Black.

"We had to do that. The father was taking her away, to begin a new life, and of course she couldn't do that with a baby, not a child her age. We kept her and Carrots for four weeks, and even then it was too long; she'd grown too attached to him. But it was all arranged, you see; the father was to fetch her, and the baby was to go to a home, and Sister and I talked it over, and we decided the only way to do it was to tell the poor child that Carrots had died in the night. So we told her that. But it was worse even than we thought. She turned dead white, and then she screamed. . . . I think I shall hear the sound of that scream to my dying day.

"It was terrible. High-pitched, queer. Then she fainted dead away, and we thought she would never come round and that she would die. We called in the doctor, which we don't do as a rule— we attend to our patients ourselves—and he said the whole thing was monstrous and that the shock of losing her baby might turn her mental. She came to, eventually. But do you know what had happened? She had lost her memory. She didn't recognise us, nor her father when he came, nor anyone. She remembered nothing of what had happened. Her memory had gone quite dead. She was well physically and mentally, but for that. The doctor said then it was the most merciful thing that could have happened. But if it ever came back, he said, it would be like waking up to hell for that poor little girl."

Black summoned the waiter and paid his bill.

"I'm sorry we've ended the evening on such a note of tragedy," he said, "but thank you very much for the story all the same. And I think you should include it in your memoirs when you come to write them. By the way, what happened to the baby?"

Matron reached for her gloves and her bag.

"They took him in at the St. Edmund's Home at Newquay," she said. "I had a friend on the Board of Governors and got it arranged, but it was quite a business. We called him Tom Smith— it seemed a safe, sound name—but I shall always think of him as Carrots. Poor lad, he will never know that in his mother's eyes he was destined to be the saviour of the world."

Black took Matron back to Sea View and promised to write as soon as he returned home, confirming the booking of the room. Then he ticked her and Carnleath

off the list in his notebook, and beneath them wrote the words "St. Edmund's Home, Newquay." It seemed a pity to come all this way to the southwest and not drive a few miles further on what would be only a matter of routine. The matter of routine proved harder than he thought.

Homes for the offspring of unmarried mothers are not usually willing to discuss the whereabouts of the children handed to their care, and the superintendent of St. Edmund's Home was no exception to this rule.

"It doesn't do," he explained to Black; "the children know nothing but the home that brought them up. It would unsettle them if the parents ever tried to get in touch with them in after life. It might lead to all sorts of complications."

"I quite understand," said Black, "but in this case there could be no complications. The father was unknown, and the mother is dead."

"I have only your word for that," said the superintendent. "I'm sorry, but it's strictly against the rules to break silence. I can tell you one thing. The last we heard of the boy, he was going steady, in a good job as travelling salesman. I regret I cannot tell you any more than that."

"You've told me quite enough," said Black.

He went back to his car and looked at his notes.

It was not only in his mind that the superintendent's words had rung a bell, but in his notes as well.

The last person to see Lady Farren alive, except the butler, had been a travelling salesman touting orders for garden furniture.

Black drove north, to London.

The firm who made the garden furniture had its headquarters in Norwood, Middlesex. Black obtained the address by putting a call through to Sir John. The catalogue had been kept amongst all the other papers and letters belonging to Lady Farren.

"What is it? Are you on to anything?" Sir John asked over the telephone.

Black was cautious.

"Just a final checkup," he said; "I believe in being thorough. I will get in touch with you again as soon as possible."

He went to see the manager of the firm, and this time Black did not disguise his identity. He gave the manager his card and explained that he was employed by Sir John Farren to enquire into the last hours of the late Lady Farren, who—doubtless the manager had seen in the newspapers—had been found shot a week before. On the morning of her death she had given an order for garden seats to a travelling salesman for this firm. Would it be possible, Black asked, to see the man?

The manager was extremely sorry, but three salesmen were all away, and when they were travelling it was not possible to contact them. The distances they covered were large. Could Mr. Black give him the name of the particular salesman he wished to question? Yes, Tom Smith. The manager consulted his book. Tom Smith was quite a young fellow. This was his first round. He would not be due back at Norwood for another five days. If Mr. Black cared to see Smith at the earliest possible date, the manager suggested he should go to see him at his lodgings, on the evening of the fourth day, when he might have returned. He gave Black the address.

"Can you tell me," said Black, "if by any chance this young man has red hair?"

The manager smiled.

"Sherlock Holmes?" he said. "Yes, Tom Smith has a shock of red hair. You could warm your hands at it."

Black thanked him and left the office.

He wondered whether he should motor down to see Sir John right away. Was there any purpose in waiting four or five days to question young Smith? The pieces of the jigsaw fitted. The story was conclusive. Lady Farren must have recognised her son, and that was that. Yet . . . had she? The butler had taken in Lady Farren's glass of milk to the drawing-room after the salesman had left, and had found her perfectly normal. The pieces fitted, but there was still one little odd-shaped bit that was missing. Black decided to wait.

On the fourth evening he went down to Norwood about half-past seven, on the chance of finding that Tom Smith had returned. His luck held. The landlady, who opened the door to him, told him that Mr. Smith was having his supper, would he please come inside. She showed Black into a small sitting-room, where a young fellow, hardly more than a boy, was seated at the table, eating a plateful of kippers.

"Gentleman to see you, Mr. Smith," she said, and left the room.

Smith put down his knife and fork and wiped his mouth. He had a thin, rather pinched face, like a ferret, and his eyes were pale blue and close together. His red hair stuck up from his head like a brush. He was quite small in size.

"What's up?" he said. He was plainly on the defensive before Black had opened his lips to speak.

"My name is Black," said the detective pleasantly. "I'm from a private-enquiry agency, and I want to ask you a few questions if you don't mind."

Tom Smith rose to his feet. His eyes looked smaller than ever.

"What are you getting at?" he said. "I've not been doing anything."

Black lit a cigarette and sat down.

"I'm not suggesting you have," he said, "and I'm not here to look at your order book, if that's what's scaring you. But I happen to know that you visited a Lady Farren on your rounds just recently, and she gave you an order for two garden seats."

"What about it?"

"That's all. Tell me what happened at the interview."

Tom Smith continued to watch Black suspiciously. "All right," he said, "let's say I did go to this Lady Farren, let's say she did give me a couple of orders; I'll make it all right with the firm when I see them, if they've got wind of it. I can say I asked the cheque to be made out to me, through a mistake, and it won't happen again."

Black was reminded of Miss Marsh. Reminded, too, of the Reverend Henry Warner. Even of Mr. Johnson and his touchy self-defence. Why did people invariably lie when questioned about something else?

"I think," said Black, "it would be much simpler for you, and for your relations with your firm, if you told me the truth straightaway. If you do, I won't report on you, either to the firm or to the superintendent at St. Edmund's."

The young man shifted uneasily from one foot to the other. "You've come from them?" he said. "I might have known it. Always down on me, right from the start. Never had a chance, not me." A note of self-pity crept into his voice. He almost whined. The baby destined to save the world, thought Black, had obviously not made a conspicuous success of the job up to date.

"I'm not interested in your childhood," he said, "only in your very immediate past, and the interview you had with Lady Farren. You may not know it, but the lady is dead."

The boy nodded.

"Saw it in the evening paper," he said; "that's really what decided me to do it. She couldn't split on me."

"Do what?" asked Black.

"Spend the money," said Tom Smith, "and cross the order off my book, and say nothing to no one about it. Easy done."

Black smoked his cigarette, and he had a sudden vision of crowded tents, and lorries, and mattresses, dumped in a field where the hops grew beside tall poles, and bursts of laughter, and the smell of beer, and a shifty-eyed, redheaded fellow like this boy, hiding behind a lorry.

"Yes," said Black, "easy done, as you say. Tell me more."

Tom Smith became easier in manner. The detective wasn't going to say anything. Not if he told the truth. All right.

"Lady Farren was on the list of the big nobs in that district," he said, "plenty of money, I was told, and she'd be sure to give me an order. So I called there, and the butler showed me in, and I gave the lady my catalogue, and she chose two seats, and I asked for a cheque. She wrote it out, and I took it. No more to it than that."

"Wait a minute," said Black. "Was Lady Farren pleasant to you? Did she take any particular notice of you?"

The boy looked surprised.

"Notice of me?" he said. "No, why should she? I wasn't anyone. Just a chap trying to sell her garden seats."

"What did she say to you?" persisted Black.

"She just looked through the catalogue, and I stood by waiting, and she marked two items with a pencil, and then I said would she make out the cheque to bearer— I tried it on, see; she had that dumb sort of face that's easy to fool—and she didn't bat an eye, but went to the desk and wrote out the cheque.

"Twenty quid it was. Ten pound a seat. And I said good morning, and she rang for the butler, and he showed me out. I went off and cashed the cheque right away. I put the money in my wallet, and even then I wasn't sure about spending it or not, but when I saw in the paper the lady was dead, I said to myself, 'Here I go.' Well, you can't blame me. It's the first chance I ever had to make a bit of money no one knew anything about."

Black extinguished his cigarette.

"First chance, and you use it dishonestly," he said, "your choice, and your future. Ashamed of yourself?"

"No one's ashamed till he's caught out," said Tom Smith. And suddenly he smiled. The smile illuminated the pale ferret face, deepened the light blue eyes. The furtiveness went, and in its place shone a strange, engaging innocence.

"I see now that dodge didn't work," he said. "I'll try something else next time."

"Try saving the world," said Black.

"Eh?" said Tom Smith.

Black said good-bye and wished him good luck, and as he walked away down the street he was conscious that the boy had come out on to the doorstep and was watching him.

That afternoon Black went down to report to Sir John Farren, but before being shown into the library, he asked the butler to have a word with him alone. They went to the drawing-room.

"You brought the traveller into this room, and you left him with Lady Farren, then after five minutes or so Lady Farren rang, and you showed the salesman out. After that, you came in again with Lady Farren's glass of milk. Is that correct?"

"Quite correct, sir," said the butler.

"When you came with the glass of milk, what was her ladyship doing?"

"She was just standing, sir, much where you are now, and she was glancing through the catalogue."

"She looked just as usual?"

"Yes, sir."

"What happened then? I've asked you this before, but I must just check again before reporting to Sir John."

The butler considered.

"I gave her ladyship the milk. I asked if there were orders for the chauffeur, and she said no, Sir John would be driving her in the afternoon. She told me she had ordered two garden seats, and she showed me them marked in the catalogue. I said they would be useful. I saw her put the catalogue down on the desk, and she walked towards the window, to drink the glass of milk."

"She said nothing else? She didn't refer to the salesman at all who had brought the catalogue?"

"No, sir. Her ladyship didn't remark on him. But I remember I did, just as I was leaving the room, but I'm sure her ladyship didn't hear what I said, because she never answered me."

"What did you say?"

"I said, joking-like, her ladyship enjoyed a bit of humour, that if the traveller called again I'd know who he was because of his hair.

"'Proper little Carrots he is, and no mistake,' I said. Then I closed the door and went to my pantry."

"Thank you," said Black, "that's all."

He stood looking out across the garden. Presently Sir John came into the room.

"I expected you in the library," he said. "Have you been here long?"

"Only a few minutes," said Black.

"Well. And what's the verdict?"

"The same as before, Sir John."

"You mean, we're back where we started from? You can't show me any reason why my wife should have killed herself?"

"None at all. I have come to the conclusion that the doctor's opinion was right. A sudden impulse, owing to her condition, made Lady Farren go to the gun room, take up your revolver, and shoot herself. She was happy, contented, and as you and everybody else knows, Sir John, she had led a blameless life.

"There was absolutely no motive for what she did."

"Thank God," said Sir John.

Black had never before considered himself a sentimentalist. Now he was no longer so sure.

RIVETS

by SIXTRA

COPYRIGHT, 1953, FIELD ENTERPRISES, INC.

RIVETS

©1953, Field Enterprises, Inc.
All rights reserved

RIVETS

COPYRIGHT, 1953, FIELD ENTERPRISES, INC.

RIVETS

©1953, Field Enterprises, Inc.
All rights reserved

RIVETS

COPYRIGHT, 1953, FIELD ENTERPRISES, INC.

RIVETS

3-27

©1953, Field Enterprises, Inc.
All rights reserved

RIVETS

COPYRIGHT, 1953, FIELD ENTERPRISES, INC.

RIVETS

ADVENTURES IN TWO WORLDS

by A. J. CRONIN

Fans of Dr. Cronin's novels know that he was a doctor before he became a writer. His autobiography, Adventures in Two Worlds, *is a series of anecdotes about his experiences in these two fields. After taking his medical degree in Glasgow, he became a ship's doctor on a vessel sailing to India. His first general practice came when he went to his native Scotland to be the assistant of a certain Doctor Cameron.*

SCOTLAND AGAIN, and real Scots weather—sad contrast to the sunny skies and spicy breezes of the tropics. On the deserted little platform of Dundonald Junction I stood in the blinding wind and rain, wondering if I should take a cab. Economy denied the cab, dignity demanded it—not my own dignity, but that of my new position.

At length I beckoned to the red-faced cabby in the long green coat, who, from beside the one fly-blown four-wheeler that graced the station exit, had been considering me for the last three minutes with a stealthy, speculative eye.

"How much to Tannochbrae village? Dr. Cameron's house."

Auld Geordie cautiously came over. None of your southern alacrity, none of that "Cab, sir!" nonsense about Geordie. He knew his worth, did old Geordie Dewar, and never sold himself for less.

"How much luggage have ye got?" he parried, though the luggage was plainly seen—one portmanteau upon the pavement, and a small black Gladstone bag, a very new bag, which I gripped in my right hand. Then he added:

"You'll be Cameron's new assistant, I'm thinkin'?"

"Just so!"

COPYRIGHT, 1935, 1937, 1951, 1952 BY
A. J. CRONIN, AND PUBLISHED BY MCGRAW-HILL
BOOK COMPANY, INC., NEW YORK

"Two shillings to you, then— Doctor."

He threw a cunning emphasis upon the title, but for all that I kept my head and said sternly: "I mean the short cut." I who had never been in Tannochbrae before! "Not the long way you proposed to wander round with me!"

"As Goad's my Maker. . . ." protested Geordie.

A lively argument ensued, at the end of which a compromise— one shilling and "the price of a pint"—was effected with expressions of good will on both sides.

The portmanteau was slung upon the roof, old Geordie climbed rheumily upon the box, and I was rattled off along the stony moorland road.

At the end of the voyage home, Captain Hamble had pressed me to remain with him on the *Rawalpindar* but at the same time had honestly advised me against lapsing into a routine which, to his knowledge, had turned many an eager and ambitious young man into a lazy and lackadaisical ship's surgeon. The captain had been extremely kind to me and in Calcutta had taken me ashore many times to lunch at the Grand Hotel and to see the sights—the great temples and gilded palaces, the teeming bazaars where sacred cattle roamed and ravaged the stalls at will, the gorgeous botanical gardens filled with exotic birds and blossoms, the grisly burning ghats that lined the waters of the Hoogly. All this had fascinated me, had stirred within me a long-ing to record my impressions of so exciting a scene. Yet I was fully aware of the sound sense in Hamble's warning, and hearing from a classmate at the University that there was an assistantship vacant in Tannochbrae—"Not much, mind you. . . . Regular country practice . . . , and he's a hard nut, old Cameron, though a rare good sort at heart"—I had, not without reluctance, quitted my berth in the ship.

So here I was, hunched in this mouldy four-wheeler, clattering down the cobbled street of a small West Highland village. Halfway down we swung to the right, into the drive of Arden House, a soundly built white stone dwelling with a coach house at the side and a semicircular spread of lawn in front.

The rain dripped miserably as I sprang up the front steps and rang the bell. After a minute, the door opened and the housekeeper, a thin, elderly woman, dressed entirely in black, confronted me. Her hair was tightly drawn, her person spotless, and in her bleak face was stamped authority mingled with a certain grudging humanity; she had the look, indeed, of one tempted terribly to smile, who guards perpetually against a single sign of levity, lest it ruin her self-esteem.

For a few seconds she inspected me, my bag, my hat, even my boots; then, with a slight elevation of her brows, my luxurious background of horse and cab.

"Ye've a cab!" she observed severely, as though I had arrived in the state coach drawn by four cream horses. A pause. "Well! I suppose you'd better come in. Don't forget to wipe your feet."

I dutifully wiped my feet and "came in," feeling that I had made a bad beginning.

"The doctor's out," she announced. "He's fair run off his legs, poor man, since the last assistant left. Aah! He was no good, that one—no good ataaal" And with a faint shake of her head, as though, in her considered judgement, I would not prove much better, she left me marooned on the hearthrug.

Somehow I had to smile. Then I glanced round the big, comfortable room—the dining room, it was —with warm red curtains and Turkey-red carpet, a blazing coal fire, and furniture of sound mahogany. No aspidistra, thank God! A big bowl of apples on the dresser, a full glass barrel of biscuits, and whisky in the square-cut decanter. No pictures, no photographs, but, of all things, three yellow violins hanging on the walls. A good—oh, a decent room to live in. I was warming myself pleasantly at the blaze when the door was flung open and Cameron came stamping in.

"That's right," said Cameron, without a handshake or a word of preamble, "warm your backside at the fire while I work myself to death outside. Dammit to hell! I thought Stirrock said ye would be here this mornin'. Janet! Janet!" —at the pitch of his lungs—"For God's sake bring in our tea."

He was a medium-sized, oldish man with a face beaten bright crimson by Scots weather and Scots whisky, and a pugnacious little grey imperial, now dewed with raindrops. He stooped slightly, so that his head had a forward, belligerent thrust. He wore gaiters, cord breeches, and a big, baggy tweed jacket of a nondescript, vaguely greenish colour, the side pockets stuffed to the bursting point with everything from an apple to a gum-elastic catheter. About him there hung invariably the odour of drugs, carbolic, and strong tobacco.

Obtaining a good three-quarters of the fire, he inspected me sideways and asked abruptly:

"Are ye strong? Sound in wind and limb?"

"I hope so!"

"Married?"

"Not yet."

"Thank God! Can ye play the fiddle?"

"No!"

"Neither can I—but I can make them bonny. Do ye smoke a pipe?"

"I do!"

"Humph! Do ye drink whisky?"

My dander had been rising under this interrogation. I don't like you, I thought, as I looked at the odd, unprofessional figure beside me, and I never will. I answered surlily:

"I drink what I like, and when I like!"

The spark of a smile gleamed in Cameron's sardonic eye.

"It might be worse," he murmured, and then: "Sit in and have your tea."

Janet had swiftly and silently

set the table—cake, buns, toast, preserve, brown bread, home-baked scones, cheese, and ban-nocks—and now, with the big brown teapot, she brought in a huge dish of cold ham and poached eggs.

"There's no falderals in this house," Cameron explained briefly as he poured the tea—he had beau-tiful hands, I noticed, hard-skinned, yet supple. "Breakfast, middle-day dinner, high tea, and supper—plain food and plenty. We work our assistant here, but—by your leave—we don't starve him."

We were well through the meal when Janet came in with more hot water. Only then did she say im-passively:

"There's a man been waiting this last half hour—young Lachlan Mackenzie, him that has the stead-ing up Inverbeg way. His bairn's badly, he makes out."

Cameron arrested a piece of oat-cake halfway to his mouth to let out his favourite oath:

"Dammit to hell!" he cried, "and me up at Inverberg this mornin' and passed his very door. Th'in-fernal eediot! I'll wager the child's been sick for days. Do they all think I'm made of steel?" He checked himself. Then, with a sigh which seemed to let off all his boiling steam, he added in quite a different voice, "All right, Janet. All right. Let him come in here the now."

In a moment Mackenzie stood in the doorway, cap in hand—a poor, shiftless-looking crofter, very much abashed by his surround-ings, and terribly nervous under the doctor's interrogating eye.

"It's the boy, Doctor," he mut-tered, twisting his cap. "The wife thinks it's the croup."

"How long has he been poorly, Lachlan?"

This friendly use of his name gave the young fellow confidence.

"Two days, Doctor—but we didna' think it was the croup. . . ."

"Ay, ay, Lachlan. The croup! Just so, just so." A pause. "How did ye get in?"

"I just walkit in, Doctor—it's no that far."

Not far! It was seven miles from Inverbeg to Tannochbrae.

Cameron rubbed his cheek slowly.

"All right, Lachlan man! Don't you worry. Away with Janet now and have your tea while the gig's bein' got round."

Silence in the dining room when he had gone. Cameron reflectively stirred his tea. Almost apologeti-cally he said:

"I can't be hard on a poor devil like that. It's a weakness I never seem to get over. He owes me for his wife's last confinement—he'll never pay it. But I'll get out the gig, drive seven miles, see the child, drive seven miles back. And what do you think I'll mark against him in the book? One and six—if I don't forget. And what does it matter if I do forget? He'll never pay me a red bawbee in any case. Oh, dammit to hell! What a life for a man who loves fiddles!"

Silence again; then I ventured:

"Shall I do the call?"

Cameron took a long pull at his

tea. The bright satire was back in his eye as he said:

"That's a braw wee black bag ye've got—ay, I see it on the sofa —brand-new and shiny, with your stethoscope and all the new contrivances inside, bonny and complete. No wonder ye're fair itchin' to use it." He looked me straight in the face. "All right! Ye can go. But let me warn you, my lad, in a practice like mine it's not the bag that matters—it's the man!" He got up. "Do the call then, and I'll do the surgery. Take some antitoxin with you to be safe. It's on the right-hand shelf as you go in the back room. Here! I'll show ye. I'm not wantin' you to drive seven miles to find out that croup is liable to mean diphtheria."

The gig was waiting outside the front porch, with Lachlan already in the back, and Jamie, the groom, standing ready with the waterproof sheet. We set off through the wet, blustery night.

In the village the rain fell heavily enough, but when we crossed the bridge and breasted the hill it broke upon us in torrents. The wind drove full into our teeth like a hurricane.

Fifteen minutes, and I was half drenched; my hat saturated, trickles of water oozing down my neck, and my precious bag, which I held upon my knees, streaming like a wet seal. I wanted to curse the weather, the practice, and Cameron; but I shut my teeth and said nothing.

It was bad, bad going. The road was dark, too, the gig lamps so blurred by a film of mud that Jamie had difficulty in keeping the horse upon the road. Away to the right, behind massed firs, were the lights of Darroch, vague, unfriendly; and to the left, lying like a great dark beast, the amorphous bulk of the Ardfillan Hills.

We went on through the pitch blackness and the rain in silence. Then from ahead came the quick lapping of water against some hidden shore.

"The loch!" said Jamie, by way of explanation. They were the only words spoken during the journey.

The unseen road wound now by this angry, unseen water. Then, three miles on, we bore sharply to the left and stopped finally at a small steading where a single illuminated window seemed somehow swamped and hopeless in the great void of sodden blackness.

As we climbed out of the gig, Lachlan's wife opened the door. She looked no more than a girl despite her clumsy sacking apron and uncouth brogues. A coil of hair fell carelessly down her neck, and her big eyes were dark and youthful against the anxious pallor of her face. She helped me out of my wet coat in silence; then, though she still said not a word, her worried eye indicated the kitchen bed. I walked over to it, my boots squelching on the stone-flagged floor.

A little boy of three lay tossing under a single blanket, his brow damp with sweat, his face completely livid as he gasped for breath. I asked for a spoon, but did not use it; instead, with my finger I depressed the child's tongue. Yes! The whole of the fauces covered with thick, greenish-white membrane. Laryngeal diphtheria!

"I've made him some gruel, Doctor," the mother murmured, "but he doesna' . . . doesna' seem to fancy it."

"He can't swallow," I said.

Because I was nervous my voice sounded unsympathetic, even harsh.

"Is he bad, then, Doctor?" she whispered, with a hand at her breast.

Bad! I thought, with my fingers on the pulse. She doesn't dream how bad he is! Bending down, I made a complete and careful examination. There was no doubt at all—the child was dying. What a horrible position, I thought again, that this should be my first case.

I went to my bag, opened it, filled my big syringe with 8,000 units of antidiphtheritic serum. The child barely moaned as the needle sank into his thigh and the serum slowly filtered in. To gain time I went back to the fire. Jamie and Lachlan were in the room now, too, for it was the only warm place in the house. They stood together by the door. I could feel their eyes on me, watchful, expectant, together with the terrified eyes of the mother. I was the centre of that humble room. They looked to me to do something for the child.

What was I to do? I knew very well what I should do. But I was afraid. I returned to the bed. If anything, the boy was worse. In half an hour, before the serum could act, he would be dead from obstruction of the windpipe. Another wave of fear came over me. I had to make up my mind. Now —at once—or it would be too late.

Automatically I faced round. I felt myself so young, so utterly inept and inexperienced in the face of the great elemental forces which surged within the room. I said in a manner wholly unimpressive:

"The boy has diphtheria. The membrane is blocking the larynx. There's only one thing to do. Operate. Open the windpipe below the obstruction."

The mother wrung her hands, and screamed:

"Oh, no, Doctor, no!"

I turned to Jamie.

"Lift the boy onto the table."

There was a second's hesitation; then slowly Jamie went over and lifted the almost senseless child on to the scrubbed pine table. But at that Lachlan broke down.

"I canna' stand it! I canna' stand it!" He cried weakly, and looked around desperately for an excuse. "I'll away and put the horse in the stable."

Blubbering, he rushed out.

Now the mother had recovered herself. Pale as a ghost, her hands clenched fiercely, she looked at me.

"Tell me what to do, and I'll do it."

"Stand there and hold his head back tight!"

I swabbed the skin of the child's throat with iodine. I took a clean towel and laid it across those glazing eyes. The case was far beyond an anaesthetic; madness to think of using it. Jamie was holding the oil lamp near. Setting my teeth, I picked up the lancet. I made the incision with a steady hand, but I felt my legs trembling beneath me. A deep incision, but not deep enough. I must go deeper, deeper —go boldly in, yet watch all the time for the jugular vein. If I cut that vein . . . ! I widened the incision, using the blunt end of the scalpel, searching desperately for the white cartilage of the trachea. The child, roused by pain, struggled like a fish in a strangling net. God! would I never find it? I was muddling hopelessly, messing about—I knew it—the child would die; they would say that I had killed him. I cursed myself in spirit. Beads of sweat broke out on my brow, as I remembered, suddenly, MacEwen's fatal words: *"You will never be a surgeon."*

The child's breathing was terrible now, thin, infrequent; the whole of his tiny thorax sucked and sobbed over each frightful, useless breath. The neck veins were engorged, the throat livid, the face blackening. Not a minute longer, I thought! He's finished, and so am I. For one sickening instant I had a quick vision of all the operations I had known—of the cold, immaculate precision of the Infirmary theatre, and then, by frightful contrast, this struggling, desperate thing dying under my knife upon a kitchen table by the flare of an oil lamp, while the wind howled and stormed outside. Oh, God, I prayed, help me, help me now.

I felt my eyes misting. A great emptiness possessed my whole being. And then under my searching knife the thin white tube sprang into view. Swiftly I incised it, and in the instant the child's gasping ceased. Instead, a long clear breath of air went in through the opening. Another—another. The cyanosis vanished, the pulse strengthened. Swept by a terrific reaction, I felt that I was going to collapse. Afraid to move, I kept my head down to hide the smarting tears that sprang into my eyes. I've done it, I thought; oh, God, I've done it after all!

Later I slipped the tiny silver tracheotomy tube into the opening. I washed the blood from my hands, lifted the boy back to bed. The temperature had fallen a point and a half. As I sat by the bedside, watching, cleaning the tube of mucus, I felt a queer, benign interest in the child—I studied his little face, no longer strange to me.

From time to time the mother replenished the fire so silently she was like a shadow in the room. Jamie and Lachlan were asleep upstairs. At five in the morning I gave another 4,000 units of serum. At six the child was sleeping, far less restive than before. At seven I rose and stretched myself. Smiling, I said:

"He'll do now, I expect!" And I explained to the mother the method of cleaning out the tube. "In ten days it'll all be all healed up good as new."

Now there was no terror in her eyes, but a gratitude—moving and inarticulate—like the gratitude of some dumb creature to a god.

The horse was harnessed, the gig brought round. We all drank a cup of tea standing. The rain had stopped long since. And at half past seven Jamie and I were off, striking through the pale glory of the morning. Strangely, Jamie was no longer taciturn; he had a word for this and that—a word of comradeship which fell graciously upon my ears.

It was close on nine when, tired, unshaven, and clutching the mud-splashed bag, I stumbled into the dining room of Arden House. Cameron was there, fresh as a new pin, whistling a little tune softly, between his teeth—he had an exasperating habit of whistling in the morning!—as he inspected a dish of bacon and eggs.

He looked me up and down; then with a dry twinkle in his eye, before I could speak, he declared: "There's one guid thing has happened anyway! Ye've taken the newness off your bag."

Another experience in Scotland.

WHEN THE AUTUMN RUN of salmon came into the loch, these were days to make a fisherman's pulse beat faster. Dr. Cameron well knew my ruling passion and in this season gave me many an afternoon off—from kindness of heart, no doubt, yet perhaps also because he was very partial to a slice of "brandered" grilse.

It was on one of these excursions that I made acquaintance with the strange character known on the lochside as Houseboat Tam, and thereafter I seldom went fishing without calling upon him. If I failed to do so, then Tam like as not would call on me, swimming up silently behind my dinghy and bursting triumphantly into view with a loud laugh or a friendly halloo. He would stay for a moment treading water, smiling naïvely, exchanging a word or two of news, then down would go his wet, black head, and he would glide away, striking through the water like a seal to where his old houseboat lay moored in Sandy Bay. It was here that Tam Douglas lived his solitary life, though to call Tam's home a houseboat was flattery of the first degree.

In her early days the boat had been a coal scow, plying between Levenford and Overton on the Fourth and Clyde Canal. With the finish of the barge trade she had lain for years mouldering in the mud of the Leven Estuary. In course of time a ramshackle superstructure had been added to her hull, and with a lick of paint on her sodden timbers, she was tugged up to the loch in the hope that she might be sold for a fishing bothy.

But no one wanted the old tub.

Sun-blistered, wind-scoured, rain-battered, she lay deserted, forgotten, and alone in the cove named Sandy Bay. Weather had toned her first hard ugliness into something not unbeautiful. She harmonised with her background, had the look of a strange, unwanted creature that has found safe anchorage at last.

It was then that she was taken by Tom Douglas—that, was Tam's proper name! Some said Tom had got her for a pound, others for a wager he would swim across the loch—for even then Tom was marvellous as a swimmer—yet it was equally probable that Tom had simply boarded the old hulk and made her, quite calmly, his own. Nobody cared very much, and it was all so long ago no one had a note of it. The fact is that Tom was not an institution in those days. He was just a young fellow come to the loch to recover from a serious and, indeed, a most mysterious illness.

A student, was he? No one knew. And what had been the matter with him? Brain fever, some declared, contracted through overstudy for a bursary examination. But the knowing ones implied that Tom must have been "that way" from his birth. For, to speak plainly, Tom was inclined to be a little queer; simple, you understand. He was quiet and friendly, not a soul had one word against him. He was just fey or, as they say in those parts, plain wuddy. You might come on him, for instance, standing all by himself under a rowan tree, not gathering the rowans for jelly, like an ordinary body, but talking to the tree. Talking to the tree, no less! Or again, about the gloaming, you might find him on the loch shore listening to the lapping of the waves upon the shingle and smiling to himself as though he found it oddly beautiful. As if a man had never heard the sound of waves before!

He came from a place in Fife, near Kirkcaldy. But he had no folks that anyone heard tell of.

"I'm just by myself," Tom would answer, smiling, when pressed upon the subject.

He brought little money with him to Tannochbrae. And the little he had was soon gone; Tom never was any good with money. Yet he stayed on. He had come to love the place. The sweet stretch of water and wood and mountain had entered into his being, enslaved his simple mind. The loch had him for its own.

That was why he took the deserted houseboat. And in that boat he became, gradually, not Tom Douglas, but Wuddy Houseboat Tam. He lived like a hermit, cooked his own food, washed his own dishes, darned his own socks. His hair grew long, his beard unkempt. He became in course of time a character. Pleasure launches, bearing their load of tourists up the loch in summer, came to make a detour to "take in" the sight of Houseboat Tam. And Tam was proud, proud for the English tourists to take a look at him.

He would be on the deck of his

boat, cutting up a cabbage for his dinner. And, as the steamer went past, like as not Tam would take care to knock a leaf of cabbage overboard, offhandedly, as though he hadn't meant it. Then, swish! Tam would take a straight header into the loch, clothes and all, and come up cool as you like with the cabbage in his mouth. The tourists loved it, especially the lady tourists, and many a good half crown came to Tam that way.

For the rest, Tam lived like a wild thing on the bounty of the loch. He was a marvellous fisher and a natural cook. A cut of fresh-caught salmon grilled on wood embers in his little galley, with a flavouring of wild thyme and parsley, was the most exquisite dish you could imagine. I had it often, and it was the finest fish I had ever eaten. In the autumn there were nuts and brambles, blaeberries and wild rasps. Tam knew all the places; he knew the roots, too, that were edible, the herbs and simples.

The winter, of course, was Tam's worst time. With ice on the water and sleet blinding down the loch in bitter sqalls, Tam stayed shivering below hatches with little enough to eat for days on end. He must have suffered severely—having insufficient clothing and still less food—but no one ever heard Tam complain. He was the gentlest, kindest, humblest creature, whose little odd streaks of vanity merely made him the more lovable. He was accepted even by the pharisees of the village as part of the Creator's scheme of things. Nobody worried about him, and he worried nobody.

When I came to Tannochbrae, Tam was close on fifty years of age, yet he looked little more than thirty. The spartan rigour of his life, the constant exercise, in and out of the clean loch water, had given him the body of an athlete. Tall as a beech, muscular, upright, his skin weathered to a fine bronze, he might have stood for the statue of Poseidon. He had a striking head, with long, dark hair, a noble brow, and gentle, hazel eyes. But his tattered clothing, unkempt beard, his old canvas shoes tied on with string made him frowsy and ridiculous. To see Tam naked was to see a god. Dressed in his clothes he looked a tinker.

That first summer following my arrival was both glorious and warm. But the succeeding winter came cruelly hard, not perhaps so iron-hard as that famous winter when the loch froze over and they drove a horse and cart upon the ice at Darroch, but raw and bitter. For a whole fortnight the country lay under deep snow, and we had many patients, from the sheer severity of the weather.

Stiff work it was, getting about, with deep drifts on the roads. And there was need to get about; I made the weary drive up to Marklea, at the head of the loch, every day, and every other night, in that freezing fortnight.

On the Thursday of the second week I was snatching a cup of hot coffee in the kitchen of the Marklea Arms when the landlady casually remarked:

"You didn't see Wuddy Tam stirring about his boat, Doctor, when you drove past the cove today?"

Holding the steaming cup in both my hands—they were perished by the cold—I reflected for a minute, then shook my head. She went on:

"In the ordinary way when the weather's like this he'll win round to the back door for a drop broth or suchlike. Not charity, you understand. Tam would never take that. It's payment in kind, so to speak. For come the spring he'll leave a salmon or a dozen trout at the house and never take a penny piece for't." She paused. "But he hasna' been near us for ten days now."

"Are you worrying about him, then?"

She frowned doubtfully.

"I'm just hereaway thereaway. Maybe my notion's all wrong. But what with this awfu' frost and all, I'd an idea he might be ill. A crying shame it would be if the poor creature was stricken down with not a soul to tend to him."

I finished my coffee, pulled on my driving gloves.

"Well," I said, "I'll keep my eye skinned as I go past."

An hour later, having finished my calls, I started back on the road to Tannochbrae. I was driving myself, in a hired trap with a cob from the stables, for Cameron had taken Jamie and the gig on the Overton round. And, as I came opposite Sandy Bay, I drew up and stared across the fifty yards or so of water toward Tam's houseboat.

No smoke from the tiny tin chimney. Not a sign of life. I hailed the boat. A loud, long yell, which seemed to vibrate across the desolation of snow and blue-grey, icy water.

No answer. Nothing but stillness. And silence.

I swore impatiently. My impulse was to go on, to get back to Tannochbrae, a warm fire, and my dinner. But instinct and a sense of compunction restrained me. I leaped out of the trap, crossed the snowy shingle, and went down to the waterside. Several boats lay drawn up, boats used by the Marklea Anglers' Club and beached on this safe shore against the winter. I threw off the covering tarpaulin, chose the stoutest skiff, launched it with an effort, and poled a passage through the pack ice to the houseboat. Clambering aboard, I ducked my head and went below.

Tam lay on his narrow bunk in the tiny cabin, the atmosphere of which was frigid as an igloo. Dressed in his tinker's clothes, covered by an old rug, Tam lay on his back shivering.

"Man, man," I cried, "what's the matter that you didn't answer me?"

Tam looked up dazedly.

"I didn't hear ye. I didn't hear anything."

"How long have you been this way?"

"A week—or thereabouts," Tam muttered, his teeth chattering with ague.

"A week!" I echoed.

I stood cudgelling my brains. Tam was ill, his wretched cabin unfit even for a dog, his locker—lying open—empty of food or stimulant. His condition, moreover, made it impossible to drive him back these two snow-bogged miles to the Marklea Arms. What could one do about it? Suddenly I reached a decision.

I climbed on deck, sculled ashore, and got into the trap. Whipping up the cob, I turned into a narrow side road opposite the cove and drove up the hill to Saughend farm. In five minutes I was there, pealing on the front-door bell, asking to see the mistress of the house immediately.

For all my urgency, Elizabeth Robb was in no hurry to appear. Saughend, unlike the neighbouring crofts and steadings, was a large farm with a fine residence and ample barns. Ever since her husband Robin Robb had died, three years before, Elizabeth had managed the farm herself and, for that matter, managed it admirably. The sense of her possessions, of her own competency, added to a natural brusqueness, gave to the widow a proud and highhanded air. Yet she was a fine woman, with a full bosom, a good, honest figure, sloe-black eyes, and neat feet. On these neat feet Elizabeth was always on the move, full of life and energy; at least, since her widowhood, her energy had been relentless. In Tannochbrae they said she was turning sour; and the knowing ones—in a Scottish village there are always

knowing ones—slyly adduced a reason, which was nonsense, of course, for many suitors had come after the widow Robb, or after her fortune, and had been firmly turned away.

At this moment, indeed, it looked as though I might also be shown to the door, for when in a few hasty phrases I had described the situation and put forward my plea, Elizabeth made a wry face.

"I'm not so sure about all this," she said. "We're overbusy for an upset of that kind. And we're not overfond of fusty auld tykes at Saughend."

But I was not to be put off, and in the end she allowed herself, with a rather bad grace, to be persuaded. She gave some sharp orders. Two men went back with me and carried Tam up to the farm.

"Here!" exclaimed Elizabeth, viewing Tam's dilapidated state with manifest disfavour. "Bring him upstairs! And be careful not to make a midden of my stair carpet!"

From his horizontal position, Tam gazed at her like a scolded schoolboy.

"I'm sorry." He shivered. "I'll go back to my boat tomorrow."

"Humph!" muttered Elizabeth, under her breath. "And a real good riddance of right bad rubbish. Here! Along the passage. Watch my clean wallpaper!"

And she acidly indicated the way to a good room where a new-lit fire smoked and crackled. Having made up her mind, under sufferance, to be charitable, she had decided apparently to do it in style. With the two farm hands I got Tam undressed and into bed. Then I made a more extensive examination. Finally I went downstairs to where Elizabeth waited for me in the parlour.

"It's a localized pleurisy," I announced cheerfully. "That, and exposure! Not quite so bad as I thought. He's coming round now. He ought to be off your hands in a few days. He's got a wonderful constitution, you know."

She compressed her lips with native irony.

"In the meantime I'm to drop all my work—and the Almighty knows I have plenty—in order to nurse him."

"It won't be for long," I assured her, smiling. "The minute Tam's better he'll be off like a shot. He's a shy fish. If he had his way, he wouldn't stay under a house roof for love nor money."

"Indeed!" she said with due asperity. And as that seemed to be all, I went away.

Next afternoon I called at Saughend again. Elizabeth met me at the door.

"You and your exposure," she said in a tone of just remonstrance. "Did you know that the poor man was starving? Not one bite of food had passed his lips for four days, and him with a heavy chill on him."

I made a deprecating gesture.

"Well! It's the way he lives, you see. . . ."

She cut me short.

"A crying scandal," she declared vigorously, "for anyone to live that way. And I'd no idea. Not the slightest. And him living almost at my doorstep. I've never taken any notice of the man, or I'd soon have set him right. His clothes—why, I burnt them the minute I set eyes on them! They're not fit for a human being. And, mind ye, he is a human being— ay, and a gey decent human being, if I'm a judge."

She broke off, eyeing me warily. It appeared as if she might have said a great deal more, but, with an effort, she recollected herself and led the way upstairs.

At first I didn't recognize Tam, for on entering the room I had the shock of my life. Tam was washed, shaved, and dressed in a fine flannel nightshirt. For all his pleurisy, he looked marvellous.

"Why, Tam"—I managed to find my tongue at last—"you seem better today."

"I am better," said Tam in his simple style. "She's looked after me a treat. But I think I'll get back to the boat the morn."

"You'll do no such thing," said Elizabeth Robb severely from the doorway. "You're far from better yet, you foolish fellow, and well you know it."

Tam was indeed not yet quite right—his temperature was above 100°, and there was still a faint crackle in his side.

Downstairs again, I said casually:

"By the bye, I'll not be at Marklea tomorrow, Mistress Robb, so I'll not bother to look in here till the day after."

"I beg your pardon," she said,

folding her hands firmly beneath her bosom, "but you seem to forget ye're dealing with a sick man. You'll oblige me, Marklea or no Marklea, by calling at this house tomorrow without fail. I suppose, because the poor man hasna' the siller to pay you, you think you can neglect him. But I'll pay you your fee, and there's an end o't."

Next day I called again. Tam, with a large bowl of beef tea at his elbow, was well on the way to recovery.

"She's unco kind, ye know, Doctor," he remarked mildly. "But I'd better get back to the boat the morn."

Elizabeth Robb did not deign to answer. But in the front parlour afterward she addressed me quite determinedly.

"He must not go back to that awful boat until he's cured and better. He's no trouble at all, at all. He's a decent, simple chap." Here her voice turned almost dreamy. "A most remarkable man, in fact, with not a word of harm to say against anybody. And some of the things he does say—clever, you wouldn't believe it. Do you know, Doctor, that he doesna' smoke, and he doesna' even know the taste of drink? To think that all these years he's been living like that all by himself."

A surge of indignation seemed to rise in her throat. But in a moment she went on:

"As for looks—well, you wouldna' call the Duke his master —a handsome, well-made, well-set-up man as I ever saw the like of."

Here, catching my eye upon her, she blushed, and, suddenly conscious of that blush, virtuously compressed her lips.

"You'll call tomorrow, Doctor," she concluded formally, and showed me to the door.

So I made my visit the following morning, and the next morning, and the next. And every time I came there was some fresh eulogy on Tam:

"Do you know, Doctor. . . ."

The thaw set in, the snow melted, and the green of the country reappeared.

One day when I arrived Tam was up, dressed in a good broadcloth suit, and looking solid, sensible, and well.

"That's a grand suit you've got, Tam," I declared.

"Not bad," Tam answered with his gentle, guileless smile. "It belonged to Mr. Robb. The late Mr. Robb, ye know." He smoothed the lapels approvingly. "It fits me gey well."

"Isn't it about time, Tam?" I demanded suddenly, inspecting Tam in his beautiful suit, fine laundered linen, sound boots, and air of high prosperity. "Isn't it about time that you were getting back to your boat?"

Tam looked mild and absentminded.

"I haven't thought so much about the boat lately," he murmured. "It's pretty nice up here at the farm."

At that moment Elizabeth came bustling in, looking pleased and blooming, happier than she had done for months. She gazed admiringly at Tam.

"Doesn't he look grand?" she remarked with a proprietary air. "He's promised to come out for a stroll with me this afternoon. I want to ask his opinion about the lower Saughend field. I've a rare notion he might make a farmer yet if he went the right way about it." She gave a little conscious laugh. "Will you be calling in again tomorrow, Doctor?"

"No," I answered gravely. "There's nothing more for me to do. I'll not look back."

But I did look back. Within the month, I was best man at their wedding.

Later, Dr. Cronin practiced medicine in the coal mining district of Wales, first in Tregenny, then in Tredegar which he left for London.

SOME EIGHT WEEKS later, on a crisp December morning, I came out, before breakfast, to the front porch, of "The Glen." The little town lay tranquilly before me, and as I gazed at its familiar outlines, the thought of our impending departure gave me a pang of regret. For three years now we had lived in Tredegar. Here we had really taken up the yoke of married life, here our first child had been born. The work which I had done might not rank high in the social or professional scale. I didn't wear a frock coat and a stiff collar, but more often than not leggings and hobnail boots. I usually walked straight into my patients' houses without knocking. I had no bedside manner to speak of, and could discourage a malingerer with the rudest adjectives. Yet I had made many friends among the miners and officials of the surrounding collieries. They never directly paid me fees—as I have explained, my quarterly cheque came from the society—but always at Christmas I received evidence of their regard in a host of homely presents. There would be a couple of ducks or chickens from one, a print of fresh butter from another, a hand-tufted rug from a third . . . nor should I neglect to mention old Mrs. Griffiths, whom I had almost (but, to be honest, not quite) cured of her rheumatism, and who hobbled across the bridge on New Year's Eve to offer us her blessings and a fine fat goose.

There was a quality in this gratitude which moved me profoundly—something which went deep down to the very roots of life. Then why should I be leaving? Most of my classmates at the University had already settled down permanently in steady provincial practices. Alas, in me the urge to move forward was not to be denied. The previous month I had handed in my resignation—in another ten days we should be gone.

Suddenly, as I stood there, regretful, yet feeling my heart lift up at the prospect of new adventure, I heard a faint and distant concussion, less an actual detonation than a vibration of the air, as though a great harp string had been plucked by a giant hand, behind me. It came from the neighbouring valley, lasted only for a moment, then vanished, so slight, so swift to come and go, it seemed of little consequence. Yet to one acquainted with this district, surrounded by so many mines, it had an ominous significance, and I listened intently, anxiously, for a confirmation of my fear. Nothing happened, however, and a few minutes later I went in to breakfast. But I had barely begun my first cup of coffee when I heard a hooter sound the alarm, six long blasts—and almost at once the telephone rang. It was George Conway, secretary of the Medical Aid Society. Briefly he told me that a disaster had occurred in the Ystfad Colliery at Pengelly across the mountain, they had sent out a routine call for aid. Would I go over at once?

Hastily, I swallowed a few mouthfuls of food, finished my coffee, and set off across the ridge on my motor bike. It was no more than two miles by mountain track to Pengelly, and I reached the village in less than five minutes. Yet already the news of the calamity was travelling through the narrow streets. Doors in the terraces were open, men and women rushing downhill toward the colliery. As they ran, more ran with them. They ran as if they could not help themselves, as if the pit had suddenly become a magnet drawing them irresistibly toward it.

When I arrived, five hundred men and women had gathered on the outskirts of the pit yard, and there were more outside. They stood in silence, the women mostly in shawls, the men without overcoats. It had been snowing here and their figures were very black against the white snow. They stood like some vast chorus, massed in silence under the clear sky. They were not the actors in the drama, but they were of it none the less.

Eight o'clock had just struck when I pushed my way into the pit yard and entered the wooden colliery office, where a number of the surface crew, all in their working clothes, were collected. The mine manager, Dai Jenkins, whom I knew well, was there with his deputy, Tom Lewis, looking at the crowd. As I entered the deputy was saying:

"Will I have the yard gates shut?"

"No," answered the other. "Have a fire lighted in the yard, a large fire. It's cold for them standing there, and God knows they may stand long enough."

In the pause which followed I asked what had happened. At first Jenkins did not seem to hear, then, turning upon me his strained and harassed gaze, he told me that water had broken into the pit from the old workings. Both main shafts were flooded and both morning shifts, sixty-one men in all, were entombed. They were waiting for the first rescue party to bring heavy pumping equipment from the emergency centre at Gilfach. They could not tell how things were underground, having lost all contact with the trapped men. They could only wait for the moment, until the rescue party arrived. As he spoke, more people came crowding into the office—two of the underviewers, a young inspector of mines, another colliery manager from further down the valley, and a party of volunteers from the neighbouring colliery. There was no confusion, no babble of voices, but an attitude of such deep gravity it filled me with foreboding.

Suddenly, in the midst of this tense expectancy, the mine telephone whirred—not the public-service instrument upon the manager's desk, but the wall attachment of the colliery system which communicated only with the underground workings. Instantly, there was a mortal silence, then, in three strides, Jenkins was at the phone. He spun the little handle violently, lifted the receiver.

"Hello, hello!" Then his face paled, he half turned to the others: "My God . . . it's Roberts."

At first I did not understand. Then I realised, with a contraction of my heart, that a voice, the voice of a man not yet dead, was rising out of the dark tomb of the flooded mine, fleeing in despairing hope over waterlogged wires to us, on the surface, two miles away.

"Hello, hello." Jenkins was listening now, he listened for three minutes with strained intentness, then rapidly, in a hard clear voice, he began to speak. "Listen to me, Roberts, bach. You must make for the old Penygroes shaft. You can't come out this way—both shafts are water-sealed, and it may be days before we clear them. You must travel the old workings. Go right up the slant. Break through the frame dam at the top east side. That takes you into the upper level of the old workings. Don't be afraid of water, that's all in the bottom levels. Go along the road, it's all main road, don't take the trenches nor the right dip, keep bearing due east for fifteen hundred yards until you strike the old Penygroes shaft."

A thick, roaring noise came over the wire, audible in the room, and Jenkins' voice rose feverishly to a shout.

"Do you hear me? The rescue party will meet you there. Do you hear me?" But his words were lost as a water blast tore out the wires and left the instrument dead in his hand. He let it fall—it swung dangling, while he stood there, bowed, motionless. At last, wiping his brow, he revealed to us what Roberts had told him.

The first shift underground had been working their heading in the usual way, drilling and shot-firing to bring down the coal. But

Roberts, the undermanager, after the last two shots, found a thin trickle of water coming from the middle of the coal face. There appeared to be no pressure behind it, but it had a bad smell of blackdamp; he knew it was not virgin coal water, and he did not like the look of it.

Immediately the men began to "tub" the water—to try to get rid of it by letting it through the pack walls on the low side of the drawing road. Meanwhile, Roberts felt it his duty to warn the second shift of twenty-three men working further underground, two hundred yards up the branch. He started off and had almost reached the other face when he heard a terrific bang. He knew it was an inrush. He had expected trouble but nothing so sudden or terrible as this. Instinctively, he turned back, but after going ten yards he saw the water rushing down the main haulage, roof-high, in a great swell of sound. The gas thrown back by the rushing water extinguished his lamp but as he stood, petrified, for ten seconds in the sounding darkness, he knew that the men of his first shift, all of them, were drowning, or already drowned, in that frightful flood. The speed of the water was ferocious, its volume that of a tidal wave. On and out it swept, reached the pit shaft, spouted and cascaded, swirling the bodies of the first shift in a backlash, at pit bottom, drowning the ponies in their stalls there. As fast as one might think, the water had risen in the two main shafts, sealing the pit absolutely and preventing all access to the workings from the surface.

The suddenness of the calamity was unbelievable and deadly, but Roberts and his mates on the second shift were still alive. They were at the top of the slant and the inrush went away from them. They were altogether twenty-two men and a boy of fourteen, standing together without speech—they knew enough to make them silent. But Roberts had recovered himself—long familiar with the mine, he remembered a return airway through which he might lead the party to a higher level. Starting off, he found the airway, began to crawl along it, on his stomach, followed by the others. But before he had gone thirty yards, he felt himself turning sick and sleepy, and hurriedly he ordered his men back. The airway was full of blackdamp, carbon monoxide driven from the old waste workings by the water, and Roberts knew then that every escape road was blocked. Trapped in the high dead end of the branch, the water and blackdamp rising steadily about them, they had perhaps half an hour to live. It was then, in this last extremity, that Roberts had remembered the telephone.

When Jenkins finished speaking —and his account, terse and technical, was briefer by far than the explanation I have given here— for a full minute no one said anything. Then, in an even voice, Mr. Deakin, the mines inspector, broke out:

"If they get through to the old

workings there's just a chance."

Jenkins nodded, turned to his deputy.

"Take ten men and go to old Penygroes shaft. Make an inspection—as quick and complete as you can. Find out the condition of the shaft. Then hurry back to me."

Meantime three trucks had rolled into the yard bringing the pumping gear, and the manager left the office to start off its erection. It would take hours to complete this heavy task, and I sensed that Jenkins had little faith in it. All his hopes were centred in these old workings which honeycombed the deep, surrounding strata. If only they could be penetrated we might reach the trapped men.

Alone in the office, I now telephoned George Conway in Tredegar, giving him the facts of the disaster, asking if I should stay on duty at the pit. The secretary endorsed my desire to remain, indeed he insisted I hold myself, from now on, at Jenkins' disposal —Dr. Davies would take over my practice until further notice.

As I rejoined the group outside, the deputy came back from the old Penygroes shaft. There was rubbish and blackdamp in the shaft, he told Jenkins, a man lowered on a crab rope had come out pretty sick, but he believed the shaft could be cleared of gas and stowing in twenty-four hours.

Immediately, then, the necessary gear was assembled, and leaving the pump erection at the main headstocks to proceed, a party of picked men led by the manager and his deputy went out across the troubled ground toward the old shaft. Following the instructions I had been given, I went with them. It had turned colder and a few thin snowflakes began to fall, trembling gently out of the unseen sky.

The disused shaft lay in a wretched place of wasteland known as the Common, all hummocks and subsidences from the network of tunnels underneath, now covered with snow and swept by a bitter wind. Small wonder they called it "troubled land." Here they began to fit headgear, winding engine, and a fan.

In spite of the fire in the pit yard nearby, everybody had left the yard and stood gathered at the Common. They stood well back from the riggers who were raising the headstocks, working fast and hard.

Within three hours they had fitted headgear, steam winding engine, and fan; then they began to free the shaft of blackdamp. When the gas was finally cleared out, a fresh relay, standing ready, went in and started to remove the stowing which blocked the road into the waste. These men worked fast, so fast that they were clearing the stowing from the main road at the rate of six feet an hour. There was more stowing than they had thought. But the relays launched themselves in waves, they battered into the obstruction, there was something frantic and abandoned in their assault. It was more than human progress; as one relay slipped in another staggered out.

"This road runs due west," said Jenkins to the inspector. "It ought to take us pretty near the mark."

"Yes," the other answered, "and we ought to be near the end of that damned stowing."

All day long this work went on, and by midnight the relays had cleared one hundred and forty feet of the old main road. Two hours later they broke through into clear road, into an open section of the old waste. A loud cheer rang out, a cheer which ascended the shaft and thrilled into the ears of those who still waited on the surface.

But there was no second cheer. Immediately beyond, by the light of torches, it was seen that the main road ran into a dip or trough which was full of water and impassable.

Dirty, covered with coal dust, wearing no collar and tie, the inspector stared at Jenkins.

"Oh, my good God!" he said hopelessly. "If only we'd known this before."

Jenkins remained unmoved.

"We must expect difficulties. We must blast a new road above the trough."

There was something so sternly inflexible in the manager's words that even the inspector was impressed.

"My God!" he said, exhausted to the verge of collapse. "That's the spirit. Come on, then, and we'll blast your blasted roof."

They began to blast the roof, to blast down the iron-hard whinstone into the water so that the

trough might be filled and a road established above water level. A compressor was brought down to supply the drills; the finest diamond drill bores were used. The work was killing. It proceeded in darkness, dust, sweat, and the fumes of high explosive. It proceeded in a sort of insane frenzy. Only Jenkins remained calm. He was there, the motive, the directing force. For a full eighteen further hours he did not leave the Penygroes shaft. Yet he ordered the others to take some rest.

Emergency cots and blankets had been brought into the long "lamp room" in the pit yard, and here, with the inspector and other officials, I stretched out and got six hours' sleep. Fresh from this respite, the inspector pleaded with Jenkins to knock off.

"Take some sleep, for God's sake. You're killing yourself."

But the manager shook his head. All that day, and the next, he snatched only an odd half hour on his office couch.

The whinstone blasting was proving incredibly difficult, an almost insuperable task. As the hours moved on, with only the slowest progress, insensibly hope began to fade. Nothing was said, but the expressions of the rescuers reflected a growing desperation.

On the evening of the third day, Jenkins told me to spell off for the night. As I passed through Pengelly on my way home the streets were deserted, every door closed, not a single child at play. Many of the shops were shuttered. A still agony lay upon the terraces, the stillness of despair. From opposite ends of the street two women approached. They were friends. They passed each other with averted faces. Not a word. Silence: even their footsteps silenced by the snow. Within the houses the same silence. In the houses of the entombed men the breakfast things were laid out upon the table in preparation for their return. It was the tradition. Even at night the blinds remained undrawn.

I returned to the pit early next morning. They had lowered the water level in the main shaft—not the Penygroes shaft—sufficiently to allow divers to descend. The divers had to contend with a maximum head of eighteen feet of water in the levels. In spite of this they fought their way along the levels as far as the fall. They made an arduous, exhaustive search. No one knew better than they how useless this search would be. All that the divers found was thirty-eight drowned bodies.

The divers came back. They reported the absence of any living soul. They reported that at least another month would be required to dewater the levels completely. Then they started to bring out the bodies: the drowned men, roped together, dangling out of the mine into the brightness of the day they did not see, laid silently on stretchers, and given to their womenfolk in that snow-trodden yard.

Everything now was concentrated on the approach by Penygroes. Yet any hope that remained seemed forlorn. It was fully realised that the men unaccounted for might never have reached the waste. Moreover, eight days had now elapsed since the date of the disaster, and it was a slender chance that these men might still be alive. Nevertheless, in a fresh frenzy of endeavour, efforts above the trough were redoubled. The rescuers spurted, strained every nerve. Six days after blasting was begun the last charge was fired, they broke through and regained the old main roadway beyond the trough. Exhausted but jubilant, the rescuers pressed forward. They were met, sixty paces due west, by a complete fall of whinstone roof. They drew up hopelessly.

"Oh, my God!" the inspector moaned. "There might be a half mile of this. We'll never reach them, never. This is the end at last." Utterly spent, he leaned against the whinstone rock and buried his face in his arm.

"We must go on," Jenkins said with sudden loudness, and a note of hysteria in his voice. "We must go on."

At that moment, when all seemed lost, a faint, unearthly sound was heard in that unfathomable darkness, an almost ghostly tapping: tap, tap . . . , tap, tap . . . , tap, tap, tap, tap, like a weak tattoo beat out upon a tribal drum.

"For God's sake, listen . . . ! Can't you hear it . . . ? The jowling."

Jowling is the name given to

that method of signifying one's position by striking the rock face with a hammer; many men have been saved by jowling their rescuers toward them. Everyone stood stock-still, with straining ears. Feebly, wearily, as though by one long since exhausted, the tapping was repeated.

"By God, you're right," cried the inspector. "They're there . . . , close to us . . . , just through the rock. They hear us."

"Stand back, behind there," shouted Jenkins through cupped hands.

A final wild blaze of effort, then, with a rending crash of whinstone, we were through, through to the imprisoned men.

There they lay, huddled together, with their backs against the branch wall, silent and spectral forms, clothed by their own comradeship, a few guttered-out pit candles at their feet.

But they were alive, every man of them; yes, the boy was alive as well, crying softly to himself as we came forward.

They were all too weak to stir themselves, nor would I permit them to be moved until I had administered to each one a pint of strong bouillon laced with brandy, glucose solution, and a hypodermic of strychnine.

"They'll recover, Doctor?" Jenkins asked anxiously.

"Yes . . . , every one of them."

Slowly, carefully, we brought them out. News of the rescue had preceded us and as we came forth to the surface there arose in a great volume of sound, soberly, yet spontaneously, swelling to the sky from the huge congregation assembled on the troubled wasteland of the Common, that favourite Welsh hymn, "O God, our help in ages past."

It was a moment of emotion that rent the heart, a sight I shall never forget. Yet through it all, the triumph of achievement, the gladness of reunion, one could not forget the thirty-eight coffins, ranged in the hall of Emmanuel Chapel, not a hundred yards along the street. The mass funeral was held the day before we left Tredegar. I attended it. A sad leave-taking of the valleys of South Wales. Yet it brought home to me, who from custom had perhaps grown heedless and indifferent, the endless hazards faced by these brave men.

Years later, in a famous London club, a plump, pink-cheeked habitué, having finished an excellent dinner and a pint of burgundy, was standing, newspaper in hand, his back to a glowing fire, holding forth to a little coterie on the damnable iniquity of the current miners' strike.

"Another sixpence an hour," he complained. "There's no satisfying these cursed blighters. What the devil do they want?"

"Only the right to live!" I interposed mildly.

I was a new member at the time and should certainly have held my tongue. Instead, I told of this disaster, and of these thirty-eight "cursed blighters" who had no further need of those extra six pennies an hour which their comrades had dared to claim.

His next step was a practice in London where he treated both rich and poor and did special work for cases suggested by the sister of the convent mentioned below.

As TIME WENT ON I came to know the convent well. How can I describe the peace of this little citadel of goodness—quiet, ordered, immaculate, with its tiny courtyard garden shaded by two lime trees, placed in the very heart of the great and bustling city. In crossing its threshold one entered a world of brooding and mysterious tranquillity. The chapel was small but of singular beauty, the interior paneled in unpainted wood, the altar of rose marble, surmounted by a large plain crucifix. The candles flickered and shed a soft radiance on the brass doors of the tabernacle and on the white flowers on either side. Against the walls, the Stations of the Cross showed vaguely, and dim, too, were the black figures of the nuns, kneeling in silence, which is felt nowhere so intensely as in a convent church, a stillness which might flood the pure in heart with a delirious ecstasy of calm and joy, but which, at this stage of my life, always pierced me with a stabbing remorse. Then, indeed, I was conscious, although perhaps incompletely, of a lack of purpose in my existence, of a void which

no amount of five-guinea fees could fill. I realised that there were certain vital questions and inner promptings which I was evading, throwing conveniently into the discard of the future, and at such moments, filled with self-dissatisfaction, I would swear passionately to reform, a resolution which, unfortunately, once I returned to the diversions of the outside world and the exciting rush of practice, I failed lamentably to carry out.

Despite my lack of virtue, I became friendly with all the good Sisters, who did their best for me by offering the one gift that was theirs to give—prayer. They were of all nationalities. Mother Cécile was, of course, the one who had captured my heart. Yet I loved also old Sister Josephine, stout and voluminously robed, with myopic eyes, reduced by steel-rimmed spectacles, the mistress of novices; and the cherry-cheeked Belgian sister, Marie Emmanuel, who controlled the kitchen, and was always smiling; nor must I omit young Sister Bridget, pale and hollow-cheeked, from Limerick in Ireland, afflicted, poor child, with tuberculosis of the lungs, whose sad yet calm blue eyes revealed to me her knowledge that she soon must die.

But if these good sisters had earned my affection, it was Sister Caterina, the Italian nun, who caught and held my hand. Black-haired and saffron-skinned, with visionary yet intelligent sloe-black eyes, Caterina was a pure romantic, a throwback to the past, who had her being exclusively in quatrocento Italy. Her knowledge of this period was encyclopaedic, and when we had the opportunity to talk together she would tell me how the Della Scala dynasty arose in Verona and the Estensi in Ferara, how Ravenna had fought Padua, and Lucia defeated Florence.

Then she would talk of the Renaissance painters: Pinturicchio, the saintly Fra Angelico, Fra Bartelomeo, a little less holy, alas; then Michelangelo, lying on his back for seven years to paint the ceiling of the Sistine chapel; and Raphael, poor fellow, misled by a bad woman, La Fornarina, but decorating the loggia of the Vatican, just before his untimely death.

There were the sculptors too, and the great architects, Donatello and Brunelleschi, constructing the dome of Santa Maria del Fiore, and the great Bramante, studying the Pantheon and Constantine's basilica, the better to design St. Peter's. And, of course, the poets, Cavalcanti, Lapo Gianni, and Dante, whom she would quote by the hour. Then came the saints of sunny Italy—she knew all of them,

all the good deeds they had done, the miracles they had performed. Familiar with all the mediaeval legends, she had also, I fancy, a vivid imagination which, I assure you, did not diminish the interest of her stories. Of these there remains vividly in my mind one which might, perhaps, better acquaint you with Sister Caterina than any description I could give of her. I can still hear her warm yet dreamy voice as she began: *"Di unmonaco che ande al servizio di Dio."*

Over two hundred years ago, in a remote country district in southern Italy, there lived two boys who were inseparable companions. Mario, clever and self-assured, son of a prosperous landowner, was the leader. His faithful follower was Anselmo, not very forward at his books, whose father was the village cobbler.

As the two roamed the countryside, Mario would discourse gravely upon his future. His pious parents had destined him for the Church, a prospect which did not displease him, since he was of a ceremonious disposition and had often been fired by the dignity and splendour of the ritual. In particular, he aspired to be a great preacher. One day, as the two boys lay among the vines on a sun-bleached hillside, Mario exclaimed:

"Truly, I would give much to have the gift of tongues."

Anselmo looked at his friend with loyal and loving eyes, and mumbled:

"I will pray, Mario, every day, that you may have that gift."

Struck by the incongruity of the remark—for Anselmo was not noticeably devout—Mario burst out laughing. In condescending affection he threw his arm across his companion's narrow shoulders. "*Amico mio*, I am deeply obliged. But, all the same, I think I shall study rhetoric."

In due course Mario entered the abbey of the Capuchins. For a few lonely months Anselmo hung about the village. Then, unable to bear the separation, he followed his friend to the monastery where he became a lay brother, a servant of the Order, carrying out the menial duties of the house. The difference in their spheres kept the two friends apart, but at least Anselmo was under the same roof as Mario, and as he laboured in the fields, tended the animals, or scrubbed the refectory floor, he was able to exchange a speaking glance, even a few words with his beloved comrade.

In the fullness of time, Mario was ordained. On the eve of Easter Sunday, when he was to preach his inaugural sermon, as he passed through the cloisters a shadowy figure lay in wait for him.

"Good luck, Mario . . . ! I shall be there . . . and praying for you."

Next morning, when Mario mounted the pulpit, the first person he saw, immediately beneath him, squeezed against a pillar in the corner of the nave, gazing up at him with ardent and expectant eyes, was Anselmo.

Encouraged by that silent tribute, Mario gave of his best. It was a spirited sermon; few better had been heard in that old monastery church. And it was followed, at intervals, by sermons of greater fluency and power, sermons which stirred the members of the chapter and brought tears of pride to the eyes of the lay brother, always pressed in obscurity against the pillar beneath the pulpit.

Gradually, Mario's fame as a preacher grew. When invitations came for him to preach at other churches in the province his Superior bade him accept, and since it was the custom that none should journey unattended from the abbey, he readily acceded to Mario's request that Anselmo should accompany him.

The years passed, and together these two travelled throughout the length and breadth of Italy. Inevitably, preferment came to Father Mario. He was made preacher in ordinary to the king, finally Lord Bishop of Abruzzo. Here, in his episcopal palace, Bishop Mario lived in lordly style. Flattered by society, sought out by princes of the Church, courted by nobles, he had become a power. His figure was turned portly, his bearing dignified. Now, indeed, he barely deigned to notice that submissive, ever-willing little brother who, though grown bowed and shrunken, still served him with self-effacing docility, tending with loving care his splendid vestments, polishing his jewelled shoe buckles, brewing to perfection that cup of French chocolate which broke the episcopal fast.

But one Sunday, as he preached, Bishop Mario was conscious of a vague deficiency in his surroundings. It was an odd, unsettling sensation, and, gazing down, he became aware that Anselmo was not in his accustomed place. Taken aback, the bishop paused for a moment, and had difficulty in picking up the thread of his discourse. Fortunately, the sermon was nearly over. At its close he hastened to the sacristy and demanded that Anselmo be sent for immediately.

There was a pause. Then an old priest quietly answered:

"He died a quarter of an hour ago."

A look of shocked incredulity came into the bishop's face as he was told:

"For months he has been suffering from an incurable complaint. He did not wish to trouble Your Grace with the knowledge of it."

A wave of sorrow welled up within Mario, but sharper than his grief was that strange sense of personal deprivation.

In an altered voice he said:

"Take me to him."

Silently, he was led out behind the stables to a small, bare, narrow cell where, on the straw-covered plank bed, wrapped in his worn habit, lay all that was left of Mario's boyhood friend.

The bishop seemed to meditate. Could it be that he weighed against this naked poverty the grandeur of his own apartments?

He glanced inquiringly toward the priest.

"This is where he lived?"

"Yes, my Lord."

"And how . . . how did he spend his days?"

"My Lord Bishop," said the old priest, looking surprised, "he served you."

"But beyond that?"

"My Lord, he had little time to spare. But every day, in the garden, he fed the birds from his own platter. He spoke often to the little children at the palace gates. I fear he fostered a crew of beggars at the palace kitchen. And then . . . he prayed."

"Prayed?" as though the word was strange to him.

"Yes, my Lord, for a lay brother he prayed prodigiously. And always, when I asked him why, he would smile and whisper, 'For a good intention.'"

The bishop's expression was inscrutable, but a knife was striking at his heart. Yet if he had not properly appreciated Anselmo's worth, if his manner toward him in these last years had been haughty, he could not stay to reproach himself. He must leave immediately for Rome, where in St. Peter's he was to preach before a gathering of archbishops.

On the following day when he slowly ascended to the pulpit, the vast basilica was crowded. It was an honour long anticipated, a glowing moment in his proud career. But when, in the bated hush, he began to speak, the dullest platitudes issued from his lips He could read the surprise and disappointment in the congregation. The sweat broke upon his brow. He glanced beneath him, but those rapt eyes were no longer in the shadow of the pulpit. In confusion, Mario hurried through his discourse. Then, hot with shame, he left the precincts of St. Peter's.

Deeply injured in his pride, furious that he should have permitted so imbecile a fancy to disconcert him, he set to work to prepare his next sermon with meticulous care. That he, the Bishop of Abruzzo, the greatest preacher in Italy, should owe it all to a dull, obscure lay brother. . . . Why, the thing was madness! And yet, when he came to deliver the address the words were lifeless. This ruinous obsession went on, from bad to worse, until one day Bishop Mario broke down completely and had to be assisted from the pulpit. To those who helped him he turned and muttered, brokenly:

"It is true. . . . He was the substance. . . . I am the empty husk."

His physicians agreed that he had been working too hard, was in need of a change; and, that he might more readily regain his health and powers, a visit to the high Pyrenees was proposed. But Mario demurred. He preferred, instead, to go to the monastery where he had been ordained, where Anselmo had first come to serve him, where indeed, the little lay brother now was buried.

There Mario spent his time in seclusion, walking in solitary meditation in the garden of the abbey, visiting every day the shady graveyard beneath the olive trees. A great change had taken place in him—the fleshy arrogance had melted from him, his manner was subdued. One afternoon the Prior came unexpectedly upon him kneeling beside Anselmo's grave. As Mario rose the Superior placed his hand upon his shoulder.

"Well, my son. . . ." He smiled, between deference and affection. "Do you pray that eloquence may be restored to you?"

"No, Father," Mario replied gravely. "I ask for a greater blessing." In a low voice he added, "Humility."

Dr. Cronin became the victim of gastric ulcers—which led him to give up his doctor's practice and become a writer.

THE HIGHLAND CLACHAN of Inveraray, little more than a cluster of whitewashed cottages huddled about the castle of the Duke of Argyll, lies among a wild grandeur of mountains at the head of the lovely inlet of the sea which was once the haunt of that delectable fish, the Loch Fyne herring. But the herring, for no known reason other than that it is unpredictable in its habits, had for some years before abandoned these waters, extinguishing a profitable industry, sending the trawler fleet to Lossie-mouth and Frazerburgh, leaving the village in all its native soli-tude. Dalchenna farm, which I had rented, was some two miles down the lonely loch shore, and despite the remoteness of the scene, we fell in love with it at first sight. The farmhouse was a snug building, with nasturtiums and scarlet fuchsias climbing its grey stone walls; on all sides green meadows surrounded us; beyond were woods of alder carpeted with bluebells and mitred bracken into which, as we approached, a roe deer bounded; while above tow-ered the heather-clad hills, source of a stream, filled with trout, that tumbled down in golden spate toward the loch.

For the two boys, aged four and seven, who really had no recollec-tion of anything but city life, the place was truly a wonderland. Barelegged and in kilts, they roamed the woods in company with my wife, climbed the hills, bathed, boated on the loch, fished in the stream, chased the rabbits, gathered shells and starfishes on the shore, helped Will, the herds-man, to milk the cows, and Annie, the dairymaid, to churn the but-ter. For the mother and her sons, the day was one long, perpetual delight—they grew brown as ber-ries, ate like hawks, and slept like hunters. But for me, alas—for the poor parent who was the instigator of the scheme—the picture was somewhat different.

Having emphatically declared before my entire household that I *would* write a novel—tacitly im-plying, of course, that it was the fault of every other member of the household that I had not written twenty novels—I found myself faced with the unpleasant neces-sity of justifying my rash remarks. All I could do was to retire, with a show of courage and deep pur-pose, to the attic of the house which had been at once selected as "the room for Daddy to write in." Here I was confronted by a square deal table, by a pile of two-penny exercise books, a diction-ary, and a thesaurus. Nor must I forget the pablum prescribed by Dr. Bennett and treasured in some suitable domestic background, for I am proud of that bland stimulus. Too often in the bad old days brandy has been the chief inspira-tion of novelists.

It was the morning following our arrival. Amazingly, for that latitude, the sun shone. Our little dinghy danced entrancingly at an-chor on the loch, waiting to be rowed. My car stood in the garage, waiting to be driven. The trout in the river lay head to tail, waiting to be caught. The hills stood fresh and green, waiting to be climbed. And I—I stood at the window of the little upstairs room. Winc-ingly, I looked at the sun, the loch, the boat, the car, the river, and the mountains; then sadly turned and sat down before my deal table, my exercise books, and my diction-ary. "What a fool you are," I said to myself gloomily, and I used an adjective to magnify my imbecil-ity. How often during the next three months was I to repeat that assertion—each time with stronger adjectives.

But in the meantime I was going to begin. Firmly I opened the first exercise book, firmly I jogged my fountain pen out of its habitual inertia. Firmly I poised that pen and lifted my head for inspiration.

It was a pleasant view through that narrow window: a long green field ran down to a bay of the loch. There was movement. Six cows, couched in the shadow of a hawthorn hedge, ruminated with steady rhythm; an old goat with an arresting beard tinkled his bell in search, I thought, of dandelions; a yellow butterfly hovered indecisively above a scarlet spurt of fuchsias; some white hens pottered about, liable to sudden excitements and pursuits.

It had all a seductive, dreamlike interest. I thought I might contemplate the scene for a minute or two before settling down to work. I contemplated. Then somebody knocked at the door and said, "Lunchtime." I started, and searched hopefully for my glorious beginning, only to find that the exercise book still retained its blank virginity.

I rose and went downstairs, and as I descended those whitescrubbed wooden steps I asked myself angrily if I were not a humbug. Was I like the wretched poet d'Argenton in Daudet's *Jack*, with his "Parva domus, magna quies" and his *Daughter of Faust*, which, as the days slipped on, never pro-gressed beyond that stillborn opening sentence: "In a remote valley of the Pyrenees . . . teeming with legends." Was I like that? I carved the mutton glumly. My two young sons, removed by their nurse to a remote distance in order that they might on no account disturb the novelist, had returned in high spirits. The younger, aged four, now lisped breezily:

"Finished your book yet, Daddy?"

The elder, always of a corrective tendency, affirmed with the superior wisdom of his two additional years:

"Don't be silly. Daddy's only half finished."

Whereupon their mother smiled upon them reprovingly:

"No, dears, Daddy can only have written a chapter or two."

I felt not like a humbug, but a criminal. Determinedly I called to mind the aphorism of an old schoolmaster of mine. "Get it down," he used to declare. "If it stays in your head it'll never be anything. Get it down." So after lunch I went straight upstairs and began to get my ideas down.

I could fill a volume with the emotional experiences of those next three months. Although the theme of the novel I wished to write was already outlined in my mind—the tragic record of a man's egotism and bitter pride—I was, beyond these naïve fundamentals, lamentably unprepared. Most novelists who suddenly blaze into print in their thirties have practised their vice secretly for years.

But I, until this moment, had written nothing but prescriptions and scientific papers. It took great determination to drive me through my inhibitions, like a circus rider through a paper hoop.

I had no pretensions to technique, no knowledge of style or form. The difficulty of simple statement staggered me. I spent hours looking for an adjective. I corrected and recorrected until the page looked like a spider's web; then I tore it up and started all over again.

Yet once I had begun, the thing haunted me. My characters took shape, spoke to me, excited me. When an idea struck me in the middle of the night I would get up, light a candle—we had, of course, no electricity in this remote spot—and sprawl on the floor until I had translated it to paper. I was possessed by the very novelty of what I did. At first my rate of progress was some eight hundred laboured words a day. By the end of the second month I was readily accomplishing two thousand.

For the next three months, through all that lovely summer, while the others enjoyed themselves, I remained chained to my desk. Despite their pleadings that I should take a day off, I kept myself on the rack relentlessly, all day and part of the night, coming down late for my peptonised meals, answering the children absently, seemingly anxious only to get back to my private treadmill.

Although at the time I maintained a stoic, a sphinxlike silence, I will now confess to the miseries I went through. There were redeeming moments when, carried away by what I had written, living with my characters in the drama they were enacting, I dared to hope that I was doing something fine; but for the most part I felt that all my drudgery was quite useless, that I was wasting my time in sheer futility.

The worst moment came when I was halfway through the book, and the typescript of the first chapters arrived from a secretarial bureau in London. As I read the opening pages, a wave of horror swept over me. I thought, Have I written this awful stuff? No one will ever read it. No one will ever publish it. I simply can't go on!

I had the impulse there and then to throw up the whole project, destroy everything I had written. It was irresistible. I got up with a set face, took the manuscript to the back door, and flung it in the ash heap.

When the news was known, a dire silence fell upon the house. At lunch, the very children were silent. I remember so well—it started to rain, a dank Scots afternoon, and, scared by my scowl, my wife and the two boys left me without a word.

Drawing a sullen satisfaction from my surrender, or, as I preferred to phrase it, my return to sanity, I went for a walk in the drizzling rain. Halfway down the loch shore I came upon old Angus, the farmer, patiently and laboriously ditching a patch of the bogged and peaty heath which made up the bulk of his hard-won little croft. As I drew near, he gazed up at me in some surprise; he knew of my intention and, with that inborn Scottish reverence for "letters," had tacitly approved it. When I told him what I had just done, and why, his weathered face slowly changed, his keen blue eyes, beneath misted sandy brows, scanned me with disappointment and a queer contempt. He was a silent man, and it was long before he spoke. Even then his words were cryptic.

"No doubt you're the one that's right, Doctor, and I'm the one that's wrong. . . ." He seemed to look right through me. "My father ditched this bog all his days and never made a pasture. I've dug it all *my* days and I've never made a pasture. But, pasture or no pasture"—he placed his foot on the spade—"I cannot help but dig. For my father knew and I know that if you only dig enough, a pasture can be made here."

I understood. I watched his dogged figure, working away, determined to see the job through at all costs. In silence I tramped back to the house, drenched, shamed, furious, and picked the soggy bundle from the ash heap. I dried it in the kitchen oven. Then I flung it on the table and set to work again with a kind of frantic desperation. I would not be beaten, I would not give in. Night after night, keeping myself awake by sheer will power, I wrote harder than ever. At last, toward the end of September, I wrote *"Finis."* The relief was un-

believable. I had kept my word. I had created a book. Whether it was good, bad, or indifferent I did not know.

With a sigh of incredible relief, I packed the manuscript in an old cardboard box, tied it with farmyard twine. Then, having found a publisher's address in a two-year-old almanac, I dispatched the untidy parcel and promptly forgot about it. Like a man who has lost a heavy burden, I began to bathe and fish and row with the boys, to roam the hills and the moors with them, to behave once again like a normal human being.

The days succeeded one another, and nothing happened. That nondescript package might well have disappeared forever into the void. By stern parental edict the subject was taboo in the family, and when the younger son inadvertently made innocent reference to "Daddy's book," he received the blackest of looks.

In point of fact, I had no illusions—I was fully aware that aspiring authors acquire rejection slips more readily than cheques, and that first manuscripts usually come back a score of times before being accepted—if indeed they are ever accepted at all. My surprise and delight may therefore be imagined when, one morning in October, I received a wire from the head of the publishing firm which I had selected, informing me that the novel had been accepted for publication, offering an advance of fifty pounds, and asking me to come to London immediately.

As we read the telegram, a

stunned awe fell upon the farm living room. Fifty pounds, cash down, seemed a lot of money, and perhaps later there might even be a little more, on account of royalties. Pale and rather shaky, I muttered:

"Maybe, with luck and economy, I can make a living as a writer. Get the timetable and find out when the next train leaves for London."

Looking back upon the events which followed, it seems incredible, even now, how swiftly, how amazingly, from that uncertain moment, the flood tide of success was loosed. This first novel, *Hatter's Castle*, written despairingly on twopenny exercise books, thrown out and rescued from the rubbish heap at the eleventh hour, was published in the spring of 1930. It was acclaimed by critics, chosen by the Book Society, translated into twenty-one languages, serialised, dramatised, and filmed. It went into endless editions, has sold, to date, approximately three million copies, and goes on selling still. It launched me upon a literary career with such an impetus that, once and for all, I hung up my stethoscope and put away that little black bag—my medical days were over.

The author here tells some of the experiences which have brought him to a truer faith.

FROM AUSTRIA I WENT to Italy. Every morning, during my brief stay in the battered little Italian village of Castelmare, near Livorno, I would see old Maria Bendetti. Small, slight, and shrunken, barefooted, clad in rusty black, a black scarf bound about her head, her frail shoulders bowed beneath the big wicker basket on her back, she typified the prevailing tragedy. Her thin brown face, so set and careworn, seemed moulded by calamity into lines of irreparable sadness.

She sold fish, those odd and unappetizing Mediterranean fishes which, eked out by a scant ration of macaroni or spaghetti, formed the meagre diet of this broken seaside community. I had known the village in its days of carefree, joyous peace. Now there was no music and laughter in the little square, where bomb-gutted buildings sprawled drunkenly among the dusty rubble, a scene of utter heartbreak, over which the scent of flowering oleanders lay poignantly, as upon a tomb. The place was dead, and because I had loved it so well, its final desolation saddened me anew.

Most of the young men and women had moved away. But the children and older people remained, moving, it seemed to me like ghosts, wresting a hand-to mouth existence from the sea with their patched-up boats and mended nets.

And among these was Maria. Occasionally she was accompanied by her niece, a thin barelegged waif of ten, who trotted beside her and cried in a shrill insistent voice, *"Pesci . . . pesci freschi!"* as though determined to establish beyond all doubt that their fish were of the freshest quality.

One morning, as they passed through the ruined square, I spoke to them. Yes, they had been through the bombardment; the war had been a bad affair, they agreed. They now lived, with the utmost frugality, in a dark little cave of a room in the Via Eustachia, a narrow street in what remained of the poorest quarter of the town.

In a culmination of that mood which burned within me, which was, of course, the reflex of my own pessimism and discontent, I asked abruptly:

"Why don't you leave the village? Here there is no future . . . all destroyed . . . completely finished."

There was a pause. The old woman slowly shook her head.

"This is our home. We do not think it is finished."

As the two moved away it appeared that they exchanged a secret glance.

That glance provoked my curiosity. During the next few days I found myself observing their movements with a queer, unwilling interest. In the early part of

the day they had their fixed and visible routine, but in the afternoon, astonishingly, they were nowhere to be found. Several times after my picnic lunch I walked to the Via Eustachia only to discover that the little room was empty. Could it be that the two were less simple than I had supposed, that their absence every afternoon concealed some underhand affair, smuggling perhaps, or some devious working of the black market?

Prompted by this thought, I went earlier one day to the Via Eustachia, at an hour when I usually took a siesta on the beach, and stationed myself in a doorway near the old woman's room. I had not long to wait. A few minutes after one o'clock Maria and her niece emerged. Each carried upon her back an empty wicker basket, and hand in hand, with an air of purpose, they set off briskly along the shattered street. Stealthily, almost, I followed them.

Through the piles of rubble went the old woman and the child. At the outskirts of the village they took a sun-baked path which led down to the dry bed of the river. Here, as I took up a vantage point on the high bank, I saw to my surprise that other figures were working with pick and spade in the flinty channel. Maria and the girl unslung their baskets and set to work. At first, I fancied they were digging some kind of bait, then I made out that the child was filling her small basket with white sand while Maria, stooping and making her selection with great care, was gathering a load of square white stones. When the panniers were full, the two shouldered their loads and slowly ascended the steep and narrow path.

They passed close to me, yet if they were conscious of my presence, they gave no sign. When they had gone a few paces ahead I followed.

The way led to the summit of the ruined town, a plateau dominating the landscape, which, in my wanderings, I had not reached before, the one site in all the wasted terrain that had escaped destruction. There, amidst a grove of acacia trees, a larger group of the village people were at work. Quietly, talking in low tones, with a restraint which gave to their actions a strange solemnity, they were mixing mortar, carving and facing the fine white stones, forming the walls of a large new structure.

For an instant I was puzzled; then, all at once, from the shape already risen, I realised what they were building. I caught my breath sharply. These people, who had barely a roof above their heads, upon whom lay the blight of overwhelming destruction, these women, children, and old men whom I had seen merely as beaten and extinguished shadows, had chosen, as their first united act, to construct, solely by their own effort, a new and splendid church. Not a makeshift chapel, but a finer, larger place of worship than ever they had had before.

Maria and the child emptied out their loads. They stood for a moment to recover their breath, then turned to make a fresh descent. As the old woman passed me, with beads of perspiration still upon her brow, she gave me, unexpectedly, from her dark, wise eyes a quick, faint smile, a smile impenetrable in its sweetness, which held, beneath its deep serenity, a touch of friendly malice, as though to say: "Are we finished, then, after all?" All her life was written in that look—the past, the present, and the future. Courage was there, and high endurance, with trust, patient and unshakable—the will to live from day to day, to accept, and above all, to hope.

Confused and humbled, I stood motionless as the old woman and the little girl passed out of sight together. And suddenly my chest heaved, a stab went through me, a stab of anguished self-compunction at my own proneness to despair. What matter the rubble and the ruins? If the very young and the very old could show such faith, there was hope for the world after all.

I stood there a long time, and as I went down at last, consoled and lifted up, the first star was rising, pale yet luminous, in the eternal sky, and in the soft mist that crept up from the waters the ravaged village disappeared. There rose instead a shining city of the spirit.

Another reassuring experience

AND THEN I WAS IN FRANCE. That same month of June, as I drove through the orchards of Normandy, within view of Mont-Saint-Michel, a turn of the road brought me suddenly to an old French château. The sight of this stately dwelling, set in a verdant park behind an avenue of lime trees, caused me to draw up. And as an old countryman was passing, I inquired:

"Who lives there?"

He stopped and smiled—a spontaneous smile which lit up his weathered face, wrinkled and ruddy as a ripe cider apple.

"Why, none other than Monsieur le Maire."

Surprised by this answer, I exclaimed:

"But surely . . . that must be the home of an important person . . . some nobleman. . . ."

The old man nodded his head in amiable indulgence.

"Oh, yes. Monsieur le Maire is certainly a marquis. . . . He has one of the best names in France. But he is also mayor of our village. And that, monsieur . . . , that is how we know him."

Something in the peasant's tone and manner—he would not be drawn further, but ambled off along the dusty lane—whetted my curiosity, gave me the feeling that I had stumbled on a story. And as I had time on my hands, instead of pushing on toward Saint-Malo as I had intended, I turned off at the adjoining village and put up at the tavern there—the Pomme d'Or. I felt a strong desire to meet Monsieur le Maire.

This, the landlord of the inn assured me, would not be difficult—the mayor was accessible to everyone—and following his voluble directions I crossed the pretty village square and entered the little red-roofed town hall. Here, in a tiny, bare whitewashed room, seated at a scrubbed deal table, under the flag of France, I found the man I sought.

He was of middle age, slight and spare, clean-shaven, with well-marked features, rather hollow cheeks, and a penetrating yet strangely tranquil gaze. He was dressed very plainly, in corduroy breeches, stout stockings and boots, and an old-fashioned Norfolk jacket with narrow lapels and a belt at the back. And he wore, round his waist, the tricolour sash that was the badge of his office. Although he held himself erect as he rose to greet me, I thought that he did not look particularly robust, and he seemed tired, as from a hard day's work. Nevertheless, he smiled cordially and offered me his hand, declaring that he had just been marrying a young couple from an outlying farm, an exercise of his civil functions

which—he added—always de-
lighted him. When I gave him my
card his eye showed a friendly interest and after some moments of
animated questioning he startled
me—for I had not expected such
hospitality—by inviting me to dinner.

The cool of evening was falling
when we left the town hall and
walked down the single street.
Passing a group of young men returning from the fields, some
women washing clothes by the
bridge, a band of children playing outside the school, one could
not but remark the extraordinary
blending of familiarity and respect with which these people of
the village greeted my companion. There was nothing of deference in their manner, still less of
servility, but rather a kind of
camaraderie, a sense of affection,
understanding, and good-fellow-
ship.

Then we came to the wrought-
iron gates of the château, passed
into the avenue, and immediately
I was struck by signs of straitened
circumstances which had not been
apparent to me from a distance.
There were deep ruts in the drive-
way, weeds sprouting between the
cobblestones of the courtyard,
great cracks in the ornamental
urns which flanked the balustrade
of the terrace. When we entered
the mansion itself—despite the
ageless beauty of the exterior—this
impression was borne out by the
silence of the lofty rooms, the absence of servants, the complete
negation of all that grandeur and
display which might normally

have been found in such a setting.
At the end of the vaulted hall a
small table covered with a checked
cloth was set with cutlery and
china, and here, after another
place had been laid, an aged
white-haired man, quiet and slow-
moving, served the dinner.

Now, indeed, the austerity of
this establishment was fully confirmed by the frugality of our re-
past. A thin soup was set before
us, followed by a dish of cooked
vegetables eaten with dark bread,
then came, finally, a cup of un-
sweetened black coffee. Despite
the control which I imposed upon
myself, some hint of perplexity
must have been visible in my expression. For suddenly, to my embarrassment, my host broke into a
low chuckle of amusement.

"If I had known you were coming we should have tried to do
better." Immediately he was serious again. "You see, sir, we are
glad here even of the simplest
fare. For there have been times in
our little community when we did
not eat at all."

When we had finished our coffee he conducted me outside to a
seat upon the terrace, silently
offered me a cigarette. Darkness
had fallen and, except for the faint
hooting of owls in the tall pine
woods behind, the stillness was
absolute. The moon was not risen,
but before us, in the hollow of the
valley, the lights of the hamlet
made a cluster of low stars. The
sight seemed to fascinate the man
beside me—his gaze remained
steadfastly upon it.

"Do you believe that a place

. . like that village you now see . . can have a soul?" The question came unexpectedly, and before I could answer it my companion went on, "Perhaps that sounds absurd to you. Yet it is a belief I cling to with all my heart."

There was a pause, then, drawing deeply on his cigarette, suppressing the slight cough which seemed always to trouble him, he began to speak, in a low tone, gazing straight ahead.

He was, he told me, one of a family of three, but both his brothers had been killed in World War I. He himself had spent four years in the trenches in that conflict, had been gassed with chlorine, wounded by shrapnel in the chest. He made this admission lightly, without self-consciousness, remarking with a faint smile that it was not the Boche gas but the Caporal tobacco, which he smoked incessantly, that really had affected his lungs.

In the troubled interim of peace which followed, both his parents had died. Then came World War II. When the Germans broke through, they occupied the château, made it a general staff headquarters, and, suspecting that he was heading a resistance movement, threw him into prison. In this fashion he had spent another four years of his life.

He smiled again, in a reminiscent fashion, and lit another cigarette.

"Someday I would like to tell you of that time in prison. The trials of an active nature with nothing to do. In desperation I bribed my jailor with my cuff links to bring me string. And with this string I made fish nets . . . scores of fish nets. And while I made these nets, I thought. . . . Ah, yes, monsieur, I thought deeply. Heaven knows I am no philosopher, yet it was the result of these reflections in my cell which changed completely my outlook upon life."

He paused in that same gently reflective manner.

"When we were freed by the forces of liberation, for which, believe me, sir, we owe the United States our eternal gratitude, I came back here. This place, the home of my family for centuries, was in a state of indescribable dilapidation and neglect, while I, of course, was ruined." His lips curved with deprecating humour. "In prison I had not been clever enough to beat the depreciation of the franc by black-market speculation. What inflation had begun, taxation finished off. As I surveyed the wreck of my estate I was tempted to throw up the sponge and go away to escape, anywhere, to the furthest ends of the earth. And then, through the mist of my own misfortunes, I became aware of the condition of the village—and of the people there—which was worse, far worse than mine.

"In the severe fighting of the liberation many of the houses had been reduced to rubble. Food was scarce, inflation and black marketing were rife, currency had no value, and for many a poor peasant the slowly accumulated savings of a lifetime, hidden in a stocking in the chimney corner, had suddenly become valueless. Everything we had believed in seemed gone. People were not only without homes, bread, or money, they were without heart, without faith. Yes, they had lost their belief in God, in France, in themselves. And in this desperate plight the new enemy crept in. Yes, monsieur, here in this remote countryside, far from the great cities, in the heart of our beautiful France, we were threatened by Communism. A mechanic at the garage, named Martin, was the leader. He had suffered severely —his business was gone, the piece of land he had bought and cultivated had become so densely overgrown by briars in the war years he had neither the means nor the will to reclaim it. In brief, he was in the mood to preach revolution, he did preach it, and soon he had a large number of the people under his influence."

My host paused here, stared broodingly into the night, before resuming.

"I must confess to you that my family had always kept themselves aloof from the village, had never taken but the remotest interest in it, except as a recruiting ground for their servants, gardeners, footmen. But suddenly, I, the sole survivor of my line, felt a strange responsibility. Perhaps you remember the parable of the lost talent. That, monsieur, in my moment of supreme despondency, was how I felt—that I must go out and seek, without rest, until I found it . . . the talent of the lost happiness

and well-being of a ruined village

"It so happened that the office of mayor was vacant. No one wanted it. It was an anachronism according to Martin, part of the derelict system that had deceived and exploited the people. Without ostentation I put myself forward . . . and was appointed. And then, instead of looking to the villagers to serve me, I began to serve them."

Again that reflective pause, that quiet smile directed toward me

"I shall not bore you by detailing my indifferent efforts. There were some fields at the end of this property—these I divided up among such as were eager to till them. For others I established a fishery in the bay—my nets proved not altogether useless, you see— and arranged for a distribution of the catch in Rennes. I used every effort to provide opportunities for work. But the essential thing was to place myself at the disposal of everyone, to be always on hand, to give advice, to settle disputes, to offer all possible assistance.

"Oh, it was not easy. Naturally the people did not trust me, suspected me of an ulterior motive, sneered at me behind my back. But gradually, almost in spite of themselves, some began to come my way. There remained, however, Martin and his following. Every time I passed the derelict garage they would shout abuse, spit on the pavement. Ah, how they hated me."

He turned toward me quickly.

"Make no mistake, monsieur, I did not commit the folly of hating them back. I understood how they felt, indeed I sympathised with them; they were Frenchmen, just as much as I. In those years in prison I had realised how false were the old standards of patriotism. In the old days in the trenches we used to say that a man cannot fight on an empty stomach. How much truer to say that he will not fight *for* an empty stomach. He must *have* something—here in the country, he must have a home, a patch of land, chickens and a cow; above all, a decent, rewarding way of life, to make him a loyal and contented citizen."

His voice suddenly grew intensely serious.

"All over the world, monsieur, that fact is becoming more and more evident. We cannot preach democracy and at the same time tolerate conditions which deny a living wage and equal opportunity to vast sections of our population. Happy people are never Communists. Revolution springs only from discontent and misery. If through our own stupidity we drive the masses in desperation, to that extremity, we have only ourselves to blame."

For a long moment he was silent; then, with a return to his former tranquillity, he went on:

"I need not tell you that we, in France, have felt the good will of America. One day, in the spring of 1948, there arrived in our village the first exciting evidence of *le bon plan Marshal*. It was a tractor, a splendid agricultural machine, complete with plough, harrow, cultivator; in short, with all

equipment. I assure you, as it stood there in the square, brand new, its bright vermilion paint gleaming in the sun, it was the centre of attention. Everyone flocked to see it.

"Well, sir, toward evening, when the crowd had gone and the commotion subsided, I saw a solitary figure viewing the machine, at first from a distance, then coming nearer, inspecting the engine, testing the controls, even caressing the heavy tire treads with his hands. To my surprise, I saw that it was Martin. Approaching unobserved, I spoke to him.

"'Good evening, Martin. It is a nice machine.'

"He started in confusion, angry at being caught there, admiring this product of the hated capitalists. But honesty compelled him to be truthful. He glared at me doggedly.

"'Yes,' he muttered, 'it is a fine job. Any fool could tell you that.'

"I gazed back at him, and as I did so a sudden idea, call it if you wish an inspiration, came to me. You will recollect that this man was a mechanic who knew and loved machinery. Remember also his derelict farm with only a broken wooden plough to work it. Almost involuntarily, the words came from me.

"'I am glad you approve of it, Martin. It is yours.'

"At first he did not understand. Perhaps he imagined I had gone mad. Then he thought I was making game of him, and his face turned dusky with anger. But he knew that the machine was under my jurisdiction, and something in my look, which was serious and calm, though I assure you, sir, I was not calm inside, must have told him I was in earnest. He went deadly pale. The struggle within him was painful to observe. He tried to speak but his lips began to tremble; although he set his jaw hard, the muscles of his face were out of his control. I could see the moisture forming in his eyes. Without a word, without even a sign, I turned and walked away."

My companion leaned forward and placed his hand upon my arm, his expression half quizzical, half grave.

"After that, no more trouble. One act of generosity can do more to dispel malice and envy than a hundred burnings at the stake. Of course we all use the tractor in the village. But it is Martin's. He is proud of it. With it he has not only reclaimed his farm. He has reclaimed himself."

When he concluded there was a long silence, a silence filled with meaning, in which, through the veils of vapour that now lay upon the dew-drenched fields, the lights of the tiny hamlet seemed somehow to burn brighter. Slowly I turned and grasped his hand.

"Yes," I said in a low voice, "your village has a soul. I believe that you have saved it."

Next morning it was early as I drove away from the Pomme d'Or. But already, though the place was only half awake, Monsieur le Maire was at his post. He waved as he threw up the window of his little bureau. And in that simple action, it was for me as though a window had been thrown open to the splendour and mystery of service and self-sacrifice. Even now I have the vision of that slight spare figure, that humble aristocrat with his pale, hollow-cheeked face, his cough, his Caporal cigarette, his comic little sash, viewing the world with unfailing sympathy, helping his neighbours, bringing together the highest and the lowest, striving simply, earnestly, unfalteringly, to keep alight the flame of freedom in the country that he loves.

And I thought that if only all of us would work like that, steadfastly and selflessly, forgetting personal expediency, in the cause of the brotherhood of men, then the troubles of this stricken world would end.

THE
SILENT WORLD

By Captain J. Y. Cousteau

with Frédéric Dumas

*This volume is a report of the adventures of the authors and others who
have pioneered in the exploration of the comparatively unknown world
below the surface of the sea. These menfish garb themselves in goggles,
aqualungs, flippers, arm themselves with knives and "shark billies," and
usually carry a camera. The following excerpts contain some high-
points in their encounters with life—and death—under the sea.*

The Drowned Museum

THERE are finer treasures in the
Mediterranean, waiting within
range of the lung. She is the
mother of civilization, the sea girt
with the oldest cultures, a museum in sun and spray. The grand-
est of undersea discoveries, to our
taste, are the wrecks of pre-Chris-
tian ships on the floor. Twice we
have visited classic wrecks and recovered riches beyond gold, the
art and artifacts of ancient times.
We have located three more such

vessels which await salvage.

No cargo ship of antiquity is
preserved on land. The Viking
ships that have been found buried
in the earth and the Emperor Tra-
jan's pleasure barges which were
recovered by draining Lake Nemi
in Italy, are splendid evidence of
noncommercial vessels of ancient
times, but little is known of the
merchant ships that brought nations together.

My first clue to the classic ships

COPYRIGHT, 1953, BY
HARPER & BROTHERS, NEW YORK

appeared in the Bay of Sanary, where forty years ago a fisherman brought up a bronze figurehead. He died before I came to Sanary and I have never been able to learn where he found it.

Years later Henri Broussard, leader of the Undersea Mountain-Climbing Club of Cannes, came up from an aqualung dive with a Greek amphora. The graceful two-handled earthenware jar was the cargo cask of antiquity, used for wine, oil, water and grain. The cargo ships of Phoenicia, Greece, Carthage and Rome carried thousands of amphoras in racks in the hold. The bottom of the amphora is conical. On land it was punched into the earth. On shipboard it probably fitted in holes in the cargo racks. Broussard reported that he saw a pile of amphoras in sixty feet of water. He did not guess that it indicated a wreck, because the ship was completely buried.

We dived from the *Élie Monnier* and found the amphoras tumbled and sharded on a bed of compacted organic matter in a dusty gray landscape of weeds. With a powerful suction hose we tunneled down to find the ship. A hundred amphoras came out of the shaft, most of them with corks still in place. A few had well-preserved waxen seals bearing the initials of ancient Greek wine merchants.

For several days we siphoned mud and amphoras. Fifteen feet down we struck wood, the deck planking of a freighter, one of two ancient cargo vesels that

have been found. We were not equipped to carry out full-scale salvage and our time was limited. We went away with amphoras, specimens of wood, and the knowledge of a unique hydro-archeological site which awaits relatively simple excavation. We believe the hull is preserved and could be raised in one piece. What things that wreck might tell of the shipbuilding and international commerce of the distant past!

Of ancient ships we know a smattering from murals and vase paintings and can make fairly sound guesses at the science of their navigators. Their cargo ships were short and broad and probably could not work to windward. The few existing lighthouses were fires kept burning on shore and there were no beacons or buoys on rocks and shoals. The skippers must have hated to lose sight of land and always tried to moor at night. The pilots must have inherited a knowledge of generations to risk voyaging a ship. Sentenced to skirt the shore, the ships were prey to sudden Mediterranean storms and treacherous rocks. Most of them that foundered, therefore, must have gone down in relatively shallow littoral waters, within diving range. Naval battles and piracy added to the toll of wrecks in shallow depths. I believe there are hundreds of ancient hulks preserved in accessible mud.

A ship that settled in less than sixty feet of water has probably vanished in the scattering action of tide and current, but if it landed deeper it lies in the calm museum of the floor. If the ship fell on rock bed and could not be wholly swallowed, it was overcome by the intense life of the sea. Algae, sponges, hydrozoa, and gorgonians enveloped it. Hungry fauna sought food and shelter in the wreck. Generations of shellfish died and were crunched by other animals that rained excremental sand and mud which mounted as the wreck broke down. After centuries the simultaneous enveloping and consuming actions reached a common level and the sea bottom healed, leaving perhaps a scar.

A diver needs trained eyes to find the signs of such a wreck— a slight anomaly of the bottom contour, an odd-shaped rock, or the graceful curve of a weed-grown amphora. Broussard's amphoras must have been deck cargo. Amphoras in the hold would have been covered with the ship. Many ancient ships have been lost beyond trace when coral or sponge divers, ignorant of the probability that amphoras point to a ship beneath, removed the jars without noting their location.

Unmistakable were the signs of the only other classic cargo vessel ever found, the Galley of Mahdia. The designation is a misnomer; the ship had no tiers of oars; it was a pure sailing vessel which was specially designed to carry an incredible load for its day, at least four hundred tons. The argosy of Mahdia was built by the imperial Romans nearly two thousand years ago for the express task of looting the art treasures of Greece. Our finding of the argosy climaxed an archeological detective story.

In June, 1907, one of the gnome-like Greek divers who roam far and deep in the Mediterranean was prospecting for sponges off Mahdia on the Tunisian east coast, when he found one hundred and twenty-seven feet down row after row of huge cylindrical objects, half buried in the mud. He reported that the bottom was covered with cannons.

Admiral Jean Baehme, in command of the French Tunisian naval district, sent helmet divers to investigate. The objects consisted of sixty-three cannons lying in apparent order in a scattered oval on the sea plain, along with other large rectangular forms. All were heavily encrusted with marine life. The divers raised one of the cylinders. When the organisms were removed, marble fluting was revealed. The "cannons" were Greek Ionic columns.

Alfred Merlin, the government director of antiquities in Tunisia, sent the news to the famous archeologist and art historian, Salomon Reinach. Reinach aroused art patrons to finance a salvage effort. Two Americans subscribed, an expatriate who styled himself the Duke of Loubat, after a Papal patent, and James Hazen Hyde, who gave $20,000. Reinach guaranteed no results, but Hyde was willing to back the effort. The expedition was in charge of a Lieutenant

Tavera, who engaged expert civilian divers from Italy and Greece, equipped with the latest helmet diving suits.

The depth was a serious problem at that stage of diving technique. That year the Royal Navy Deep Diving Committee was working out the first tables of stage decompression for operations to one hundred and fifty feet, of which Tavera did not yet have knowledge. Several divers were so heavily stricken with the bends that they could never work again. The difficult and dangerous operation was pursued for five years.

The argosy was a museum of classic sculpture. It held not only capitals, columns, plinths and horizontal members of the Ionic order, but carved *kraters,* or garden vases, as tall as a man. The divers found marble statuary and bronze figures scattered across the floor as though they had been deck cargo, strewn as the ship side-slipped down like a falling leaf.

Merlin, Reinach and other experts attributed the art to Athens of the first century B.C. They believed that the argosy had foundered about 80 B.C., while carrying the systematically gathered loot of the Roman Dictator Lucius Cornelius Sulla, who had sacked Athens in 86 B.C. The evidence was that the architectural members constituted a complete prefabricated temple or sumptuous villa which Sulla's art commissioners had taken apart in Athens for shipment to Rome. The ship

was way off course for a journey from Greece to Rome, a not uncommon dilemma of the clumsy sailing ships of that era. Enough *objets d'art* were brought up to fill five rooms in the Museum Alaoui in Tunis, where they may be seen today. In 1913 the salvage operation was broken off when financial aid ran out.

We first heard of the argosy in 1948, when we made an undersea archeological investigation of the supposed sunken commercial harbor of ancient Carthage. The summer before, Air General Vernoux, commanding in Tunisia, had personally taken some curious aerial photos of the shallow water off Carthage. Through the clear sea were seen distinct geometrical forms that startlingly resembled the moles and basins of a commercial harbor. The photos were examined by Father Poidebard, a Jesuit scholar, who was also an Air Force chaplain. He found underwater remains of the ports of Tyre and Sidon in the early twenties and was eager to look into the Carthage discovery.

Father Poidebard came aboard the *Élie Monnier* and we took a ten-man diving team to examine the harbor. We found no trace of masonry or man-made construction, and to check our conclusions we had a powerful dredge cut trenches through the "harbor" features. The dredgings held no traces of building material.

Then in the Tunisian archives and in the Alaoui Museum we came upon the story of the argosy of Mahdia. Merlin's monographs and Lieutenant Tavera's report led us to believe there were many treasures still left in the wreck. I had a thrill when I came across the name of Admiral Jean Baehme: he was my wife's grandfather. When we found Tavera's clear detailed sketches, showing the bearings of the wreck, we went for it.

We lay off shore in dazzling Sunday morning sunlight, studying the sketches. There were three drawings of landmarks which could be aligned to bring us over the argosy. The first alignment was a castle sighted past a stone buttress in a ruined jetty. We saw the castle immediately, but there were four piers of the fallen jetty which could be lined up on it.

The second bearing was to bring a small bush on the dunes in line with the crest of a hill. In the thirty-five years since Tavera had drawn the lonely bush, a veritable forest had grown up around it. The last clue was a change in color of a distant olive grove lined up on a foreground windmill. We squinted through the glasses until our eyes wavered but saw no windmill. We made disparaging remarks about Lieutenant Tavera, now a deceased admiral, and wished he had studied treasure-map cartography from Robert Louis Stevenson.

We went ashore to look for the ruins of the mill. We loaded a truck with wooden beams and muslin to construct a signal beacon on the site. Up and down the dusty road we went, questioning the natives. No one remembered

the mill, but someone suggested the old eunuch might know. We found him hobbling down the road, a withered octogenarian with a bald head and fluffy white sideburns. It was difficult to imagine him as he once must have been, the sleek and proud factotum of an Arabian Nights' harem. His blank eyes lighted encouragingly. "Windmill? Windmill?" he squeaked. "I'll take you to it." Carrying our gear, we followed him several miles across country to a pile of rubble. We hurried to build the beacon. The ancient looked worried and mumbled to me, "I remember another mill further on." He took us to a second heap of stones. As we regarded it with pain, he thought of still another ruined mill. The coast of Mahdia seemed to be a graveyard of windmills.

We returned to the *Élie Monnier* and held council. We decided to exert the maximum possibilities of aqualung search technique to rediscover the wreck as though we knew nothing of its location. That was not greatly exaggerating the situation. We had two facts—the wreck was somewhere near and it was in one hundred and twenty-seven feet of water. Echo sound established that the floor was nearly level with slight variations in depth. We cruised until we found the depth area closest to Tavera's sounding.

On the sea floor we laid a steel wire grid covering one hundred thousand square feet. It was patterned like an American football field more than doubled in size, with fifty feet between each cross-line. The object of the undersea game was for divers to swim to and fro along the stripes, surveying the terrain right and left for signs of the wreck. It took us two days to canvas the grid. We would have found a watch dropped on the field. There was no Roman freighter in our web.

Lieutenant Jean Alinat proposed that he go down on the undersea sled. We towed Alinat around the outskirts of the grid. He found nothing. So passed the fifth unfruitful day of the argosy hunt. That night we indicated our desperation by deciding to search closer to shore.

Next morning Commandant Tailliez waved the sled aside and elected to be towed on a shotline by an auxiliary tender. In our campaigns against the unmanageable sea, I believe I felt the low point that morning, the sixth day of failure. I mentally composed a report to my superiors in Toulon which would explain why it was necessary for me to work two naval vessels and thirty men for a week on a wreck that was salved in 1913. Father Poidebard was beginning to remind me of an angry admiral.

A lookout shouted. Out on the sunny water bobbed a tiny dot of orange plastic, the personal signal buoy Tailliez carried on his belt. When the little buoy comes up, the diver has marked something important. Tailliez broke water, tore out his mouth grip, and yelled, "A column! I found a column."

The old records indicated that one pillar had been dragged away from the wreck and abandoned when operations were terminated. The argosy was ours. We ran into Mahdia for the night and broke out champagne for all hands. What occurred in the bistros that night illumines the problem of a crew that has found undersea treasure. The town buzzed with the news that we had found the fabled golden statue of the galley, a mythological object locally venerated for a third of a century. Philippe's mollusk-eaten pillar became a fortune in gold. Admirers thronged aboard to congratulate us.

We began work at daybreak. Dumas and I went down and found the main wreck site. It looked nothing like a ship. The fifty-eight remaining columns were vague cylinders covered with thick blankets of vegetation and animals. They lay pounded, flattened into the muddy basement. We called on our imaginations to flash the picture of a ship. She must have been a whale of a vessel in her day. Tape measurements on the distribution of the columns outlined a ship perhaps one hundred and thirty feet long by forty feet wide, twice the displacement of the *Élie Monnier*, hanging in the sky above.

The argosy was lost in a bare prairie of mud and sand that spread beyond sight into the clear depths. It was an oasis for fish.

Big rock bass swam in the drowned museum. We noticed there were no commercial varieties of sponges growing on the columns. The thoroughgoing Greek sponge divers of our day had apparently gleaned them all. Perhaps they had also lifted small art objects as a belated patriotic recovery of the Roman pillage.

We were confronted with a semi-industrial salvage operation. We were heirs to the great advances in diving science since Tavera's brave men had dared the wreck, and we had, in fact, a set of unique diving tables newly worked out under Lieutenant Jean Alinat's direction. They were designed for aqualung work, in which men could go down and come back quickly in a series of short dives, without building up the nitrogen saturation of prolonged single plunges. The latest helmet diving tables for a man who was to work forty-five minutes at the depth of the argosy required him to return by stages to decompress. He had to halt four minutes at a depth of thirty feet, proceed to twenty feet and spend twenty-six minutes, and halt for another twenty-six minutes at ten feet, before surfacing.

It cost him almost an hour to return from a three-quarter-hour dive. Alinat's schedule, in contrast, sent a man down for three fifteen-minute dives, alternated by three-hour rest periods. The independent diver needed only five minutes of stage decompression at ten feet after the third dive, one-twelfth

of the helmet diver's decompression wait.

To make Alinat's theories work for an efficient attack on the Roman ship, the two-man teams had to go down and come up on a rigid timetable. They would not be expected to consult their own wrist watches. We devised a "shooting clock," a rifleman on deck who fired into the water five minutes after they had gone down, again at ten minutes, and discharged three rounds at fifteen minutes as the imperative signal to surface. The shock impact of bullets could be heard distinctly in the wreck.

On the first day I saw a diver surface, holding up a small glittering object, and my heart leaped, for we had hoped to find Greek bronzes. It was merely a bullet from the shooting clock. The floor became covered with them. It would have been fun to have been hiding behind a column when the next sponge diver sneaked down and saw the bottom gleaming with gold.

The timetable was also threatened by the fact that the *Élie Monnier* swung wide in wind and current off its one anchor, so that the divers had long unpredictable diagonals to swim on their way to work, a drain of time and energy. Dumas hoisted out on deck a slingload of miscellaneous dockyard scrap he had foraged, such as rusted girder bolts and hunks of plate. The divers laughed at the boyish simplicity of Didi's solution. Holding a fifteen-pound scrap iron against his belly, a diver could go sailing down, using his body as a hydrofoil to control his slanting glide. He could come on the wreck from any approach by adjusting his ballast. He could drag, sideslip, or plunge; arrive rested; and drop his iron commutation ticket.

Didi dutifully obeyed the shooting clock, until one day he spied something fascinating as he climbed from his third dive. The sun was still aglow on the floor. Dumas could not resist a lightning dive at it. He found nothing of interest and returned. At dinner he remarked on a twinge in his shoulder. We kidnapped him instantly, locked him in the recompression chamber on deck, and dialed the inside pressure to four atmospheres. We could not take chances on the bends, which can hit a diver some time after he surfaces. There was a phone from the recompression chamber to a loudspeaker in the divers' ready room. After we had eaten Dumas took the mike and broadcast a diatribe against shipmates who starved a pal. We cooled him off for an hour. It was the only time we have used the recompression chamber on our dives.

The world of the argosy was twilight blue in which flesh was a greenish putty color. The far-off sun gleamed on the chromed regulators, winked on the frames of the masks, and ensilvered our exhaust bubbles. The blond basement suffused a reflected light strong enough to make a color movie of the divers at work. I believe it was the first color film made at such a depth.

The Athenian marbles were dark bluish shapes, blurred with blankets of marine life. We dug under with our hands, dog-fashion, to pass cargo slings under them. As the stones ascended, color grew on the crust and, at the surface, they swung into the air ablaze with life. As they drained on deck, the Joseph's coat of flora and fauna faded into the earth shade of death. We scraped, scrubbed and hosed the snowy marble volutes and bared them to their first sun since ancient Athens.

Of the stones on the floor, we took four columns, two capitals and two bases. We raised two mysterious leaden parts of ancient anchors, which were found near the supposed outlines of the ship in positions that indicated the anchors had been stowed when the vessel sank. She must have met her fate suddenly. The anchor parts, each weighing three-quarters of a ton, were oblongs with reinforced holes in the middle, obviously to take wooden posts that had rotted away. Such straight metal shapes could not have been the arms or hooks of the anchors. We dug around for the arms and found none. The finds could only have been the stocks, or top cross-bars. The rest of the anchors must have been made of wood. Here was a puzzle. Why did the ancients put the greatest weight at the top of the anchor?

We argued over evidence and

supposition and formed a possible explanation. The ancient ships did not have anchor chain, but used rope. A modern anchored ship driven by wind or current keeps its hooks fast by means of the horizontal stress on the lower end of the anchor chain. The Roman anchor rope drew taut in such conditions and would have lifted the wooden hooks if the top had not been weighted with a leaden stock, which provided the horizontal stress.

We worked six days in the Roman argosy, increasingly absorbed with its clues to original seamanship. We wanted to dig for the ship itself. Tavera's records indicated that the helmet divers had excavated extensively in the stern. I selected marbles from a compact area on the starboard side amidships and sent them up to clear an area for excavation. We lowered a powerful water hose to blow away the earth. A slight current conveniently carried off the mud we raised. We supposed that the heavily laden vessel had burst her top framing outward in the crash and that the main deck had been hammered in by the deck cargo. The theory seemed to be borne out.

Two feet down we stubbed our fingers on a solid deck covered with leaden plates. The sea washed mud into the hole almost as fast as we clawed, but we felt enough of the sturdy deck to estimate that the Roman ship is two-thirds intact. We dug up an Ionic capital which was encased entirely in mud. No mollusks or plants had reached it. It scrubbed down to the pristine beauty of the days when it was carved, before Christ was born.

I am confident that amidships there is unbreached cargo. I am certain that then as now the crew lived in the forecastle, the least desirable place of a ship, and that there are intimate possessions and tools buried there that could tell us about what kind of men sailed the Roman ship.

We were merely scratching at history's door in our few days in the huge argosy. We found iron nails corroded to needle thicknesses and bronze nails worn to bright threads. We turned up a millstone, with which the sea cooks had ground grains carried in amphoras. We brought up yard-long pieces of Lebanon cedar ribs covered with the original yellow varnish. (It would be useful to know how to make marine varnish that will survive twenty centuries of immersion.) I dug down five feet at the prow against the sliding sands and embraced the cedar stempost. I could barely touch fingertips around it.

Four years later in New York I met the president of the French Alliances of the United States and Canada, a lively old gentleman named James Hazen Hyde, and linked his name with that of the patron who had helped salve the treasures of Mahdia. It was the same man. He invited me to dinner at the Plaza and I showed him the color film of the divers in the wreck. "Fascinating," he said. "You know I've never seen the things that were brought up. In those days one had a lot of money and a steam yacht. I was cruising in the Aegean while they were diving. I never got to the museum at Tunis. Salomon Reinach sent me photographs of the *kraters* and statues, I got a nice letter from Merlin, and the Bey of Tunis gave me a decoration. It is interesting indeed to see it after forty-five years."

Sea Companions

PERHAPS our most beguiling companion of the sea has been the seal. Once the Mediterranean abounded in monk seals, *Monachus albiventer*, a species known in ancient times from the Black Sea to the eastern Atlantic. During the introduction of commercial sealing in the seventeenth century, the monk seals were ruthlessly exterminated by men who shared the mores of the Newfoundlander Abraham Kean, who boasted that he was the biggest animal killer in history—he had killed one million seals. But, occasionally we would hear old fishermen speak of living monk seals.

The trail of the extinct seals grew warm in La Galite, a group of tiny islands thirty-five miles north of Tunisia, which is famous for its lobsters that are kept alive in submerged pots until boats call from Tunis or Metropolitan France. La Galite had a garrulous, red-haired mayor who declared positively that he had seen living monk seals. "One evening everyone saw a seal pillaging a lobster pot near the jetty. He made such a mess that when he came up to breathe he wore the lobster pot like a queer hat." We roared at the picture. "We have all seen it," the mayor exclaimed. "I will show you the caves where the seals live."

Monsieur le Maire conducted us to three caves that had no traces of animals. At the fourth cave, Tailliez, Dumas and Marcel Ichac, the Himalayan explorer, went ashore to arouse whatever creatures inhabited it. Jean Alinat and I dived toward the cave mouth; he took a post fifteen feet in front of me behind a rock, while I trained the camera toward the underwater ramp. The shore party threw a stone into the cave. To their amazement, two big frightened monk seals lumbered out, a gray female and a huge white bull, and plowed into the water in a cascade of stones. *Monachus albiventer* had re-entered zoology.

In the shadowy cave mouth I saw a big white outline, which I took to be an unusual fish. While I was not unprepared to see a monk seal, the idea of seeing a white one was not admissible—an adult albino seal is a great rarity. Alinat was close enough to see that it was a seal and he made urgent gestures for me to start the camera. The seal stopped six feet from Alinat. The old albino was unique himself, but he had never seen a double-tailed fish that exuded clouds of bubbles. The bull stretched his paw, rolled his enormous eyes from side to side and pointed his mustache with a marvelous gesture. He swam straight for me. Alinat was close enough to caress the hoary white flank as it passed.

We hurried back aboard ship and put on dry clothes for an exploration of the cave. Inside, a flashlight inspection discovered a tunnel mouth large enough to admit a man. It was a twenty-foot crawl to the inner chamber, twenty feet in diameter and filled with a strong animal odor. In the center of the chamber our flashlights discovered the undismantled skeleton of a great monk seal. Here was the ghetto in which the species had survived, where they bore children out of sight of murdering man, and here they crawled to die when their only enemy shot them. We could not dismiss the impression that the skeleton was a tomb. It lay as well-kept as a monument.

Our search for the monk seal led us further, to Port Etienne, a French outpost near the Spanish Gold Coast. There, in a corrugated iron hut, we met a lonely man, M. Caussé, who declared that the seals were his only friends. "I have learned a whistle that brings them to me," Caussé told us. "On my Sundays, I go early and crawl quietly on the sand to their midst, and we spend the day on the beach." We looked at him and wondered which was extinct, monk seals and Caussé, or our civilization.

He was acquainted with two hundred survivors of the supposedly extinct colonies of Gold Coast seals. After he had introduced us to a herd, we put on bathing trunks to emulate our host's sociable belly crawls. Philippe and Didi, in mask and fins, swam in from the sea. They were careful about overly familiar contact with mammals twice their size, which could bite through flesh and bone with their powerful jaws. Twenty seals were bathing in the surf, including a large dark male, a mother and infant, and several playful adolescents.

Floating in the water, Dumas closely studied the seals' diving technique. They closed their nostrils, turned on their sides, caressed the water with their cheeks, and vanished without a splash. Dumas, the most "liquid" of us, looked awkward as he tried to copy them. A heavy swell labored on the rocks, shaking up muddy water full of nettling micro-organisms and stinging jellyfish, but Didi and Philippe were too absorbed in their swimming lesson to notice the inconveniences. The seals seemed to enjoy the visit of the amateurs. A big bull quietly submerged behind Tailliez and popped up to surprise him, face-to-face. Philippe cupped his hand and splashed the seal in the face. The seal puffed and blew like a small boy. Dumas flailed with laughter. The laugh turned to a shout. He rolled over and thrust his mask into the water. He saw the departing rump of a seal which had sneaked up and tickled his back with its whiskers.

I had determined when we first saw the lost colony to take a pup back to France and train him to dive with us like a hunting dog. We kidnapped an eighty-pound adolescent in a net lowered from the cliff. As we hauled the net reproachful eyes watched from the surf. Caussé's eyes expressed the same disappointment. "Don't worry," I said, "we'll take very good care of him. We'll make a friend of him."

The sailors named the pup "Dumbo." They erected the notorious antishark cage on deck and spread a rug in it for him. The pup sulked, lay prostrate and refused to eat. Dumbo had not eaten for six days when we put in at Casablanca. Worried, we tried to hire the public saltwater swimming pool to jolly the pup out of his torpor. While we were negotiating for the pool, an amiable Arab fisherman climbed aboard and looked at our dolorous seal through the bars of the former human zoo. "Say," said the visitor, "seals simply love octopus. You should try it." I clutched his arm. "Please get us some octopus."

The fisherman went ashore and cut an olive branch and lashed it to a pole. He stuck the branch into the water by the stone piers of a jetty and flirted the silvery leaves before a crevice. An octopus, thinking that the leaves were small fishes, reached out a tentacle and curled it around the lure. When the octopus had embraced it with all tentacles, our friend jerked the cephalopod out on the jetty. He took three small octopi in twenty minutes.

We threw them in Dumbo's cage. The pup bounded up and swallowed them like spaghetti. From that moment on, Dumbo gobbled up every kind of fish we could buy. He became wonderfully gregarious, but the vigorous pup had revealed an alarming aspect of his friendship: he ate $200 worth of fish a month. We figured that he would eat a thousand dollars' worth of food a month when fully grown.

We thought of throwing him in the Mediterranean, but realized that Dumbo, now unafraid of humans, would pop up beside some fisherman, bawl for food and be slain in a panic. We couldn't ship him back to the Gold Coast. Even then, would his colony accept the sophisticated foreign traveler? We sadly decided to give him to the Marseilles zoo, where he was installed in a big pool of his own. We visited him several times. From Africa, Caussé sent him Christmas greetings. But soon Dumbo no longer recognized his benefactors of the *Élie Monnier*. He turned away from us and barked at a little old woman in black who came every day to give him a fish.

We visited the luxuriant waters of the Cape Verde Islands where every dive was a marvel for us. We imagined what observations

Charles Darwin, who explored there in 1831 during the famous oceanographic voyage of H.M.S. *Beagle*, could have made with our equipment. "While looking for marine animals, with my head about two feet above the rocky shore," Darwin wrote, "I was more than once saluted by a jet of water, accompanied by a slight grating noise. . . . I found out that this was a cuttle fish. . . . I observed that one which I kept in the cabin was slightly phosphorescent in the dark."

We were permited to observe the cuttlefish, or octopus, with our heads below the water. We saw the great rays and mantas swimming in the depths. Under Boavista Island, blue lobsters were so numerous that there were not enough crevices to house them. The homeless ones wandered on the bottom along crowded boulevards between the dwellings of the home owners. It looked like slow-motion city traffic.

The turtles of Brava astonished us by the duration of their submersions. A captured turtle in a zoo pool surfaces often for breath, but here in the wild they rested on the bottom for hours. Only once did we see a turtle ascend to breathe. Their metabolism is possibly so low that turtles require little oxygen, except when paddling energetically to escape.

Fifty feet down off Brava we discovered a large tunnel which passed completely through a small island. In the dark interior, one could look back reassuringly at the emerald glow of the entrance, swim on through shafts of silvery light falling from potholes in the rock above, and turn a corner to find the inviting green of the sea at the far exit. The cave entrances were exuberant with bright silver-blue fish, as animated as a wedding party. The gatherings were exactly that; a mass marriage of large blue jacks was taking place. Their bellies were dilated with eggs. Jacks were everywhere in the waters outside, in swiftly moving forage parties of four to thirty fish, but here they gathered by the hundreds in a glittering mass circling in the shadows. They were quite excited by the invasion of the divers, and gathered around us reprovingly, like guests at a genteel reception glaring at uninvited drunks.

We would enter the cave slowly from dark corners so as not to disturb them, and witness the excited flutterings of their long love dances in the nuptial suite. We made ourselves as inconspicuous as possible out of respect for one of nature's secret ceremonies, perhaps never before witnessed by man.

Our best companion in the reefs was the tragicomic trumpet fish, found everywhere in great numbers in the Cape Verdes. The trumpet fish has a head like a horse, and a disproportionately tiny tail, separated by a long pipe of a body, sometimes two feet in length. The hapless trumpet fish, more properly called *poisson flûte*, or flute fish, is wretchedly equipped for locomotion. The useless tail and the stiff tubular body are handicaps for which the trumpet compensates by wildly agitating its pectoral fins to move forward and backward, slanted head down, or leaning on end as frequently as it swims horizontally. From a rocky hole a dozen of the poor chaps will be found sticking up like pencils in a cup.

These forlorn sticks have a remarkable trait. We observed it at such length that what I report here is not a hasty conclusion but a confirmed observation, recorded many times by the cinécamera.

Often a trumpet fish will leave his fellow wallflowers and swim rapidly toward a larger animal such as a parrot fish, a grunt, grouper or rock bass. He will place himself alongside or on the back of the passer-by, barely touching it, and swim along in this tandem fashion as if seeking friendship, begging for tenderness, offering his heart. There is absolutely no hostility in this gesture. The trumpet fish has no weapons to harm a fish his size, and is in fact placing himself in some danger from the other more capable fish. Nor is the trumpet trying to beg part of the other fellow's dinner.

The gesture is never reciprocated. The rock bass or parrot fish goes about his affairs, heedless of the trumpet fish, until he grows annoyed at the bore pressing his unwanted friendship. He makes a sudden spurt to dislodge the nuisance, but the lonely one follows. Later, the object of affection accelerates to full speed and leaves the trumpet fish hanging morosely in the water, rejected once again. We watched this piscine social drama many times, torn between pity and laughter.

The Gibraltar Straits are a unique place to study sea mammals. Migratory thousands of whales and porpoises pass to and fro across the narrow sill between the Mediterranean and Atlantic. Tailliez and I watched the herds romping through the gate, while Dumas was under the keel fitting an automatic movie camera to film an antic porpoise pack playing at the bow of the *Élie Monnier*.

One watches them race the bow of a ship, vaulting out of the foam for breath and dropping out of the stream like a man falling from flight, to be replaced instantly by another porpoise; and, as the bow speeds, lie on their flanks and spy the humans with quick little eyes. A mother swims with her child, which moves at a faster rhythm to keep up; they jostle each other playfully. Presto, for no apparent reason, the ranks thin out—the last porpoise sounds and a curtain of foam is drawn over the ballet of the sea.

We often watched them and occasionally dived with them. They played chasing games as if they had a brain capacity for satire. They are constructed disturbingly like men. They are warm-blooded and breathe air and are the size and weight of men. Dr. Longet dissected a porpoise on an operating table on deck. We watched uneasily as he removed lungs like ours and a brain as big as a man's, deeply corrugated in the fashion that is supposed to mark human genius. Porpoises have smiling lips and shining eyes. They are gregarious and, more than that, social. There are probably more porpoises in the sea than there are men on earth.

The powerful horizontal flukes of the porpoises speed them to the surface to take an instant breath, then they dive like a living torpedo. We took slow-motion movies of their ventholes to measure the time they need to snatch a breath. The films showed that they fill their lungs in one-eighth of a second. When they went down they left a silvery dotted line of bubbles, revealing that porpoises do not hermetically seal their blowholes under water.

Swimming under water among them with naked ears we heard their mouselike squeaks, a comical cry for such splendid animals. The porpoise's shrill pip may have a further use than mere conversation in the herd. One day, forty miles out in the Atlantic on a

course for Gibraltar, the *Élie Monnier* was running its honest twelve knots when a crowd of porpoises overtook from astern. They were headed on the exact bearing for the center of Gibraltar Strait, although land was far out of sight. I ran with them for a while, then subtly altered course five or six degrees, trying to deviate them. The pack accepted the detour for a few minutes, then abandoned the bow and resumed its original heading. I swung back on the porpoise course—they were running true for the Straits.

Wherever they came from the porpoises had secure knowledge of where the ten-mile gate lay in the immense sea. Are the porpoises equipped with sonic or ultrasound apparatus by which their squeaks give them the feel of unseen bottom topography? Things happen exactly as though they receive bearings from Gibraltar. They probably bounce their mouselike chirps from the floor. Perhaps deep in their racial instinct there is a knowledge of the course which winds through the far unseen hills and plains to the door of their Mediterranean playland.

Monsters We Have Met

FISHING is one of man's oldest occupations and fish stories entered folklore very early. Poets and nature fakers added their touches to marine superstitions that persist to our day. The popu-

lar press still cannot resist unsubstantiated stories of sea monsters.

When the helmet diver appeared a century ago, the saga gained the ultimate dramatic ingredient, a human hero to descend and give battle to the fiends. Their sanguinary engagements have been portrayed by dry writers ashore. The lonely, hardworking divers may be forgiven for their silent endorsement of the sagas. Indeed the helmet diver, imprisoned in his casque, and almost always working in filthy harbors and channels, is unable to determine whether an interference with his air pipe is caused by a giant squid or a rotted spar. Doubt leaves room for interpretation.

A naked man swimming in the sea mingles with and observes life around him and may be watched by other swimmers, and the recording eye of the lens. His advent means the end of superstition.

If I may put aside the sea snake, the villains of undersea myth are sharks, octopi, congers, morays, sting rays, mantas, squids and barracudas. We have met all but the giant squid, which lives beyond our depth range. Save for the shark, about which we are still puzzled, the monsters we have met seem a thoroughly harmless lot. Some are indifferent to men; others are curious about us. Most of them are frightened when we approach closely. I write here of some of our "monsters"—and of the shark later.

Our experiences, of course, have been mainly in the Mediterranean with shorter periods in the Atlantic and Red Sea. Perhaps the monsters of the Mediterranean have been tamed, and the wild ones live in your ocean. Consider the case of the slandered octopus.

The octopus owes most of its notoriety to Victor Hugo, who, in *Toilers of the Sea*, related the manner in which the octopus ingests food, in this case a human being. "You enter in the beast," he wrote. "The hydra incorporates itself with the man; the man is amalgamated with the hydra. You become one. The tiger can only devour you; the devilfish inhales you. He draws you to him, into him; and, bound and helpless, you feel yourself emptied into this frightful sac, which is a monster. To be eaten alive is more than terrible; but to be drunk alive is inexpressible." Such was the anticipation of the octopus we took to our first dives. After meeting a few octopi, we concluded that it was more likely that to be "drunk alive" referred to the condition of the novelist when he penned the passage, than to the situation of a human meeting an octopus.

On countless occasions we have offered our persons for this libation. At first we had natural revulsion against touching the slimy surfaces of rocks and animals, but found that the fingertips conveyed no such sense. That made it easier to touch a live octopus for the first time. We saw many octopi on the floor and clinging to reefs. Dumas seized the nettle one day, by pulling an octopus from a cliff. He was somewhat apprehensive, but it was a small octopus and Didi felt he was too large a drink for it. If Dumas was timid, the octopus was downright terrorized. It writhed desperately to escape the four-armed monster, and succeeded in breaking loose. It made off by slow jet propulsion, exuding spurts of its famous ink.

Soon we were handling any size of cephalopod we found. Dumas became a sort of dancing instructor to devilfish. He would select an unwilling pupil, hold it firmly and gently and gyrate around, inducing the creature to follow. The octopod used every trick to escape. The bashful animal usually refused to fasten its suction cups to flesh. Didi tried to wrap the tentacles around his bare arm, in the familiar blood-drinking position, but without success. The octopus would not retain the grip. Didi forced the suction cups against his arm and succeeded in obtaining a brief adhesion, quite easy to remove, leaving momentary marks on his skin.

The octopus has a remarkable trace of adaptability. Dumas determined that, by patiently playing with them until he met some response. Usually octopi were most submissive when very tired. Dumas would release an exhausted octopus and let it jet away with its legs trailing. The octopus has two distinct means of locomotion. It can crawl efficiently on hard surfaces. (Guy Gilpatric once saw an octopus let loose in a library. It raced up and down the stacks, hurling books on the floor, possibly a belated revenge on authors.) Its method of swimming consists of inflating the head, or valva, with water and jetting the fluid to achieve moderate speed. Dumas could easily overtake the animal. The octopus discharged several ink bombs and then resorted to its last defense, a sudden plunge to immobility on the bottom, where it instantly assumed the local color and pattern. Keeping a sharp eye out for this camouflage stunt, Didi confronted the creature again. At the exhaustion of its psychological warfare effects, the octopus sprang hopelessly from the bottom, fanned its legs and dribbled back to the floor.

At this point Dumas found it willing to dance. Taking the student by the feet, he led it through some ballet improvisations. Several octopi induced to this state of nervous collapse responded imitatively to his figures, and ended the lesson in the attitude of a playful cat. When Didi's air was gone, the spent octopus remained extended and relaxed, watching him fly into the sky. I know this sounds like a story from Marseilles. I was careful to make several movies of it as evidence.

The ink of the octopus has been liberally diluted with journalistic fantasy. Masks protect our eyes so I cannot say whether or not the ink is optically venomous. It had no effect on naked skin and appeared to have none on a fish passing through the ink. We found that the emission was not a smoke screen to hide the creature from pursuers. The pigment did not dissipate; it hung in the water as a fairly firm blob with a tail, too small to conceal the octopus. If the ink wasn't poison or concealment, what was its function? I heard an interesting explanation from a staunch friend of the octopus, Theodore Rousseau, curator of painting at the Metropolitan Museum of Art in New York. He submitted that the ink bomb is a mock-octopus shape to divert weak-eyed pursuers. The size and shape of the puff roughly corresponds to that of the swimming octopus which deposited it.

On the flat shallow floor northeast of Porquerolles we came upon an octopus city. We could hardly believe our eyes. Scientific credence, confirmed by our own experiences, holds that the octopus lives in crannies of rock and reef. Yet here were strange villas, indisputably erected by the octopi themselves. A typical home was one roofed with a flat stone two feet long and weighing perhaps twenty pounds. One side of the stone had been raised eight inches and propped by two lintels, a stone and a red building brick. The mud floor inside had been excavated five inches. In front of the lean-to was a wall of accumulated debris: crab and oyster shells, stones, shards of man-made pottery, sea anemones and urchins. A tentacle extended from the dwelling and curled around the rubble, and the owl-like eyes of the octopus peered at me over the wall. When I went closer, the tentacle contracted, sweeping the debris up against the door, concealing the inhabitant. We made color photographs of an octopus house.

To me the observation was noteworthy, for it may prove that the octopus is capable of using tools, which involves complex conditioned reflexes which I have not seen previously credited to the octopus. By assembling materials to build a house and by lifting the rock and holding it while it inserted the pebble and brick pillars, the octopus may have promoted itself in the brain classification of species.

It is intriguing to speculate on octopus love-making, which we have never seen in the sea. It was described by Henry Lee, late keeper of the Brighton (England) Aquarium, the Boswell of the octopus. Eighty years ago Henry Lee patiently observed the first captive English octopus in a tank at Brighton. He wrote a profoundly witty book called *The Octopus, the Devilfish of Fact and Fiction*. For his Victorian audience Lee wrote, "I can say but little concerning the fertilization of eggs of the octopodae in a book intended for readers of all classes." With this pious disclaimer, Henry Lee then proceeded to describe what he had seen: "In the breeding season a curious alteration takes place in one of the arms of the male octopus. The limb becomes swollen, and from it is developed a long wormlike process, furnished with two longitudinal rows of suckers, from the extremity of which extends a slender elongated filament. When its owner offers his hand in marriage to a lady octopus she accepts, *and keeps it, and walks away with it,* for this singular outgrowth is then detached from the arm of her suitor, and becomes a moving creature, having separate life, and continuing to exist for some time after being transferred to her keeping."

A favorite haunt for another breed of monster was an encampment one hundred and thirty feet down in La Sèche du Sarranier in the Côte d'Azur. The soil was distinctive—it seemed sandy until we drew near and saw it was a field of queer round pebbles of organic origin, tinted in delicate shades of rose and mauve. There were a few stone cairns, inhabited by merous and rockfish, but the place was owned by rays. A host of sting rays, eagle rays and skates rested flat on the pebbles.

As we swam to them, they raised alertly on their wingtips, ready to flee, and when we closed in, they rose in pairs and fled. We often saw them swimming in couples, but we have not been able to capture a natural pair to see if they were sexual mates. Once I came upon two medium-sized sting rays asleep on the bottom. One awoke and started to fly. It hesitated, returned to the other and awakened it by flapping its wings. They sailed away together.

When we glided motionless into the ray kingdom, they remained, rolling their big round eyes and closely watching us. The thicker bodies were pregnant females, which retain their young for a long time, as if to launch them as capable as possible in the struggle for life. Spearing rays has no

further interest for us. The killing is simple and unworthy. In the early days we sometimes harpooned rays. One that we landed surprised us by giving birth on the sand. Tailliez picked up one of the eight-inch calves to return it to the water. The newborn infant gave him a man-sized sting.

Fishermen are sometimes hurt by boated rays and observe the rule of severing the tail when the animal is hauled in. The wounds are often infected. There is a poison gland in the tail, and the thick coat of mucus on the serrated stinger may plant infection in a wound.

Rays are no danger to a diver. Certainly the ray will never attack a man. The celebrated stinger is not an offensive weapon—it is a reactor to molestation. The stinger is located at the base of the tail, extending for only a sixth of its length. Dumas swims up behind a ray and grabs the end of the tail, an insurance against an accidental sting. The ray struggles to release its tail from his grasp, but it cannot manipulate the stinger while Dumas holds the tip. The saw-toothed weapon is placed to defend attack from behind and above. Bathers who step on a ray may receive this reflex stroke, inflicted as deeply as the frightened animal can swing. It may mean several weeks in the hospital.

While we were diving off Praia in the Cape Verdes, a shadow passed across the bottom. I thought it was a cloud scudding in the other world, until Dumas hooted and pointed up. Directly over us passed a manta ray with an eighteen-foot wingspread. It eclipsed the sun. It did not swim —it flew. The curved extremities of its wings sliced the surface film. The belly was enamel white, as white as the back was black. The supernatural sight did not remain long. Gliding without apparent effort the manta drew away from Dumas's best two-knot pursuit, flickered its wings and accelerated into the sea fog.

Fishermen fear manta rays, a superstition which is enhanced by its nocturnal prank of a violent leap into the air and a flat resounding crash of a ton of flesh on the water. Fishermen warned us that mantas killed divers by wrapping their wings around the man and smothering him, or by enveloping the diver and crushing him against the floor. But far from inspiring fear in a diver, they arouse admiration in a man lucky enough to see them in flight. We dissected a manta ray to examine its nutritive system. It had no teeth or grinders. Food was taken by a powerful water pump comprising the gill clefts and mouth, drawing large volumes of water into an elaborate filtering system, which strained morsels of plankton as fine as pablum to pass them through the little throat. Unlike the sting ray it had no stinger on its tail. The manta ray had to rely entirely on its speed to survive. It could harm nothing but plankton.

At Brava Island Dumas penetrated the camouflage of a large sea tortoise which clung to a rock, secure in its blend with the reef.

He approached from the rear and grasped the shell by either rim. The astonished turtle jerked its flippers. Didi lifted the animal and applied a slight propulsion with his fins. The outraged turtle took up the tandem glide and paddled Didi around a vertical loop. Dumas experimented with several aeronautical figures, including a worthy Immelmann, and liberated his towboat. The turtle did not understand freedom. It repeated the last loop like a comedian performing a double take, before it rowed off into the green.

In undersea fiction, the moray eel is a formidable gangster of the deep. It guards as many sunken treasures as does the literary octopus. Fishermen fear the moray on a realistic basis. Flopping out its life in the bilge boards of a boat, the moray *in extremis* will bite anything presented to its jaws. Wise fishermen crush its head as soon as it is boated. Roman historians relate that Nero threw slaves into pools of morays to amuse his friends with the sight of human beings eaten alive. This celebrated perversity, whether true or not, gave the moray a bad name for all time. Nero must have methodically starved captive morays until the fish had no choice of menu.

Morays will not attack men in the sea. They presented themselves to us with only the head and neck emerging from the hole. They looked quite fearsome. In addition to speed, camouflage and weapons, fish employ psychological effects. The moray disseminates propaganda with its evil eyes and bared fangs. If it could hiss like a wildcat, it would. The moray is also found in sunken ships, staring with basilisk eyes from encrusted aeries of pipes, and trunks. Alas, it is as prosaic as you and I and the cat. It wishes to be unmolested in the destined journey of life. It is a confirmed home body. It will hence inflict a bite on an intruder. Dumas was once reaching into the reef for lobsters under Machado light, when he took a moray bite on his finger. The puncture was unimportant and healed overnight. The next day the wound hemorrhaged and closed again. Dumas said, "The moray did not attack me. It warned my hand to get out and stay out." There was no infection. The bite was not venomous.

While we were grubbing in the harbor of ancient Carthage, we called on Dr. Heldt, director of the oceanographic station at Salambo. He and his wife had great enthusiasm for Tunisian marine fauna, and urged us to visit one of the most horrible and grand sights we would ever see, the Madrague of Sidi Daoud. A *madrague* is a gigantic tuna net originated centuries ago in the Aegean and Adriatic and brought later to Tunisia. It is a wide-meshed vertical net a mile or two in length which is stretched diagonally from the shore, terminating at sea in four roomy chambers in which big tuna are trapped during the early summer spawning season.

Tunas are migrants; some zoologists believe they cruise around the world. World travelers, or citizens of a single ocean, tuna invariably come inshore in the spawning season and swim in schools along the beaches. They always navigate with their right eyes toward the shore. Aristotle, who was no mean oceanographer, concluded that tuna were blind in the left eye, a belief still prevalent among contemporary Mediterranean fishermen. But whatever the reason honeymooning tunas keep the shore to starboard, it is the characteristic that signs their doom.

When the herd encounters the *madrague,* it turns left along the net wall to skirt the obstacle, and passes straight into the trap. Arab fishermen in boats watch the foyer of the trap and close the door when the fish have entered. They admit the tuna to a second room and close it, so that the outside door may be open for new arrivals. The fish are conducted into a third chamber, beyond which hangs the death cell itself, which is termed by an ominous Sicilian word, the *corpo.* Sixty gigantic tuna and hundreds of bonitos were in the *corpo* when we arrived in the village of Sidi Daoud to film the massacre in color.

The *corpo* had been towed inshore. On the jetty stood the master of ceremonies and head executioner, the *raïs,* a majestic individual in a red fez and American Army trousers. He hoisted a flag as the signal for the *matanza* (massacre). Hundreds of Arabs converged in steady flat-bottomed rowboats and disposed them in a hollow square around the *corpo*. The *raïs* was rowed to the center. He ordered the ritual to begin. A barbarian roar broke from the fishermen and they chanted an old Sicilian song, traditional to the *matanza*. To its cadence the boatmen hauled in the walls of the net.

Marcel Ichac filmed the spectacle from a boat above the *corpo*, while Dumas and I dived into the net to record it below. Sunk in the crystalline water we could not see both sidewalls of the *corpo*, and imagined that the fish could not, either. We had unconsciously taken on the psyche of the doomed animals. In the frosty green space we saw the herd only occasionally. The noble fish, weighing up to four hundred pounds apiece, swam around and around counter-clockwise, according to their habit. In contrast to their might, the net wall looked like a spider web that would rend before their charge, but they did not challenge it. Above the surface, the Arabs were shrinking the walls of the *corpo*, and the rising floor came into view.

Life took on a new perspective, when considered from the viewpoint of the creatures imprisoned in the *corpo*. We pondered how it would feel to be trapped with the other animals and have to live their tragedy. Dumas and I were the only ones in the creeping, constricting prison who knew the outcome, and we were destined to escape. Perhaps we were oversentimental but we were ashamed of the knowledge. I had an impulse to take my belt knife and cut a hole for a mass break to freedom.

The death chamber was reduced to a third of its size. The atmosphere grew excited, frantic. The herd swam restlessly faster, but still in formation. Their eyes passed us with almost human expressions of fright.

My final dive came just before the boatmen tied off the *corpo* to begin the killing. Never have I beheld a sight like the death cell in the last moments. In a space comparable to a large living room tunas and bonitos drove madly in all directions. The tuna's right-eyed honeymoon instinct was at last destroyed. The fish were out of control.

It took all my will power to stay down and hold the camera into the maddened shuttle of fish. With the seeming momentum of locomotives, the tuna drove at me, head-on, obliquely and crosswise. It was out of the question for me to dodge them. Frightened out of sense of time, I heard the reel run out and surfaced amidst the thrashing bodies. There was not a mark on my body. Even while running amok the giant fish had avoided me by inches, merely massaging me with backwash when they sped past.

The nets were pegged, the *raïs* gave the ceremonial sign of execution. He lifted his fez and saluted those who were about to die. The fishermen struck at the surfaced swarm with large gaffs. The sea turned red. It took five or six men whacking gaffs into a single tuna to draw it out, flapping and bending like a gross mechanical toy. The boats rocked with convulsive bleeding mounds of tuna and bonitos. The fish ended their struggles, and the bloody fishermen leaped into the pink water of the *corpo* to wash and relax.

More than any other fish, the great liche is the ocean's nobility, aloof from nets and hooks, living in liberty below fifteen fathoms, deigning to touch the terrestrial world at remote capes, lonely reefs and deep wrecks. The liche is the color of the ocean; elongated, powerful, swift and lissome, with a lemony stripe on its seasilver sides. Sometimes alone, more often in troops, the liche appears from liquid nothingness into the diver's world and casts its fawn's eye upon him. Then all other fish seem shabby provincials. The liche is a cosmopolite, unimpresed on its long passage from Sidon to the Pillars of Hercules by the sight of men, who are one day worth an investigatory pause and the next are pedestrians to be shouldered out of the way.

We have seen them counterlit against the sky, circling a rock needle aureoled in foam. Like tunas, liches are big, migratory carnivores. Men betray the tuna with nets and catch them on lines, but the liche will not be taken. So successfully do they elude hooks and trawls that fishermen and scientists believe the liche is rare and does not exceed three feet in length. Yet, we have counted far

more liche than tuna, and are not surprised to see six-footers. The sight of liche is to us the badge of an adventurous dive.

Barracudas are no danger to divers. Despite undersea fairy tales, I know of no reliable evidence of a barracuda's attacking a diver. Many good-sized barracudas passed us in the Red Sea, in the Mediterranean and the tropical Atlantic, giving no sign of aggressiveness.

A diver is too busy avoiding a certain truly dangerous undersea animal to fret over barracudas. This real-life peril of the deep is the commonplace sea urchin, a burrowing thistle-like echinoderm with sharp, brittle spines. It is in no way aggressive, it is merely omnipresent. The urchin may not measure up to the demands of the monster-mongers, but when one bumps into an urchin there is villain enough. Its spines penetrate the flesh and break off. They are extremely difficult to remove and may become infected. We keep a sharper eye out for sea urchins than we do for barracudas.

A larger nuisance is the stinging jellyfish, whose varicolored crystal cups hang in the water like small naval mines. They are pleasingly patterned in dark blue, brown and yellow. Many varieties of jellyfish can deal a shocking sting. The most prevalent and dangerous is the Portuguese man-of-war, whose arrival at the seashore has spoiled many a resort season. The animal floats on the surface dangling its long poisonous filaments. I made a dive off

Bermuda, through a colony of men-of-war, so crowded together it was hard to find a place to enter. Safe below the surface, I looked up at a ceiling of injurious threads, fringing the sky to the limit of sight. Among the filaments swam small Nomeus fish, of the perch-pike family, who have an absolution from the man-of-war. It never stings them.

Two important living enemies of undersea man are fire coral and sea poison ivy, which inflict burns that may last for days. They are allergenic phenomena—a few persons are immune and others suffer no pain on the first contact, but the second exposure brings a severe rash. Anti-histamine creams heal the burns of sea ivy and fire coral in a few hours.

Such are some of the monsters we have met. If none have eaten us, it is perhaps because they have never read the instructions so generously provided in marine demonology.

Shark Close-ups

ON a goggle dive at Djerba Island off Tunisia in 1939 I met sharks under water for the first time. They were magnificent gunmetal creatures, eight feet long, that swam in pairs behind their servant remoras. I was uneasy with fear, but I calmed somewhat when I saw the reaction of my diving companion, Simone. She was scared. The sharks passed on haughtily.

The Djerba sharks were entered in a shark casebook I kept religiously until we went to the Red Sea in 1951, where sharks appeared in such numbers that my census lost value. From the data, covering over a hundred shark encounters with many varieties, I can offer two conclusions: The better acquainted we become with sharks, the less we know them, and one can never tell what a shark is going to do.

Man is separated from the shark by an abyss of time. The fish still lives in the late Mesozoic, when the rocks were made: it has changed but little in perhaps three hundred million years. Across the gulf of ages, which evolved other marine creatures, the relentless, indestructible shark has come without need of evolution, the oldest killer, armed for the fray of existence in the beginning.

One sunny day in the open sea between the islands of Boavista and Maio, in the Cape Verde group, a long Atlantic swell beat on an exposed reef and sent walls of flume high into the air. Such a sight is the dread of hydrographers, who mark it off sternly to warn the mariner. But the *Élie Monnier* was attracted to such spots. We anchored by the dangerous reef to dive from the steeply rolling deck into the wild sea. Where there is a reef, there is

Captain Cousteau swims under the sea with his pressurized Rolleiflex camera making color flash photos. The camera document which follows records man's most intimate and comprehensive adventure inside the sea. Captain Cousteau provides a running commentary on the great moments of fifteen years and five thousand dives by the authors and members of the Undersea Group. Most pictures are from his eight movies made under water. Some are by photographers accompanying his various expeditions, a few (such as the shot above) have been rendered from color stereophotos. When a picture is not credited to a photographer, it was made by Cousteau, Frédéric Dumas or Philippe Tailliez, members of the Undersea Research Group. (*Photo by Jean de Wouters d'Oplinter.*)

In 1942, the brilliant engineer, Émile Gagnan, and I made the first completely automatic compressed-air apparatus, the aqualung. Below, Philippe Tailliez, of the Undersea Research Group, swims in complete freedom with an aqualung, receiving breaths automatically from the demand regulator.

Old and new ways to salvage. Dumas, second from right, joins a veteran conventional diver in cutting up the sunken passenger steamer, *Chellah,* near Marseilles.

We hoist aboard an Ionic capital which has been buried in the sea bed since before Christ was born. Lieutenant Jean Alinat fingers marble carving almost as perfect as it came from the Greek sculptor's chisel over two thousand years ago. (*Photo by Marcel Ichac.*)

Frédéric Dumas swims in a sunken ship sixty feet down.

We invented an antishark cage in which Dumas goes down, feeling a
little silly. The idea was to give divers a quick refuge downstairs. We
abandoned the human zoo when we decided shark danger was negligible.

Dumas swims down toward the shark and pilot fish.

"No fate could be more horrible than to be entwined in the embrace of those eight clammy, corpselike arms, and to feel their folds creeping and gliding around you, and the eight hundred discs with their cold adhesive touch, gluing themselves to you with a grasp that nothing could relax, and feeling like so many mouths devouring you at the same time."—*Victor Hugo*

abundant life.

Small sharks came when we dropped anchor. The crew broke out tuna hooks and took ten of them in as many minutes. When we went overside for a camera dive, there were only two sharks left in the water. Under the racing swell we watched them strike the hooks and thrash their way through the surface. Down in the reef we found the savage population of the open ocean, including some extremely large nurse sharks, a class that is not supposed to be harmful to man. We saw three sharks sleeping in rocky caverns. The camera demanded lively sharks. Dumas and Tailliez swam into the caves and pulled their tails to wake them. The sharks came out and vanished into the blue, playing their bit parts competently.

We saw a fifteen-foot nurse shark. I summoned Didi and conveyed to him in sign language that he would be permitted to relax our neutrality toward sharks and take a crack at this one with his super-harpoon gun. It had a six-foot spear with an explosive head and three hundred pounds of traction in its elastic bands. Dumas fired straight down at a distance of twelve feet. The four-pound harpoon struck the shark's head and, two seconds later, the harpoon tip exploded. We were severely shaken. There was some pain involved.

The shark continued to swim away, imperturbably, with the spear sticking from its head like a flagstaff. After a few strokes the harpoon shaft fell to the bottom and the shark moved on. We swam after it as fast as we could to see what would happen. The shark showed every sign of normal movement, accelerated gradually and vanished. The only conclusion we could draw was that the harpoon went clear through the head and exploded externally, because no internal organ could survive a blast that nearly incapacitated us two harpoon lengths away. Even so, taking such a burst a few inches from the head demonstrated the extraordinary vitality of sharks.

One day we were finishing a movie sequence on trigger fish when Dumas and I were galvanized with ice-cold terror. It is a reaction unpleasant enough on land, and very lonely in the water. What we saw made us feel that naked men really do not belong under the sea.

At a distance of forty feet there appeared from the gray haze the lead-white bulk of a twenty-five-foot *Carcharodon carcharias*, the only shark species that all specialists agree is a confirmed maneater. Dumas, my bodyguard, closed in beside me. The brute was swimming lazily. In that moment I thought that at least he would have a bellyache on our three-cylinder lungs.

Then, the shark saw us. His reaction was the last conceivable one. In pure fright, the monster voided a cloud of excrement and departed at an incredible speed.

Dumas and I looked at each other and burst into nervous

laughter. The self-confidence we gained that day led us to a foolish negligence. We abandoned the bodyguard system and all measures of safety. Further meetings with sharp-nosed sharks, tiger sharks, mackerel sharks, and ground sharks, inflated our sense of shark mastery. They all ran from us. After several weeks in the Cape Verdes, we were ready to state flatly that all sharks were cowards. They were so pusillanimous they wouldn't hold still to be filmed.

One day I was on the bridge, watching the little spark jiggle up and down on the echo-sound tape, sketching the profile of the sea floor nine thousand feet below the open Atlantic off Africa. There was the usual faint signal of the deep scattering layer twelve hundred feet down. The deep scattering layer is an astounding new problem of oceanography, a mystifying physical mezzanine hovering above the bedrock of the sea. It is recorded at two to three hundred fathoms in the daytime and it ascends toward the surface at night.

The phenomenon rises and falls with the cycle of sun and dark, leading some scientists to believe it is a dense blanket of living organisms, so vast as to tilt the imagination. As I watched the enigmatic scrawls, the stylus began to enter three distinct spurs on the tape, three separate scattering layers, one above the other. I was lost in whirling ideas, watching the spark etch the lowest and heaviest layer, when I heard shouts from the deck, "Whales!" A herd of sluggish bottlenosed whales surrounded the *Élie Monnier*.

In the clear water we studied the big dark forms. Their heads were round and glossy with bulbous foreheads, the "bottle" which gives them their name. When a whale broke the surface, it spouted and the rest of the body followed softly, stretching in relaxation. The whale's lips were curved in a fixed smile with tiny eyes close to the tucks of the lips, a roguish visage for such a formidable creature. Dumas skinned down to the harpoon platform under the bow while I stuck a film magazine in the underwater camera. The whales were back from a dive. One emerged twelve feet from Dumas. He threw the harpoon with all his might. The shaft struck near the pectoral fin and blood started. The animal sounded in an easy rhythm and we paid out a hundred yards of harpoon line, tied to a heavy gray buoy. The buoy was swept away in the water—the whale was well hooked. The other whales lay unperturbed around the *Élie Monnier*.

We saw Dumas's harpoon sticking out of the water; then it, the whale and buoy disappeared. Dumas climbed the mast with binoculars. I kept the ship among the whales, thinking they would not abandon a wounded comrade. Time passed.

Libera, the keen-eyed radio man, spotted the buoy and there was the whale, seemingly unhurt, with the harpoon protruding like a toothpick. Dumas hit the whale twice with dum-dum bullets. Red water washed on the backs of the faithful herd, as it gathered around the stricken one. We struggled for an hour to pick up the buoy and tie the harpoon line to the *Élie Monnier.*

A relatively small bottlenosed whale, heavily wounded, was tethered to the ship. We were out of sight of land, with fifteen hundred fathoms of water under the keel, and the whale herd diving and spouting around the ship. Tailliez and I entered the water to follow the harpoon line to the agonized animal.

The water was an exceptional clear turquoise blue. We followed the line a few feet under the surface, and came upon the whale. Thin streams of blood jetted horizontally from the bullet holes. I swam toward three other bottlenoses. As I neared them, they turned up their flukes and sounded. It was the first time I had been under water to actually see them diving and I understood the old whaler's word, "sound." They did not dive obliquely as porpoises often do. They sped straight down, perfectly vertical. I followed them down a hundred feet. A fifteen-foot shark passed way below me, probably attracted by the whale's blood. Beyond sight was the deep scattering layer; down there a herd of leviathans grazed; more sharks roamed. Above in the sun's silvery light was Tailliez and a big whale dying. Reluctantly I returned to the ship.

Back on deck I changed into another lung and strapped a tablet of cupric acetate on an ankle and one on my belt. When this chemical dissolves in water it is supposed to repulse sharks. Dumas was to pass a noose over the whale's tail, while I filmed. Just after we went under he saw a big shark, but it was gone before I answered his shout. We swam under the keel of the ship and located the harpoon line.

A few lengths down the line in a depth of fifteen feet we sighted an eight-foot shark of a species we had never before seen. He was impressively neat, light gray, sleek, a real collector's item. A ten-inch fish with vertical black-and-white stripes accompanied him a few inches above his back, one of the famous pilot fish. We boldly swam toward the shark, confident that he would run as all the others had. He did not retreat. We drew within ten feet of him, and saw all around the shark an escort of tiny striped pilots three or four inches long.

They were not following him; they seemed part of him. A thumbnail of a pilot fish wriggled just ahead of the shark's snout, miraculously staying in place as the beast advanced. He probably found there a compressibility wave that held him. If he tumbled out of it, he would be hopelessly left behind. It was some time before we realized that the shark and his courtiers were not scared of us.

Sea legends hold that the shark has poor eyesight and pilot fish guide him to the prey, in order to take crumbs from his table. Scientists today tend to pooh-pooh the attribution of the pilot as a seeing-eye dog, although dissection has confirmed the low vision of sharks. Our experiences lead us to believe they probably see as well as we do.

The handsome gray was not apprehensive. I was happy to have such an opportunity to film a shark, although, as the first wonder passed, a sense of danger came to our hearts. Shark and company slowly circled us. I became the film director, making signs to Dumas, who was co-starred with the shark. Dumas obligingly swam in front of the beast and along behind it. He lingered at the tail and reached out his hand. He grasped the tip of the caudal fin, undecided about giving it a good pull. That would break the dreamy rhythm and make a good shot, but it might also bring the teeth snapping back at him. Dumas released the tail and pursued the shark round and round. I was whirling in the center of the game, busy framing Dumas. He was swimming as hard as he could to keep up with the almost motionless animal. The shark made no hostile move nor did he flee, but his hard little eyes were on us.

I tried to identify the species. The tail was quite asymmetrical, with an unusually long top, or heterocercal caudal fin. He had huge pectorals, and the large dorsal fin was rounded with a big white patch on it. In outline and marking he resembled no shark we had seen or studied.

The shark had gradually led us down to sixty feet. Dumas pointed down. From the visibility limit of the abyss, two more sharks climbed toward us. They were fifteen-footers, slender, steel-blue animals with a more savage appearance. They leveled off below us. They carried no pilot fish.

Our old friend, the gray shark, was getting closer to us, tightening his slowly revolving cordon. But he still seemed manageable. He turned reliably in his clockwise prowl and the pilots held their stations. The blue pair from the abyss hung back, leaving the affair to the first comer. We revolved inside the ring, watching the gray, and tried to keep the blues located at the same time. We never found them in the same place twice.

Below the blue sharks there appeared great tunas with long fins. Perhaps they had been there since the beginning, but it was the first time we noticed them. Above us flying fish gamboled, adding a discordant touch of gaiety to what was becoming a tragedy for us. Dumas and I ransacked our memories for advices on how to frighten off sharks. *"Gesticulate wildly,"* *said a lifeguard.* We flailed our arms. The gray did not falter. *"Give 'em a flood of bubbles,"* *said a helmet diver.* Dumas waited until the shark had reached his nearest point and released a heavy exhalation. The shark did not react. *"Shout as loud as you can,"* *said Hans Hass.* We hooted until our voices cracked. The shark appeared deaf. *"Cupric acetate tab-*

lets *fastened to leg and belt will keep sharks away if you go into the drink*," said an Air Force briefing officer. Our friend swam through the copper-stained water without a wink. His cold, tranquil eye appraised us. He seemed to know what he wanted, and he was in no hurry.

A small dreadful thing occurred. The tiny pilot fish on the shark's snout tumbled off his station and wriggled to Dumas. It was a long journey for the little fellow, quite long enough for us to speculate on his purpose. The mite butterflied in front of Dumas's mask. Dumas shook his head as if to dodge a mosquito. The little pilot fluttered happily, moving with the mask, inside which Dumas focused in cross-eyed agony.

Instinctively I felt my comrade move close to me, and I saw his hand held out clutching his belt knife. Beyond the camera and the knife, the gray shark retreated some distance, turned, and glided at us head-on.

We did not believe in knifing sharks, but the final moment had come, when knife and camera were all we had. I had my hand on the camera button and it was running, without my knowledge that I was filming the oncoming beast. The flat snout grew larger and there was only the head. I was flooded with anger. With all my strength I thrust the camera and banged his muzzle. I felt the wash of a heavy body flashing past and the shark was twelve feet away, circling us as slowly as be-

fore, unharmed and expressionless. I thought, *Why in hell doesn't he go to the whale? The nice juicy whale. What did we ever do to him?*

The blue sharks now climbed up and joined us. Dumas and I decided to take a chance on the surface. We swam up and thrust our masks out of the water. The *Élie Monnier* was three hundred yards away, under the wind. We waved wildly and saw no reply from the ship. We believed that floating on the surface with one's head out of the water is the classic method of being eaten away. Hanging there, one's legs could be plucked like bananas. I looked down. The three sharks were rising toward us in a concerted attack.

We dived and faced them. The sharks resumed the circling maneuver. As long as we were a fathom or two down, they hesitated to approach. It would have been an excellent idea for us to navigate toward the ship. However, without landmarks, or a wrist compass, we could not follow course.

Dumas and I took a position with each man's head watching the other man's flippers, in the theory that the sharks preferred to strike at feet. Dumas made quick spurts to the surface to wave his arms for a few seconds. We evolved a system of taking turns for brief appeals on the surface, while the low man pulled his knees up against his chest and watched the sharks. A blue closed in on Dumas's feet while he was above. I yelled. Dumas turned over and resolutely faced the shark. The beast broke off and went back to the circle. When we went up to look we were dizzy and disoriented from spinning around under water, and had to revolve our heads like a lighthouse beacon to find the *Élie Monnier*. We saw no evidence that our shipmates had spied us.

We were nearing exhaustion, and cold was claiming the outer layers of our bodies. I reckoned we had been down over a half hour. Any moment we expected the constriction of air in our mouthpieces, a sign that the air supply nears exhaustion. When it came, we would reach behind our backs and turn the emergency supply valve. There was five minutes' worth of air in the emergency ration. When that was gone, we could abandon our mouthpieces and make mask dives, holding our breath. That would quicken the pace, redouble the drain on our strength, and leave us facing tireless, indestructible creatures that never needed breath. The movements of the sharks grew agitated. They ran around us, working all their strong propulsive fins, turned down and disappeared. We could not believe it. Dumas and I stared at each other. A shadow fell across us. We looked up and saw the hull of the *Élie Monnier*'s launch. Our mates had seen our signals and had located our bubbles. The sharks ran when they saw the launch.

We flopped into the boat, weak and shaken. The crew were as distraught as we were. The ship had lost sight of our bubbles and drifted away. We could not believe what they told us; we had been in the water only twenty minutes. The camera was jammed by contact with the shark's nose.

On board the *Élie Monnier*, Dumas grabbed a rifle and jumped into the small boat to visit the whale. He found it faintly alive. We saw a brown body separate from the whale and speed away, a shark. Dumas rowed around to the whale's head and gave the *coup de grâce*, point-blank with a dumdum bullet. The head sank with the mouth open, streaming bubbles from the blowhole. Sharks twisted in the red water, striking furiously at the whale. Dumas plunged his hands in the red froth and fastened a noose to the tail, which is what he had started out to do when we were diverted by our friend.

We hoisted the whale aboard and were impressed by the moon-shaped shark bites. The inch-thick leather of the whale had been scooped out cleanly, without rips, ten or fifteen pounds of blubber at a bite. The sharks had waited until we were cheated away from them before they struck the easy prey.

The whale became Surgeon Longet's biggest dissection. He swept his scalpel down the belly. Out on deck burst a slimy avalanche of undigested three-pound squids, many of them intact, almost alive. In the recesses of the stomach were thousands of black squid beaks. My mind leaped back to the fathogram of the deep scattering layer. The coincidence of the whale's lunch and the lines drawn on the fathogram may have been entirely fortuitous. It was not strict proof. But I could not dispel an unscientific picture of that dark gloaming of the scattering layer twelve hundred feet down, and whales crashing into a meadow writhing with a million arms of squids.

Standing for Dakar we met a porpoise herd. Dumas harpooned one in the back. It swam like a dog on a tether, surrounded by the pack. The mammals demonstrated a decided sense of solidarity. Save that the whale was now a porpoise, Dumas and Tailliez dived into a re-enactment of the previous drama. This time the dinghy carefully followed their air bubbles.

I watched the porpoise swimming on its leash like a bait goat a lion hunter has tied to a stake. The sharks went for the porpoise. It was cruelty to an animal but we were involved with a serious study of sharks, and had to carry it out.

The sharks circled the porpoise as they had circled us. We stood on deck remarking on the cowardice of sharks, beasts as powerful as anything on earth, indifferent to pain, and splendidly equipped as killers. Yet the brutes timidly waited to attack. Attack was too good a word for them. The porpoise had no weapons and he was dying in a circle of bullies.

At nightfall Dumas sent a *coup de grâce* into the porpoise. When it was dead, a shark passed closely by the mammal, and left entrails in the water. The other sharks passed across the porpoise, muddying the sea with blood. There was no striking and biting. The sharks spooned away the solid flesh like warm butter, without interrupting their speed.

Sharks have never attacked us with resolution, unless the overtures of our friend and the two blues may be called pressing an attack. Without being at all certain, we suppose that sharks more boldly strike objects floating on the surface. It is there that the beast finds its usual meals, sick or injured fish and garbage thrown from ships. The sharks we have met took a long time surveying submerged men. A diver is an animal they may sense to be dangerous. Aqualung bubbles may also be a deterrent.

After seeing sharks swim on unshaken with harpoons through the head, deep spear gashes on the body and even after sharp explosions near their brains, we place no reliance in knives as defensive arms. We believe better protection is our "shark billy," a stout wooden staff four feet long, studded with nail tips at the business end. It is employed, somewhat in the manner of the lion tamer's chair, by thrusting the studs into the hide of an approaching shark. The nails keep the billy from sliding off the slippery leather, but do not penetrate far enough to irritate the animal. The diver may thus hold a shark at his proper distance. We carried shark billies on wrist thongs during hundreds of dives in the Red Sea, where sharks were commonplace. We have never had occasion to apply the billy, and it may prove to be merely another theoretical defense against the creature which has eluded man's understanding.

THE NECKLACE

SHE WAS ONE of those pretty, charming young ladies, born, as if through an error of destiny, into a family of clerks. She had no dowry, no hopes, no means of becoming known, appreciated, loved and married by a man either rich or distinguished; and she allowed herself to marry a petty clerk in the office of the Board of Education.

She was simple, not being able to adorn herself, but she was unhappy, as one out of her class; for women belong to no caste, no race, their grace, their beauty and their charm serving them in the place of birth and family. Their inborn finesse, their instinctive elegance, their suppleness of wit, are their only aristocracy, making some daughters of the people the equal of great ladies.

She suffered incessantly, feeling herself born for all delicacies and luxuries. She suffered from the poverty of her apartment, the shabby walls, the worn chairs and the faded stuffs. All these things, which another woman of her station would not have noticed, tortured and angered her. The sight of the little Breton, who made this humble home, awoke in her sad regrets and desperate dreams. She thought of quiet antechambers with their oriental hangings lighted by high bronze torches and of the two great footmen in short trousers who sleep in the large armchairs, made sleepy by the heavy air from the heating apparatus. She thought of large drawing rooms hung in old silks, of graceful pieces of furniture carrying bric-a-brac of inestimable value and of the little perfumed coquettish apartments made for five o'clock chats with most intimate friends, men known and sought after, whose attention all women envied and desired.

When she seated herself for dinner before the round table, where the tablecloth had been used three days, opposite her husband who uncovered the tureen with a delighted air, saying: "Oh! the good potpie! I know nothing better than that," she would think of the elegant dinners, of the shining silver, of the tapestries peopling the walls with ancient personages and rare birds in the midst of fairy forests; she thought of the exquisite food served on marvelous dishes, of the whispered gallantries, listened to with the smile of the Sphinx while eating the rose-colored flesh of the trout or a chicken's wing.

She had neither frocks nor jewels, nothing. And she loved only those things. She felt that she was made for them. She had such a desire to please, to be sought after, to be clever and courted.

She had a rich friend, a schoolmate at the convent, whom she did not like to visit; she suffered so much when she returned. And she wept for whole days from chagrin, from regret, from despair and disappointment.

One evening her husband returned, elated, bearing in his hand a large envelope.

"Here," he said, "here is something for you."

She quickly tore open the wrapper and drew out a printed card on which were inscribed these words:

The Minister of Public Instruction and Madame George Ramponneau ask the honor of M. and Mme Loisel's company Monday evening, January 18, at the Minister's residence.

Instead of being delighted, as her husband had hoped, she threw the invitation spitefully upon the table, murmuring:

"What do you suppose I want with that?"

"But, my dearie, I thought it would make you happy. You never go out, and this is an occasion, and a fine one! I had a great deal of trouble to get it. Everybody wishes one, and it is very select; not many are given to employees. You will see the whole official world there."

She looked at him with an irritated eye and declared impatiently:

"What do you suppose I have to wear to such a thing as that?"

He had not thought of that; he stammered:

"Why, the dress you wear when we go to the theater. It seems very pretty to me."

He was silent, stupefied, in dismay, at the sight of his wife weeping. Two great tears fell slowly from the corners of her eyes toward the corners of her mouth; he stammered:

"What is the matter? What is the matter?"

By a violent effort she had controlled her vexation and responded in a calm voice, wiping her moist cheeks:

"Nothing. Only I have no dress and consequently I cannot go to this affair. Give your card to some colleague whose wife is better fitted out than I."

He was grieved but answered:

"Let us see, Matilda. How much would a suitable costume cost, something that would serve for other occasions, something very simple?"

She reflected for some seconds, making estimates and thinking of a sum that she could ask for without bringing with it an immediate refusal and a frightened exclamation from the economical clerk.

Finally she said in a hesitating voice:

"I cannot tell exactly, but it seems to me that four hundred francs ought to cover it."

He turned a little pale, for he had saved just this sum to buy a gun that he might be able to join some hunting parties the next summer, on the plains at Nanterre, with some friends who went to shoot larks up there on Sunday. Nevertheless, he answered:

"Very well. I will give you four hundred francs. But try to have a pretty dress."

The day of the ball approached, and Mme Loisel seemed sad, disturbed, anxious. Nevertheless, her dress was nearly ready. Her husband said to her one evening:

"What is the matter with you? You have acted strangely for two or three days."

And she responded: "I am vexed not to have a jewel, not one stone, nothing to adorn myself with. I shall have such a poverty-laden look. I would prefer not to go to this party."

He replied: "You can wear some natural flowers. At this season they look very chic. For ten francs you can have two or three magnificent roses."

She was not convinced. "No," she replied, "there is nothing more humiliating than to have a shabby air in the midst of rich women."

Then her husband cried out: "How stupid we are! Go and find your friend Madame Forestier and ask her to lend you her jewels. You are well enough acquainted with her to do this."

She uttered a cry of joy. "It is true!" she said. "I had not thought of that."

The next day she took herself to her friend's house and related her story of distress. Mme Forestier went to her closet with the glass doors, took out a large jewel case, brought it, opened it and said: "Choose, my dear."

She saw at first some bracelets, then a collar of pearls, then a Venetian cross of gold and jewels and of admirable workmanship. She tried the jewels before the glass, hesitated, but could neither decide to take them nor leave them. Then she asked:

"Have you nothing more?"

"Why, yes. Look for yourself. I do not know what will please you."

Suddenly she discovered in a black satin box a superb necklace of diamonds, and her heart beat fast with an immoderate desire. Her hands trembled as she took them up. She placed them about her throat, against her dress, and remained in ecstasy before them. Then she asked in a hesitating voice full of anxiety:

"Could you lend me this? Only this?"

"Why, yes, certainly."

She fell upon the neck of her friend, embraced her with passion, then went away with her treasure.

The day of the ball arrived. Mme Loisel was a great success. She was the prettiest of all, elegant, gracious, smiling and full of joy. All the men noticed her, asked her name and wanted to be presented. All the members of the Cabinet wished to waltz with her. The minister of education paid her some attention.

She danced with enthusiasm, with passion, intoxicated with pleasure, thinking of nothing, in the triumph of her beauty, in the glory of her success, in a kind of cloud of happiness that came of all this homage and all this admiration, of all these awakened desires and this victory so complete and sweet to the heart of woman.

She went home toward four o'clock in the morning. Her husband had been half asleep in one of the little salons since midnight, with three other gentlemen whose wives were enjoying themselves very much.

He threw around her shoulders the wraps they had carried for the coming home, modest garments of everyday wear, whose poverty clashed with the elegance of the ball costume. She felt this and wished to hurry away in order not to be noticed by the other women who were wrapping themselves in rich furs.

Loisel detained her. "Wait," said he. "You will catch cold out there. I am going to call a cab."

But she would not listen and descended the steps rapidly. When they were in the street they found no carriage, and they began to seek for one, hailing the coachmen whom they saw at a distance.

They walked along toward the Seine, hopeless and shivering. Finally they found on the dock one of those old nocturnal coupés that one sees in Paris after nightfall, as if they were ashamed of their misery by day.

It took them as far as their door in Martyr Street, and they went wearily up to their apartment. It was all over for her. And on his part he remembered that he would have to be at the office by ten o'clock.

She removed the wraps from her shoulders before the glass for a final view of herself in her glory. Suddenly she uttered a cry. Her necklace was not around her neck.

Her husband, already half undressed, asked: "What is the matter?"

She turned toward him excitedly:

"I have—I have—I no longer have Madame Forestier's necklace."

He arose in dismay: "What! How is that? It is not possible."

And they looked in the folds of the dress, in the folds of the mantle, in the pockets, everywhere. They could not find it.

He asked: "You are sure you still had it when we left the house?"

"Yes, I felt it in the vestibule as we came out."

"But if you had lost it in the street we should have heard it fall. It must be in the cab."

"Yes. It is probable. Did you take the number?"

"No. And you, did you notice what it was?"

"No."

They looked at each other, utterly cast down. Finally Loisel dressed himself again.

"I am going," said he, "over the track where we went on foot, to see if I can find it."

And he went. She remained in her evening gown, not having the force to go to bed, stretched upon a chair, without ambition or thoughts.

Toward seven o'clock her husband returned. He had found nothing.

He went to the police and to the cab offices and put an advertisement in the newspapers, offering a reward; he did everything that afforded them a suspicion of hope.

She waited all day in a state of bewilderment before this frightful disaster. Loisel returned at evening, with his face harrowed and pale, and had discovered nothing.

"It will be necessary," said he, "to write to your friend that you have broken the clasp of the necklace and that you will have it repaired. That will give us time to turn around."

She wrote as he dictated.

At the end of a week they had lost all hope. And Loisel, older by five years, declared:

"We must take measures to replace this jewel."

The next day they took the box which had inclosed it to the jeweler whose name was on the inside. He consulted his books.

"It is not I, madame," said he, "who sold this necklace; I only furnished the casket."

Then they went from jeweler to jeweler, seeking a necklace like the other one, consulting their memories, and ill, both of them, with chagrin and anxiety.

In a shop of the Palais-Royal they found a chaplet of diamonds which seemed to them exactly like the one they had lost. It was valued at forty thousand francs.

They could get it for thirty-six thousand.

They begged the jeweler not to sell it for three days. And they made an arrangement by which they might return it for thirty-four thousand francs if they found the other one before the end of February.

Loisel possessed eighteen thousand francs which his father had left him. He borrowed the rest.

He borrowed it, asking for a thousand francs of one, five hundred of another, five louis of this one and three louis of that one. He gave notes, made ruinous promises, took money of usurers and the whole race of lenders. He compromised his whole existence, in fact, risked his signature without even knowing whether he could make it good or not, and, harassed by anxiety for the future, by the black misery which surrounded him and by the prospect of all physical privations and moral torture, he went to get the new necklace, depositing on the merchant's counter thirty-six thousand francs.

When Mme Loisel took back the jewels to Mme Forestier the latter said to her in a frigid tone: "You should have returned them to me sooner, for I might have needed them."

She did open the jewel box as her friend feared she would. If she should perceive the substitution what would she think? What should she say? Would she take her for a robber?

Mme Loisel now knew the hor-

rible life of necessity. She did her part, however, completely, heroically. It was necessary to pay this frightful debt. She would pay it. They sent away the maid; they changed their lodgings; they rented some rooms under a mansard roof.

She learned the heavy cares of a household, the odious work of a kitchen. She washed the dishes, using her rosy nails upon the greasy pots and the bottoms of the stewpans. She washed the soiled linen, the chemises and dishcloths, which she hung on the line to dry; she took down the refuse to the street each morning and brought up the water, stopping at each landing to breathe. And, clothed like a woman of the people, she went to the grocer's, the butcher's and the fruiterer's with her basket on her arm, shopping, haggling to the last sou her miserable money.

Every month it was necessary to renew some notes, thus obtaining time, and to pay others.

The husband worked evenings, putting the books of some merchants in order, and nights he often did copying at five sous a page.

And this life lasted for ten years.

At the end of ten years they had restored all, all, with interest of the usurer, and accumulated interest, besides.

Mme Loisel seemed old now. She had become a strong, hard woman, the crude woman of the poor household. Her hair badly dressed, her skirts awry, her hands red, she spoke in a loud tone and washed the floors in large pails of water. But sometimes, when her husband was at the office, she would seat herself before the window and think of that evening party of former times, of that ball where she was so beautiful and so flattered.

How would it have been if she had not lost that necklace? Who knows? Who knows? How singular is life and how full of changes! How small a thing will ruin or save one!

One Sunday, as she was taking a walk in the Champs Elysées to rid herself of the cares of the week, she suddenly perceived a woman walking with a child. It was Mme Forestier, still young, still pretty, still attractive. Mme Loisel was affected. Should she speak to her? Yes, certainly. And now that she had paid, she would tell her all. Why not?

She approached her. "Good morning, Jeanne."

Her friend did not recognize her and was astonished to be so familiarly addressed by this common personage. She stammered:

"But, madame—I do not know—You must be mistaken."

"No, I am Matilda Loisel."

Her friend uttered a cry of astonishment: "Oh! my poor Matilda! How you have changed."

"Yes, I have had some hard days since I saw you, and some miserable ones—and all because of you."

"Because of me? How is that?"

"You recall the diamond necklace that you loaned me to wear to the minister's ball?"

"Yes, very well."

"Well, I lost it."

"How is that, since you returned it to me?"

"I returned another to you exactly like it. And it has taken us ten years to pay for it. You can understand that it was not easy for us who have nothing. But it is finished, and I am decently content."

Mme Forestier stopped short. She said:

"You say that you bought a diamond necklace to replace mine?"

"Yes. You did not perceive it then? They were just alike."

And she smiled with a proud and simple joy. Mme Forestier was touched and took both her hands as she replied:

"Oh, my poor Matilda! Mine were false. They were not worth over five hundred francs!"

THE PIECE OF STRING

ALONG ALL THE ROADS around Goderville the peasants and their wives were coming toward the burgh because it was market day. The men were proceeding with slow steps, the whole body bent forward at each movement of their long twisted legs; deformed by their hard work, by the weight on the plow which, at the same time, raised the left shoulder and swerved the figure, by the reaping of the wheat which made the knees spread to make a firm "purchase," by all the slow and painful labors of the country. Their blouses, blue, "stiff-starched," shining as if varnished, ornamented with a little design in white at the neck and wrists, puffed about their bony bodies, seemed like balloons ready to carry them off. From each of them a head, two arms and two feet protruded.

Some led a cow or a calf by a cord, and their wives, walking behind the animal, whipped its haunches with a leafy branch to hasten its progress. They carried large baskets on their arms from which, in some cases, chickens and, in others, ducks thrust out their heads. And they walked with a quicker, livelier step than their husbands. Their spare straight figures were wrapped in a scanty little shawl pinned over their flat bosoms, and their heads were enveloped in a white cloth glued to the hair and surmounted by a cap.

Then a wagon passed at the jerky trot of a nag, shaking strangely, two men seated side by side and a woman in the bottom of the vehicle, the latter holding onto the sides to lessen the hard jolts.

In the public square of Goderville there was a crowd, a throng of human beings and animals mixed together. The horns of the cattle, the tall hats, with long nap, of the rich peasant and the headgear of the peasant women rose above the surface of the assembly. And the clamorous, shrill, screaming voices made a continuous and savage din which sometimes was dominated by the robust lungs of some countryman's laugh or the long lowing of a cow tied to the wall of a house.

All that smacked of the stable, the dairy and the dirt heap, hay and sweat, giving forth that unpleasant odor, human and animal, peculiar to the people of the field.

Maître Hauchecome of Breaute had just arrived at Goderville, and he was directing his steps toward the public square when he perceived upon the ground a little piece of string. Maître Hauchecome, economical like a true Norman, thought that everything useful ought to be picked up, and he bent painfully, for he suffered from rheumatism. He took the bit of thin cord from the ground and began to roll it carefully when he noticed Maître Malandain, the harness maker, on the threshold of his door, looking at him. They had heretofore had business together on the subject of a halter, and they were on bad terms, both being good haters. Maître Hauchecome was seized with a sort of shame to be seen thus by his enemy, picking a bit of string out of the dirt. He concealed his "find" quickly under his blouse, then in his trousers' pocket; then he pretended to be still looking on the ground for something which he did not find, and he went toward the market, his head forward, bent double by his pains.

He was soon lost in the noisy and slowly moving crowd which was busy with interminable bargainings. The peasants milked, went and came, perplexed, always in fear of being cheated, not daring to decide, watching the vender's eye, ever trying to find the trick in the man and the flaw in the beast.

The women, having placed their great baskets at their feet, had taken out the poultry which lay upon the ground, tied together by the feet, with terrified eyes and scarlet crests.

They heard offers, stated their prices with a dry air and impassive face, or perhaps, suddenly deciding on some proposed reduction, shouted to the customer who was slowly going away: "All

right, Maître Authirne, I'll give it
to you for that."

Then little by little the square
was deserted, and the Angelus
ringing at noon, those who had
stayed too long scattered to their
shops.

At Jourdain's the great room
was full of people eating, as the
big court was full of vehicles of
all kinds, carts, gigs, wagons,
dumpcarts, yellow with dirt,
mended and patched, raising their
shafts to the sky like two arms
or perhaps with their shafts in
the ground and their backs in the
air.

Just opposite the diners seated
at the table the immense fireplace,
filled with bright flames, cast a
lively heat on the backs of the
row on the right. Three spits were
turning on which were chickens,
pigeons and legs of mutton, and
an appetizing odor of roast beef
and gravy dripping over the
nicely browned skin rose from the
hearth, increased the jovialness
and made everybody's mouth
water.

All the aristocracy of the plow
ate there at Maître Jourdain's,
tavern keeper and horse dealer, a
rascal who had money.

The dishes were passed and
emptied, as were the jugs of yellow cider. Everyone told his
affairs, his purchases and sales.
They discussed the crops. The
weather was favorable for the
green things but not for the wheat.

Suddenly the drum beat in the
court before the house. Everybody rose, except a few indifferent persons, and ran to the door
or to the windows, their mouths
still full and napkins in their
hands.

After the public crier had
ceased his drumbeating he called
out in a jerky voice, speaking his
phrases irregularly:

"It is hereby made known to
the inhabitants of Goderville, and
in general to all persons present
at the market, that there was lost
this morning on the road to Benzeville, between nine and ten
o'clock, a black leather pocketbook containing five hundred
francs and some business papers.
The finder is requested to return
same with all haste to the mayor's
office or to Maître Fortune Houlbreque of Manneville; there will
be twenty francs reward."

Then the man went away. The
heavy roll of the drum and the
crier's voice were again heard at
a distance.

Then they began to talk of this
event, discussing the chances that
Maître Houlbreque had of finding
or not finding his pocketbook.

And the meal concluded. They
were finishing their coffee when a
chief of the gendarmes appeared
upon the threshold.

He inquired:

"Is Maître Hauchecome of
Breaute here?"

Maître Hauchecome, seated at
the other end of the table, replied:

"Here I am."

And the officer resumed:

"Maître Hauchecome, will you
have the goodness to accompany
me to the mayor's office? The
mayor would like to talk to you."

The peasant, surprised and disturbed, swallowed at a draught his tiny glass of brandy, rose and, even more bent than in the morning, for the first steps after each rest were specially difficult, set out, repeating: "Here I am, here I am."

The mayor was awaiting him, seated on an armchair. He was the notary of the vicinity, a stout, serious man with pompous phrases.

"Maître Hauchecome," said he, "you were seen this morning to pick up, on the road to Benzeville, the pocketbook lost by Maître Houlbreque of Manneville."

The countryman, astounded, looked at the mayor, already terrified by this suspicion resting on him without his knowing why.

"Me? Me? Me pick up the pocketbook?"

"Yes, you yourself."

"Word of honor, I never heard of it."

"But you were seen."

"I was seen, me? Who says he saw me?"

"Monsieur Malandain, the harness maker."

The old man remembered, understood and flushed with anger.

"Ah, he saw me, the clodhopper, he saw me pick up this string here, M'sieu the Mayor." And rummaging in his pocket, he drew out the little piece of string.

But the mayor, incredulous, shook his head.

"You will not make me believe, Maître Hauchecome, that Monsieur Malandain, who is a man worthy of credence, mistook this cord for a pocketbook."

The peasant, furious, lifted his hand, spat at one side to attest his honor, repeating:

"It is nevertheless the truth of the good God, the sacred truth, M'sieu the Mayor. I repeat it on my soul and my salvation."

The Mayor resumed:

"After picking up the object you stood like a stilt, looking a long while in the mud to see if any piece of money had fallen out."

The good old man choked with indignation and fear.

"How anyone can tell—how anyone can tell—such lies to take away an honest man's reputation! How can anyone——"

There was no use in his protesting; nobody believed him. He was confronted with Monsieur Malandain, who repeated and maintained his affirmation. They abused each other for an hour. At his own request Maître Hauchecome was searched; nothing was found on him.

Finally the mayor, very much perplexed, discharged him with the warning that he would consult the public prosecutor and ask for further orders.

The news had spread. As he left the mayor's office the old man was surrounded and questioned with a serious or bantering curiosity in which there was no indignation. He began to tell the story of the string. No one believed him. They laughed at him.

He went along, stopping his friends, beginning endlessly his statement and his protestations, showing his pockets turned inside out to prove that he had nothing.

They said:

"Old rascal, get out!"

And he grew angry, becoming exasperated, hot and distressed at not being believed, not knowing what to do and always repeating himself.

Night came. He must depart. He started on his way with three neighbors to whom he pointed out the place where he had picked up the bit of string, and all along the road he spoke of his adventure.

In the evening he took a turn in the village of Breaute in order to tell it to everybody. He only met with incredulity.

It made him ill at night.

The next day about one o'clock in the afternoon Marius Paumelle, a hired man in the employ of Maître Breton, husbandman at Ymanville, returned the pocketbook and its contents to Maître Houlbreque of Manneville.

This man claimed to have found the object in the road, but not knowing how to read, he had carried it to the house and given it to his employer.

The news spread through the neighborhood. Maître Hauchecome was informed of it. He immediately went the circuit and began to recount his story completed by the happy climax. He was in triumph.

"What grieved me so much was not the thing itself as the lying. There is nothing so shameful as to be placed under a cloud on account of a lie."

He talked of his adventure all day long; he told it on the highway to people who were passing by, in the wineshop to people who were drinking there and to persons coming out of church the following Sunday. He stopped strangers to tell them about it. He was calm now, and yet something disturbed him without his knowing exactly what it was. People had the air of joking while they listened. They did not seem convinced. He seemed to feel that remarks were being made behind his back.

On Tuesday of the next week he went to the market at Goderville, urged solely by the necessity he felt of discussing the case.

Malandain, standing at his door, began to laugh on seeing him pass. Why?

He approached a farmer from Crequetot who did not let him finish and, giving him a thump in the stomach, said to his face:

"You big rascal."

Then he turned his back on him.

Maître Hauchecome was confused; why was he called a big rascal?

When he was seated at the table in Jourdain's tavern he commenced to explain "the affair."

A horse dealer from Monvilliers called to him:

"Come, come, old sharper, that's an old trick; I know all about your piece of string!"

Hauchecome stammered:

"But since the pocketbook was found."

But the other man replied:

"Shut up, papa, there is one

that finds and there is one that reports. At any rate you are mixed with it."

The peasant stood choking. He understood. They accused him of having had the pocketbook returned by a confederate, by an accomplice.

He tried to protest. All the table began to laugh.

He could not finish his dinner and went away in the midst of jeers.

He went home ashamed and indignant, choking with anger and confusion, the more dejected that he was capable, with his Norman cunning, of doing what they had accused him of and ever boasting of it as of a good turn. His innocence to him, in a confused way, was impossible to prove, as his sharpness was known. And he was stricken to the heart by the injustice of the suspicion.

Then he began to recount the adventures again, prolonging his history every day, adding each time new reasons, more energetic protestations, more solemn oaths which he imagined and prepared in his hours of solitude, his whole mind given up to the story of the string. He was believed so much the less as his defense was more complicated and his arguing more subtile.

"Those are lying excuses," they said behind his back.

He felt it, consumed his heart over it and wore himself out with useless efforts. He wasted away before their very eyes.

The wags now made him tell about the string to amuse them, as they make a soldier who has been on a campaign tell about his battles. His mind, touched to the depth, began to weaken.

Toward the end of December he took to his bed.

He died in the first days of January, and in the delirium of his death struggles he kept claiming his innocence, reiterating: "A piece of string, a piece of string—look—here it is, M'sieu the Mayor."

AN AFFAIR OF STATE

PARIS HAD JUST HEARD of the disaster of Sedan. The Republic was proclaimed. All France was panting from a madness that lasted until the time of the commonwealth. Everybody was playing at soldier from one end of the country to the other.

Capmakers became colonels, assuming the duties of generals; revolvers and daggers were displayed on large rotund bodies enveloped in red sashes; common citizens turned warriors, commanding battalions of noisy volunteers and swearing like troopers to emphasize their importance.

The very fact of bearing arms and handling guns with a system excited a people who hitherto had only handled scales and measures and made them formidable to the first comer, without reason. They even executed a few innocent people to prove that they knew how to kill, and in roaming through virgin fields still belonging to the Prussians they shot stray dogs, cows chewing the cud in peace or sick horses put out to pasture. Each believed himself called upon to play a great role in military affairs. The cafés of the smallest villages, full of tradesmen in uniform, resembled barracks or field hospitals.

Now the town of Canneville did not yet know the exciting news of the army and the capital. It had, however, been greatly agitated for a month over an encounter between the rival political parties. The mayor, Viscount de Varnetot, a small thin man, already old, remained true to the Empire, especially since he saw rising up against him a powerful adversary in the great, sanguine form of Dr Massarel, head of the Republican party in the district, venerable chief of the Masonic lodge, president of the Society of Agriculture and the Fire Department and organizer of the rural militia designed to save the country.

In two weeks he had induced sixty-three men to volunteer in defense of their country—married men, fathers of families, prudent farmers and merchants of the town. These he drilled every morning in front of the mayor's window.

Whenever the mayor happened to appear Commander Massarel, covered with pistols, passing proudly up and down in front of his troops, would make them shout, "Long live our country!" And this, they noticed, disturbed the little viscount, who no doubt heard in it menace and defiance and perhaps some odious recollection of the great Revolution.

On the morning of the fifth of September, in uniform, his revolver on the table, the doctor gave consultation to an old peasant couple. The husband had suffered with a varicose vein for seven years but had waited until his wife had one too, so that they might go and hunt up a physician together, guided by the postman when he should come with the newspaper.

Dr Massarel opened the door, grew pale, straightened himself abruptly and, raising his arms to heaven in a gesture of exaltation, cried out with all his might, in the face of the amazed rustics:

"Long live the Republic! Long live the Republic! Long live the Republic!"

Then he dropped into his armchair weak with emotion.

When the peasant explained that this sickness commenced with a feeling as if ants were running up and down his legs the doctor exclaimed: "Hold your peace. I have spent too much time with you stupid people. The Republic is proclaimed! The Emperor is a prisoner! France is saved! Long live the Republic!" And, running to the door, he bellowed: "Celeste! Quick! Celeste!"

The frightened maid hastened in. He stuttered, so rapidly did he try to speak. "My boots, my saber—my cartridge box—and—the Spanish dagger which is on my night table. Hurry now!"

The obstinate peasant, taking advantage of the moment's silence, began again: "This seemed like some cysts that hurt me when I walked."

The exasperated physician

shouted: "Hold your peace! For heaven's sake! If you had washed your feet oftener, it would not have happened." Then, seizing him by the neck, he hissed in his face: "Can you not comprehend that we are living in a republic, stupid?"

But the professional sentiment calmed him suddenly, and he let the astonished old couple out of the house, repeating all the time:

"Return tomorrow, return tomorrow, my friends; I have no more time today."

While equipping himself from head to foot he gave another series of urgent orders to the maid:

"Run to Lieutenant Picard's and to Sublieutenant Pommel's and say to them that I want them here immediately. Send Torcheboeuf to me too, with his drum. Quick now! Quick!" And when Celeste was gone he collected his thoughts and prepared to surmount the difficulties of the situation.

The three men arrived together. They were in their working clothes. The commander, who had expected to see them in uniform, had a fit of surprise.

"You know nothing, then? The Emperor has been taken prisoner. A republic is proclaimed. My position is delicate, not to say perilous."

He reflected for some minutes before the astonished faces of his subordinates and then continued.

"It is necessary to act, not to hesitate. Minutes now are worth hours at other times. Everything depends upon promptness of de-cision. You, Picard, go and find the curate and get him to ring the bell to bring the people together, while I get ahead of them. You, Torcheboeuf, beat the call to assemble the militia in arms, in the square, from even as far as the hamlets of Gerisaie and Salmare. You, Pommel, put on your uniform at once, that is, the jacket and cap. We, together, are going to take possession of the *mairie* and summon Monsieur de Varnetot to transfer his authority to me. Do you understand?"

"Yes."

"Act, then, and promptly. I will accompany you to your house, Pommel, since we are to work together."

Five minutes later the commander and his subaltern, armed to the teeth, appeared in the square just at the moment when the little Viscount de Varnetot, with hunting gaiters on and his rifle on his shoulder, appeared by another street, walking rapidly and followed by three guards in green jackets, each carrying a knife at his side and a gun over his shoulder.

While the doctor stopped, half stupefied, the four men entered the mayor's house and the door closed behind them.

"We are forestalled," murmured the doctor; "it will be necessary now to wait for reinforcements; nothing can be done for a quarter of an hour."

Here Lieutenant Picard appeared. "The curate refuses to obey," said he; "he has even shut himself up in the church with the beadle and the porter."

On the other side of the square, opposite the white closed front of the *mairie*, the church, mute and black, showed its great oak door with the wrought-iron trimmings.

Then, as the puzzled inhabitants put their noses out of the windows or came out upon the steps of their houses, the rolling of a drum was heard, and Torcheboeuf suddenly appeared, beating with fury the three quick strokes of the call to arms. He crossed the square with disciplined step and then disappeared on a road leading to the country.

The commander drew his sword, advanced alone to the middle distance between the two buildings where the enemy was barricaded and, waving his weapon above his head, roared at the top of his lungs: "Long live the Republic! Death to traitors!" Then he fell back where his officers were. The butcher, the baker and the apothecary, feeling a little uncertain, put up their shutters and closed their shops. The grocery alone remained open.

Meanwhile the men of the militia were arriving little by little, variously clothed but all wearing caps, the cap constituting the whole uniform of the corps. They were armed with their old rusty guns, guns that had hung on chimney pieces in kitchens for thirty years, and looked quite like a detachment of country soldiers.

When there were about thirty around him the commander explained in a few words the state of affairs. Then, turning toward his major, he said: "Now we must act."

While the inhabitants collected, talked over and discussed the matter the doctor quickly formed his plan of campaign.

"Lieutenant Picard, you advance to the windows of the mayor's house and order Monsieur de Varnetot to turn over the town hall to me in the name of the Republic."

But the lieutenant was a master mason and refused.

"You are a scamp, you are. Trying to make a target of me! Those fellows in there are good shots, you know that. No, thanks! Execute your commissions yourself!"

The commander turned red. "I order you to go in the name of discipline," said he.

"I am not spoiling my features without knowing why," the lieutenant returned.

Men of influence, in a group near by, were heard laughing. One of them called out: "You are right, Picard, it is not the proper time." The doctor, under his breath, muttered: "Cowards!" And placing his sword and his revolver in the hands of a soldier, he advanced with measured step, his eye fixed on the windows as if he expected to see a gun or a cannon pointed at him.

When he was within a few steps of the building the doors at the two extremities, affording an entrance to two schools, opened, and a flood of little creatures, boys on one side, girls on the other, poured out and began playing in the open space, chattering around the doctor like a flock of birds. He scarcely knew what to make of it.

As soon as the last were out the doors closed. The greater part of the little monkeys finally scattered, and then the commander called out in a loud voice: "Monsieur de Varnetot?" A window in the first story opened and M. de Varnetot appeared.

The commander began: "Monsieur, you are aware of the great events which have changed the system of government. The party you represent no longer exists. The side I represent now comes into power. Under these sad but decisive circumstances I come to demand you, in the name of the Republic, to put in my hand the authority vested in you by the outgoing power."

M. de Varnetot replied: "Doctor Massarel, I am mayor of Canneville, so placed by the proper authorities, and mayor of Canneville I shall remain until the title is revoked and replaced by an order from my superiors. As mayor, I am at home in the *mairie*, and there I shall stay. Furthermore, just try to put me out." And he closed the window.

The commander returned to his troops. But before explaining anything, measuring Lieutenant Picard from head to foot, he said:

"You are a numskull, you are— a goose, the disgrace of the army. I shall degrade you."

The lieutenant replied: "I'll attend to that myself." And he went over to a group of muttering civilians.

Then the doctor hesitated. What should he do? Make an assault? Would his men obey him? And then was he surely in the right? An idea burst upon him. He ran to the telegraph office on the other side of the square and hurriedly sent three dispatches: "To the Members of the Republican Government at Paris"; "To the New Republican Prefect of the Lower Seine at Rouen"; "To the New Republican Subprefect of Dieppe."

He exposed the situation fully; told of the danger run by the commonwealth from remaining in the hands of the monarchistic mayor, offered his devout services, asked for orders and signed his name, following it up with all his titles. Then he returned to his army corps and, drawing ten francs out of his pocket, said:

"Now, my friends, go and eat and drink a little something. Only leave here a detachment of ten men, so that no one leaves the mayor's house."

Ex-Lieutenant Picard, chatting with the watchmaker, overheard this. With a sneer he remarked: "Pardon me, but if they go out, there will be an opportunity for you to go in. Otherwise I can't see how you are to get in there!"

The doctor made no reply but went away to luncheon. In the afternoon he disposed of offices all about town, having the air of knowing of an impending surprise. Many times he passed before the doors of the *mairie* and of the church without noticing anything suspicious; one could have believed the two buildings empty.

The butcher, the baker and the apothecary reopened their shops and stood gossiping on the steps. If the Emperor had been taken prisoner, there must be a traitor somewhere. They did not feel sure of the revenue of a new republic.

Night came on. Toward nine o'clock the doctor returned quietly and alone to the mayor's residence, persuaded that his adversary had retired. And as he was trying to force an entrance with a few blows of a pickax the loud voice of a guard demanded suddenly: "Who goes there?" M. Massarel beat a retreat at the top of his speed.

Another day dawned without any change in the situation. The militia in arms occupied the square. The inhabitants stood around awaiting the solution. People from neighboring villages came to look on. Finally the doctor, realizing that his reputation was at stake, resolved to settle the thing in one way or another. He had just decided that it must be something energetic when the door of the telegraph office opened and the little servant of the directress appeared, holding in her hand two papers.

She went directly to the commander and gave him one of the dispatches; then, crossing the square, intimidated by so many eyes fixed upon her, with lowered head and mincing steps, she rapped gently at the door of the barricaded house as if ignorant that a part of the army was concealed there.

The door opened slightly; the hand of a man received the message, and the girl returned, blushing and ready to weep from being stared at.

The doctor demanded with stirring voice: "A little silence, if you please." And after the populace became quiet he continued proudly:

"Here is a communication which I have received from the government." And, raising the dispatch, he read:

"Old mayor deposed. Advise us what is most necessary. Instructions later.
"For the Subprefect,
"SAPIN, Counselor."

He had triumphed. His heart was beating with joy. His hand trembled, when Picard, his old subaltern, cried out to him from the neighboring group:

"That's all right; but if the others in there won't go out, your paper hasn't a leg to stand on." The doctor grew a little pale. If they would not go out—in fact, he must go ahead now. It was not only his right but his duty. And he looked anxiously at the house of the mayoralty, hoping that he might see the door open and his adversary show himself. But the door remained closed. What was to be done? The crowd was increasing, surrounding the militia. Some laughed.

One thought, especially, tortured the doctor. If he should make an assault, he must march at the head of his men; and as with him dead all contest would cease, it would be at him and at him alone that M. de Varnetot and the three guards would aim. And their aim was good, very good! Picard had reminded him of that.

But an idea shone in upon him, and turning to Pommel, he said: "Go, quickly, and ask the apothecary to send me a napkin and a pole."

The lieutenant hurried off. The doctor was going to make a political banner, a white one, that would, perhaps, rejoice the heart of that old legitimist, the mayor.

Pommel returned with the required linen and a broom handle. With some pieces of string they improvised a standard, which Massarel seized in both hands. Again he advanced toward the house of mayoralty, bearing the standard before him. When in front of the door, he called out: "Monsieur de Varnetot!"

The door opened suddenly, and M. de Varnetot and the three guards appeared on the threshold. The doctor recoiled instinctively. Then he saluted his enemy courteously and announced, almost strangled by emotion: "I have come, sir, to communicate to you the instructions I have just received."

That gentleman, without any salutation whatever, replied: "I am going to withdraw, sir, but you must understand that it is not because of fear or in obedience to an odious government that has usurped the power." And, biting off each word, he declared: "I do not wish to have the appearance of serving the Republic for a single day. That is all."

Massarel, amazed, made no reply; and M. de Varnetot, walking off at a rapid pace, disappeared around the corner, followed closely by his escort. Then the doctor, slightly dismayed, returned to the crowd. When he was near enough to be heard he cried: "Hurrah! Hurrah! The Republic triumphs all along the line!"

But no emotion was manifested. The doctor tried again. "The people are free! You are free and independent! Do you understand? Be proud of it!"

The listless villagers looked at him with eyes unlit by glory. In his turn he looked at them, indignant at their indifference, seeking for some word that could make a grand impression, electrify this placid country and make good his mission. The inspiration came, and turning to Pommel, he said: "Lieutenant, go and get the bust of the ex-emperor, which is in the Council Hall, and bring it to me with a chair."

And soon the man reappears, carrying on his right shoulder Napoleon III in plaster and holding in his left hand a straw-bottomed chair.

Massarel met him, took the chair, placed it on the ground, put the white image upon it, fell back a few steps and called out in sonorous voice:

"Tyrant! Tyrant! Here do you fall! Fall in the dust and in the mire. An expiring country groans under your feet. Destiny has called you the Avenger. Defeat and shame cling to you. You fall conquered, a prisoner to the Prussians, and upon the ruins of the crumbling Empire the young and radiant Republic arises, picking up your broken sword."

He awaited applause. But there was no voice, no sound. The bewildered peasants remained silent. And the bust, with its pointed mustaches extending beyond the cheeks on each side, the bust, so motionless and well groomed as to be fit for a hairdresser's sign, seemed to be looking at M. Massarel with a plaster smile, a smile ineffaceable and mocking.

They remained thus face to face, Napoleon on the chair, the doctor in front of him about three steps away. Suddenly the commander grew angry. What was to be done? What was there that would move this people and bring about a definite victory in opinion? His hand happened to rest on his hip and to come in contact there with the butt end of his revolver under his red sash. No inspiration, no further word would come. But he drew his pistol, advanced two steps and, taking aim, fired at the late monarch. The ball

entered the forehead, leaving a little black hole like a spot, nothing more. There was no effect. Then he fired a second shot, which made a second hole, then a third; and then, without stopping, he emptied his revolver. The brow of Napoleon disappeared in white powder, but the eyes, the nose and the fine points of the mustaches remained intact. Then, exasperated, the doctor overturned the chair with a blow of his fist and, resting a foot on the remainder of the bust in a position of triumph, he shouted: "So let all tyrants perish!"

Still no enthusiasm was manifest, and as the spectators seemed to be in a kind of stupor from astonishment the commander called to the militiamen: "You may now go to your homes." And he went toward his own house with great strides, as if he were pursued.

His maid, when he appeared, told him that some patients had been waiting in his office for three hours. He hastened in. There were the two varicose-vein patients, who had returned at daybreak, obstinate but patient.

The old man immediately began his explanation: "This began by a feeling like ants running up and down the legs."

MISS HARRIET

THERE WERE SEVEN of us in a four-in-hand, four women and three men, one of whom was on the box seat beside the coachman. We were following at a footpace the broad highway which serpentines along the coast.

Setting out from Etretat at break of day in order to visit the ruins of Tancarville, we were still asleep, chilled by the fresh air of the morning. The women especially, who were but little accustomed to these early excursions, let their eyelids fall and rise every moment, nodding their heads or yawning, quite insensible to the glory of the dawn.

It was autumn. On both sides of the road the bare fields stretched out, yellowed by the corn and wheat stubble which covered the soil like a bristling growth of beard. The spongy earth seemed to smoke. Larks were singing high up in the air, while other birds piped in the bushes.

At length the sun rose in front of us, a bright red on the plane of the horizon, and as it ascended, growing clearer from minute to minute, the country seemed to awake, to smile, to shake and stretch itself, like a young girl who is leaving her bed in her white, airy chemise. The Count d'Etraille, who was seated on the box, cried:

"Look! Look! A hare!" And he pointed toward the left, indicating a piece of hedge. The leveret threaded its way along, almost concealed by the field, only its large ears visible. Then it swerved across a deep rut, stopped, again pursued its easy course, changed its direction, stopped anew, disturbed, spying out every danger and undecided as to the route it should take. Suddenly it began to run with great bounds from its hind legs, disappearing finally in a large patch of beetroot. All the men woke up to watch the course of the beast.

René Lemanoir then exclaimed: "We are not at all gallant this morning," and, looking at his neighbor, the little Baroness of Stérennes, who was struggling with drowsiness, he said to her in a subdued voice: "You are thinking of your husband, Baroness. Reassure yourself; he will not return before Saturday, so you have still four days."

She responded to him with a sleepy smile.

"How rude you are." Then, shaking off her torpor, she added: "Now let somebody say something that will make us all laugh. You, Monsieur Chenal, who have the reputation of possessing a larger fortune than the Duke of Richelieu, tell us a love story in which you have been mixed up, anything you like."

Léon Chenal, an old painter who had once been very handsome, very strong, who was very proud of his physique and very amiable, took his long white beard in his hand and smiled; then after a few moments' reflection he became suddenly grave.

"Ladies, it will not be an amusing tale, for I am going to relate to you the most lamentable love affair of my life, and I sincerely hope that none of my friends has ever passed through a similar experience.

I

"At that time I was twenty-five years old and was making daubs along the coast of Normandy. I call 'making daubs' that wandering about with a bag on one's back from mountain to mountain under the pretext of studying and of sketching nature. I know nothing more enjoyable than that happy-go-lucky wandering life in which you are perfectly free, without shackles of any kind, without care, without preoccupation, without thought even of tomorrow. You go in any direction you please without any guide save your fancy, without any counselor save your eyes. You pull up because a running brook seduces you or because you are attracted in front of an inn by the smell of potatoes frying. Sometimes it is the perfume of clematis which decides you in your choice, or the naïve glance of the servant at an inn. Do not despise me for my affection of these rustics. These girls have soul as well as feeling, not to mention firm cheeks and fresh lips, while their hearty and willing kisses have the flavor of wild fruit. Love always has its price, come whence it may. A heart that beats when you make your appearance, an eye that weeps when you go away, these are things so rare, so sweet, so precious, that they must never be despised.

"I have had rendezvous in ditches in which cattle repose and in barns among the straw still steaming from the heat of the day. I have recollections of canvas spread on rude and creaky benches and of hearty, fresh, free kisses, more delicate, free from affectation and sincere than the subtle attractions of charming and distinguished women.

"But what you love most amid all these varied adventures are the country, the woods, the risings of the sun, the twilight, the light of the moon. For the painter these are honeymoon trips with Nature. You are alone with her in that long and tranquil rendezvous. You go to bed in the fields amid marguerites and wild poppies and, with eyes wide open, you watch the going down of the sun and descry in the distance the little village with its pointed clock tower which sounds the hour of midnight.

"You sit down by the side of a spring which gushes out from the foot of an oak, amid a covering of fragile herbs, growing and redolent of life. You go down on your knees, bend forward and drink the cold and pellucid water, wetting your mustache and nose; you drink it with a physical pleasure, as though you were kissing the spring, lip to lip. Sometimes, when you encounter a deep hole along the course of these tiny brooks, you plunge into it, quite naked, and on your skin, from head to foot, like an icy and delicious caress, you feel the lovely and gentle quivering of the current.

"You are gay on the hills, melancholy on the verge of pools, exalted when the sun is crowned in an ocean of blood-red shadows and when it casts on the rivers its red reflection. And at night under the moon, as it passes the vault of heaven, you think of things, singular things, which would never have occurred to your mind under the brilliant light of day.

"So in wandering through the same country we are in this year I came to the little village of Benouville, on the Falaise, between Yport and Etretat. I came from Fécamp, following the coast, a high coast, perpendicular as a wall, with projecting and rugged rocks falling sheer down into the sea. I had walked since the morning on the close-clipped grass as smooth and as yielding as a carpet. Singing lustily, I walked with long strides, looking sometimes at the slow and lazy flight of a gull, with its short white wings, sailing in the blue heavens, sometimes at the green sea or at the brown sails of a fishing bark. In short, I had passed a happy day, a day of list-lessness and of liberty.

"I was shown a little farmhouse where travelers were put up, a kind of inn, kept by a peasant, which stood in the center of a Norman court, surrounded by a double row of beeches.

"Quitting the Falaise, I gained the hamlet, which was hemmed in by trees, and I presented myself at the house of Mother Lecacheur.

"She was an old, wrinkled and austere rustic, who always seemed to yield to the pleasure of new customs with a kind of contempt.

"It was the month of May: the spreading apple trees covered the court with a whirling shower of blossoms which rained unceas-ingly both upon people and upon the grass.

"I said:

"'Well, Madame Lecacheur, have you a room for me?'

"Astonished to find that I knew her name, she answered:

"'That depends; everything is let, but, all the same, there will be no harm in looking.'

"In five minutes we were in per-fect accord, and I deposited my bag upon the bare floor of a rustic room furnished with a bed, two chairs, a table and a washstand. The room opened into the large and smoky kitchen, where the lodgers took their meals with the people of the farm and with the farmer himself, who was a wid-ower.

"I washed my hands, after which I went out. The old woman was fricasseeing a chicken for din-ner in a large fireplace in which hung the stewpot, black with smoke.

"'You have travelers then at the present time?' I said to her.

"She answered in an offended tone of voice:

"'I have a lady, an English lady, who has attained to years of maturity. She is occupying my other room.'

"By means of an extra five sous a day I obtained the privilege of dining out in the court when the weather was fine.

"My cover was then placed in front of the door, and I com-menced to gnaw with hunger the lean members of the Normandy chicken, to drink the clear cider and to munch the hunk of white bread which, though four days old, was excellent.

"Suddenly the wooden barrier which opened on to the highway was opened, and a strange person directed her steps toward the house. She was very slender, very tall, enveloped in a Scotch shawl with red borders. You would have believed that she had no arms, if you had not seen a long hand ap-pear just above the hips holding a white tourist umbrella. The face of a mummy, surrounded with sausage rolls of plaited gray hair, which bounded at every step she took, made me think, I know not why, of a sour herring adorned with curling papers. Lowering her eyes, she passed quickly in front of me and entered the house.

"This singular apparition made me curious. She undoubtedly was my neighbor, the aged English lady of whom our hostess had spoken.

"I did not see her again that day. The next day, when I had begun to paint at the end of that beautiful valley which, you know, extends as far as Etretat, lifting my eyes suddenly, I perceived something singularly attired standing on the crest of the declivity; it looked like a pole decked out with flags. It was she. On seeing me she suddenly disappeared. I re-entered the house at midday for lunch and took my seat at the common table so as to make the acquaintance of this old and original creature. But she did not respond to my polite advances, was insensible even to my little attentions. I poured water out for her with great alacrity; I passed her the dishes with great eagerness. A slight, almost imperceptible movement of the head and an English word murmured so low that I did not understand it, were her only acknowledgments.

"I ceased occupying myself with her, although she had disturbed my thoughts. At the end of three days I knew as much about her as did Madame Lecacheur herself.

"She was called Miss Harriet. Seeking out a secluded village in which to pass the summer, she had been attracted to Benouville some six months before and did not seem disposed to quit it. She never spoke at table, ate rapidly, reading all the while a small book treating of some Protestant propaganda. She gave a copy of it to everybody. The curé himself had received no less than four copies at the hands of an urchin to whom she had paid two sous' commission. She said sometimes to our hostess abruptly, without preparing her in the least for the declaration:

"'I love the Saviour more than all; I worship him in all creation; I adore him in all nature; I carry him always in my heart.'

"And she would immediately present the old woman with one of her brochures which were destined to convert the universe.

"In the village she was not liked. In fact, the schoolmaster had declared that she was an atheist and that a sort of reproach attached to her. The curé, who had been consulted by Madame Lecacheur, responded:

"'She is a heretic, but God does not wish the death of the sinner, and I believe her to be a person of pure morals.'

"These words 'atheist,' 'heretic,' words which no one can precisely define, threw doubts into some minds. It was asserted, however, that this Englishwoman was rich and that she had passed her life in traveling through every country in the world, because her family had thrown her off. Why had her family thrown her off? Because of her natural impiety?

"She was, in fact, one of those people of exalted principles, one of those opinionated puritans of whom England produces so many,

one of those good and insupportable old women who haunt the
tables d'hôte of every hotel in
Europe, who spoil Italy, poison
Switzerland, render the charming
cities of the Mediterranean unin-
habitable, carry everywhere their
fantastic manias, their petrified
vestal manners, their indescribable toilets and a certain odor of
India rubber, which makes one
believe that at night they slip
themselves into a case of that material. When I meet one of these
people in a hotel I act like birds
which see a manikin in a field.

"This woman, however, ap-
peared so singular that she did
not displease me.

"Madame Lecacheur, hostile by
instinct to everything that was not
rustic, felt in her narrow soul a
kind of hatred for the ecstatic ex-
travagances of the old girl. She
had found a phrase by which to
describe her, I know not how, but
a phrase assuredly contemptuous,
which had sprung to her lips, invented, probably, by some confused and mysterious travail of
soul. She said: 'That woman is a
demoniac.' This phrase, as uttered
by that austere and sentimental
creature, seemed to me irresistibly
comic. I myself never called her
now anything else but 'the demoniac,' feeling a singular pleasure in pronouncing this word on
seeing her.

"I would ask Mother Leca-
cheur: 'Well, what is our demoniac about today?' To which
my rustic friend would respond
with an air of having been scan-
dalized:

"'What do you think, sir? She
has picked up a toad which has
had its leg battered and carried it
to her room and has put it in her
washstand and dressed it up like a
man. If that is not profanation I
should like to know what is!'

"On another occasion, when
walking along the Falaise, she had
bought a large fish which had just
been caught, simply to throw it
back into the sea again. The sailor
from whom she had bought it,
though paid handsomely, was
greatly provoked at this act—more
exasperated, indeed, than if she
had put her hand into his pocket
and taken his money. For a whole
month he could not speak of the
circumstance without getting into
a fury and denouncing it as an
outrage. Oh yes! She was indeed a
demoniac, this Miss Harriet, and
Mother Lecacheur must have had
an inspiration of genius in thus
christening her.

"The stableboy, who was called
Sapeur because he had served in
Africa in his youth, entertained
other aversions. He said with a
roguish air: 'She is an old hag who
has lived her days.' If the poor
woman had but known!

"Little kindhearted Céleste did
not wait upon her willingly, but I
was never able to understand
why. Probably her only reason
was that she was a stranger, of
another race, of a different tongue
and of another religion. She was
in good truth a demoniac!

"She passed her time wandering
about the country, adoring and
searching for God in nature. I
found her one evening on her

knees in a cluster of bushes. Having discovered something red through the leaves, I brushed aside the branches, and Miss Harriet at once rose to her feet, confused at having been found thus, looking at me with eyes as terrible as those of a wild cat surprised in open day.

"Sometimes when I was working among the rocks I would suddenly descry her on the banks of the Falaise, standing like a semaphore signal. She gazed passionately at the vast sea glittering in the sunlight and the boundless sky empurpled with fire. Sometimes I would distinguish her at the bottom of an alley, walking quickly with her elastic English step, and I would go toward her, attracted by I know not what, simply to see her illuminated visage, her dried-up features, which seemed to glow with an ineffable, inward and profound happiness.

"Often I would encounter her in the corner of a field, sitting on the grass under the shadow of an apple tree with her little Bible lying open on her knee, while she looked meditatively into the distance.

"I could no longer tear myself away from that quiet country neighborhood, bound to it as I was by a thousand links of love for its soft and sweeping landscapes. At this farm I was out of the world, far removed from everything, but in close proximity to the soil the good, healthy, beautiful green soil. And, must I avow it, there was something besides curiosity which retained me at the residence of Mother Lecacheur. I wished to become acquainted a little with this strange Miss Harriet and to learn what passes in the solitary souls of those wandering old English dames.

II

"We became acquainted in a rather singular manner. I had just finished a study which appeared to me to display genius and power as it must have, since it was sold for ten thousand francs fifteen years later. It was as simple, however, as that two and two make four, and had nothing to do with academic rules. The whole of the right side of my canvas represented a rock, an enormous rock covered with sea wrack, brown, yellow and red, across which the sun poured like a stream of oil. The light, without which one could see the stars concealed in the background, fell upon the stone and gilded it as if with fire. That was all. A first stupid attempt at dealing with light, with burning rays, with the sublime.

"On the left was the sea, not the blue sea, the slate-colored sea, but a sea of jade, as greenish, milky and thick as the overcast sky.

"I was so pleased with my work that I danced from sheer delight as I carried it back to the inn. I wished that the whole world could have seen it at one and the same moment. I can remember that I showed it to a cow which was browsing by the wayside, exclaiming at the same time: 'Look at that, my old beauty; you will not often see its like again.'

"When I had reached the front of the house I immediately called out to Mother Lecacheur, shouting with all my might: "'Ohé! Ohé! My mistress, come here and look at this.'

"The rustic advanced and looked at my work with stupid eyes which distinguished nothing and did not even recognize whether the picture was the representation of an ox or a house.

"Miss Harriet came into the house and passed in rear of me just at the moment when, holding out my canvas at arm's length, I was exhibiting it to the female innkeeper. The 'demoniac' could not help but see it, for I took care to exhibit the thing in such a way that it could not escape her notice. She stopped abruptly and stood motionless, stupefied. It was her rock which was depicted, the one which she usually climbed to dream away her time, undisturbed.

"She uttered a British 'Oh,' which was at once so accentuated and so flattering that I turned round to her, smiling, and said: "'This is my last work, mademoiselle.'

"She murmured ecstatically, comically and tenderly: "'Oh, monsieur, you must understand what it is to have a palpitation.'

"I colored up of course and was more excited by that compliment than if it had come from a queen. I was seduced, conquered, vanquished. I could have embraced her—upon my honor.

"I took my seat at the table beside her, as I had always done. For the first time she spoke, drawling out in a loud voice: "'Oh! I love nature so much.'

"I offered her some bread, some water, some wine. She now accepted these with the vacant smile of a mummy. I began to converse with her about the scenery.

"After the meal we rose from the table together and walked leisurely across the court; then, attracted by the fiery glow which the setting sun cast over the surface of the sea, I opened the outside gate which faced in the direction of the Falaise, and we walked on side by side, as satisfied as any two persons could be who have just learned to understand and penetrate each other's motives and feelings.

"It was a misty, relaxing evening, one of those enjoyable evenings which impart happiness to mind and body alike. All is joy; all is charm. The luscious and balmy air, loaded with the perfumes of herbs, with the perfumes of grass wrack, with the odor of the wild flowers, caresses the soul with a penetrating sweetness. We were going to the brink of the abyss which overlooked the vast sea and rolled past us at the distance of less than a hundred meters.

"We drank with open mouth and expanded chest that fresh breeze from the ocean which glides slowly over the skin, salted as it is by long contact with the waves.

"Wrapped up in her square

shawl, inspired by the balmy air and with teeth firmly set, the Englishwoman gazed fixedly at the great sun ball as it descended toward the sea. Soon its rim touched the waters, just in rear of a ship which had appeared on the horizon, until by degrees it was swallowed up by the ocean. We watched it plunge, diminish and finally disappear.

"Miss Harriet contemplated with passionate regard the last glimmer of the flaming orb of day.

"She muttered: 'Oh! Love—I love——' I saw a tear start in her eye. She continued: 'I wish I were a little bird so that I could mount up into the firmament.'

"She remained standing as I had often before seen her, perched on the riverbank, her face as red as her flaming shawl. I should have liked to have sketched her in my album. It would have been an ecstatic caricature. I turned my face away from her so as to be able to laugh.

"I then spoke to her of painting, as I would have done to a fellow artist, using the technical terms common among the devotees of the profession. She listened attentively to me, eagerly seeking to divine the sense of the obscure words, so as to penetrate my thoughts. From time to time she would exclaim: 'Oh! I understand; I understand. This is very interesting.' We returned home.

"The next day on seeing me she approached me eagerly, holding out her hand, and we became firm friends immediately.

"She was a brave creature with an elastic sort of a soul which became enthusiastic at a bound. She lacked equilibrium, like all women who are spinsters at the age of fifty. She seemed to be pickled in vinegary innocence, though her heart still retained something of youth and of girlish effervescence. She loved both nature and animals with a fervent ardor, a love like old wine, mellow through age, with a sensual love that she had never bestowed on men.

"One thing is certain: a mare roaming in a meadow with a foal at its side, a bird's nest full of young ones squeaking, with their open mouths and enormous heads, made her quiver with the most violent emotion.

"Poor solitary beings! Sad wanderers from table d'hôte to table d'hôte, poor beings, ridiculous and lamentable, I love you ever since I became acquainted with Miss Harriet!

"I soon discovered that she had something she would like to tell me but dared not, and I was amused at her timidity. When I started out in the morning with my box on my back she would accompany me as far as the end of the village, silent, but evidently struggling inwardly to find words with which to begin a conversation. Then she would leave me abruptly and, with jaunty step, walk away quickly.

"One day, however, she plucked up courage:

"'I would like to see how you paint pictures. Will you show me? I have been very curious.'

"And she colored up as though she had given utterance to words extremely audacious.

"I conducted her to the bottom of the Petit-Val, where I had commenced a large picture.

"She remained standing near me, following all my gestures with concentrated attention. Then suddenly, fearing, perhaps, that she was disturbing me, she said to me: 'Thank you,' and walked away.

"But in a short time she became more familiar and accompanied me every day, her countenance exhibiting visible pleasure. She carried her folding stool under her arm, would not consent to my carrying it, and she sat always by my side. She would remain there for hours, immovable and mute, following with her eye the point of my brush in its every movement. When I would obtain by a large splotch of color spread on with a knife a striking and unexpected effect she would, in spite of herself, give vent to a half-suppressed 'Oh!' of astonishment, of joy, of admiration. She had the most tender respect for my canvases, an almost religious respect for that human reproduction of a part of nature's work divine. My studies appeared to her to be pictures of sanctity, and sometimes she spoke to me of God with the idea of converting me.

"Oh! He was a queer good-natured being, this God of hers. He was a sort of village philosopher without any great resources and without great power, for she always figured him to herself as a being quivering over injustices committed under his eyes and helpless to prevent them.

"She was, however, on excellent terms with him, affecting even to be the confidante of his secrets and of his whims. She said:

" 'God wills,' or, 'God does not will,' just like a sergeant announcing to a recruit: 'The colonel has commanded.'

"At the bottom of her heart she deplored my ignorance of the intention of the Eternal, which she strove, nay, felt herself compelled, to impart to me.

"Almost every day I found in my pockets, in my hat when I lifted it from the ground, in my box of colors, in my polished shoes standing in the mornings in front of my door those little pious brochures which she, no doubt, received directly from Paradise.

"I treated her as one would an old friend, with unaffected cordiality. But I soon perceived that she had changed somewhat in her manner, but for a while I paid little attention to it.

"When I walked about, whether to the bottom of the valley or through some country lanes, I would see her suddenly appear, as though she were returning from a rapid walk. She would then sit down abruptly, out of breath, as though she had been running or overcome by some profound emotion. Her face would be red, that English red which is denied to the people of all other countries; then without any reason she would grow pale, become the color of the ground and seem ready to faint away. Gradually, however, I would see her regain her ordinary color, whereupon she would begin to speak.

"Then without warning she would break off in the middle of a sentence, spring up from her seat and march off so rapidly and so strongly that it would sometimes put me to my wit's end to try and discover whether I had done or said anything to displease or offend her.

"I finally came to the conclusion that this arose from her early habits and training, somewhat modified, no doubt, in honor of me, since the first days of our acquaintanceship.

"When she returned to the farm after walking for hours on the wind-beaten coast her long curled hair would be shaken out and hanging loose, as though it had broken away from its bearings. It was seldom that this gave her any concern, though sometimes she looked as though she had been dining *sans cérémonie,* her locks having become disheveled by the breezes.

"She would then go up to her room in order to adjust what I called her glass lamps. When I would say to her in familiar gallantry which, however, always offended her:

"'You are as beautiful as a planet today, Miss Harriet,' a little blood would immediately mount into her cheeks, the blood of a young maiden, the blood of sweet fifteen.

"Then she would become abruptly savage and cease coming to watch me paint. But I always thought:

"'This is only a fit of temper she is passing through.'

"But it did not always pass away. When I spoke to her sometimes she would answer me, either with an air of affected indifference or in sullen anger, and she became by turns rude, impatient and nervous. For a time I never saw her except at meals, and we spoke but little. I concluded at length that I must have offended her in something, and accordingly I said to her one evening:

"'Miss Harriet, why is it that you do not act toward me as formerly? What have I done to displease you? You are causing me much pain!'

"She responded in an angry tone, in a manner altogether *sui generis:*

"'I am always with you the same as formerly. It is not true, not true,' and she ran upstairs and shut herself up in her room.

"At times she would look upon me with strange eyes. Since that time I have often said to myself that those condemned to death must look thus when informed that their last day has come. In her eye there lurked a species of folly, a folly at once mysterious and violent—even more, a fever, an exasperated desire, impatient, at once incapable of being realized and unrealizable!

"Nay, it seemed to me that there was also going on within her a combat in which her heart struggled against an unknown force that she wished to overcome—perhaps, even something else. But what could I know? What could I know?

III

"This was indeed a singular revelation.

"For some time I had commenced to work as soon as daylight appeared on a picture, the subject of which was as follows:

"A deep ravine, steep banks dominated by two declivities, lined with brambles and long rows of trees, hidden, drowned in milky vapor, clad in that misty robe which sometimes floats over valleys at break of day. At the extreme end of that thick and transparent fog you see coming or rather already come, a human couple, a stripling and a maiden embraced, interlaced, she with head leaning on him, he inclined toward her, and lip to lip.

"A ray of the sun glistening through the branches has traversed the fog of dawn and illuminated it with a rosy reflection just behind the rustic lovers, whose vague shadows are reflected on it in clear silver. It was well done; yes indeed, well done.

"I was working on the declivity which led to the Val d'Etretat. This particular morning I had, by chance, the sort of floating vapor which was necessary for my purpose. Suddenly an object appeared in front of me, a kind of phantom; it was Miss Harriet. On seeing me she took to flight. But I called after her, saying: 'Come here; come here, mademoiselle, I have a nice little picture for you.'

"She came forward, though with seeming reluctance. I handed her my sketch. She said nothing but stood for a long time motionless, looking at it. Suddenly she burst into tears. She wept spasmodically, like men who have been struggling hard against shedding tears but who can do so no longer and abandon themselves to grief, though unwillingly. I got up, trembling, moved myself by the sight of a sorrow I did not comprehend, and I took her by the hand with a gesture of brusque affection, a true French impulse which impels one quicker than one thinks.

"She let her hands rest in mine for a few seconds, and I felt them quiver, as if her whole nervous system was twisting and turning. Then she withdrew her hands abruptly or, rather, tore them out of mine.

"I recognized that shiver as soon as I had felt it; I was deceived in nothing. Ah! The love shudder of a woman, whether she is fifteen or fifty years of age, whether she is one of the people or one of the *monde*, goes so straight to my heart that I never had any difficulty in understanding it!

"Her whole frail being trembled, vibrated, yielded. I knew it. She walked away before I had time to say a word, leaving me as surprised as if I had witnessed a miracle and as troubled as if I had committed a crime.

"I did not go in to breakfast. I took a walk on the banks of the

Falaise, feeling that I could just as soon weep as laugh, looking on the adventure as both comic and deplorable and my position as ridiculous, fain to believe that I had lost my head.

"I asked myself what I ought to do. I debated whether I ought not to take my leave of the place, and almost immediately my resolution was formed.

"Somewhat sad and perplexed, I wandered about until dinnertime and entered the farmhouse just when the soup had been served up.

"I sat down at the table, as usual. Miss Harriet was there, munching away solemnly without speaking to anyone, without even lifting her eyes. She wore, however, her usual expression, both of countenance and manner.

"I waited patiently till the meal had been finished. Then, turning toward the landlady, I said: 'Madame Lecacheur, it will not be long now before I shall have to take my leave of you.'

"The good woman, at once surprised and troubled, replied in a quivering voice: 'My dear sir, what is it I have just heard you say? Are you going to leave us after I have become so much accustomed to you?'

"I looked at Miss Harriet from the corner of my eye. Her countenance did not change in the least, but the underservant came toward me with eyes wide open. She was a fat girl of about eighteen years of age, rosy, fresh, strong as a horse, yet possessing a rare attribute in one in her position—she was very neat and clean. I had kissed her at odd times in out-of-the-way corners in the manner of a mountain guide, nothing more.

"The dinner being over, I went to smoke my pipe under the apple trees, walking up and down at my ease from one end of the court to the other. All the reflections which I had made during the day, the strange discovery of the morning, that grotesque and passionate attachment for me, the recollections which that revelation had suddenly called up, recollections at once charming and perplexing, perhaps, also, that look which the servant had cast on me at the announcement of my departure—all these things, mixed up and combined, put me now in an excited bodily state with the tickling sensation of kisses on my lips, and in my veins something which urged me on to commit some folly.

"Night having come on, casting its dark shadows under the trees, I descried Céleste who had gone to shut the hen coops at the other end of the inclosure. I darted toward her, running so noiselessly that she heard nothing, and as she got up from closing the small traps by which the chickens went in and out, I clasped her in my arms and rained on her coarse, fat face a shower of kisses. She made a struggle, laughing all the same, as she was accustomed to do in such circumstances. What made me suddenly loose my grip of her? Why did I at once experience a shock? What was it that I heard behind me?

"It was Miss Harriet who had come upon us, who had seen us and who stood in front of us, as motionless as a specter. Then she disappeared in the darkness.

"I was ashamed, embarrassed, more annoyed at having been surprised by her than if she had caught me committing some criminal act.

"I slept badly that night; I was worried and haunted by sad thoughts. I seemed to hear loud weeping, but in this I was no doubt deceived. Moreover, I thought several times that I heard someone walking up and down in the house and that someone opened my door from the outside.

"Toward morning I was overcome by fatigue, and sleep seized on me. I got up late and did not go downstairs until breakfast time, being still in a bewildered state, not knowing what kind of face to put on.

"No one had seen Miss Harriet. We waited for her at table, but she did not appear. At length Mother Lecacheur went to her room. The Englishwoman had gone out. She must have set out at break of day, as she was wont to do, in order to see the sunrise.

"Nobody seemed astonished at this, and we began to eat in silence.

"The weather was hot, very hot, one of those still, sultry days when not a leaf stirs. The table had been placed out of doors under an apple tree, and from time to time Sapeur had gone to the cellar to draw a jug of cider, everybody was so thirsty. Céleste brought the dishes from the kitchen, a ragout of mutton with potatoes, a cold rabbit and a salad. Afterward she placed before us a dish of strawberries, the first of the season.

"As I wanted to wash and freshen these, I begged the servant to go and bring a pitcher of cold water.

"In about five minutes she returned, declaring that the well was dry. She had lowered the pitcher to the full extent of the cord and had touched the bottom, but on drawing the pitcher up again it was empty. Mother Lecacheur, anxious to examine the thing for herself, went and looked down the hole. She returned announcing that one could see clearly something in the well, something altogether unusual. But this, no doubt, was pottles of straw which, out of spite, had been cast down it by a neighbor.

"I wished also to look down the well, hoping to clear up the mystery, and perched myself close to its brink. I perceived indistinctly a white object. What could it be? I then conceived the idea of lowering a lantern at the end of a cord. When I did so the yellow flame danced on the layers of stone and gradually became clearer. All four of us were leaning over the opening, Sapeur and Céleste having now joined us. The lantern rested on a black-and-white, indistinct mass, singular, incomprehensible. Sapeur exclaimed:

"'It is a horse. I see the hoofs. It must have escaped from the meadow during the night and fallen in headlong.'

"But suddenly a cold shiver attacked my spine; I first recognized a foot, then a clothed limb; the body was entire, but the other limb had disappeared under the water.

"I groaned and trembled so violently that the light of the lamp danced hither and thither over the object, discovering a slipper.

"'It is a woman! Who—who—can it be? It is Miss Harriet.'

"Sapeur alone did not manifest horror. He had witnessed many such scenes in Africa.

"Mother Lecacheur and Céleste began to scream and to shriek and ran away.

"But it was necessary to recover the corpse of the dead. I attached the boy securely by the loins to the end of the pulley rope; then I lowered him slowly and watched him disappear in the darkness. In the one hand he had a lantern and held onto the rope with the other. Soon I recognized his voice, which seemed to come from the center of the earth, crying:

"'Stop.'

"I then saw him fish something out of the water. It was the other limb. He bound the two feet together and shouted anew:

"'Haul up.'

"I commenced to wind him up, but I felt my arms strain, my muscles twitch, and was in terror lest I should let the boy fall to the bottom. When his head appeared over the brink I asked:

"'What is it?' as though I only expected that he would tell me what he had discovered at the bottom.

"We both got onto the stone slab at the edge of the well and, face to face, hoisted the body.

"Mother Lecacheur and Céleste watched us from a distance, concealed behind the wall of the house. When they saw issuing from the well the black slippers and white stockings of the drowned person they disappeared.

"Sapeur seized the ankles of the poor, chaste woman, and we drew it up, inclined, as it was, in the most immodest posture. The head was in a shocking state, bruised and black, and the long gray hair, hanging down, was tangled and disordered.

"'In the name of all that is holy, how lean she is!' exclaimed Sapeur in a contemptuous tone.

"We carried her into the room, and as the women did not put in an appearance, I, with the assistance of the lad, dressed the corpse for burial.

"I washed her disfigured face. By the touch of my hand an eye was slightly opened; it seemed to scan me with that pale stare, with that cold, that terrible look which corpses have, a look which seems to come from the beyond. I plaited up, as well as I could, her dishevelled hair, and I adjusted on her forehead a novel and singularly formed lock. Then I took off her dripping wet garments, baring not without a feeling of shame, as though I had been guilty of some profanation her shoulders and her chest and her long arms, slim as the twigs of branches.

"I next went to fetch some flowers, corn poppies, blue beetles, marguerites and fresh and perfumed herbs, with which to strew her funeral couch.

"Being the only person near her, it was necessary for me to perform the usual ceremonies. In a letter found in her pocket, written at the last moment, she asked that her body be buried in the village in which she had passed the last days of her life. A frightful thought then oppressed my heart. Was it not on my account that she wished to be laid at rest in this place?

"Toward the evening all the female gossips of the locality came to view the remains of the defunct, but I would not allow a single person to enter; I wanted to be alone, and I watched by the corpse the whole night.

"By the flickering light of the candles I looked at the body of this miserable woman, wholly unknown, who had died so lamentably and so far away from home. Had she left no friends, no relatives behind her? What had her infancy been? What had been her life? When had she come thither all alone, a wanderer, like a dog driven from home? What secrets of suffering and of despair were sealed up in that disagreeable body, in that spent and withered body, that impenetrable hiding place of a mystery which had driven her far away from affection and from love?

"How many unhappy beings there are! I felt that upon that human creature weighed the eternal injustice of implacable nature! Life was over with her without her ever having experienced, perhaps, that which sustains the most miserable of us all—to wit, the hope of being once loved! Otherwise why should she thus have concealed herself, have fled from the face of others? Why did she love everything so tenderly and so passionately, everything living that was not a man?

"I recognized also that she believed in a God and that she hoped for compensation from him for the miseries she had endured. She had now begun to decompose and to become, in turn, a plant. She who had blossomed in the sun was now to be eaten up by the cattle, carried away in herbs and in the flesh of beasts, again to become human flesh. But that which is called the soul had been extinguished at the bottom of the dark well. She suffered no longer. She had changed her life for that of others yet to be born.

"Hours passed away in this silent and sinister communion with the dead. A pale light at length announced the dawn of a new day, and a bright ray glistened on the bed, shedding a dash of fire on the bedclothes and on her hands. This was the hour she had so much loved, when the waking birds began to sing in the trees.

"I opened the window to its fullest extent; I drew back the curtains so that the whole heavens might look in upon us. Then, bending toward the glassy corpse, I took in my hands the mutilated head and slowly, without terror or disgust, imprinted a long, long kiss upon those lips which had never before received the salute of love."

. . . .

Léon Chenal remained silent. The women wept. We heard on the box seat Count d'Etraille blow his nose from time to time. The coachman alone had gone to sleep. The horses, which felt no longer the sting of the whip, had slackened their pace and dragged softly along. And the four-in-hand, hardly moving at all, became suddenly torpid, as if laden with sorrow.

THE DEVIL

THE PEASANT WAS STANDING opposite the doctor, by the bedside of the dying old woman, and she, calmly resigned and quite lucid, looked at them and listened to their talking. She was going to die and she did not rebel at it, for her life was over—she was ninety-two.

The July sun streamed in at the window and through the open door and cast its hot flames onto the uneven brown clay floor which had been stamped down by four generations of clodhoppers. The smell of the fields came in also, driven by the brisk wind and parched by the noontide heat. The grasshoppers chirped themselves hoarse, filling the air with their shrill noise, like that of the wooden crickets which are sold to children at fair time.

The doctor raised his voice and said: "Honoré, you cannot leave your mother in this state; she may die at any moment." And the peasant, in great distress, replied: "But I must get in my wheat, for it has been lying on the ground a long time, and the weather is just right for it; what do you say about it,

Mother?" And the dying woman, still possessed by her Norman avariciousness, replied yes with her eyes and her forehead and so urged her son to get in his wheat and to leave her to die alone. But the doctor got angry and, stamping his foot, he said: "You are no better than a brute; do you hear? And I will not allow you to do it. Do you understand? And if you must get in your wheat today, go and fetch Rapet's wife and make her look after your mother. I *will* have it. And if you do not obey me I will let you die like a dog when you are ill in your turn; do you hear me?"

The peasant, a tall thin fellow with slow movements who was tormented by indecision, by his fear of the doctor and his keen love for saving, hesitated, calculated and stammered out: "How much does La Rapet charge for attending sick people?"

"How should I know?" the doctor cried. "That depends upon how long she is wanted for. Settle it with her, by Jove! But I want her to be here within an hour; do you hear?"

So the man made up his mind. "I will go for her," he replied; "don't get angry, Doctor." And the latter left, calling out as he went: "Take care, you know, for I do not joke when I am angry!" And as soon as they were alone the peasant turned to his mother and said in a resigned voice: "I will go and fetch La Rapet, as the man will have it. Don't go off while I am away."

And he went out in his turn.

La Rapet, who was an old washerwoman, watched the dead and the dying of the neighborhood, and then as soon as she had sewn her customers into that linen cloth from which they would emerge no more, she went and took up her irons to smooth the linen of the living. Wrinkled like a last year's apple, spiteful, envious, avaricious with a phenomenal avarice, bent double, as if she had been broken in half across the loins by the constant movement of the iron over the linen, one might have said that she had a kind of monstrous and cynical affection for a death struggle. She never spoke of anything but of the people she had seen die, of the various kinds of deaths at which she had been present, and she related, with the greatest minuteness, details which were always the same, just like a sportsman talks of his shots.

When Honoré Bontemps entered her cottage he found her preparing the starch for the collars of the village women, and he said: "Good evening; I hope you are pretty well, Mother Rapet."

She turned her head round to look at him and said: "Fairly well, fairly well, and you?"

"Oh, as for me, I am as well as I could wish, but my mother is very sick."

"Your mother?"

"Yes, my mother!"

"What's the matter with her?"

"She is going to turn up her toes; that's what's the matter with her!"

The old woman took her hands out of the water and asked with sudden sympathy: "Is she as bad as all that?"

"The doctor says she will not last till morning."

"Then she certainly is very bad!" Honoré hesitated, for he wanted to make a few preliminary remarks before coming to his proposal, but as he could hit upon nothing, he made up his mind suddenly.

"How much are you going to ask to stop with her till the end? You know that I am not rich, and I cannot even afford to keep a servant girl. It is just that which has brought my poor mother to this state, too much work and fatigue! She used to work for ten, in spite of her ninety-two years. You don't find any made of that stuff nowadays!"

La Rapet answered gravely: "There are two prices: forty sous by day and three francs by night for the rich, and twenty sous by day and forty by night for the others. You shall pay me the twenty and forty." But the peasant reflected, for he knew his mother well. He knew how tenacious of life, how vigorous and unyielding she was. He knew, too, that she might last another week, in spite of the doctor's opinion, and so he said resolutely: "No, I would rather you would fix a price until the end. I will take my chance one way or the other. The doctor says she will die very soon. If that happens, so much the better for you and so much the worse for me, but if she holds out till to-morrow or longer, so much the better for me and so much the

worse for you!"

The nurse looked at the man in astonishment, for she had never treated a death as a speculative job, and she hesitated, tempted by the idea of the possible gain. But almost immediately she suspected that he wanted to juggle her. "I can say nothing until I have seen your mother," she replied.

"Then come with me and see her."

She washed her hands and went with him immediately. They did not speak on the road; she walked with short, hasty steps, while he strode on with his long legs, as if he were crossing a brook at every step. The cows lying down in the fields, overcome by the heat, raised their heads heavily and lowed feebly at the two passers-by, as if to ask them for some green grass.

When they got near the house Honoré Bontemps murmured: "Suppose it is all over?" And the unconscious wish that it might be so showed itself in the sound of his voice.

But the old woman was not dead. She was lying on her back on her wretched bed, her hands covered with a pink cotton counterpane, horribly thin, knotty paws, like some strange animal's or like crabs' claws, hands closed by rheumatism, fatigue and the work of nearly a century which she had accomplished.

La Rapet went up to the bed and looked at the dying woman, felt her pulse, tapped her on the chest, listened to her breathing and asked her questions so as to hear her speak; then, having looked at her for some time longer, she went out of the room, followed by Honoré. His decided opinion was that the old woman would not last out the night, and he asked: "Well?" And the sick nurse replied: "Well, she may last two days, perhaps three. You will have to give me six francs, everything included."

"Six francs! Six francs!" he shouted. "Are you out of your mind? I tell you that she cannot last more than five or six hours!" And they disputed angrily for some time, but as the nurse said she would go home as the time was slipping away, and as his wheat would not come to the farmyard of its own accord, he agreed to her terms at last.

"Very well then, that is settled; six francs, including everything, until the corpse is taken out."

"That is settled, six francs."

And he went away with long strides to the wheat which was lying on the ground under the hot sun which ripens the grain, while the sick nurse returned to the house.

She had brought some work with her, for she worked without stopping by the side of the dead and dying, sometimes for herself, sometimes for the family who employed her as seamstress also, paying her rather more in that capacity. Suddenly she asked:

"Have you received the last sacrament, Mother Bontemps?"

The old peasant woman said no with her head, and La Rapet, who was very devout, got up quickly. "Good heavens, is it possible? I will go and fetch the curé," and she rushed off to the parsonage so quickly that the urchins in the street thought some accident had happened when they saw her trotting off like that.

The priest came immediately in his surplice, preceded by a choirboy, who rang a bell to announce the passage of the Host through the parched and quiet country. Some men, working at a distance, took off their large hats and remained motionless until the white vestment had disappeared behind some farm buildings; the women who were making up the sheaves stood up to make the sign of the cross; the frightened black hens ran away along the ditch until they reached a well-known hole through which they suddenly disappeared, while a foal, which was tied up in a meadow, took fright at the sight of the surplice and began to gallop round at the length of its rope, kicking violently. The choirboy, in his red cassock, walked quickly, and the priest, the square biretta on his bowed head, followed him, muttering some prayers. Last of all came La Rapet, bent almost double, as if she wished to prostrate herself; she walked with folded hands, as if she were in church.

Honoré saw them pass in the distance, and he asked: "Where is our priest going to?" And his man, who was more acute, replied: "He is taking the sacrament to your mother, of course!"

The peasant was not surprised and said: "That is quite possible," and went on with his work.

Mother Bontemps confessed, received absolution and extreme unction, and the priest took his departure, leaving the two women alone in the suffocating cottage. La Rapet began to look at the dying woman and to ask herself whether it could last much longer.

The day was on the wane, and a cooler air came in stronger puffs, making a view of Epinal, which was fastened to the wall by two pins, flap up and down. The scanty window curtains, which had formerly been white but were now yellow and covered with flyspecks, looked as if they were going to fly off and seemed to struggle to get away, like the old woman's soul.

Lying motionless, with her eyes open, the old mother seemed to await the death which was so near and which yet delayed its coming, with perfect indifference. Her short breath whistled in her throat. It would stop altogether soon, and there would be one woman less in the world, one whom nobody would regret.

At nightfall Honoré returned, and when he went up to the bed and saw that his mother was still alive he asked: "How is she?" just as he had done formerly when she had been sick. Then he sent La Rapet away, saying to her: "Tomorrow morning at five o'clock without fail." And she replied: "Tomorrow at five o'clock."

She came at daybreak and found Honoré eating his soup, which he had made himself, before going to work.

"Well, is your mother dead?" asked the nurse.

"She is rather better, on the contrary," he replied with a malignant look out of the corners of his eyes. Then he went out.

La Rapet was seized with anxiety and went up to the dying woman, who was in the same state, lethargic and impassive, her eyes open and her hands clutching the counterpane. The nurse perceived that this might go on thus for two days, four days, eight days, even, and her avaricious mind was seized with fear. She was excited to fury against the cunning fellow who had tricked her and against the woman who would not die.

Nevertheless, she began to sew and waited with her eyes fixed on the wrinkled face of Mother Bontemps. When Honoré returned to breakfast he seemed quite satisfied and even in a bantering humor, for he was carrying in his wheat under very favorable circumstances.

La Rapet was getting exasperated; every passing minute now seemed to her so much time and money stolen from her. She felt a mad inclination to choke this old ass, this headstrong old fool, this obstinate old wretch—to stop that short, rapid breath, which was robbing her of her time and money, by squeezing her throat a little. But then she reflected on the danger of doing so, and other thoughts came into her head, so she went up to the bed and said to her: "Have you ever seen the devil?"

Mother Bontemps whispered: "No."

Then the sick nurse began to talk and to tell her tales likely to terrify her weak and dying mind. "Some minutes before one dies the devil appears," she said, "to all. He has a broom in his hand, a saucepan on his head, and he utters loud cries. When anybody has seen him all is over, and that person has only a few moments longer to live"; and she enumerated all those to whom the devil had appeared that year: Josephine Loisel, Eulalie Ratier, Sophie Padagnau, Séraphine Grospied.

Mother Bontemps, who was at last most disturbed in mind, moved about, wrung her hands and tried to turn her head to look at the other end of the room. Suddenly La Rapet disappeared at the foot of the bed. She took a sheet out of the cupboard and wrapped herself up in it; then she put the iron pot onto her head so that its three short, bent feet rose up like horns, took a broom in her right hand and a tin pail in her left, which she threw up suddenly so that it might fall to the ground noisily.

Certainly when it came down it made a terrible noise. Then, climbing onto a chair, the nurse showed herself, gesticulating and uttering shrill cries into the pot which covered her face, while she menaced the old peasant woman, who was nearly dead, with her broom.

Terrified, with a mad look on her face, the dying woman made a superhuman effort to get up and escape; she even got her shoulders and chest out of bed; then she fell back with a deep sigh. All was over, and La Rapet calmly put everything back into its place; the broom into the corner by the cupboard, the sheet inside it, the pot onto the hearth, the pail onto the floor and the chair against the wall. Then with a professional air she closed the dead woman's enormous eyes, put a plate on the bed and poured some holy water into it, dipped the twig of boxwood into it and, kneeling down, she fervently repeated the prayers for the dead, which she knew by heart, as a matter of business.

When Honoré returned in the evening, he found her praying. He calculated immediately that she had made twenty sous out of him, for she had only spent three days and one night there, which made five francs altogether, instead of the six which he owed her.

THE MOUNTEBANKS

COMPARDIN, the clever manager of the Eden Réunis Theater, as the theater critics invariably called him, was reckoning on a great success and had invested his last franc in the affair without thinking of the morrow or of the bad luck which had been pursuing him so inexorably for months past. For a whole week the walls, the kiosks, shop fronts and even the trees had been placarded with flaming posters, and from one end of Paris to the other carriages were to be seen which were covered with fancy sketches by Chéret, representing two strong, well-built men who looked like ancient athletes. The younger of them, who was standing with his arms folded, had the vacant smile of an itinerant mountebank, and the other, who was dressed in what was supposed to be the costume of a Mexican trapper, held a revolver in his hand. There were large-type advertisements in all the papers that the Montefiores would appear without fail at the Eden Réunis the next Monday.

Nothing else was talked about, for the puff and humbug attracted people. The Montefiores, like fashionable knickknacks, succeeded that whimsical jade, Rose Péché, who had gone off the preceding autumn between the third and fourth acts of the burlesque, *Ousca Iscar,* in order to make a study of love in company of a young fellow of seventeen who had just entered the university. The novelty and difficulty of their performance revived and agitated the curiosity of the public, for there seemed to be an implied threat of death or at any rate, of wounds and of blood in it, and it seemed as if they defied danger with absolute indifference. And that always pleases women; it holds them and masters them, and they grow pale with emotion and cruel enjoyment. Consequently all the seats in the large theater were let almost immediately and were soon taken for several days in advance. And stout Compardin, losing his glass of absinthe over a game of dominoes, was in high spirits, seeing the future through rosy glasses, and exclaimed in a loud voice: "I think I have turned up trumps, by George!"

The Countess Regina de Villégby was lying on the sofa in her boudoir, languidly fanning herself. She had only received three or four intimate friends that day, Saint Mars Montalvin, Tom Sheffield and her cousin, Mme de Rhouel, a Creole, who laughed as incessantly as a bird sings. It was growing dusk, and the distant rumbling of the carriages in the avenue of the Champs Elysées sounded like some somnolent rhythm. There was a delicate perfume of flowers; the lamps had not been brought in yet, and chatting and laughing filled the room with a confused noise.

"Would you pour out the tea?" the countess said, suddenly touching Saint Mars's fingers, who was beginning an amorous conversation in a low voice, with her fan. And while he slowly filled the little china cup he continued: "Are the Montefiores as good as the lying newspapers make out?"

Then Tom Sheffield and the others all joined in. They had never seen anything like it, they declared; it was most exciting and made one shiver unpleasantly, as when the *espada* comes to close quarters with the infuriated brute at a bullfight.

Countess Regina listened in silence and nibbled the petals of a tea rose.

"How I should like to see them!" giddy Mme de Rhouel exclaimed.

"Unfortunately, Cousin," the countess said in the solemn tones of a preacher, "a respectable woman dare not let herself be seen in improper places."

They all agreed with her. Nevertheless, Countess de Villégby was present at the Montefiores' performance two days later, dressed all in black and wearing a thick veil, at the back of a stage box.

Mme de Villégby was as cold as a steel buckler. She had married as soon as she left the convent in which she had been educated, without any affection or even liking for her husband; the most skeptical respected her as a saint, and she had a look of virgin purity on her calm face as she went down the steps of the Madeleine on Sundays after high mass.

Countess Regina stretched herself nervously, grew pale and trembled like the strings of a violin on which an artist had been playing some wild symphony. She inhaled the nasty smell of the sawdust, as if it had been the perfume of a bouquet of unknown flowers; she clenched her hands and gazed eagerly at the two mountebanks whom the public applauded rapturously at every feat. And contemptuously and haughtily she compared those two men, who were as vigorous as wild animals that have grown up in the open air, with the rickety limbs that look so awkward in the dress of an English groom.

Count de Villégby had gone back to the country to prepare for his election as councilor general, and the very evening that he started Regina again took the stage box at the Eden Réunis. Consumed by sensual ardor, as if by some love philter, she scribbled a few words on a piece of paper—the eternal formula that women write on such occasions.

"A carriage will be waiting for you at the stage door after the performance—*An unknown woman who adores you.*"

And then she gave it to a box opener, who handed it to the Montefiore who was the champion pistol shot.

Oh, that interminable waiting in a malodorous cab, the overwhelming emotion and the nausea of disgust, the fear, the desire of waking the coachman who was nodding on the box, of giving him her address and telling him to drive her home! But she remained with her face against the window, mechanically watching the dark passage illuminated by a gas lamp at the "actors' entrance" through which men were continually hurrying who talked in a loud voice and chewed the end of cigars which had gone out. She sat as if she were glued to the cushions and tapped impatiently on the bottom of the cab with her heels.

When the actor, who thought it was a joke, made his appearance, she could hardly utter a word, for evil pleasure is as intoxicating as adulterated liquor. So face to face with this immediate surrender and this unconstrained immodesty, he at first thought that he had to do with a streetwalker.

Regina felt various sensations and a morbid pleasure throughout her whole person. She pressed close to him and raised her veil to show how young, beautiful and desirable she was. They did not speak a word, like wrestlers before a combat. She was eager to be locked up with him, to give herself to him and, at last, to know that moral uncleanness of which she was, of course, ignorant as a chaste wife; and when they left the room in the hotel together, where they had spent hours like amorous deer, the man dragged himself along and almost groped his way like a blind man, while

Regina was smiling, though she exhibited the serene candor of an unsullied virgin, like she did on Sundays after mass.

Then she took the second. He was very sentimental, and his head was full of romance. He thought the unknown woman, who merely used him as her plaything, really loved him, and he was not satisfied with furtive meetings. He questioned her, besought her, and the countess made fun of him. Then she chose the two mountebanks in turn. They did not know it, for she had forbidden them ever to talk about her to each other under the penalty of never seeing her again, and one night the younger of them said with humble tenderness as he knelt at her feet:

"How kind you are to love me and to want me! I thought that such happiness only existed in novels and that ladies of rank only made fun of poor strolling mountebanks like us!"

Regina knitted her golden brows.

"Do not be angry," he continued, "because I followed you and found out where you lived and your real name and that you are a countess and rich, very rich."

"You fool!" she exclaimed, trembling with anger. "People make you believe things as easily as they can a child!"

She had had enough of him; he knew her name and might compromise her. The count might possibly come back from the country before the elections, and then the mountebank began to love her.

She no longer had any feeling, any desire for those two lovers whom a fillip from her rosy fingers could bend to her will. It was time to go on to the next chapter and to seek for fresh pleasures elsewhere.

"Listen to me," she said to the champion shot the next night, "I would rather not hide anything from you. I like your comrade; I have given myself to him and I do not want to have anything more to do with you."

"My comrade!" he repeated.

"Well, what then? The change amuses me!"

He uttered a furious cry and rushed at Regina with clenched fists. She thought he was going to kill her and closed her eyes, but he had not the courage to hurt that delicate body which he had so often covered with caresses, and in despair and hanging his head, he said hoarsely:

"Very well, we shall not meet again, since it is your wish."

The house at the Eden Réunis was as full as an overfilled basket. The violins were playing a soft and delightful waltz of Gungl's, which the reports of a revolver accentuated.

The Montefiores were standing opposite to one another, as in Chéret's picture, and about a dozen yards apart. An electric light was thrown on the younger, who was leaning against a large white target, and very slowly the other traced his living outline with bullet after bullet. He aimed with prodigious skill, and the black dots showed on the cardboard and marked the shape of his body. The applause drowned the orchestra and increased continually, when suddenly a shrill cry of horror resounded from one end of the hall to the other. The women fainted; the violins stopped, and the spectators jostled each other. At the ninth ball the younger brother had fallen to the ground, an inert mass, with a gaping wound in his forehead. His brother did not move, and there was a look of madness on his face, while the Countess de Villégby leaned on the ledge of her box and fanned herself calmly, as implacably as any cruel goddess of ancient mythology.

The next day between four and five, when she was surrounded by her usual friends in her little warm Japanese drawing room, it was strange to hear in what a languid and indifferent voice she exclaimed:

"They say that an accident happened to one of those famous clowns, the Monta—the Monte—what is the name, Tom?"

"The Montefiores, madame!"

And then they began to talk about Angèle Velours, who was going to buy the former Folies at the Hôtel Drouot before marrying Prince Storbeck.

ON CATS

CAPE OF ANTIBES. SEATED ON A BENCH, the other day at my door, in the full sunlight, with a cluster of anemones in flower before me, I read a book recently published, an honest book, something uncommon and charming,—"The Cooper" by George Duval. A large white cat that belonged to the gardener jumped upon my lap, and by the shock closed the book, which I placed at my side in order to caress the animal.

The weather was warm; a faint suggestive odor of new flowers was in the air, and at times came little cool breezes from the great white summits that I could see in the distance. But the sun was hot and sharp, and the day was one of those that stir the earth, make it alive, break open the seed in order to animate the sleeping germs, and cleave the buds so that the young leaves may spring forth. The cat rolled itself on my knees, lying on its back, its paws in the air, with claws protruding, then receding. The little creature showed its pointed teeth beneath its lips, and its green eyes gleamed in the half-closed slit of its eyelids. I caressed and rubbed the soft, nervous animal, supple as a piece of silk, smooth, warm, delicious, dangerous. She purred with satisfaction, yet was quite ready to scratch, for a cat loves to scratch as well as to be petted. She held out her neck and rolled again, and when I took my hand from her, she raised herself and pushed her head against my lifted hand.

I made her nervous, and she made me nervous also, for, although I like cats in a certain way, I detest them at the same time,— those animals so charming and so treacherous. It gives me pleasure to fondle them, to rub under my hand their silky fur that sometimes crackles, to feel their warmth through this fine and exquisite covering. Nothing is softer, nothing gives to the skin a sensation more delicate, more refined, more rare, than the warm, living coat of a cat. But this living coat also communicates to me, through the ends of my fingers, a strange and ferocious desire to strangle the animal I am caressing. I feel in her the desire she has to bite and scratch me. I feel it,—that same desire, as if it were an electric current communicated from her to me. I run my fingers through the soft fur and the current passes through my nerves from my fingertips to my heart, even to my brain; it tingles throughout my being and causes me to shut my teeth hard.

And if the animal begins to bite and scratch me, I seize her by the neck, I give her a turn and throw her far from me, as I would throw a stone from a sling, so quickly and so brutally that she never has time to revenge herself.

I remember that when I was a child I loved cats, yet I had even then that strange desire to strangle them with my little hands; and one day at the end of the garden, at the beginning of the woods, I perceived suddenly something gray rolling in the high grass. I went to see what it was, and found a cat caught in a snare, strangling, suffocating, dying. It rolled, tore up the ground with its claws, bounded, fell inert, then began again, and its hoarse, rapid breathing made a noise like a pump, a frightful noise which I hear yet. I could have taken a spade and cut the snare, I could have gone to find the servant or tell my father. No, I did not move, and with beating heart I watched it die with a trembling and cruel joy. It was a cat! If it had been a dog, I would rather have cut the copper wire with my teeth than let it suffer a second more. When the cat was quite dead, but yet warm, I went to feel of it and pull its tail!

These little creatures are delicious, notwithstanding, delicious above all, because in caressing them, while they are rubbing against our skin, purring and rolling on us, looking at us with their yellow eyes which seem never to see us, we realize the insecurity of their tenderness, the perfidious selfishness of their pleasure.

Some women, also, give us that sensation,—women who are charming, tender, with clear yet false eyes, who have chosen us entirely for their gratification. Near them, when they open their arms and offer their lips, when a man folds them to his heart with pounding pulses, when he tastes the joy of their delicate caresses, he realizes well that he holds a perfidious, tricky cat, with claws and fangs, an enemy in love, who will bite him when she is tired of kisses.

Many of the poets have loved cats. Baudelaire has sung to them divinely.

I had one day the strange sensation of having inhabited the enchanted palace of the White Cat, a magic castle where reigned one of the most undulant, mysterious, troubling animals, the only one, perhaps, of all living creatures that one never hears walk.

This adventure occurred last year on the same shore of the Mediterranean. At Nice, there was atrocious heat, and I asked myself as to whether there was not, somewhere in the mountains above us, a fresh valley where one might find a breath of fresh air.

Thorence was recommended to me, and I wished to see it immediately. To get there I had first to go to Grasse, the town of perfumes, concerning which I shall write some day, and tell how the essences and quintessences of flowers are manufactured there, costing up to two thousand francs the liter. I passed the night in an old hotel of the town, a poor kind of inn, where the quality of the food was as doubtful as the cleanliness of the rooms. I went on my way in the morning.

The road went straight up into the mountains, following the deep ravines, which were overshadowed by sterile peaks, pointed and savage. I thought that my advisers had recommended to me a very extraordinary kind of summer excursion, and I was almost on the point of returning to Nice the same day, when I saw suddenly before me, on a mountain which appeared to close the entrance to the entire valley, an immense and picturesque ruined castle, showing towers and broken walls, of a strange architecture, in profile against the sky. It proved to be an ancient castle that had belonged to the Templars, who, in bygone days, had governed this county of Thorence.

I made a detour of this mountain, and suddenly discovered a long, green valley, fresh and reposeful. Upon its level were meadows, running waters, and willows; and on its sides grew tall pine-trees. In front of the ruins, on the other side of the valley, but standing lower, was an inhabited castle, called the Castle of the Four Towers, which was built about the year 1530. One could not see any trace of the Renaissance period, however. It was a strong and massive square structure, apparently possessing tremendous powers of resistance, and it was supported by four defensive towers, as its name would indicate.

I had a letter of introduction to the owner of this manor, who would not permit me to go to the hotel. The whole valley is one of the most charming spots in summer that one could dream of. I wandered about there until evening, and after dinner I went to the apartment that had been reserved for me. I first passed through a sort of sitting-room, the walls of which were covered by old Cordova leather; then I went through another room, where, by the light of my candle, I noticed rapidly, in passing, several old portraits of ladies—those paintings of which Theophile Gautier has written.

I entered the room where my bed was, and looked around me. The walls were hung with antique tapestries, where one saw rose-colored donjons in blue landscapes, and great fantastic birds sitting under foliage of precious stones! My dressing-room was in one of the towers. The windows wide on the inside, going through the entire thickness of the walls, were, in reality, nothing but loopholes, through which one might kill an approaching enemy.

I shut my door, went to bed, and slept. Presently I dreamed; usually one dreams a little of something that has passed during the day. I seemed to be traveling; I entered an inn, where I saw at a table before the fire a servant in complete livery, and a mason,—a strange association which did not astonish me. These people spoke of Victor Hugo, who had just died, and I took part in their conversation. At last I went to bed in a room, the door of which I could not shut; and suddenly,

I saw the servant and the mason, armed with sabers, coming softly toward my bed.

I awoke at once, and a few moments passed before I could recollect where I was. Then I recalled quickly my arrival of the day before at Thorence, the occurrences of the evening, and my pleasant reception by the owner. I was just about to close my eyes, when I saw distinctly in the darkness, in the middle of my room, at about the height of a man's head, two fiery eyes watching me.

I seized a match, and while striking it I heard a noise, a light, soft noise, like the sound of a wet rag thrown on the floor, but after I had lighted the candle I saw nothing but a tall table in the middle of the room. I rose, went through both apartments, looked under the bed and into the closets, and found nothing. I thought then that perhaps I had continued dreaming after I was awake, and so I went to sleep again, but not without trouble.

I dreamed again. This time I traveled once more, but in the Orient, in the country that I love. I arrived at the house of a Turk, who lived in the middle of a desert. He was a superb Turk,—not an Arab, but a Turk, fat, friendly, and charming. He was dressed in Turkish attire, with a turban on his head, and a whole shopful of silk on his back,—a real Turk of the Theatre Français, who made me compliments while offering me sweetmeats, sitting on a voluptuous divan.

Then a little black boy took me

to a room—all my dreams ended in this fashion in those days! It was a perfumed room decorated in sky blue, with skins of wild beasts on the floor, and before the fire,—the idea of fire pursued me even in the desert,—on a low chair was a woman, lightly clothed, who was waiting on me. She was of the purest Oriental type, with stars tatooed on her cheeks and forehead and chin; she had immense eyes, a beautiful form, and slightly brown skin,—a warm and exciting skin.

She looked at me, and I thought: "This is what I understand to be the true meaning of the word hospitality. In our stupid and prudish northern countries, with their hateful mawkishness of ideas, and silly notions of morality, a man would never receive a stranger in this fashion."

I went up to the woman and spoke to her, but she replied only by signs, not knowing a word of my language, which the Turk, her master, understood so well. All the happier that she would be silent, I took her by the hand and led her toward my couch, where I placed myself by her side. . . .

But one always awakens at those moments! So I opened my eyes and was not greatly surprised to feel beneath my hand something soft and warm, which I caressed lovingly. Then my mind clearing, I recognized that it was a cat, a big cat rolled up against my cheek, sleeping there with confidence. I left it there and composed myself to sleep once more. When daylight appeared he was gone; and I really thought I had dreamed he had been with me; for I could not understand how he could have come in and gone out, as my door was locked.

When I related my dream and my adventure to my agreeable host (not the whole of it!) he began to laugh and said: "He came in through his own door," and raising a curtain, he showed me a little round hole in the wall. I learned then that the old habitations of this country have long, narrow runways through the walls, which go from the cellar to the garret, from the servants' rooms to the rooms of the *seigneur,* and these passages render the cat king and master of the interior of the house. He goes where it pleases him, visits his domain at his pleasure, sleeps in all the beds, sees all, hears all, knows all the secrets, all the habits, all the shames of the house. Everywhere he is at home, the animal that moves without noise, the silent prowler, the nocturnal rover of the hallowed walls. And I thought of Baudelaire.

ANDERSON COLLEGE
LIBRARY
ANDERSON, INDIANA